Y0-BUD-645

ITALIAN PHYSICAL SOCIETY

PROCEEDINGS

OF THE

INTERNATIONAL SCHOOL OF PHYSICS « ENRICO FERMI »

COURSE XXXV

edited by L. GRATTON
Director of the Course

VARENNA ON LAKE COMO
VILLA MONASTERO
12 th - 24 th JULY 1965

High-Energy Astrophysics

1966

ACADEMIC PRESS · NEW YORK AND LONDON

Varenna, Italy. Scuola internazionale di fisica

SOCIETÀ ITALIANA DI FISICA

RENDICONTI

DELLA

SCUOLA INTERNAZIONALE DI FISICA
«ENRICO FERMI»

XXXV Corso

a cura di L. Gratton
Direttore del Corso

VARENNA SUL LAGO DI COMO
VILLA MONASTERO
12 - 24 LUGLIO 1965

Astrofisica delle alte energie

1966

ACADEMIC PRESS • NEW YORK AND LONDON

QB
461
.V34

ACADEMIC PRESS INC.
111 Fifth Avenue
New York 3, N. Y.

United Kingdom Edition
Published by
ACADEMIC PRESS INC. (London) Ltd.
Berkeley Square House, London W. 1

Copyright © 1966, by Società Italiana di Fisica

ALL RIGHTS RESERVED

NO PART OF THIS BOOK MAY BE REPRODUCED IN ANY FORM,
BY PHOTOSTAT, MICROFILM, OR ANY OTHER MEANS,
WITHOUT WRITTEN PERMISSION FROM THE PUBLISHERS.

Library of Congress Catalog Card Number: 66-14728

Library
UNIVERSITY OF MIAMI

PRINTED IN ITALY

INDICE

E. M. BURBIDGE – Radio galaxies and quasi-stellar radio sources.

R. GIACCONI, H. GURSEY, J. R. WATERS, B. ROSSI, G. CLARK, G. GARMIRE, M. ODA and M. WADA – Some observational aspects of X-ray astronomy.

G. BURBIDGE – X-ray and γ-ray sources.

PREFACE.

L. GRATTON

These lectures on High-Energy Astrophysics appear more than one year after they have actually been delivered at Varenna. This lapse of time may appear somewhat too large in such a rapidly growing subject. However, the main reason for the delay was just this rapid growth; indeed some of the Authors were so desirous to include their own latest contributions to the field, that they were reluctant to send their manuscripts. Obviously this could not go on indefinitely and the Editor had finally to put a dead line, which proved to be about June 1966.

The result was that some of the papers, especially those concerned with the observational facts, were brought up to date to the middle of 1966, and this certainly adds much value to the book. Among the few important results which could not be included, let me quote here only the recent identification of the source *Sco* X-1 with a peculiar optical object, probably an *ex-Nova*, by a group of researchers, among whom some of the contributors to this volume.

On the other side, it seems that no decisive advances on the theoretical side of the problems have been made between June 1965 and the middle of 1966; hence in this connection we feel confident that the reader will find reasonably complete and up to date information.

The time spent at Varenna will certainly be remembered by all who were there as a very happy one. For this let me express here my best thanks to everybody, to the teachers for their splendid lectures, to both teachers and students, for the lively discussions which followed each lecture and lasted often during the promenades along the lake and during many after-sessions around tables scattered with espresso-cups and glasses of beer and fine Italian wine (how many bright ideas were suggested by it and perhaps are still on their way to materialization!).

Finally a warm thank is also due to the Italian Society of Physics and its efficient secretary, Prof. GERMANÀ, to whose untiring efforts a large part of the success of the E. FERMI Courses is due.

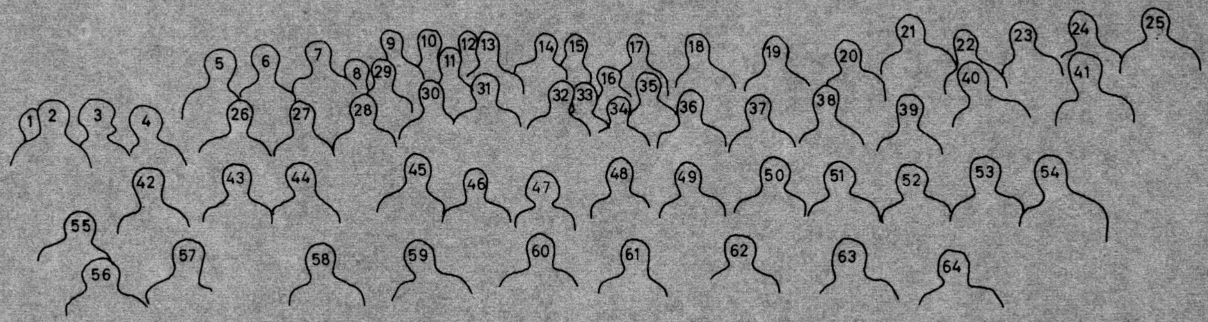

1. N. Bel
2. V. Kourganoff
3. E. Asseo
4. S. Souffrin
5. C. Navach Fasano
6. M. G. Sussi
7. A. Saggion
8. K. Y. Shen
9. S. Refsdal
10. F. Occhionero
11. C. Long
12. E. J. Callan
13. M. Simon
14. G. Silvestro
15. J. M. Bardeen
16. R. Fanti
17. K. S. Thorne
18. G. R. Isaak
19. D. Shalitin
20. D. K. Sen
21. L. M. Bianchi
22. T. C. Weekes
23. N. Dallaporta
24. R. James
25. D. F. Falla
26. P. Giannone
27. K. Elsässer
28. V. De Sabbata
29. D. Bramanti
30. R. G. Mc Lenaghan
31. H. D. Greyber
32. R. Giacconi
33. A. Braccesi
34. G. Swarup
35. A. Finzi
36. J. J. M. Beenakker
37. J. K. Bienlein
38. K. Ono
39. R. R. Daniel
40. F. Pacini
41. P. Veron
42. J. Oostens
43. D. Boccaletti
44. A. Caruso
45. L. Gratton
46. D. W. Sciama
47. C. Giovannini
48. E. M. Burbidge
49. G. Szamosi
50. G. Burbidge
51. W. Fowler
52. A. Sandage
53. H. Burkhardt
54. R. Gallino
55. J. P. Wright
56. N. Lund
57. R. Hakim
58. A. Renzini
59. M. Perinotto
60. G. Noci
61. A. Hamoui
62. J. Kleczek
63. I. H. Thompson
64. N. Virgopia

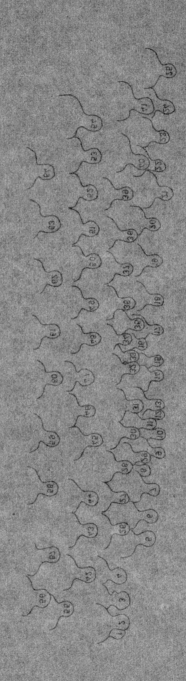

SOCIETÀ ITALIANA DI FISICA

SCUOLA INTERNAZIONALE DI FISICA « E. FERMI »

XXXV CORSO - VARENNA SUL LAGO DI COMO - VILLA MONASTERO - 12 - 24 Luglio 1965

High-Energy Astrophysics.

L. GRATTON

Cattedra di Astrofisica dell'Università - Roma
IV Sezione del Centro di Astrofisica del C.N.R.

1. – Introduction. - High-energy astrophysics.

E ogni permutanza credi stolta,
Se la cosa dimessa in la sorpresa,
Come 'l quattro nel sei non è raccolta. (*)
DANTE, *Paradiso*, Canto v, 58-60.

The history of the last hundred years shows that on several occasions the astrophysical demand of sources of very large quantities of energy has presented exceedingly difficult problems to physics, which could be satisfactorily solved only when some important advance in the very fundaments of physics became available. For instance, when it became evident that the life of the Sun was by some order of magnitude larger than 10^7 y, it was impossible to explain its present rate of radiation, until the discovery, mainly by BETHE (following earlier suggestions by ATKINSON and HOUTERMANS), of the thermonuclear reactions leading to the synthesis of He in the solar interior.

The equivalence of mass and energy predicted by the theory of relativity, while providing an enormous amount of energy stored in material bodies, has put also a definite upper limit to it; indeed, if $\mathscr{M}$ is the mass contained in a certain volume, measured from its gravitational effect upon an external test particle, the energy which may be extracted from it by any conceivable process cannot evidently exceed $\mathscr{M}c^2$.

(*) And let him deem every permutation foolish, if the thing laid down be not contained in that which is taken up, as four in six.

As a matter of fact, with the sole exception of the process of annihilation of particles and antiparticles, all known physical processes lie far below this limit. The most effective nuclear process (the synthesis of one ^{56}Fe atom out of 56 H atoms) cannot extract from a body (consisting initially of pure hydrogen) more than the 0.88% of its rest energy.

Recent astrophysical evidence had led to suspect that in some cases the limit set by the relativity theory is much more closely approached. In other words some observations suggest that from certain regions of space large amounts of energy are released under the form of electromagnetic waves and others, the total quantity released being perhaps a considerable fraction of $\mathcal{M}c^2$, if $\mathcal{M}$ is the total (gravitational) mass which under any reasonable assumption we can admit to have been initially enclosed in the body from which the observed phenomena originate. It seems thus that a more efficient mechanism than nuclear reactions has to be considered.

Some different mechanism must be invoked any way in the case of supernovae outbursts, since it is generally agreed that supernovae are stars whose matter has reached the end of nuclear evolution, that is the stage at which all possible nuclear reactions are exothermic.

Gravitational collapse has been suggested as a possible mechanism by means of which a quantity of energy can be released which may be a considerable fraction of the rest energy of a body. Whether this mechanism works in all cases is however by no means certain.

In all these cases the astrophysical results point towards rather unstable phenomena, suggesting explosive or, at any rate, very violent events. This is in contrast with the evolution of normal astrophysical objects, which occurs in a slow peaceful way. Compare, for instance, the rate of energy release in the Sun, about 2 erg s^{-1} g^{-1}, with that of a supernova, at maximum brightness, which is probably 10^9 times larger. In a similar way, although the masses of quasistellar radio sources are very uncertain, the present evidence suggests that their emission rate per gram is at least 10^5 times larger than that of an average galaxy.

The words « High-Energy Astrophysics » as a general title for those developments which deal with these phenomena, are thus meant to indicate not merely processes in which large amounts of energy are involved, but, mainly, those in which the rate of energy release per second and gram is very high as compared with the more usual processes going on in normal stars and galaxies.

The problem of finding a suitable energy source, that is a physical process or some physical processes, by means of which large amounts of energy stored in rather small volumes are released under the form of electromagnetic waves or others, is however only one of the difficulties. Another equally important problem arises from the fact that, if our interpretation of the low-frequency emission, and perhaps also of a part of the optical spectrum is correct, a very important fraction of the electromagnetic spectrum is due to synchrotron radiation, that is to magnetic bremsstrahlung. In turn this is indicative of the existence of magnetic fields and of a large quantity of high-energy (relativistic) electrons, whose total energy is itself a very considerable fraction of $\mathcal{M}c^2$, if the initial mass $\mathcal{M}$ is to be kept within reasonable limits.

How such a large amount of energy has been transferred into this high-energy plasma, whichever was the form under which it was stored in the initial body? Is there any connection between the high-energy particles associated with the radio emission from these bodies and primary cosmic rays?

To find a suitable mechanism of acceleration of individual particles to relativistic energies seems an exceedingly difficult problem; perhaps even more difficult than that of the energy source itself. Indeed, generally speaking, the tendency in Nature is towards a fragmentation of any amount of energy in fractions as small as possible; as a consequence by far the largest quantities of energy permanently concentrated in single units are the rest energies of baryons. Of course, this is due to the very low average energy density of the universe; the breaking of the rest energy of baryons into smaller units being prevented only by the law of conservation of baryons.

A mechanism which concentrates very large amounts of energy in single particles, is thus in a way something which is going against this general tendency. In other words it produces a very large decrease of entropy in a certain system which must be accompanied by a correspondingly larger increase in another (interacting) system, if we wish to respect the 2nd principle of thermodynamics. The kind of the interaction constitutes a very hard problem indeed and it may be that we have to seek the solution in a completely different and unexpected direction.

Parallel to all these considerations goes the problem of the evolutionary course followed by the objects involved in the processes of high-energy astrophysics. Are they completely different objects from ordinary stars and galaxies or simply peculiar evolutionary stages of these more common objects? If so, how do they fit into the general evolution of stars and galaxies?

Of course the urgency of introducing evolutionary ideas comes from the explosive or short-lived character of these objects. After all, we can hope to understand the structure of a star (we do in fact understand it) or of a galaxy even without knowing much about their origin and their final fate; the reason is that their life is very long (from 10^8, for the shortest-lived stars, to 10^{11} years) compared with the time necessary to restore dynamical equilibrium. But the lives of a supernova and of a quasi-stellar radio source, as such, are so short that the problem of their evolution cannot be ignored from the very beginning. In other words the problem is essentially a dynamical one and must be stated as such.

2. – Supernovae, neutron stars and gravitational collapse.

These our actors,
As I foretold you, were all spirits and
Are melted into air, into thin air:
And, like the baseless fabric of this vision,
The cloud-capp'd towers, the gorgeous palaces,
The solemn temples, the great globe itself,
Yea, all which it inherit, shall dissolve
And, like this insubstantial pageant faded,
Leave not a rack behind.

W. SHAKESPEARE, *The Tempest*, Act IV, 148-156.

The detailed study of the different problems will be the subject of the following lectures. I will, therefore limit myself to two astrophysical problems, giving a general sketch from an historical point of view, mainly for the benefit of the students who are not especially acquainted with them.

Supernova outbursts have been known since several centuries, but for a long time they have been mistaken with ordinary novae. The first realization that they implied much larger amounts of energy (by many orders of magnitude) was due to ZWICKY, who also suggested that the outburst might be connected with the collapse of a more or less ordinary star into a highly condensed state in which its matter consisted essentially of a gas of neutrons (ZWICKY 1958).

The theory of neutron stars was, thus, associated from the beginning with the outbursts of supernovae. After the pioneer work by LANDAU (see LANDAU and LIFSHITS 1959), OPPENHEIMER and others (OPPENHEIMER and VOLKOFF, 1939), it was revived more recently by CAMERON (1959), HAMADA and SALPETER (1961) and others, mainly following the work of BURBIDGE, BURBIDGE, FOWLER and HOYLE (1957) who showed that a star which has reached the end point of its nuclear evolution should undergo a violent collapse; important contributions are due also to CHIU (1965).

In the case of the supernova outbursts, it seems that the primary energy source is not a difficulty; gravitational collapse of a body of more or less the Sun mass provides a sufficient amount of energy, the binding energy of the final body, which is radiated away during the collapse. If the final product is a zero-temperature neutron star the energy released is amply enough.

The discovery by ROSSI and his coworkers (GIACCONI, 1964) and by FRIEDMAN (1965) of a number of discrete sources of X-rays, almost certainly galactic, one of which is coincident with the Crab Nebula (the famous remnant of the 1054 Supernova), connected quite naturally neutron stars with these sources. Although it seems now that the connection, if it exists, cannot be too direct, the idea cannot be completely dismissed. We shall hear more about it during these lectures. However the most recent work by BAHCALL and WOLF (1965 *a*, *b*), FINZI (1965) and others makes it rather improbable that we shall ever be able to observe a neutron star through its direct radiation. We may quote on this connection also recent contributions by MORRISON and SARTORI (1965), DE SABBATA and GUALDI (1965) etc....

A problem of enormous theoretical interest is associated with a neutron star or, more generally, with a cold body at the end of its nuclear evolution. It was known since Oppenheimer's work that no equilibrium state exists for a neutron star if its mass exceeds a certain critical value somewhat less than one solar mass. It was also known that for a smaller mass there exist two equilibrium solutions, one stable and the other unstable, the latter corresponding to a more centrally condensed configuration with a lower energy content. In other words, the stable solution is, really, « metastable »; given a sufficiently strong perturbation the body will collapse into the unstable state and, from this, the collapse will continue indefinitely. An indefinite collapse will ensue anyway in the case of a mass larger than the critical mass, since no equilibrium is possible.

It is maintained by WHEELER (1964) and others that, although this cannot be rigorously proved, no equation of state of the neutron matter can prevent the collapse of the body inside its own Schwarzschild's singularity, a fact which is described some times as the « squeezing of matter out of existence ». Although the question may have no practical importance, it is nevertheless very important in principle. It might well be that by such considerations as these, we may be led to modify some of our basic physical laws, like the field equations of general relativity from one side, or the conservation of baryons from another.

However the possibility that the collapse might be halted by a suitable equation of state cannot be ruled out entirely. This point was discussed by CHIU (1965), GRATTON and SZAMOSI (1964) and by MARX and NÉMETH (1965); but it must be avowed that we ignore completely the behaviour of matter compressed to such high densities (well beyond nuclear densities).

Some exploratory work on this field is due to BAHCALL and WOLF (1965*a*) and also to HAGEDORN (1965); it seems that at very large densities the concept of individual particles fails. The thermodynamics of hadrons (strongly interacting particles) leads to a mass spectrum which is entirely different from its free-particle analogue. Thus, the independent-particle model may, at best, give only a very rough suggestion of what might happen.

Several recent developments have also appeared on the dynamics of the collapse and will be revised in these lectures. After OPPENHEIMER and SNYDER'S (1939) early work, important contributions have recently been made by BURBIDGE, BURBIDGE, FOWLER and HOYLE (1964), MCVITTIE (1964), MISNER and SHARP (1964), BONDI (1964), MAY and WHITE (1965) and FIR-

MANI (1965). However the most detailed computations (based on classical mechanics) are due to COLGATE and WHITE (1964).

But speaking as an astrophysicist, I would like to venture the opinion that the most urgent problem is to extract from the spectra of supernovae all the information they contain. At present practically all we know about an individual supernova comes from the study of the Crab Nebula (WOLTJER 1958), which is being observed nine centuries after its outburst and might not be typical. It is well possible that a complete interpretation of the spectrum of a Supernova near maximum might give a clue as to the mechanism of the collapse and to the acceleration of (individual) electrons to relativistic energy which is required to explain the present synchrotron radiation of the Crab Nebula.

3. – Radiogalaxies, quasi-stellar radio sources and related objects.

There was Chaos at first, and Darkness and Night,
and Tartarus vasty and dismal;
But the Earth was not there, nor the Sky, nor the Air,
till at length in the bosom abysmal
Of Darkness an egg, from the whirlwind conceived,
was laid by the sable-plumed Night.
And out of that egg, as the Seasons revolved
sprang Love, the entrancing, the bright,
Love brilliant and bold with his pinions of gold,
like a whirlwind, refulgent and sparkling.

ARISTOPHANES, *The Birds*, 693-697.

Ordinary galaxies, like our own or the Andromeda Nebula, do not radiate very strongly in the radio-frequency range; besides the 21 cm emission due to interstellar hydrogen, they possess a rather faint continuous which is interpreted as synchroton radiation from an extended halo of relativistic electrons moving in the general galactic magnetic field.

It has been found, however, that there exists a number of galaxies which are very strong radio-emitters; some very-well-known examples are the radio-sources *Centaurus* A (connected with NGC 5128, a peculiar elliptical nebula), *Cygnus* A, *Virgo* A (connected with M 87) etc. In general the galaxies associated with these radio-sources are very bright giant galaxies showing some peculiarities like dark bands rather exceptional for their types, bright « jets » whose light is often strongly polarized, or other similar uncommon features.

The radio-flux does not come from the same volume as the optical light; most often it is emitted by two sources more or less symmetrical relative to the optical object and far apart from it along its axis of rotation. It has been also remarked that radiogalaxies occur mostly as single objects or in poor clusters (MATTHEWS, MORGAN and SCHMIDT 1964); when they appear in a cluster they are the dominating feature, being by far the largest and brightest galaxy in it and lying usually near its center.

The energy requirements to explain the radio-sources are exceedingly high. The energy stored in the high-energy plasma (including the magnetic energy of the field) can be estimated from the radio-spectrum; since the magnetic field is not known, only minimum values can be obtained. This ranges up to 10^{61} erg, equivalent to 10^7 rest solar masses; the actual values however, may be considerably higher.

It is generally agreed that the plasma clouds have been ejected during some violent event which must have taken place near the center of the optical object at least some 10^6 years ago (since the distance of the clouds from it are 10^6 light years). Now the observed radio-fluxes are of the order of 10^{45} erg/s, which makes at least 10^{58} erg emitted under the form of radio-waves since the time of the ejections. All these are minimum values, the actual energy release may have been 100 or perhaps 10 000 times larger.

Evidence for a very violent event near the center of the galaxy M 82 has been discussed in a famous paper by LYNDS and SANDAGE (1963) and a very inspiring discussion of similar events in a number of galaxies has been published by Margaret and Geoffrey BURBIDGE and SANDAGE (1963). They come to the conclusion that the amounts of energy released range from 10^{55} to 10^{61} erg; the events manifest themselves through their effects during times which may last 10^6 or more years. Large mass motions and large fluxes of relativistic particles are generated during these events.

The most spectacular discovery of the last few years in the entire realm of astrophysics was certainly that of the quasi-stellar objects, known as quasi-stellar radio sources (QSS). The first recognition by SCHMIDT (1963) of the extragalactic nature of the radio-source 3C 273 (after the beautiful observations of a group of Australian radioastronomers) and by GREENSTEIN and MATTHEWS (1963) of that of 3C 48, has been followed by a number of remarkable discoveries. After the work of these workers, of SANDAGE and others, many puzzling features of these extraordinary objects have become known. The last discovery announced so far has been that by SANDAGE of the existence of some other objects, apparently not connected with radio-sources, but probably identical with QSS in all other respects.

Dr. SANDAGE will summarize in his lecture the brilliant work done by himself and his colleagues of the large American observatories. I will say only that their results open an enormous field for theoretical investigations. Some tentative models for strong radio-sources and for QSS have been suggested by HOYLE and FOWLER (1963*a*, *b*) and by FOWLER (1964). An entirely different point of view, however, has been taken by GOLD (1963) and his collaborators and also by others (WOLTJER 1964, FIELD 1964); according to these authors QSS, or in general strong radio-sources are actually multiple systems (clusters of stars) rather than single bodies.

But it seems that, at least in the case of QSS, the single-body theory is more acceptable, due to the very small diameters and the light variations of the optical objects. A very simple model based on the adiabatic equilibrium of a single body of very large mass (10^9 solar masses or more) has been proposed by GRATTON (1964). This model leaves completely open the question of how the body has been formed, but it suggests that it will eventually expand into a large (dark) gas cloud of the size of a galaxy.

If this view is correct, QSS should be placed at the initial stage of the evolution of galaxies or, perhaps, of clusters of galaxies. Although this permits a more straightforward interpretation of the observational results, I know that many people will express considerable doubts; these are mainly due to the fact that this model leaves unanswered the question of the energy source, since neither nuclear nor gravitational sources can be assumed. On the contrary, the contraction of such a body from an infinitely expanded state would require a considerable amount of energy.

I think, however, that at the present stage, the most we can hope for is a very crude sketch and we must not be too exacting concerning some possible inconsistencies. Perhaps it is better to have a rough model based on simple physics, rather than elaborated theories which try to explain more than it is known.

About hundred years ago Lord KELVIN proposed his famous theory of the origin of the Sun heath. I wish to quote his very words from the French magazine « Les Mondes » (1863):

> « Qu'une théorie météorique de quelque nature soit certainement la vraie et complète explication de la chaleur solaire, c'est ce dont on ne saurait douter, en considérant les raisons suivantes:
>
> 1) Aucune autre explication naturelle, excepté l'action chimique, ne peut se concevoir.
>
> 2) La théorie d'une action chimique est tout à fait insuffisante, parce que l'action la plus énergique que nous connaissions, s'opérant entre des substances équivalent à toute la masse du Soleil, ne développerait que trois mille années de chaleur.
>
> 3) Au moyen de la théorie météorique on peut, sans difficulté, rendre raison de vingt millions d'années de chaleur. »

If we take into account the fast progress of the physics of strongly interacting particles, I wonder what we will say within, say, ten years from now, with respect to QSS!

BIBLIOGRAPHY

BAHCALL, J. N. and R. A. WOLF, 1965*a*, *Phys. Rev. Letters.*, **14**, 343.
BAHCALL, J. N. and R. A. WOLF, 1965*b*, Preprint.
BONDI, H., 1964, *Proc. R. S.*, **281**, 39.
BURBIDGE, E. M., G. R. BURBIDGE, W. A. FOWLER and F. HOYLE, 1957, *Rev. of Mod. Phys.*, **29**, 547.
BURBIDGE, E. M., G. R. BURBIDGE, W. A. FOWLER and F. HOYLE, 1964, *Ap. J.*, **139**, 909.
BURBIDGE, G. R., E. M. BURBIDGE and A. R. SANDAGE, 1963, *Rev. of Mod. Phys.*, **35**, 947.
CAMERON, A. G. W., 1959, *Ap. J.*, **130**, 884.
CHIU, H. J., 1965, Paper presented at the *Buenos Aires Meeting of COSPAR*; summarizes earlier work (preprint).
COLGATE, S. A. and R. H. WHITE, 1964, UCRL 7777 (preprint).
DE SABBATA, V. and C. GUALDI, 1965, *Nuovo Cimento* (in press).
FIELD, G. B., 1964, *Ap. J.*, **140**, 1434.
FINZI, A., 1965, *La ricerca scientifica* (in press).
FIRMANI, C., 1965, *Thesis* (Univ. of Roma).
FRIEDMAN, H., 1965, Paper presented at the *Buenos Aires Meeting of COSPAR* (preprint).
FOWLER, W. A., 1964, *Rev. of Mod. Phys.*, **36**, 545.
GIACCONI, R., 1964, Paper presented at the *Austin Conference on Relativistic Astrophysics* (preprint).
GOLD, T. A., W. I. AXFORD and E. C. RAY, 1963, *Dallas Symposium on Quasi Stellar Radio Sources etc.*, p. 93.
GRATTON, L., 1964, Paper presented at the *Austin Conference on Relativistic Astrophysics*.
GRATTON, L. and G. SZAMOSI, 1964, *Nuovo Cimento*, **33**, 1056.
GREENSTEIN, J. L. and T. A. MATTHEWS, 1963, *Nature*, **197**, 1041.
HAGEDORN, R., 1965, Preprint.
HAMADA, I. and E. E. SALPETER, 1961, *Ap. J.*, **134**, 683.
HOYLE, F. and W. A. FOWLER, 1963*a*, *M. N.*, **125**, 169.
HOYLE, F. and W. A. FOWLER, 1963*b*, *Nature*, **197**, 533.
LANDAU, L. D. and E. M. LIFSHITZ, 1959, *Statistical Physics*, p. 340 (London).
LYNDS, C. R. and A. R. SANDAGE, 1963, *Ap. J.*, **137**, 1005.
MARX, G. and J. NÉMETH, 1965, Preprint.
MATTHEWS, T. A., W. W. MORGAN and M. SCHMIDT, 1964, *Ap. J.*, **140**, 35.
MAY, M. M. and R. H. WHITE, 1965, UCRL 14242 (preprint).
MISNER, C. W. and D. H. SHARP, 1964, *Phys. Rev.*, **136**, 571.
MORRISON, P. and L. SARTORI, 1965 (preprint).
OPPENHEIMER, J. R. and G. VOLKOFF, 1939, *Phys. Rev.*, **55**, 374.
OPPENHEIMER, J. R. and H. SNYDER, 1939, *Phys. Rev.*, **56**, 455.
SCHMIDT, M., 1963, *Nature*, **197**, 1040.
MCVITTIE, G. C., 1964, *Ap. J.*, **140**, 401.
WHEELER, J. A., 1964, *The superdense star and the critical nucleon number*, in: H. J. CHIU and W. F. HOFMANN: *Gravitation and Relativity*, p. 195. A book by Wheeler and others on this subject is in press.
WOLTJER, L., 1958, *B.A.N.*, **14**, 39.
WOLTJER, L., 1964, *Nature*, **201**, 803.
ZWICKY, F., 1958, *Supernovae*, in: *Enc. of Phys.*, vol. **51**, p. 766 (Berlin).

Observational Properties of Radio Galaxies and Quasi-Stellar Sources.

A. SANDAGE

Mount Wilson and Palomar Observatories,
Carnegie Institution of Washington,
California Institute of Technology

1. – Introduction.

Discrete radio sources have been known for less than twenty years, but in this short interval some of the most baffling results of science have been discovered. Galaxies, once thought to be quiescent gravitating aggregates of stars, are now known to be the sites of violent events. Large-scale motions of gas and plasma have been observed, with the material apparently being shot out of the central regions of the galaxies involved. As soon as optical identification with galaxies was achieved, it was realized that new energy sources of unprecedented power were involved. Radio-brightness distributions of the sources showed that multiple structure (radio doubling) was involved, and these data, obtained by ingenious radio techniques, provided some insight into the explosive mechanisms.

These results—well known to radio astronomers working actively in the field—have only recently begun to dominate the research of optical astronomers working with large reflectors. But dominate they do, and now much of the dark, moonless time with the 200- and 120-inch reflectors is used for optical identification work, measurement of red-shifts and velocity fields, and photometry of radio sources.

It is my privilege in these lectures to trace the history of the subject from the first discovery of discrete sources, through the intense cataloguing phases and early optical identifications, to the discovery of quasi-stellar sources, and finally to the use of these data in cosmology.

2. – Discrete radio sources.

2·1. *Discovery and early surveys.* – The first discrete radio source was discovered in 1946 by HEY, PARSONS, and PHILIPS (1946*a*) in a survey of the sky for the distribution of radio noise at 64 MHz using a Yagi antenna system of beam width 6° by 15°. Their contour map showed a region of high intensity near the galactic center and a second region in the direction of *Cygnus*. Each of these closed contours had previously been found by REBER (1944) in his pioneering survey of the radio sky with a 30-foot paraboloid working at 160 MHz ($\lambda = 1.8$ meters). But these results did not, in themselves, show the existence of discrete sources because the closed contours observed on the maps could just as well have been due to a surface distribution of radiation. However, the discovery by HEY, PARSONS, and PHILIPS (1946*b*) of rapid fluctuations in the intensity of the *Cygnus* region showed that the source must be of small angular dimensions and therefore discrete.

The fluctuations were confirmed by BOLTON and STANLEY (1948) in Australia, and RYLE and SMITH (1948) in England. In addition to observing the fluctuations, BOLTON and STANLEY were able to estimate an upper limit of 8′ of arc to the angular size by observing the amplitude of the modulation of the varying signal. These workers were also able to give the first moderately accurate radio position from their sea interferometer data. These data of HEY, PARSON, and PHILIPS, together with the confirmations, established the existence of *Cygnus* A, or 3C 405.

BOLTON (1948) then made a survey for other sources over about one quarter of the celestial sphere, again using the sea interferometer at 100 MHz. In addition to *Cygnus* A, he found six other objects, among which were *Taurus* A, *Coma* A, *Hercules* A, and *Centaurus* A. The limit of his sensitivity was 200 flux units (f.u.) at 100 MHz [1 flux unit is 10^{-26} W/m^2 (Hz)].

RYLE and SMITH (1948), working with a Michelson-type radio interferometer at 80 MHz, found, during the course of their polarization work on the *Cygnus* source, a new source of greater intensity than *Cygnus* A in the direction of *Cassiopeia*, together with twenty-eight fainter sources. [It is of considerable interest that the *Cassiopeia* source also appears on Reber's contour map (1944).] Thus by 1948 at least eight sources were known and listed. The period of intense cataloguing then began.

A survey by RYLE, SMITH, and ELSMORE (1950) was made at Cambridge with an East-West interferometer working at 110 λ separation at a frequency of 80.6 MHz [3.7 meters]. The results constitute the 1C catalogue in which fifty sources are listed with positions having probable errors of several minutes in R.A. and about a degree in declination. The flux limit of the catalogue is 25 f.u. at 81 MHz.

A survey by STANLEY and SLEE (1950), again with the sea interferometer working as a Lloyd's mirror at 100 MHz, listed eighteen sources between declinations of $\pm 50°$. The tabulated positions show accuracies of about $\pm 10^m$ of time and $\pm 3°$ in declination. Following MOXON (1946), these authors were among the first to give data on the spectral energy distribution of the continuum radiation, obtained by observing the sources at different frequencies.

A survey by MILLS (1952*a*), using a Michelson-type interferometer working at 101 MHz, gave 77 sources between declination $+50°$ and $-90°$ to a flux limit of 50 f.u. at 101 MHz. Other surveys by HANBURY BROWN and HAZARD (1953*a*), SHAIN and HIGGINS (1954), and BOLTON, STANLEY, and SLEE (1954) added 164 more sources.

Then, in 1955, a very extensive survey was completed at Cambridge (RYLE and HEWISH, 1955) with a new radio telescope that consisted of four antennas working as an interferometer at 91 MHz (3.3 meters). The declination coverage was $-3°$ to $+83°$ with tabulated position accuracies of about $\pm 2'$ of arc in R.A. and $\pm 12'$ in declination. The catalogue, designated as 2C (SHAKESHAFT *et al.*, 1955), comprised 1936 entries and had a limit of about 10 f.u. at 81 MHz.

For the purposes of this review, the 2C survey conveniently marks the end of the intense initial cataloguing efforts by many radio astronomers. The next phase began with improved values of positions and with strong and successful attempts to improve the reliability of the catalogues with the elimination of spurious entries.

2·2. *Recent surveys.* – To check the conclusions drawn from the 2C catalogue, MILLS and SLEE (1957) made a small-sample survey of a region of the sky between $+10°$ and $-20°$ declination and 0^h to 8^h R.A. in 1956 with the newly completed Mills cross-antenna system. A check of the regions of overlap between the 2C survey and this new catalogue showed that many of the catalogued sources were not common to the two lists. Further analysis showed that both surveys were affected by confusion for sources fainter than about 40 f.u. at 81 MHz in the 2C catalogue and 20 f.u. in the MS list. Confusion results when the angular resolution of the instruments is too poor for the sensitivity of the receiver. Near the flux limit of the instruments the discrete sources are not clearly resolved, giving a spurious record. To remedy this, the Cambridge group made a new survey at 158 MHz, which is twice the frequency of the 2C—a circumstance which gives four times the resolution of the 2C catalogue. The 3C catalogue (EDGE *et al.*, 1959) contains 471 entries between $-22°$ and $+71°$ to a flux limit of 7 f.u. at 159 MHz. The reliability of the catalogue is discussed by EDGE, SCHEUER, and SHAKESHAFT (1958) and later by BENNETT and SMITH (1961), with the conclusion that all but 5 per cent of the 3C sources are real.

Based on the results of the 3C and on new surveys by LESLIE (1961) at 178 MHz, using the same Cambridge telescope, BENNETT (1962*a*, *b*) produced a revised 3C catalogue covering declinations between $-5°$ and $+90°$, containing 328 entries to a limit of 9 f.u. Subsequent work by many observers has shown that the reliability of the 3CR is virtually 100 per cent. It now forms the principal finding list for sources in the northern hemisphere brighter than 9 f.u. at 178 MHz, providing for radio astronomy what the Shapley-Ames catalogue of bright galaxies has provided for optical astronomy.

Paralleling this development in the north are the MILLS, SLEE and HILL (1958, 1960, 1961) surveys made with the pencil-beam Mills cross-instrument working at 86 MHz. The beam width to half power is $0°.8$ in both co-ordinates. A total of 2270 sources are listed to a level of about 7 f.u. at 85 MHz. A survey by KELLERMAN and HARRIS (1960) was made with the California Institute of Technology interferometer, working at 960 MHz, to check the reliability of the MSH lists in declination ranges $+10°$ to $-20°$ around the sky, and from $-20°$ to $-50°$ from 17^h to 5^h of R.A. KELLERMAN and HARRIS confirmed 77 per cent of the MSH sources brighter than 15 f.u. at 86 MHz, with a smaller percentage of fainter levels. Part of the failure to detect all of the MSH sources must lie in the different frequencies used (86 MHz for MSH, 960 MHz for KH). A steep spectrum would place some sources below the limit of detection at 0.5 f.u. HILL and MILLS (1962) and BENNETT and SMITH (1961) have discussed the reliability of the MSH and the 3C catalogues. It is concluded that the two surveys are substantially correct for flux densities greater than 20 f.u. at 86 MHz and 8 f.u. at 158 MHz, but the MSH list is less reliable below this level. As previously stated, BENNETT and SMITH further conclude that 5 per cent of the 3C sources do not exist and 20 per cent appear to be blank. As noted above, most—or all—of these difficulties have now been eliminated in the 3CR.

The most recent southern survey is that made at Parkes with the Australian 210-foot parabola (BOLTON, GARDNER, and MACKEY, 1964) in the declination range $-20°$ to $-60°$ as part of a complete program from $+20°$ to $-90°$. The measurements were made at three frequencies. The catalogue contains 297 sources brighter than 4 f.u. at 400 MHz. The reliability of the Parkes catalogue is believed to be very high. This feature, together with the relatively high radio position accuracy ($\pm 0'.6$ of arc in both co-ordinates for 90 per cent of the sources), makes the Parkes catalogue of very great value for southern sources.

A variety of special surveys are available—made for various purposes other than cataloguing. Among these are the California Institute of Technology lists (HARRIS and ROBERTS, 1960; known as CTA; WILSON and BOLTON, 1960, known as CTB; the survey of normal galaxies by HANDBURY-BROWN and HAZARD, 1961*a*, *b*), the survey of Shapley-Ames galaxies by HEESCHEN and

WADE (1964), and the survey of the 3C for confirmation of sources and for spectral data by PAULINY-TOTH, WADE, and HEESCHEN (1966) which provides good positional accuracy.

New surveys to fainter flux levels are now in progress—one of which is the fourth Cambridge catalogue. Segments of the 4C have been published (SCOTT, RYLE, and HEWISH, 1961) in a restricted declination region from 40° to 44° and from 50° to 52°. The flux level is about 3 f.u. at 178 MHz. The deepest survey is that of RYLE and NEVILLE (1962) near the north celestial pole. Special techniques of aperture synthesis allowed positions to be determined to $\pm 15''$ arc for 87 sources to a flux level of 0.25 f.u. at 178 MHz.

Finally, the first results from the Bologna cross-type antenna have appeared (BRACCESI *et al.*, 1965) in a catalogue listing 654 sources between declinations $-20°$ and $-30°$ and R.A. 0^h to 13^h in an area of 0.41 sr. The frequency is 408 MHz and the intensity limit is 1 f.u. at this frequency.

The number of discrete radio sources available for study is therefore enormous. The Bologna and the 4C results suggest that the number of sources per steradian exceeds 1000 to 1 f.u. This source-density gives well over 10 000 sources over the entire sky to 1 f.u., and the numbers can be increased at will by going to fainter levels.

2'3. *Early radio positions and optical I.D.* – Little progress in understanding the nature of radio sources could be made until they had been identified with optical objects. In the earliest days it was not even known if the sources were outside the solar system, but parallax measurements by RYLE and SMITH in 1948 and 1949 of *Cygnus* A and *Cassiopeia* A were sufficiently accurate to demonstrate that these sources were more distant than $2 \cdot 10^{16}$ cm, which placed them outside the solar system (RYLE, 1950).

The first suggestions for optical identifications were made by BOLTON, STANLEY, and SLEE (1949). They compared the radio positions of the objects discovered by BOLTON (1948) with known astronomical objects and suggested that *Taurus* A was coincident with the Crab Nebula, *Virgo* A with NGC 4486, and *Centaurus* A with NGC 5128. Each of the three identifications has withstood the test of time and are known to be correct. As each new survey was completed, the optical sky was searched for coincidences with positions of radio objects, and additional identifications were suggested. The most notable early successes were those of RYLE, SMITH, and ELSMORE (1950) in suggesting that the Andromeda Nebula and several other nearby galaxies were radio sources, and the several investigations of HANBURY BROWN and HAZARD (1951, 1952, 1953*a*, *b*) on other bright normal galaxies. In 1961 a summary of normal galaxies found to be radio sources was given by RYLE, SMITH, and ELSMORE, and one by HANBURY BROWN (see also the survey by HEESCHEN and WADE, 1964).

Aside from identifications of bright optical galaxies by special radiosurveys at the optical positions, the identification problem of the majority of the radio sources was one of accurate radio positions, and until the positions became highly accurate little progress was made in identification.

The first major break in the problem was made by BAADE and MINKOWSKI (1954*a*, *b*) in two papers that have become classics. Armed with accurate radio positions from each of the three principal groups (Cambridge, Jodrell Bank, Australian workers), BAADE and MINKOWSKI succeeded in identifying many sources with optical objects. Among them were *Cassiopeia* A, *Cygnus* A, *Puppis* A, NGC 1275, and a confirmation of the Crab Nebula, *Virgo* A, and *Centaurus* A. Besides the positive identification of *Cygnus* A, the importance of which will be discussed below, BAADE and MINKOWSKI's papers established beyond doubt the earlier conclusions of various workers such as OORT and WESTERHOUT (1951), and in particular MILLS (1952*a*), that the discrete sources are divided into two classes—those occurring in the galaxy and those which are extragalactic. A further subdivision into four classes was established by BAADE's and MINKOWSKI's work where the galactic sources were divided into (I) remnants of supernovae of which *Taurus* A, *Cassiopeia* A, and *Puppis* A are examples (see HARRIS, 1962 for a discussion complete to that date), and (II) galactic H II regions characterized by a thermal spectrum where the radio flux is independent of frequency except at low frequencies where the gas is optically thick (many references, among which are WILSON and BOLTON, 1960). The extragalactic sources are divided into (III) normal galaxies such as M31, M101, etc., which are intrinsically weak radio emitters (see HANBURY BROWN and HAZARD, 1959, 1961*a*, *b*), and (IV) strong radio sources identified with elliptical galaxies that may or may not be optically peculiar, of which NGC 5128, NGC 1316, NGC 1275, and NGC 4486 are examples. Also included in class IV are the quasi-stellar sources discussed later. Classes I and II are generally concentrated toward the galactic plane and have large angular diameters, circumstances which together with the flat spectrum of class II often permit a class identification on the basis of the radio data alone. Class III sources are easily recognized because of the ready identification with known bright galaxies. Class IV objects are the most difficult to identify because the optical galaxies are often very faint, very small in angular diameter, and occur in regions where similar optical galaxies are very numerous per square degree. These circumstances proved to be the barrier preventing wholesale optical identifications until the radio positions became exceedingly precise ($\pm 10''$ in both co-ordinates), beginning only in 1960-1963.

The identification of *Cygnus* A with the brightest member of a faint cluster of galaxies was made only when relatively precise positions were available. The history of the radio position work is given by BAADE and MINKOWSKI (1954*a*), where a table of radio positions available to 1952, as obtained by seven different teams, is shown. The most precise position was due to SMITH (1951), who used a new Cambridge interferometer on *Taurus* A, *Cassiopeia* A, *Cygnus* A, and *Virgo* A employing three different methods. Smith's positional accuracy for *Cygnus* A was quoted as $\pm 1''$ in R.A. and $\pm 60''$ in declination-values which proved to be realistic because the actual difference between his position and the optical object that was finally identified is 0.8 second of time in R.A. and $46''$ of arc in declination. A later position by MILLS (1952*b*) is nearly as accurate.

The identification of *Cygnus* A was highly important in one respect but somewhat unfortunate in another. Coming in 1954 before many identifications were available, a prediction was made from the characteristics of *Cygnus* A that most of the radio sources would be so distant that they would be well beyond the optical power of the 200-inch telescope working to its limit. The argument was as follows: *Cygnus* A is the second brightest radio source in the sky, second only the supernova remnant *Cassiopeia* A. The radio flux is 8100 f.u. at 178 MHz. Minkowski's redshift of $\Delta\lambda/\lambda_0 = 0.0570$ ($cz = 17100$ km/s symbolic velocity) showed that *Cygnus* A was at the relatively great distance of $1.7 \cdot 10^8$ parsec if the Hubble expansion rate is 100 km/s Mparsec. The galaxy involved is of apparent visual magnitude $\mathscr{V}_c = 14.36$, and apparent blue magnitude $\mathscr{B}_c = 15.51$ after correcting for galactic absorption and for aperture effect—the measurements being reduced to an isophote of 25 mag/square second of arc surface brightness (see HUMASON *et al.*, 1956, Appendix A for the method). If all radio galaxies were similar to *Cygnus* A in radio power, a discrete source observed at 10 f.u., being 810 times fainter than *Cygnus* A, would be 28 times further away, neglecting cosmological effects due to different world models. The object would be 7.3 magnitudes fainter, if we neglect the effects of red-shifts on the observed heterochromatic magnitudes, and assume similar absolute optical luminosities. But we cannot neglect the effect of red-shifts because the expected value of $\Delta\lambda/\lambda_0$ would be about 1.5 on a simple cosmological model with $q_0 = +1$ (see Sect. **5** and **7**), and the optical K dimming due to the shifting of the optical energy curve through the measuring band is very large—probably 3 mag for visual wavelengths (see HUMASON *et al.*, 1956, Appendix B for the theory of the K correction). This shows that a *Cygnus* A-type galaxy at 10 f.u. would be of optical apparent magnitude $\mathscr{V} \approx 14.44 + +10.3 = 24.7$, which is beyond the effective routine limit of the 200-inch telescope.

Variations of this argument were often used from 1954 to 1960 to suggest that most radio sources of class IV would not be optically identified and that radio observations could reach far beyond optical methods in studying the most distant reaches of space. But it is now known that this pessimistic conclusion is not valid in the majority of cases because the absolute radio power of strong radio galaxies has a spread of a factor of at least 10^5, with *Cygnus* A being nearly the strongest source intrinsically. The failure to identify optically large numbers of radio sources between 1954 and 1960 was, then, not due to the objects being so distant as to be invisible, but rather due to the relatively poor radio positions and the circumstance that most radio galaxies do not look peculiar optically. While it is true that the first galaxies to be identified were highly peculiar in some optical feature (the broad absorption band in NGC 5128, the jet in NGC 4486, and the rather chaotic filaments in NGC 1275) —circumstances which in many cases led to the initial suggestion of an identification—it is now known that most optical radio galaxies are not particularly abnormal in optical appearance. A positive identification usually results only when the radio position is accurate to about 15″ of arc in both coordinates. Positions of this accuracy have only been available since about 1962—a time which marks the beginning of wholesale optical identifications.

The situation concerning optical identifications in 1959 was summarized by DEWHIRST at the Paris radio-astronomy symposium. DEWHIRST listed fifteen optical identifications obtained from position coincidences of the 3C catalogue and optical photographs. Among these are the three identifications of BOLTON, STANLEY, and SLEE (1949), the BAADE and MINKOWSKI identifications, new cases identified with double elliptical galaxies (3C 310, 3C 315), and several sources in clusters of galaxies (3C 218, 3C 338, 3C 465, and 3C 219). Dewhirst's principal results were: 1) Double or multiple elliptical galaxies in a common envelope are frequently radio sources. These systems—hereafter called « dumbbells », the nomenclature adopted by MATTHEWS, MORGAN, and SCHMIDT (1964)—usually appear of about equal brightness and are often circular (*E*0) galaxies. 2) All identified radio sources are associated either with galactic nebulosities or with galaxies, but the bright nearby galaxies, such as M31, M101, M51, M81, etc., are not among the intrinsically powerful radio emitters. 3) The galaxies identified as intense sources are among the brightest galaxies known in optical absolute luminosities.

MINKOWSKI (1960) summarized his own investigations on identifications made in 1959 during a search for position coincidences on prints of the 48-inch Schmidt Sky Survey, using the first part of the MSH catalogue, and part of the 3C catalogue. His investigation, combined with the beautiful work by MILLS (1960), resulted in the examination of a total of 480 sources, of which only 59 objects were candidates for identification. These numbers, combined with Dewhirst's results on inspection of 430 sources of the 3C, of which only 15 identifications were noted, showed that less than 10 per cent of the sources could even be suggested to be associated with an optical object. However, this pessimistic result was later shown to be a result of poor radio positions.

One result by MILLS (1960) was that many clusters of galaxies in Abell's catalogue (1958) coincided with radio positions in the MHS list. This very important conclusion was verified by VAN DEN BERGH (1961*a*, *b*), and more recently by detailed identification studies using the precise radio positions available in 1965. About 30 per cent of all radio galaxies identified so far are in clusters or groups composed primarily of E or $S0$ systems.

BOLTON (1960) summarized the identification situation and listed 22 certain identifications and 7 less certain. Bolton's results again confirmed that no nearby bright spiral galaxies were strong radio sources, but rather the strong radio galaxies were of type E or $S0$ and were of exceedingly bright, absolute optical luminosity.

MINKOWSKI gave two further summaries, one in 1961 and the other in 1963. In the first paper, he listed 23 identifications from the MHS survey and 27 identifications from the 3C catalogue, all considered to be certain. Many of the new identifications were due to T. A. MATTHEWS of the California Institute of Technology, whose work will be described in Sect. 2·4 and 4·1. The second summary in 1963 is a critical discussion of the problem where it was shown that the abnormal number of « dumbbells » in the initial lists is a selection effect and that these double systems are not more numerous among radio sources than in the general field of nonradio galaxies.

It is fair to say that by about 1960 the identification problem had finished its first phase and had reached a stalemate with the positions available in the 3C and MSH lists. This was because the radio positions were not accurate enough to proceed further, except for the brightest sources where exceptional radio experiments had been performed, such as the early work of SMITH (1951), MILLS (1952), and later work by ELSMORE, RYLE, and LESLIE (1959). In many areas there were either many galaxies within the radio error rectangle or else nothing but stars were present. Realizing that more accurate positions were necessary, many groups proceeded to build new equipment, much of which was of the long base-line interferometric type. These instruments provided new radio positions of very high accuracy.

2·4. *Modern radio positions and optical identifications.* – The modern work on accurate radio positions can be said to begin with ELSMORE, RYLE, and LESLIE (1959). The new Cambridge aperture-synthesis interferometer was used at 178 MHz. Positions were determined for 64 radio sources in the 3C catalogue. The positional accuracies range from ± 1 to ± 2 seconds of time in R.A. and $\pm 0'.5$ to $\pm 3'.0$ in Dec. The optical positions of 10 calibrating sources were used to determine the constants of the instrument.

In 1963, READ at the California Institute of Technology determined declinations for 110 sources from 0 hours to 14 hours R.A., mostly from the 3C, with accuracies ranging from $\pm 2''.6$ to $\pm 46''$, with the average of $\pm 13''$. Again optical calibrators were used. Important catalogues by FOMALONT *et al.* (1964), CLARKE (1964), ADGIE (1964), WADE, CLARK, and HOGG (1965), and WILLS and PARKER (1966) all contain data of high accuracy. The work of

ADGIE and GENT (1966) is of exceptional importance. The positional accuracy of this catalogue ranges from $\pm 1''.0$ to $\pm 15''$ in R.A. and $\pm 1''.0$ to $\pm 24''$ in declination. There are 137 sources in the catalogue. These accuracies are so high that optical identifications are positive if any object appears at the radio position.

The situation concerning optical identifications changed abruptly between 1959 and 1962. Prior to 1959 only partial success was achieved, and then only for the brighter galaxies. Beginning with the knowledge of accurate radio positions in 1960, very great success has been attained, and indeed a new class of radio objects was isolated—the quasi-stellar sources, hereafter called QSS.

The modern search for optical identifications has been conducted principally by 1) the Cambridge group (LONGAIR, 1965; WILLS and PARKER, 1966; SHAKESHAFT and LONGAIR, 1965; and others); 2) the California Institute of Technology group (MATTHEWS, unpublished; WYNDHAM, 1965, 1966), and 3) the Mount Wilson and Palomar group (MATTHEWS and SANDAGE, 1963; SANDAGE and WYNDHAM, 1965; SANDAGE, VERON, and WYNDHAM, 1965; BOLTON, CLARKE, SANDAGE, and VERON, 1965; VERON, 1965, 1966).

The entire 3CR catalogue has been inspected by VERON and independently by WYNDHAM. Veron's analysis of the results available to June 1965 are as follows: There are 328 sources in the 3CR. The two sources 3C 129.1 and 3C 390.1 are probably erroneous; 28 sources are supernovae remnants or other structures connected with the galactic system. Of the remaining 298 sources, 40 are in low galactic latitudes in Hubble's zone of avoidance and therefore cannot be identified. Consequently, 258 sources are available for identification. Of these, 95 are positively identified galaxies, while 35 are possible galaxies; 35 are positively identified QSS, while 18 are possible QSS. In 18 fields there is no optical object at the radio position to the optical limit of the 48-inch Schmidt telescope. Finally, there were 60 fields which could not be adequately discussed due to lack of precise radio positions, or where two or more radio positions disagreed. The identification situation had improved by the middle of 1966, and more than 50 QSS were positively identified with a similar increase in the percentage of positively identified radio galaxies. Therefore, among the identified radio sources, about 28 per cent are QSS, while 72 per cent are radio galaxies; among the radio galaxies, 30 per cent are the brightest members of clusters. These encouraging results showed that more than 80 per cent of the 3CR sources either were, or could be, identified with optical objects to the limit of the 48-inch Schmidt telescope.

2'5. *Radio angular diameters and radio doubling.* – Soon after the discovery of discrete radio sources, attempts were made to find the radio angular diameters of the objects. It was soon found that most of the nongalactic sources had angular diameters smaller than the resolving power of single parabolic dishes or small parabolic cylinder arrays. In 1952 three groups developed independently and nearly simultaneously the radio analogue of Michelson's fringe visibility interferometric method of obtaining high angular resolution. The method consists of moving apart the elements of an interferometer array and measuring at each separation the amplitude of the fringes from a given source. A plot of the fringe visibility, defined as

$$\gamma = \frac{\text{fringe amplitude at base line } L}{\text{fringe amplitude at zero separation}},$$

against the base line expressed in wavelengths gives a curve which is the Fourier transform of the brightness distribution across the source in the direction of the base line of the two antennas. The angular size is obtained from the characteristics of this fringe visibility curve. The method was first used by HANBURY BROWN, JENNISON, and DAS (1952) at Jodrell Bank, by MILLS (1952c) at Sydney, and by SMITH (1952) at Cambridge to measure the angular diameter of *Cygnus* A, *Cassiopeia* A, and a few other sources.

The great discovery was made by JENNISON and DAS GUPTA (1953, 1956) when they succeeded in resolving *Cygnus* A into two separate radio components 85″ of arc apart and placed symmetrically on either side of the associated optical galaxy. Following this beautiful work, MALTBY and MOFFET (1962) at the California Institute of Technology and ALLEN *et al.* (1962) at Jodrell Bank analysed many 3C sources by these methods and found that most of the radio sources are double. The data in 1963 indicated that more than two thirds of the sources are double. The median angular separation between the sources is about 120″ with a range between 3″ and 1000″.

The same data on fringe visibilities can be used to derive the angular diameters of the separate components. Experiments at Jodrell Bank with extremely long base lines ranging up to 180 000 wavelengths have shown that most radio sources are larger than 0″.4 arc. The distribution of angular size (PALMER, 1963, Fig. 14/2) is such that 70 per cent of the sources have component sizes smaller than 200″ arc, 30 per cent smaller than 20″, and 10 per cent smaller than 2″ arc. In an attempt to resolve all of the sources, a special experiment using a 600 000 λ base line was performed by the Jodrell Bank observers in conjunction with the astronomers at the Royal Radar Establishment (ADGIE *et al.*, 1965). Even at this base line, the sources 3C 119, 3C 286, CTA 21, and CTA 102 remained unresolved, and, therefore, have angular diameters of less than 0″.1 arc. All other sources were resolved and many have double components. The smallest angular separation of double components which has so far been observed is 0″.4 arc for component B of 3C 273, each component of which is less than 0″.1 arc diameter.

Some well-known examples of source structure are as follows:

3C 33. This radio source is composed of two identical components, elongated along the line joining both components. The size of each component is $8'' \times 16''$; the separation is $250''$, *i.e.*, 200 kparsec (3C 33 is identified with a galaxy hawing a redshift of $z = 0.060$; $cz = 18.000$ km/s). The brightness distribution in each component is not uniform, but increases toward the outer edge, with a very strong gradient at the very end (MOFFET, 1964). The radio components are symmetrical about the optical galaxy.

Cygnus A. The radio structure for *Cygnus* A is very similar to 3C 33, but the separation of components is only 80 kparsec. The brightness distribution in the radio components has the same peculiarity as 3C 33.

3C 295. This source is also double with two similar components, but the elongation ($1'' \times 1''.7$) is perpendicular to the line joining the components. 3C 295 was identified by MINKOWSKI with the most remote known galaxy ($z = 0.461$); the separation of the components is about $4''$, *i.e.*, 16 kparsec.

3C 196. This source is identified with a QSS. It is double, both components having a size of $2''$ separated by $5''$.

MSH 14-121. This source was identified with a QSS. Its structure and position were studied by HAZARD (1964) by lunar occultation. The structure is double, the size of the components being, respectively, $5''$ and $< 5''$. The separation is $37''$. The « star » is located *between* the radio components in a quiet radio region (VERON, 1965).

Fornax A. Identified with the bright elliptical galaxy NGC 1316, which has a dark lane across it. The radio source is composed of two very large components symmetrical about the galaxy; the total size is about 1°. ARP (1964) showed that two faint optical extensions go into the radio components.

Centaurus A. This radio source is formed by two small components very near the center of the galaxy and two very large components with some structure (BOLTON and CLARK, 1960).

3. – Optical evidence for explosions: M82.

The unexpected results that most radio sources are double, with the individual components straddling the optical source, immediately suggested to many people that some ejection process has taken place in the radio sources. In the absence of better terminology, the unknown process has been called a violent event. It is here envisaged that an explosion of some sort has taken place, sending confined clouds of relativistic electrons outward from the central optical region—these electrons interacting with a magnetic field producing the radio emission.

The evidence for the explosion was indirect, based mainly on the radio-doubling observations. In the case of *galactic* radio sources the evidence is more direct, especially for the Crab Nebula (3C 144) where direct observation of the explosion was secured by the Chinese, and perhaps by the American Indians (MILLER, 1955). But supernova remnants are of much smaller order of magnitude as regards energy than galaxies, and no direct connection between the phenomenon necessarily exists.

But in 1963 direct optical evidence for an explosion was obtained for the source 3C 231, which coincides with the nearby peculiar optical galaxy M 82. LYNDS (1961), then at the National Radio Astronomy Observatory in Green Bank, showed that M82 is a radio source with an almost flat radio spectrum of index 0.2. LYNDS took a series of spectrograms with the Lick 120-inch and showed that strong emission lines of hydrogen, [S II] [N II] and [O I] were present at large distances above and below the fundamental plane along the minor axis. Direct photographs were then obtained by SANDAGE with an 80 Å total half-width interference filter at H_α using the 200-inch reflector. Large-scale filaments of hydrogen rising along the minor axis from the central regions were visible on the photographs. The spectrographic plates showed the emission lines to be inclined relative to laboratory comparison spectra, indicating large-scale motions along the minor axis. Analysis of the data (LYNDS and SANDAGE, 1963) showed that a nearly linear velocity-distance relation exists for the H_α filaments along the mirror axis and that an expulsion of $6\cdot10^6$ solar masses of hydrogen took place from the central regions of the galaxy about $1.5\cdot10^6$ years ago as seen from the earth. The kinetic energy of the moving gas is about 10^{55} erg.

The direct photographic evidence for the explosion has been reproduced in many places, among which should be mentioned the review article on violent events by BURBIDGE, BURBIDGE, and SANDAGE (1963).

One of the major problems for the model of M82 is the source of excitation energy for the H_α filaments. Since the galaxy is a radio source, radiating presumably by the synchrotron mechanism at radio frequencies, SANDAGE and MILLER speculated that optical synchrotron radiation might be present at a sufficient energy density to produce ionization of the hydrogen by synchrotron photons which exist below the Lyman limit at $\lambda = 912$ Å. If this were so, it should be possible to detect the optical synchrotron emission in the outer regions of the galaxy and in the neighborhood of the H_α filaments. A special series of direct photographs were obtained with the 200-inch reflector using blue plates sensitive to radiation between $\lambda = (3\,800 \div 5\,000)$ Å, a spectral region devoid of strong emission lines. An enormous set of filaments, radiating continuous light, was found (SANDAGE and MILLER, 1964), and these occupied the same general regions as the H_α structures. Figures 1 and 2 show the H_α and the continuous blue filaments. If these blue filaments were indeed synchrotron radiation, they should be highly polarized with the electric vector perpendicular to the magnetic field. Special polarization plates were taken, again with the 200-inch Hale reflector, and the result is shown in Fig. 3. It is evident

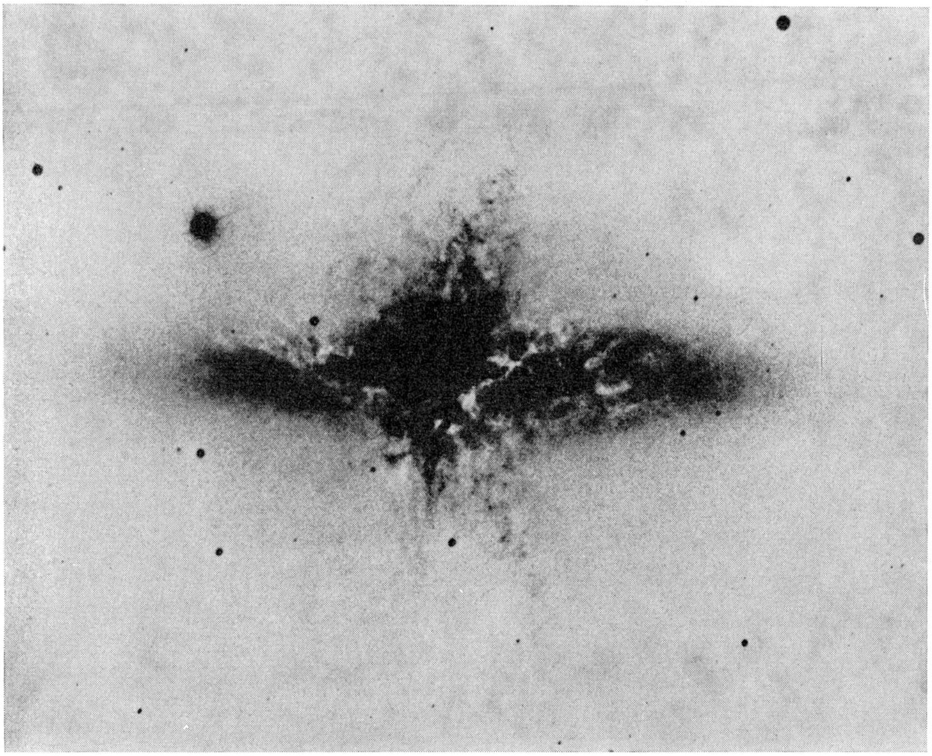

Fig. 1. – Photograph of M 82 taken with the 200-inch Hale reflector in H_α light with an interference filter of total halfwidth of 80 Å.

that a high degree of polarization is present with the electric vector along the major axis of the galaxy. This requires a relatively regular large-scale magnetic field to be present along the minor axis.

The analysis of LYNDS, SANDAGE, and MILLER of the phenomena in this galaxy, using the usual synchrotron equations, which need not be reproduced here, lead to a minimum total energy involved in the explosion between 10^{56} and 10^{59} erg. The lifetime of the source, deduced from the direct evidence from the kinematic field, is $1.5 \cdot 10^{6}$ years. If the electrons responsible for the optical synchrotron emission are not reaccelerated during this lifetime, the magnetic field must have a value less than 10^{-6} gauss. Any larger field will cause a decay of the energy of the electrons responsible for optical radiation

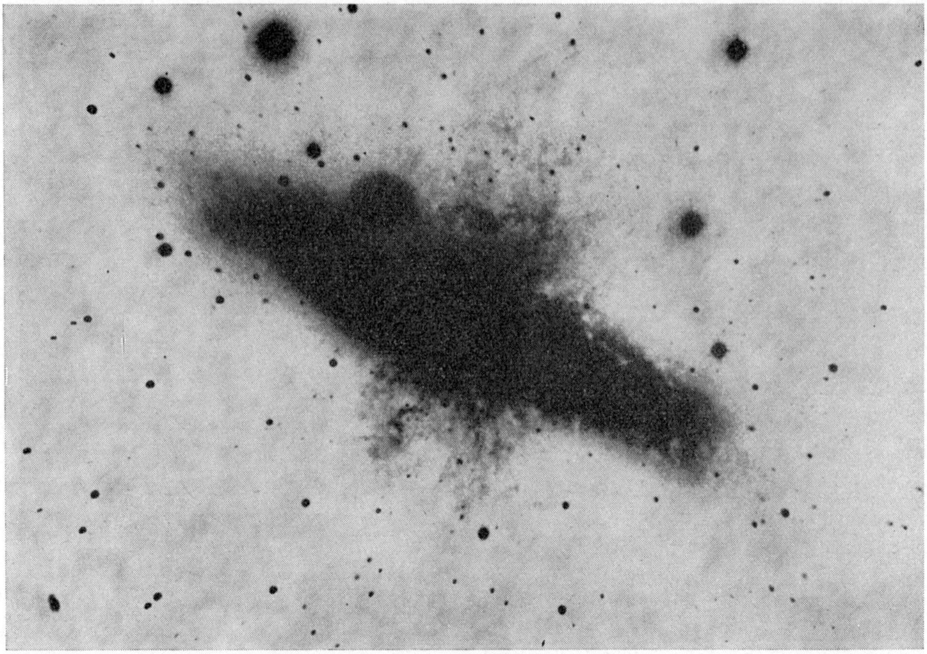

Fig. 2. – A composite negative print of M 82 from three plates taken with the 200-inch telescope in the wavelength interval 3800 to 5000 Å. The light from the filaments is shining by continuum radiation rather than emission from atomic lines.

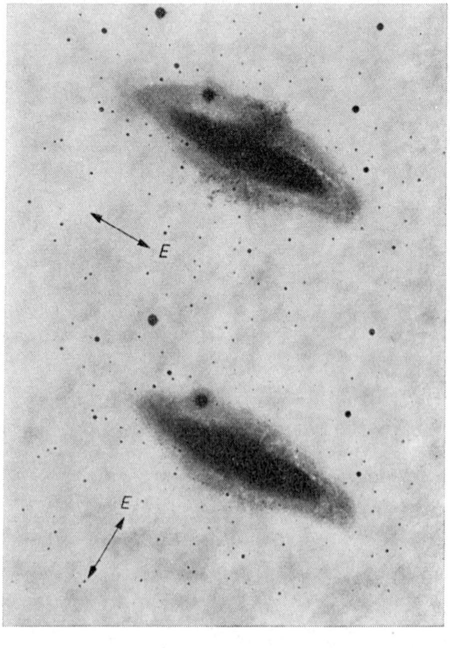

Fig. 3. – *a*) Composite of two superposed yellow-sensitive plates exposed through a Schott GG11 filter and HN38 polaroid sheet, recording the wavelength interval 5000 to 6200 Å, made with the 200-inch reflector. The electric vector of the polaroid sheet is at position angle 61.5° (north through east), which is predominantly along the major axis. The filaments radiate strongly in this position of the electric vector. *b*) Same as *a*, but with the electric vector of the polaroid sheet at 151.5°, which is predominantly along the minor axis. The filaments nearly disappear in this position of the electric vector.

at $\nu = 10^{15}$ Hz in times less than 10^6 years, which is the explosion lifetime of the source.

The energy of the electrons which produce radiation at $\nu = 10^{15}$ Hz in a field of 10^{-6} gauss is 8×10^3 GeV, which is in the low-energy cosmic-ray range.

There are, however, problems with this model of M82, notwithstanding the direct evidence of an explosion. Detailed measurements of the angular diameter of the radio source by interferometric methods shows that most of the radio radiation comes from a central region of 40″ diameter and this is much smaller than the size of the continuous filaments. Therefore, at the moment, there seems to be no connection between the radio source near the center and the optical synchrotron source which exists at distances of 5′ of arc in diameter from the nucleus along the minor axis. Consequently, the connection of explosive phenomena in M82 with the properties of radio sources in general is not clear. Nevertheless, most astronomers do believe that an explosive process is the *modus operandi* of strong radio sources.

4. – Quasi-stellar radio sources.

4·1. *Discovery.* – By 1960 angular diameters of the brighter 3C radio sources had become available, primarily through the work of the Jodrell Bank observers. Several sources such as 3C 48, 3C 286, 3C 196, and 3C 147 were known to have very small angular diameters and, hence, extremely high brightness temperatures. These sources stood out from all the others because of this characteristic. They were unidentified with optical galaxies, and because they differed so much from the galaxies in surface temperatures, they were deemed worthy of special attention. MATTHEWS of the California Institute of Technology prepared a partial list of high-surface-temperature sources for which moderately accurate radio positions had become available through the special work of the Cambridge and Caltech radio astronomers. Photographs of the 3C 48, 3C 196, and 3C 286 regions were obtained by SANDAGE in September 1960 with the 200-inch reflector. MATTHEWS found that there were single, starlike objects on the plates at the radio positions and these were the only objects within the error rectangle. SANDAGE then obtained spectrograms and photoelectric photometry of the 3C 48 object in October 1960, and these data showed that the object had unique characteristics never before observed in a celestial body. The $U-B$, $B-V$ colors were peculiar, resembling in some ways the colors of white dwarfs, old novae, and *U Gem* stars. But the spectrum was not like any of these objects. Broad emission lines were present which could not be identified. The details of this early work are given by MATTHEWS and SANDAGE (1963).

After the identification of 3C 48, 3C 196, and 3C 286 had been achieved,

SCHMIDT identified 3C 273 with a twelfth-magnitude stellar object that had an associated jet. He made the identification on a 200-inch plate which SANDAGE had previously taken during the program on the Matthews list of high-temperature sources. SCHMIDT used a precise radio position determined at Caltech, which was supplemented later by a position determined by the Australian astronomers from a lunar occultation of the radio source. Schmidt's famous investigation of the spectrum lines (1963) showed, for the first time, that these starlike objects had large red-shifts and that the emission lines could be identified with normal, red-shifted resonance features. SCHMIDT coined the name « quasi-stellar radio sources » for these objects—a name that has recently been contracted to quasars.

The identification of quasars then proceeded at a rapid rate with the discovery of 3C 147 as the fifth source (SCHMIDT and MATTHEWS, 1964), and soon thereafter the wholesale identification, based on the two-color technique (RYLE and SANDAGE, 1964), began. Identifications using radio positions and peculiar colors were made by SANDAGE and WYNDHAM (1965), SANDAGE, VERON, and WYNDHAM (1965), and BOLTON, CLARKE, SANDAGE, and VERON (1965) up to the time of the present summer school. Later identifications by VERON and by WYNDHAM (1966) had increased the sample of positive identifications to about 80 by mid-1966.

4·2. *Optical colors of quasars.* – The energy distribution of quasars differs from ordinary stars in the region of the Balmer discontinuity. Normal main-sequence stars show a strong ultra-violet deficiency near $\lambda 3700$ Å due to photon absorption by the Balmer continuum. Quasars do not have this feature. Their ultra-violet excess relative to normal stars has proved to be convenient in discovering new quasars and in verifying suggested identifications. Figure 4 shows the $U-B$, $B-V$ diagrams for all quasars for which photoelectric photometry existed to April 1966. The triangles are N-type galaxies which look like quasars on plates taken with small telescopes, but with large telescopes one can see the non-stellar image.

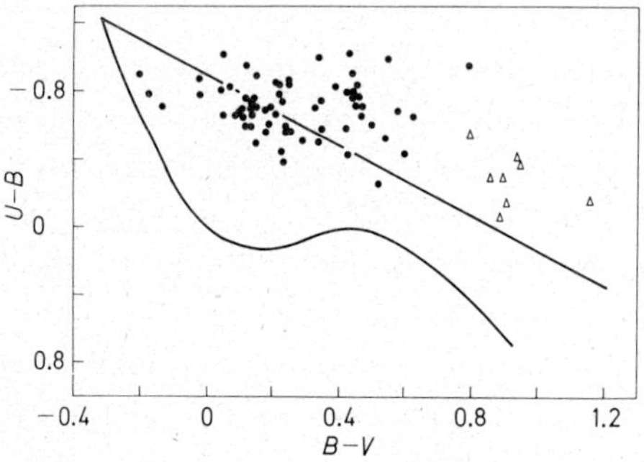

Fig. 4. – The $U-B$, $B-V$ diagram for all quasi-stellar radio sources whose photometry existed to May 1966. The triangles are eight N-type galaxies. The straight line is the black-body relation. The curved line is the relation for normal main-sequence stars.

The straight line in Fig. 4 is the black-body path. High temperature blackbodies are in the upper left, while low-temperature objects are in the lowest right. The main-sequence curve is shown. Because 99 per cent of all stars on the plane of the sky fall close to this curve, it is easy to distinguish QSS objects from ordinary stars by use of this two-color diagram.

The QSS lie on both sides of the black-body line. Those which lie below are in the region which white dwarfs occupy and it is, therefore, impossible to distinguish QSS from white dwarfs by color alone here. However, those QSS which lie above the black-body line are in a unique region populated by no other major class of astronomical objects.

4·3. *Optical variations.* – Both 3C 48 (Matthews and Sandage, 1963) and 3C 273 (Smith and Hoffleit, 1963) were discovered to be optical variables with fluctuations exceeding 0.4 mag. The most complete data are those of Smith (1964) for 3C 273 which extend from 1890 to the present. There is no doubt that this object has gone through several fluctuation cycles with a characteristic cycle time of about thirteen years.

Three-color photoelectric data exist for 3C 48 from 1960 to 1966 (Sandage, 1964, 1966). There is evidence for one short-term burst superposed on a longer-term fluctuation of several years duration. But there is yet no proof that the variations of either 3C 273 or 3C 48 are periodic. The data can equally well be explained as superposition of random variations.

All other QSS which have been adequately studied have been found to vary. Photoelectric observations at Palomar have shown that 3C 47, 196, 216, and 245 vary. Photographic observations of 3C 2, 43, and 454.3 indicate large changes of over 1 mag. in an eleven-year interval. Extensive observations of 3C 345 by Goldsmith and Kinman (1965) show large variations in a time interval as short as twenty days.

A general survey of all QSS in search for fluctuations has not yet been conducted, so there is no proof that all quasars do indeed vary. It will be important to attempt correlations of the time scale of variation (20 days for 3C 345 compared with 13 years for 3C 273) with such parameters as the radio diameter or the low-frequency cut-off in the radio spectrum due to synchrotron self-absorption.

4·4. *Radio variations.* – Early in 1964, Dent (1965) of the University of Michigan discovered that 3C 273, 3C 279, and 3C 345 have shown secular changes in their radio flux densities at 8 000 MHz. The variation in 3C 273 is beyond doubt, having increased 40 per cent in intensity in three years. Subsequent observations by Dent (1966) showed that 3C 84—which is NGC 1275, the brightest *galaxy* in the *Perseus* cluster—has also varied in radio flux.

The amplitude of the radio variations is a steep function of the frequency, and this is rather direct proof that the optical depth of the radio atmosphere

TABLE I. – *Summary of photoelectric and spectrogra*

Object	z (**)	V	$B-V$	$U-B$
				Objects in
3C 2	—	19.35	+0.79	—0.96
3C 9	2.012	18.21	+0.23	—0.74
3C 47	0.425	18.1	+0.05	—0.65
3C 48	0.367	16.2	+0.42	—0.58
3C 93	—	18.1	+0.34	—0.50
3C 138	0.759	17.9	+0.23	—0.38
3C 147	0.545	16.9	+0.35	—0.59
3C 181	1.382	18.92	+0.43	—1.02
3C 186	1.063	17.60	+0.45	—0.71
3C 191	1.946	18.4	+0.25	—0.84
3C 196	0.871	17.6	+0.60	—0.43
3C 204	1.112	18.21	+0.55	—0.99
3C 207	0.683	18.15	+0.43	—0.42
3C 208	1.110	17.42	+0.34	—1.00
3C 215	0.411	18.27	+0.21	—0.66
3C 216	—	18.3	+0.50	—0.60
3C 245	1.029	17.25	+0.45	—0.83
3C 249.1	0.311	15.72	—0.02	—0.77
3C 254	0.734	17.98	+0.15	—0.49
3C 263	0.652	16.32	+0.18	—0.56
				Non-3
3C 57	—	16.40	+0.14	—0.73
3C 232	0.534	15.78	+0.10	—0.68
3C 261	—	18.24	+0.24	—0.56
3C 279	0.536	17.75	+0.26	—0.56
3C 281	—	17.02	+0.13	—0.59
3C 446	1.403	18.39	+0.44	—0.90
MSH 03-19	0.614	16.24	+0.11	—0.65
MSH 13-011	—	17.68	+0.14	—0.66
MSH 14-121	0.942	17.37	+0.44	—0.76
CTA 102	1.038	17.32	+0.42	—0.79
0106+01	2.107	18.39	+0.15	—0.70
0922+14	0.900	17.96	+0.54	—0.52
0952+18	1.471	—	—	—
0957+00	0.908	17.57	+0.47	—0.71
1116+12	2.118	19.25	+0.14	—0.76
1217+02	0.240	16.53	—0.02	—0.87

(*) There are 55 red-shifts and 69 photoelectric values.

(**) Red-shifts due to SCHMIDT, LYNDS, M. BURBIDGE, RUBIN and FORD, and KINMAN. Photometry due to SANDAGE, except for PHL 938 which is due to KINMAN.

on QSS Complete to June 1966 (*).

Object	z (**)	V	$B-V$	$U-B$
R catalogue				
3C 268.4	1.40	18.42	+0.58	−0.69
3C 270.1	1.519	18.61	+0.19	−0.61
3C 273	0.158	12.8	+0.21	−0.85
3C 275.1	0.557	19.00	+0.23	−0.43
3C 277.1	0.320	17.93	−0.17	−0.78
3C 280.1	1.659	19.44	−0.13	−0.70
3C 286	0.846	17.30	+0.22	−0.84
3C 287	1.054	17.67	+0.63	−0.65
3C 288.1	0.961	18.12	+0.39	−0.82
3C 298	1.439	16.79	+0.33	−0.70
3C 309.1	0.903	16.78	+0.46	−0.77
3C 334	0.555	16.41	+0.12	−0.59
3C 336	0.927	17.47	+0.44	−0.79
3C 345	0.594	15.96	+0.29	−0.50
3C 351	0.371	15.28	+0.13	−0.75
3C 380	0.691	16.81	+0.24	−0.59
3C 432	1.804	17.96	+0.22	−0.79
3C 454	1.756	18.40	+0.12	−0.95
3C 454.3	—	16.10	+0.47	−0.66
ects				
1252+11	0.870	16.64	+0.35	−0.75
PHL 658	—	16.40	+0.11	−0.70
PHL 923	—	17.33	+0.20	−0.70
PHL 938	1.93	17.16	+0.32	−0.88
PHL 1078	—	18.25	+0.04	−0.81
PHL 1093	—	17.07	+0.05	−1.02
PHL 1305	—	16.96	+0.07	−0.82
PHL 1377	—	16.46	+0.15	−0.89
PHL 3740	—	18.61	+0.09	−0.65
PHL 6638	—	17.72	+0.18	−0.69
4C 39.25	0.698	—	—	—
4C 21.35	0.435	17.50	+0.06	−0.69
4C 20.33	0.871	17.65	+0.44	−0.69
4C 29.68	1.015	17.30	+0.65	−0.87
BSO 1	1.241	16.98	+0.31	−0.78
Ton 256	0.131	15.41	+0.65	−0.78

of these sources increases with decreasing ferquency. MOFFET showed that the percentage of fluctuation in 3C 273 and in others of Dent's list decreased drastically as the frequency of observation was changed from 8 000 MHz to 1 000 MHz, going to zero at about 30 cm.

4·5. *Discussion of the optical and radio variations.* – The existence of variable quasars was completely unexpected after Schmidt's discovery of the red-shifts. If the distances to the QSS are as large as the red-shifts imply, assuming Hubble's expansion law applies, then the optical and radio power emitted by the sources are very large. For 3C 48, the power radiated between $\lambda_0 = 2\,340$ Å and $\lambda_0 = 4390$ Å in the rest system is $1.3 \cdot 10^{45}$ erg/s (SANDAGE, 1964). A similar power level applies to the radio emission between 10^7 and 10^{10} Hz. How can the source modulate this very large power output in such a short time-interval? TERRELL (1964) showed that the linear diameter of a variable quasar must be smaller than the fluctuation period, otherwise the modulation amplitude would be reduced to a small fraction of its true value. These considerations suggested to some astronomers that the QSS are not at cosmological distances but are local phenomena where the red-shifts are due to causes other than the expansion of the universe. The optical and radio variations themselves do not force this conclusion because the linear diameters of the fluctuating component of the QSS can be as small as Terrell's argument requires and not be in conflict with the observations. And, indeed, as the radio astronomers increase the resolution of the measurements of angular diameters, smaller and smaller radio diameters are being found. The fluctuations themselves, then, do not force the issue of the cosmological *vs.* local hypothesis, and, in the case of NGC 1275 where variations *have* been observed, we know the source is extragalactic and at the Hubble distance. There does remain, of course, the problem of the physics involved in the mechanism of the fluctuations themselves.

4·6. *Red-shifts.* – Since Schmidt's discovery in 1963, a large number of red-shifts have been obtained for quasars. A total of 55 red-shifts were known to June 1966, principally through the work of SCHMIDT, C. R. LYNDS, MRS. BURBIDGE, and RUBIN and FORD. Table I is a summary list complete to June 1966, together with the photometry available on QSS to that date.

5. – Absolute power levels of radio galaxies and quasars.

At this writing, red-shifts exist for about 60 radio galaxies and for a comparable number of quasars. The absolute power generated by each source can be computed from 1) the observed flux density and 2) the distance determined from the Hubble law. In principle, a model of the universe must be known to make a correct calculation, but in practice the changes caused by differences in world models are very small.

A rigorous formulation starts from Robertson's equation which relates apparent luminosity to absolute luminosity, red-shift, and metric distance. The equation is

$$l = \frac{L}{4\pi R_0^2 r^2 (1+z)^2}, \tag{1}$$

where R_0 is the present value of the space dilatation factor, r is the co-moving radial co-ordinate in the Robertson-Walker line element, and z is the red-shift. A photometric distance, D, can be defined by

$$D = R_0 r(1+z) \tag{2}$$

such that

$$l = \frac{L}{4\pi D^2}. \tag{3}$$

MATTIG (1958) and SANDAGE (1961*a*, 1962) have shown that

$$D = \frac{c}{H_0 q_0^2}\{q_0 z + (q_0 - 1)[(1+2q_0 z)^{\frac{1}{2}} - 1]\} \tag{4}$$

for all Friedman-type models with the cosmological constant equal to zero. Here H_0 is the present value of the Hubble expansion rate and q_0 is the deceleration parameter defined as

$$q_0 = -\frac{\ddot{R}_0}{R_0 H_0^2}. \tag{5}$$

For the special case of steady-state cosmology where $q_0 = -1$, the photometric distance is given by

$$D = \frac{cz(1+z)}{H_0}. \tag{6}$$

If $q_0 = +1$, eq. (4) reduces to the usual form of

$$D = \frac{cz}{H_0}, \tag{7}$$

and the absolute luminosity is given, from eq. (3), by

$$L = \frac{4\pi c^2 z^2}{H_0^2}\, l. \tag{8}$$

If $H_0 = 100$ km/s Mparsec, this becomes

$$L = 1.08 \cdot 10^{44} l z^2 \text{ erg/s} , \tag{9}$$

when l is expressed in units of 10^{-16} watt/meter².

As we shall see in the last Section, the value of $q_0 = +1$ is a good approximation to the available data. Therefore, eq. (8) has been used to calculate absolute radio power levels from the apparent luminosity, l, corrected for red-shift.

The proper integrated flux l is here defined as the apparent power received from each source between rest frequencies of 10^7 to 10^{10} Hz. This can be calculated from the observed radio spectrum, assumed to be a power law with the frequency as argument, with the appropriate K-term included. The K-term corrects for 1) the change in effective bandwidth due to red-shift and 2) the selective term due to the shifting of the spectrum through the fixed frequency to which the radio receiver is tuned. It is easy to show (SANDAGE, 1967*a*) that

$$l = A(1+z)^{n-1} \int_{10^7}^{10^{10}} \nu^{-n} \, d\nu , \tag{10}$$

where the observed radio flux density S is of the form

$$S = A\nu^{-n} \text{ watt/meter}^2 \text{ hertz} . \tag{11}$$

The proper integrated flux for each radio galaxy and for each QSS which have red-shifts was calculated from eq. (10) using all radio spectral data available, or was taken from Kellerman's tabulation (1964), with the appropriate K-correction applied. Equation (9) then gives the absolute radio power in erg/s between rest frequencies of 10^7 and 10^{10} Hz.

The power levels L_R are displayed in Fig. 5, where they are plotted against distance modulus

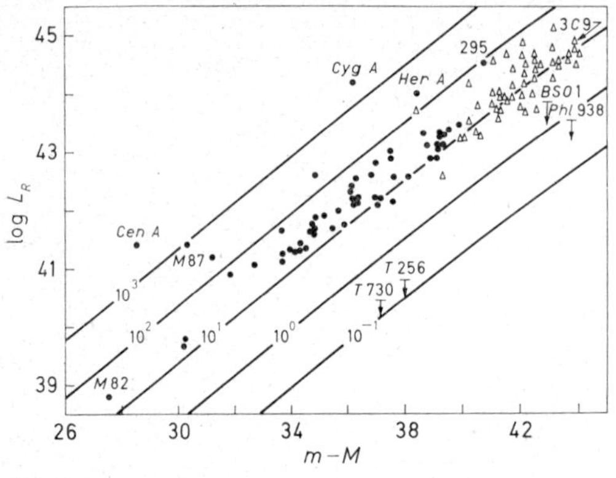

Fig. 5. – The absolute radio power, L_R, between proper frequencies of 10^7 to 10^{10} Hz, plotted against distance modulus for all radio galaxies (dots) and quasars (triangles) whose red-shifts were known to May 1966. The sloping lines are loci of constant apparent flux densities at 178 MHz.

$m-M$ calculated on the $q_0=+1$ assumption from

$$m - M = 5 \log cz + 15 \equiv 5 \log D - 5 , \tag{12}$$

where D is the photometric distance in parsec. This equation assumes a Hubble constant of $H_0 = 100$ km/s Mparsec.

The diagram contains an enormous amount of information, not only about the characteristics of presently identified radio sources but also about the prospects for future optical identifications. (The circles in the diagram represent radio galaxies while the triangles are QSS.)

The most striking, but superficial, characteristic of Fig. 5 is the correlation of L_R with distance modulus. The lower envelope of the data points is well represented by $L_R \propto D^2$. This of course, has no physical meaning but is caused entirely by observational selection due to the fact that the sample is chosen from a radio catalogue (3CR) which is complete to a given apparent flux limit. The sloping lines in Fig. 5 are loci of constant flux density S at 178 MHz. Lines of 1000, 100, 10, 1, and 0.1 flux units at this frequency are shown, and, as required by the nature of the sample, the data-points are bounded by the $S=10$ limit line, which is near the lower limit of the 3CR catalogue. The main features of the diagram are:

A) The absolute radio power of the sources varies by a factor of 10^6, ranging from 10^{39} erg/s for M82 to about 10^{45} erg/s for *Cyg* A, 3C 295, and a number of quasi-stellar sources. It is significant in this regard that the most intense radio galaxies (*Cyg* A, *Her* A, and 3C 295) rival the QSS in L_R. This shows that from the magnitude of the radio power levels alone, there can be no argument that QSS must be local because their L_R values are too large if they are at the Hubble distance. Such an argument has been used, but it is specious because radio galaxies, which are certainly at the Hubble distance, reach comparable L_R values.

B) The diagram suggests why red-shifts much larger than $z=2$ have not yet been observed. It appears that an upper limit of $L_R \simeq 10^{45}$ erg/s may exist for radio sources. This limiting line intersects the $S=10$ f.u. sloping line at $m-M=44$, which corresponds to a red-shift of $z=2$. Quasars with *larger* red-shifts must have apparent flux densities less than $S=10$ f.u. if they are to lie below the $L_R=10^{45}$ limit. Consequently, QSS with $z>2$ will appear as entries in radio catalogue only if these lists go well below 10 f.u. at 178 MHz. The 4C and 5C catalogues must therefore be used for optical identification if large red-shifted objects are to be located.

C) The diagram is useful in visualizing the problem of the radio-luminosity function. Between each successive magnitude interval in $m-M$, the volume of space sampled increases by a factor of 4. Consequently, the count of sources in vertical strips in the diagram separated by one magnitude should be in the ratio of 4 to 1 between adjacent strips. The expectation for optical identifications in radio catalogues which reach 1 or 0.1 f.u. is that many fairly bright galaxies should be found. For example, there are two radio galaxies in the present sample at $L_R \simeq 10^{41}$ erg/s in the interval of $m-M$ from 31 to 32. We would, therefore, expect for a similar fraction of completeness in a radio catalogue reaching 1 f.u. that there should be 512 radio galaxies near $L_R = 10^{41}$ erg/s in the modulus range from $m-M=35$ to 36. Since the mean absolute luminosity of radio galaxies is $\bar{M}_V = -21^{\mathrm{m}}.6$ with a dispersion of $\sigma_V = 0^{\mathrm{m}}.44$, as can be computed from the data in the last Section, these galaxies should appear at $V=14^{\mathrm{m}}$, which is very bright.

D) We have no information on the range of L_R among QSS because of the selection effect that works on the present sample. Figure 5 shows that the nearest QSS appears at a modulus of $m-M=38.5$. The quasars are so rare per unit volume of space that we must look to this modulus to find the nearest one, as long as we restrict $\log L_R$ to be equal to or greater than 42.8 (this is the intersection of the $S=10$ line with $m-M=38.5$). Any intrinsically fainter quasar than this absolute power will not be included in the 3CR catalogue because $S \leqslant 10$ f.u. with these parameters. Consequently, the entire area of the diagram lying below $S=10$ and $m-M \geqslant 39$ is denied the optical astronomer if he searches for QSS from the 3CR catalogue. If this region is filled with QSS (*i.e.*, if the range of L_R is large), the observer must discover these sources *by optical means*. It is here that the quasi-stellar galaxies (*i.e.*, the «radio quiet» quasars) lie, as discussed in the next Section.

6. – The existence of quasi-stellar galaxies.

6·1. *Discovery*. – Early in 1965 SANDAGE and VERON (1965) were conducting a search for blue stellar objects by the two-color photographic method (RYLE and SANDAGE, 1964) in an effort to discover quasars. In their general search near 3CR radio positions, they had previously noticed that many ultraviolet objects were present over the two-color plates in places other than the radio positions. The frequency of such objects was about four per square degree (SANDAGE, 1965). It was soon realized that these objects were similar to those found and catalogued by HARO and LUYTEN in 1962. Photoelectric photometry of a number of these so-called interlopers showed a distribution of color indices very similar to that in Fig. 4. A series of inductive arguments led SANDAGE to the conclusion that a large number of the Haro-Luyten-type blue objects were not stars but were quasi-stellar objects whose apparent radio flux was smaller than the limit of existing radio catalogues. The arguments will not be repeated here. Reference to the original paper (SANDAGE, 1965) should be made. This hypothesis that many of the PHL objects are extragalactic was partially tested by obtaining red-shifts for three of the candidate objects. BSO1 (SANDAGE and VERON, 1965) and Tonantzintla 730 and 256 (IRIARTE and CHAVIRA, 1957) all proved to have appreciable red-shifts, a result which would not have been obtained if all the high-latitude blue objects had been stars.

SANDAGE (1965) estimated that about 80 per cent of the objects in the PHL catalogue would be extragalactic. This result was criticized by KINMAN (1965) and by LYNDS and VILLERE (1965) who pointed out that the known frequency distribution of white dwarfs required that a large number of the PHL objects were nearby stars of this type. KINMAN produced spectrographic data for 12 Tonantzintla objects, all of which proved to be stars associated with our Galaxy, whereas the statistics of SANDAGE required that one half should be quasi-stellar galaxies. Neither KINMAN nor LYNDS questioned the *existence* of the new class of extragalactic objects, but rather indicated that the percentage of QSG to blue halo stars was lower than Sandage's estimates. Indeed, in the course of further observations, KINMAN produced new evidence himself for the reality of the new class. His spectra of PHL 938 showed that this object was a radio-quiet QSS with a red-shift of $z=1.93$.

By the middle of 1966, *UBV* photoelectric photometry had been completed by SANDAGE of an unbiased sample of one of the PHL fields. These data, combined with proper-motion measurements by LUYTEN, showed that between 17 and 20 per cent of the PHL objects could be extragalactic radio-quiet QSS (*i.e.*, quasi-stellar galaxies), between 13 and 16 per cent are probably white dwarfs, and 63 per cent are subdwarf stars characteristic of globular-cluster main-sequence stars. If the sample is restricted only to those objects listed as very blue in the PHL catalogue, the percentages are 41 to 50 per cent QSG, between 41 and 50 per cent white dwarfs, 9 per cent horizontal-branch stars, and there are no subdwarfs.

These preliminary values suggest a surface density of about 0.8 extragalactic QSG per square degree to $V=18.5$ apparent magnitude. This is to be compared with the surface density of 0.01 QSS per square degree identified from the 3CR radio catalogue. Thus, the radioquiet QSG might be as much as 80 times more numerous than the quasi-stellar radio sources which are visible to a limit of 9 f.u. These objects are expected to fill the lower right portion of Fig. 5, and many of them will be identified as weak radio sources in catalogues whose limiting flux density is as low as 0.1 f.u.

7. – Observational cosmology using radio sources.

BOLTON (1960) was among the first to suggest that the radio objects which had been identified with galaxies formed a homogeneous set as regards absolute luminosity. His visual estimates of apparent luminosities from 48-inch Schmidt plates, together with the redshift data then available, permitted him to conclude that « the radio galaxies appear to be mainly systems of high absolute brightness ». BOLTON found that $\bar{M}_{pg} = -19.9$ with a dispersion of somewhat less than 1 mag. This absolute luminosity is based on a distance scale given by a Hubble constant of $H_0 = 100$ km/s Mparsec.

The small dispersion in absolute luminosity, and the ability to obtain large red-shifts by use of the emission lines of the optical spectra make radio galaxies ideal systems for a study of the Hubble law of the expansion of the universe. Beginning in 1963, SANDAGE obtained photoelectric intensity measurements of all identified radio galaxies with known red-shifts. Measurements were made with several aperture sizes so as to obtain « asymptotic » magnitude values to a given isophotal contour. New tables of the K dimming were computed from Oke's energy distribution curves of nearby E galaxies, and these have been published in the 1964 Padua Galileo Conference (SANDAGE, 1967*b*) and are not reproduced here.

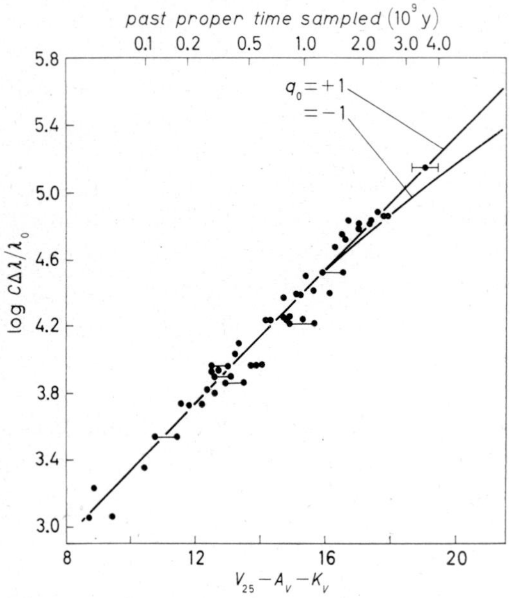

Fig. 6. – The red-shift-corrected apparent-magnitude relation for 46 radio galaxies whose red-shifts were known to April 1965 ($L_R \geqslant 2 \cdot 10^{40}$ erg/s). Two theoretical lines for different cosmological models are shown.

These new results confirm Bolton's conclusion that strong radio galaxies are confined to a narrow range of absolute luminosities, and that they can indeed be used to study the cosmological problem. Figure 6 shows the Hubble diagram for 46 radio galaxies available to June 1965. Plotted is the correlation between red-shift and the apparent visual magnitude corrected for 1) aperture effect to an isophote of about 25 mag. per square second of arc, 2) visual absorption due to interstellar extinction in our own Galaxy, and 3) the K dimming. Dumbbells are indicated by two points connected by a horizontal line, showing the combined light and the light of the brightest component. The lines for two different q_0 values are drawn, as taken from the theory of homogeneous and isotropic expanding spaces (SANDAGE, 1961*a*). The slope of these lines is 5 in the limit of small red-shift. This is the theoretical slope if red-shifts increase directly with distance, as in Hubble's law.

Figure 7 shows the Hubble diagram for the first-ranked cluster galaxy for 20 clusters of galaxies. The two theoretical lines are identical in slope and in zero point with the relations in Fig. 6. This proves that radio galaxies reach the same absolute luminosity as the brightest galaxy in the great clusters. It suggests that a necessary, but not sufficient, condition for a galaxy to become a strong radio source is that it be the most luminous and, therefore, the most massive type of system known. Galaxies whose luminosities differ from the first-ranked cluster member by more than about one magnitude are not capable of generating radio energy at a level of $2\cdot10^{40}$ erg/s.

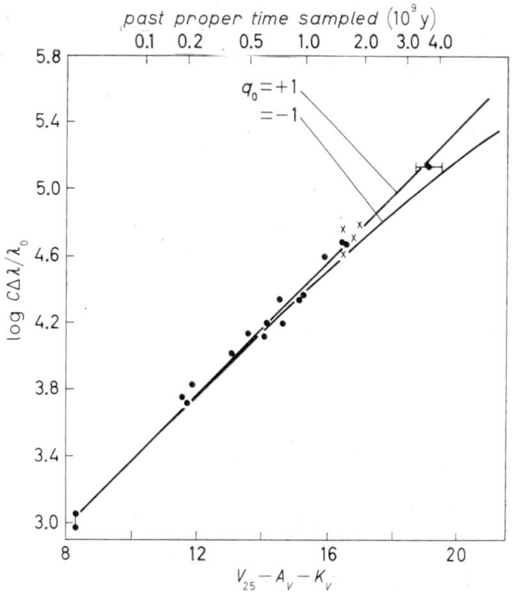

Fig. 7. – Same as Fig. 6 but for the first-ranked galaxy in clusters of galaxies.

Figure 8 shows the Hubble diagram for radio galaxies and for QSS. The $q_0=+1$ line through the quasars is displaced toward brighter luminosities by $\Delta V \simeq 3^m.1$, which proves that the quasars are indeed sixteen times brighter than the brightest ellip-

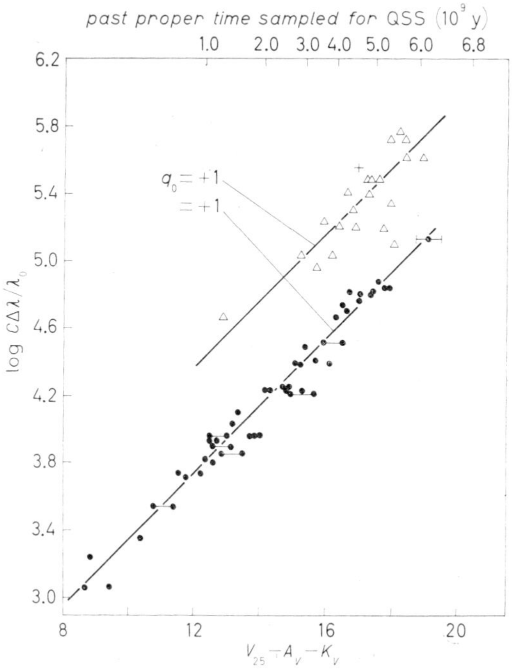

Fig. 8. – Same as Fig. 6 but with the quasars included as triangles. The data were complete to July 1965. More recent data available in 1966 show that the scatter of the QSS about the $q_0=+1$ line is much larger. This, at the moment, restricts the use of QSS in discussions of the value of q_0.

tical galaxies known, in the mean. The scatter of the quasars about the line is large, and data available to June 1966 on a three-times larger sample of quasars show that the scatter is too large for QSS to be used for a cosmological determination of q_0.

Figure 9 shows the most recently available data for the Hubble diagram, where the radio galaxies and the first-ranked, nonradio cluster galaxies are combined. Curves for various values of the deceleration parameter are shown for comparison. The value $q_0 = -1$ represents the steady-state model. Friedman exploding models of zero cosmological constant are represented by a continuum of q_0 values such that $q_0 \geqslant 0$. The value $q_0 = +0.5$ separates the Friedman models into the oscillating and the ever-expanding cases. The radius of curvature of the universe is given by the well-known equation

$$\frac{kc^2}{R_0^2} = H_0^2(2q_0 - 1) \tag{13}$$

(see *e.g.* SANDAGE, 1961*a*), which shows that the three-dimensional subspace of the four-dimensional space-time continuum is Euclidean if $q_0 = +0.5$. Larger values of q_0 represent spaces of constant positive curvature of finite volume. Values of q_0 between 0 and $+0.5$ are spaces of negative curvature of infinite volume.

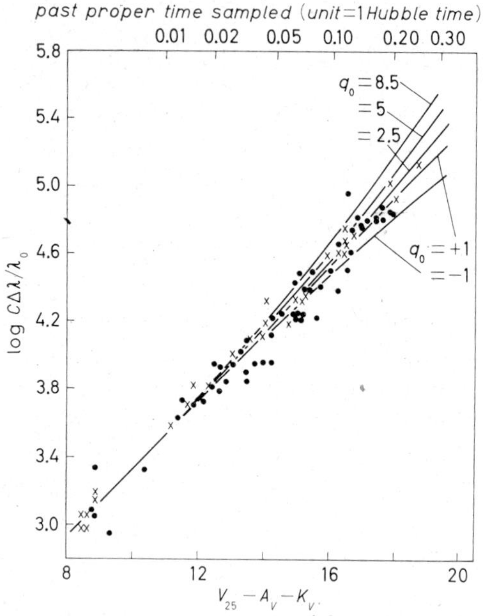

Fig. 9. – Combined data for radio galaxies and first-ranked cluster members: × brightest cluster galaxy; • radio galaxies. Several theoretical relations for different values of q_0 are shown.

The present data can be used to 1) reassess the validity of Hubble's linear expansion law and 2) make a preliminary determination of the value of q_0. Least squares solutions with the data of Fig. 7, letting the slope of the correlation remain an unknown, gives

$$\begin{aligned} V_c = {} & 4.910 \log c\,\Delta\lambda/\lambda_0 - 0.115\,\Delta\lambda/\lambda_0 - 6.47 \\ & \pm 0.055 \qquad\qquad \pm 0.323 \qquad\qquad \pm 0.23 \end{aligned} \tag{14}$$

for the nonradio cluster data of Fig. 7. The radio galaxy data combined with the cluster data, as in Fig. 9, gives

$$V_c = \underset{\pm 0.085}{4.971} \log c\,\Delta\lambda/\lambda_0 - \underset{\pm 0.553}{1.014}\,\Delta\lambda/\lambda_2 - \underset{\pm 0.36}{6.67}\,. \tag{15}$$

The slope coefficient of the leading term gives the exponent on the distance in Hubble's law. It is easy to show that eqs. (14) and (15) require the expansion law to be of the form

$$c\frac{\Delta\lambda}{\lambda_0} = Hr^{0.982\pm0.011} \tag{16}$$

from eq. (14), and

$$c\frac{\Delta\lambda}{\lambda_0} = Hr^{0.994\pm0.017} \tag{17}$$

from eq. (15) in the limit as $z \to 0$. These exponents are so close to 1.0, which is the theoretical requirement, that new solutions were made with this as a condition. The results are

$$V_c = 5 \log c\,\Delta\lambda/\lambda_0 - \underset{\pm 0.309}{0.551}\,\Delta\lambda/\lambda_0 - \underset{\pm 0.04}{6.80} \tag{18}$$

for the combined data.

The coefficient of the redshift term is related to q_0 by $1.086(1-q_0)$. Combining equations (15) and (18) with a solution from the radio galaxies alone then gives

$$q_0 = +1.65 \pm 0.3\,. \tag{20}$$

This differs from the steady-state value of $q_0 = -1$ by nine times the probable error. Therefore, the data suggest that steady-state cosmology does not fit the observations. Of the two available theories of cosmology, we must conclude that the present data fit the Friedman model best. But, if this is so, the solutions are not complete. Corrections must be applied for the evolution of the stellar content of the elliptical galaxies plotted in Fig. 6, 7, and 9 during the light travel time (SANDAGE, 1961*b*). A presently incomplete analysis of this evolutionary effect shows that q_0 will be reduced from 1.65 to a value close to $q_0 = +0.5 \pm 0.3$, which is the critical value between open and closed Friedman spaces. It is therefore evident that no decision between *various* Friedman models is yet possible, but there is every hope that future work on the stellar content of elliptical galaxies will solve this problem.

BIBLIOGRAPHY

ABELL, G. O., 1958, *A. J. Supp.*, **3**, 211.
ADGIE, R. L., 1964, *Nature*, **204**, 1028.
ADGIE, R. L. and H. GENT, 1966, *Nature*, **209**, 549.
ADGIE, R. L., *et al.*, 1965, *Nature*, **208**, 275.
ALLEN, L. R., *et al.*, 1962, *M. N.*, **124**, 477.
ARP, H. C., 1964, *Ap. J.*, **139**, 1378.
BAADE, W. and R. MINKOWSKI, 1954*a*, *Ap. J.*, **119**, 206.
BAADE, W. and R. MINKOWSKI, 1954*b*, *Ap. J.*, **119**, 215.
BENNETT, A. S., 1962*a*, *M. N.*, **125**, 75.
BENNETT, A. S., 1962*b*, *Mem. R.A.S.*, **68**, 163.
BENNETT, A. S. and F. G. SMITH, 1961, *M. N.*, **122**, 71.
BERGH, S. VAN DEN, 1961*a*, *Ap. J.*, **134**, 970.
BERGH, S. VAN DEN, 1961*b*, *A. J.*, **66**, 562.
BOLTON, J. G., 1948, *Nature*, **162**, 141.
BOLTON, J. G., 1960, *Observations of Calif. Inst. Tech. Rad. Obs.*, No. **5**.
BOLTON, J. G. and B. CLARK, 1960, *Pub. A.S.P.*, **72**, 29.
BOLTON, J. G. and G. J. STANLEY, 1948, *Nature*, **161**, 312.
BOLTON, J. G., F. F. GARDNER and M. B. MACKEY, 1964, *Aust. J. Phys.*, **17**, 340.
BOLTON, J. G., G. J. STANLEY and O. B. SLEE, 1949, *Nature*, **164**, 101.
BOLTON, J. G., G. J. STANLEY and O. B. SLEE, 1954, *Aust. J. Phys.*, **7**, 110.
BOLTON, J. G., M. CLARKE, A. SANDAGE and P. VÉRON, 1965, *Ap. J.*, **142**, 1289.
BRACCESI, A., M. CECCARELLI, *et al.*, 1965, Preprint from the Bologna radio project.
BROWN, R. HANBURY, 1962, *Problems in Extragalactic Research*, ed. G. C. MCVITTIE (New York), p. 79.
BROWN, R. HANBURY and C. HAZARD, 1951, *M. N.*, **111**, 357.
BROWN, R. HANBURY and C. HAZARD, 1952, *Phil. Mag.*, **43**, 137.
BROWN, R. HANBURY and C. HAZARD, 1952*a*, *M. N.*, **113**, 123.
BROWN, R. HANBURY and C. HAZARD, 1953*b*, *Nature*, **172**, 853.
BROWN, R. HANBURY and C. HAZARD, 1959, *M. N.*, **119**, 297.
BROWN, R. HANBURY and C. HAZARD, 1961*a*, *M. N.*, **122**, 479.
BROWN, R. HANBURY and C. HAZARD, 1961*b*, *M. N.*, **123**, 279.
BROWN, R. HANBURY, R. C. JENNISON and M. K. DAS GUPTA, 1952, *Nature*, **170**, 1061
BURBIDGE, G. R., E. M. BURBIDGE and A. R. SANDAGE, 1963, *Rev. Mod. Phys.*, **35**, 947.
CLARKE, M. E., 1964, *M. N.*, **127**, 405.
DENT, W. A., 1965, *Science*, **148**, 1458.
DENT, W. A., 1966, *Ap. J.*, **144**, 843.
DEWHIRST, D. W., 1959, *Paris Symposium on Radio Astronomy*, ed. R. N. BRACEWELL (Stanford, California: Stanford University Press), p. 507.
EDGE, D. O., P. A. G. SCHEUER and J. R. SHAKESHAFT, 1958, *M. N.*, **118**, 183.
EDGE, D. O., J. R. SHAKESHAFT, W. B. MCADAM, J. E. BALDWIN and S. ARCHER, 1959, *Mem. R.A.S.*, **67**, 37.
ELSMORE, B., M. RYLE and R. R. LESLIE, 1959, *Mem. R.A.S.*, **68**, 61.
FOMALONT, E. B., T. A. MATTHEWS, D. MORRIS and J. D. WYNDHAM, 1964, *A. J.*, **69**, 772.
GOLDSMITH, D. W. and T. D. KINMAN, 1965. *Ap. J.*, **142**, 1693.

HARO, G. and W. J. LUYTEN, 1962, *Bull. Obs. Ton.*, No. **22**, 1.
HARRIS, D. E., 1962, *Ap. J.*, **135**, 661.
HARRIS, D. E. and J. A. ROBERTS, 1960, *Pub. A.S.P.*, **72**, 237.
HAZARD, C., 1964, *Quasi-Stellar Sources and Gravitational Collapse*, Chap. 11, ed. ROBINSON, SCHILD and SCHUCKING (Chicago).
HEESCHEN, D. S. and C. M. WADE, 1964, *A. J.*, **69**, 277.
HEY, J. S., S. J. PARSONS and J. W. PHILIPS, 1946*a*, *Nature*, **157**, 296.
HEY, J. S., S. J. PARSONS and J. W. PHILIPS, 1946*b*, *Nature*, **158**, 234.
HILL, E. R. and B. Y. MILLS, 1962, *Aust. J. Phys.*, **15**, 437.
HUMASON, M. L., N. U. MAYALL and A. R. SANDAGE, 1956, *A. J.*, **61**, 97.
IRIARTE, B. and E. CHAVIRA, 1962, *Bull. Obs. Ton.*, No. **16**, 3.
JENNISON, R. C. and M. K. DAS GUPTA, 1953, *Nature*, **172**, 996.
JENNISON, R. C. and M. K. DAS GUPTA, 1956, *Phil. Mag.*, Ser. 8, **1**, 65.
KELLERMAN, K. I., 1964, *Ap. J.*, **140**, 969.
KELLERMAN, K. I. and D. E. HARRIS, 1960, *Observations Calif. Inst. Tech. Rad. Obs.*, No. **7**.
KINMAN, T. D., 1965, *Ap. J.*, **142**, 1241.
LESLIE, P. R. R., 1961, *M. N.*, **122**, 51.
LONGAIR, M. S., 1965, *M. N.*, **129**, 419.
LYNDS, C. R., 1961, *Ap. J.*, **134**, 659.
LYNDS, C. R. and A. R. SANDAGE, 1963, *Ap. J.*, **137**, 1005.
LYNDS, C. R. and G. VILLERE, 1965, *Ap. J.*, **142**, 1296.
MALTBY, P. and A. T. MOFFET, 1962, *Ap. J. Supp.*, **7**, 141.
MATTIG, W., 1958, *A. N.*, **284**, 109.
MATTHEWS, T. A. and A. R. SANDAGE, 1963, *Ap. J.*, **138**, 30.
MATTHEWS, T. A., W. W. MORGAN and M. SCHMIDT, 1964, *Ap. J.*, **140**, 35.
MILLER, W. C., 1955, *A.S.P. Leaflet*, No. 314.
MILLS, B. Y., 1952*a*, *Aust. J. Sci. Res.*, **5**, 266.
MILLS, B. Y., 1952*b*, *Aust. J. Sci. Res.*, **5**, 456.
MILLS, B. Y., 1952*c*, *Nature*, **170**, 1063.
MILLS, B. Y., 1960, *Aust. J. Phys.*, **13**, 550.
MILLS, B. Y. and O. B. SLEE, 1957, *Aust. J. Phys.*, **10**, 162.
MILLS, B. Y., O. B. SLEE and E. R. HILL, 1958, *Aust. J. Phys.*, **11**, 360.
MILLS, B. Y., O. B. SLEE and E. R. HILL, 1960, *Aust. J. Phys.*, **13**, 676.
MILLS, B. Y., O. B. SLEE and E. R. HILL, 1961, *Aust. J. Phys.*, **14**, 497.
MINKOWSKI, R., 1960, *Proc. Nat. Acad. Sci.*, **46**, 13.
MINKOWSKI, R., 1961, *Proc. Fourth Berkeley Symposium on Mathematical Statistics and Probability*, ed. J. NEYMAN (Berkeley), **4**, 245.
MINKOWSKI, R., 1963, *Proc. Nat. Acad. Sci.*, **49**, 779.
MOFFET, A. T., 1964, *Science*, **146**, 764.
MOXON, L. A., 1946, *Nature*, **158**, 758.
OORT, J. H. and G. WESTERHOUT, 1951, *B.A.N.*, **426**, 323.
PALMER, H. P., 1963, *Radio Astronomy Today* (Cambridge, Mass.).
PAULINY-TOTH, I. I. K., C. M. WADE and D. S. HEESCHEN, 1966, *Ap. J. Supp.*, **13**, 65.
READ, R. B., 1963, *Ap. J.*, **138**, 1.
REBER, G., 1944, *Ap. J.*, **100**, 279.
RYLE, M., 1950, *Rept. Prog. Phys.*, **13**, 184.
RYLE, M. and A. HEWISH, 1955, *Mem. R.A.S.*, **67**, 97.
RYLE, M. and A. C. NEVILLE, 1962, *M. N.*, **125**, 39.
RYLE, M. and A. SANDAGE, 1964, *Ap. J.*, **139**, 419.

RYLE, M. and F. G. SMITH, 1948, *Nature*, **162**, 462.
RYLE, M., F. G. SMITH and B. ELSMORE, 1950, *M. N.*, **110**, 508.
SANDAGE, A., 1961*a*, *Ap. J.*, **133**, 355.
SANDAGE, A., 1961*b*, *Ap. J.*, **134**, 916.
SANDAGE, A., 1962, *Ap. J.*, **136**, 319.
SANDAGE, A., 1964, *Ap. J.*, **139**, 416.
SANDAGE, A., 1965, *Ap. J.*, **141**, 1560.
SANDAGE, A., 1966, *Ap. J.*, **144**, 1234.
SANDAGE, A., 1967*a*, *Ap. J.*, in press.
SANDAGE, A., 1967*b*, *Proc. Padua Conference on Cosmology*, ed. L. ROSINO, in press.
SANDAGE, A. and W. C. MILLER, 1964, *Science*, **144**, 382.
SANDAGE, A. and P. VÉRON, 1965, *Ap. J.*, **142**, 412.
SANDAGE, A. and J. D. WYNDHAM, 1965, *Ap. J.*, **141**, 328.
SANDAGE, A., P. VÉRON and J. D. WYNDHAM, 1965, *Ap. J.*, **142**, 1307.
SCHMIDT, M., 1963, *Nature*, **197**, 1040.
SCHMIDT, M. and T. A. MATTHEWS, 1964, *Ap. J.*, **139**, 781.
SCOTT, P. F., M. RYLE and M. HEWISH, 1961, *M. N.*, **122**, 95.
SHAIN, C. A. and C. A. HIGGINS, 1954, *Aust. J. Phys.*, **7**, 130.
SHAKESHAFT, J. R. and M. S. LONGAIR, 1965, *Observatory*, **85**, 30.
SHAKESHAFT, J. R., M. RYLE, J. E. BALDWIN, B. ELSMORE and J. H. THOMSON, 1955, *Mem. R.A.S.*, **67**, 106.
SMITH, F. G., 1951, *Nature*, **168**, 555.
SMITH, F. G., 1952, *Nature*, **170**, 1065.
SMITH, H., 1964, *Quasi-Stellar Sources and Gravitational Collapse*, Chap. 16, ed. ROBINSON, SCHILD and SCHUCKING (Chicago).
SMITH, H. and D. HOFFLEIT, 1963, *Nature*, **198**, 650.
STANLEY, G. J. and O. B. SLEE, 1950, *Aust. J. Sci. Res.*, **3**, 234.
TERRELL, J., 1964, *Science*, **145**, 918.
VÉRON, P., 1965, *Ap. J.*, **141**, 1284.
VÉRON, P., 1966, *Ap. J.*, **144**, 861.
WADE, C. M., B. G., CLARK and D. E. HOGG, 1965, *Ap. J.*, **142**, 406.
WILLS, D. and E. A. PARKER, 1966, *M. N.*, **131**, 503.
WILSON, R. W. and J. G. BOLTON, 1960, *Pub. A.S.P.*, **72**, 331.
WYNDHAM, J. D., 1965, *A. J.*, **70**, 384.
WYNDHAM, J. D., 1966, *A. J.*, **144**, 459.

Radio Galaxies and Quasi-Stellar Radio Sources.

E. M. BURBIDGE

University of California - San Diego, Cal.

1. – Introduction.

In these lectures I shall concentrate on what can be deduced about radio galaxies and quasi-stellar radio sources from their optical spectra, discussing particularly the physical conditions (such as, for example, the temperature, density, and source of ionization of the gaseous component), and the kinematics of the constituent parts of radio galaxies. I shall try to relate the properties of radio galaxies to the normal galaxies on the one hand, and to the quasi-stellar radio sources on the other hand, and also to various theories that have been put forward to explain the source of the large energies needed to account for the radio emission. These lectures are intended to link closely with those given by Dr. SANDAGE, and I shall have frequent occasion to refer to what is contained in his lectures.

2. – Power levels of radio emission.

Before turning to the optical spectra, let us consider the power levels of radio emission from galaxies and QSRS, in order to have in mind the order of magnitude of the phenomena we are trying to account for. Our own galaxy is a radio emitter, at a level of only about 10^{38} erg/s—a small energy output compared with the optical luminosity, which, our galaxy being a normal spiral with mass of order $10^{11}\,M_\odot$, must be about 10^{44} erg/s. It is quite probable that, among the spiral and irregular galaxies at least, every normal galaxy may be a radio emitter at this level or less; a galaxy emitting a total radio power of 10^{38} erg/s, at a distance $D = 15$ Mparsec (about the distance of the

Virgo cluster of galaxies) would appear as a source with a flux level P given by

$$P = \frac{10^{38}}{4\pi D^2} \times \frac{10^{-7} \times 10^{4}}{10^{10}} \text{ W m}^{-2}(\text{Hz}^{-1}) \text{ per steradian,}$$

$$\approx 4 \cdot 10^{-28} \text{ W m}^{-2}(\text{Hz}^{-1}) \text{ sr}^{-1} ,$$

assuming for simplicity that the source has a flat radio spectrum with cut-offs at 10 MHz and 10^4 MHz. The unit « 10^{-26} W $m^{-2}(Hz^{-1})$ sr^{-1} » is called a « flux unit » or « f.u. »; the third Cambridge catalogue extends to a faint limit of 9 flux units at 178 MHz. Therefore, as new catalogues going to fainter flux levels become available (*e.g.* the 4C catalogue), we can expect to find many more identifications with relatively nearby normal spiral and irregular galaxies.

We shall define the « radio galaxies » as those galaxies emitting radio fluxes at least 10 times as high as that from our galaxy. As discussed by Dr. SANDAGE, radio fluxes for the strongest radio-emitting galaxies such as *Cygnus A* are as large as 10^{45} erg/s, or 10 times the normal optical luminosity output. The QSRS 3C 273 has a radio output of about 10^{45} erg/s, if the cosmological interpretation of the red-shifts of these objects is correct so that 3C 273 is at the large distance of 470 Mparsec. Thus, with this proviso, the magnitude of the *radio* (not optical) phenomenon that has to be explained is similar in the two kinds of object.

3. – General description of optical spectra of radio galaxies and information they yield.

The information that we can get from the spectrum of any galaxy, be it a normal galaxy or a strong radio emitter, is limited by the fact that even the nearest extragalactic objects are at a sufficiently large distance that we usually receive in the spectrograph slit the integrated light coming from many stars and from the interstellar gas of the galaxy. The stars will give an absorption-line spectrum, while the gas will give emission lines. It is much easier to derive information from the spectra if *gas* is present; we can then study both the physical conditions in the gas and its one-dimensional velocity field. As we shall see presently, the various stages of ionization represented in the spectrum and the relative intensities of the emission lines seen will yield information on the electron densities, temperatures, and ionization conditions, as well as perhaps some knowledge of the relative abundances of the elements in the gas.

Wavelength measurements of the emission lines as a function of position in the object (assuming it is an extended object in the sky) will yield the

Doppler displacements and therefore give

$$v = c\frac{\Delta\lambda}{\lambda},$$

i.e., the line-of-sight component of the velocity with respect to the observer. For example, the line-of-sight velocity field in the radio galaxy M82, as described by Dr. SANDAGE, was most revealing in the evidence it gave for the occurrence of an explosive event in the center of that object.

If no emission lines are present in the spectrum, then we have *a priori* no evidence for the presence of excited gas, and all we shall observe are absorption lines from the stars. Taking arbitrary relative numbers of stars of various spectral types, one can synthetize a composite spectrum to match that observed, and so infer the stellar population that is contributing most of the light of the galaxy (MORGAN and MAYALL, 1957). One can also derive the velocity dispersion $\langle v^2 \rangle$ of the stars. Then we have

$$M\langle v^2 \rangle + \Omega = 0$$

from the virial theorem, where M is the total mass of the galaxy and

$$\Omega = -G\int_0^R \frac{M(r)\,\mathrm{d}M}{r}.$$

Thus if we assume the stars have a constant mass-to-light ratio, independent of position in the galaxy, and if we measure the luminosity distribution, we derive Ω in terms of M and the virial equation can be solved for M.

Among the galaxies that are strong radio emitters, a wide variety of spectra is found. It is fairly characteristic, but by no means universal, that rather strong emission lines are seen. If so, the lines are usually of hydrogen together with forbidden lines of common light elements in several stages of ionization (somewhat like gaseous nebulae in our own galaxy that are excited by hot central stars). In *Cygnus* A, BAADE and MINKOWSKI (1954) observed the lines given in Table I. In some radio galaxies, however, the emission lines are not strong, and in some they are not present at all. A study by SCHMIDT (1965) of the red-shifts of 31 rather distant radio galaxies provides a very useful illustration of this diversity. He classified the objects according to an index which he called S_6, defined as the sum of the estimated strengths of the 6 emission lines most commonly seen, on a scale going from 1 (just visible) to 6 (strongest lines encountered). His results are given in Table II; his red-shifts z $(= \Delta\lambda/\lambda_0)$ corrected for solar motion are also tabulated. On this scale,

TABLE I. – *Emission lines in Cygnus* A, *from* BAADE *and* MINKOWSKI.

λ observed	Identification		$c\,\Delta\lambda/\lambda_0$ (km/s)
3619.9	3425.8	[Ne V]	17010
3937.2	3727.5	[O II]	16930
4087.5	3868.7	[Ne III]	16930
4189.6	3967.5	[Ne III]	16820
5234.3	4958.9	[O III]	16660
5284.6	5006.8	[O III]	16955
6642.5	6300.2	[O I]	16770
6718.6	6363.9	[O I]	16720
6916.6	6548.1	[N II]	16870
6928.0	6562.8	H_α	16300
6949.2	6583.6	[N II]	16670

SCHMIDT estimated S_6 for *Cyg* A to be 18. He found no correlation between S_6 and any of the radio properties of the galaxies, such as radio power output, radio brightness distribution, or radio spectral index.

The radio galaxy 3C 295, which has the largest red-shift found so far for a galaxy (MINKOWSKI, 1960), does not have strong lines; the single line seen (on which MINKOWSKI based his red-shift determination of $\Delta\lambda/\lambda_0 = 0.4614$) is [O II] λ3727. The radio output is $2\cdot10^{45}$ erg/s (MATTHEWS, MORGAN and SCHMIDT, 1964).

One may sum up by noting that in the spectral region (3400 ÷ 6800) Å, the emission lines usually found are the Balmer lines of hydrogen, the forbidden lines of [O III], [O II], [Ne III], [N II], [S II], [Ne V], and occasionally helium lines. In general, the lines found can be duplicated in other galaxies that are not radio galaxies, *e.g.*, in irregulars that have much interstellar gas, and the spectra also find their counterparts among planetary nebulae of various degrees of excitation.

It is worth noting one case of mis-identification of a radio source (*Her* A) with a galaxy, some years ago, which arose through a combination of an inaccurate radio position, the expectation that strong emission lines were characteristic of radio galaxies, and the chance occurrence of a peculiar, irregular (but not radio-emitting!) galaxy with very strong emission lines near the inaccurate radio position. The correct identification proved to have $S_6 = 2$ (the only emission line seen being weak [O II] λ 3727) on Schmidt's scale (GREENSTEIN, 1962).

Because of the general similarity of the spectra of radio galaxies with those of planetary nebulae, let us review the mechanism of emission in those objects. This will also be useful later when we turn to the spectra of the QSRS.

In planetary nebulae, hydrogen and helium lines are produced by recom-

TABLE II. – *Emission line strengths in Schmidt's* 31 *radio galaxies.*

Radio object	Mag.	z (correlated for solar motion)	S_6
3C 17	19	0.2201	7
3C 26	19	0.2106	11
3C 28	$18\frac{1}{2}$	0.1959	2
3C 33	16	0.0600	12
3C 78	14	0.0289	1:
3C 79	19	0.2561	16
3C 88	14	0.0302	2
3C 98	15	0.0306	8
M05-43	16	0.0342	15:
3C 171	$19\frac{1}{2}$	0.2387	12
3C 198	$17\frac{1}{2}$	0.0809	7
3C 219	$18\frac{1}{2}$	0.1745	8
3C 234	$17\frac{1}{2}$	0.1846	17
3C 264	13	0.0206	0
3C 277.3	$17\frac{1}{2}$	0.0857	2
3C 310	16	0.0543	2
3C 315	$17\frac{1}{2}$	0.1086	3
3C 317	16	0.0351	3
3C 327	17	0.1041	15
3C 353	17	0.0307	2
3C 382	16	0.0586	5
3C 386	16	0.0008	0
3C 388	16	0.0917	1
3C 433	17	0.1025	7
3C 436	19	0.2154	5
3C 445	17	0.0568	15
3C 452	18	0.0820	5
3C 456	$19\frac{1}{2}$	0.2337	7:
3C 459	18	0.2205	3
M23-112	$16\frac{1}{2}$	0.0825	7
3C 465	15	0.0301	1

bination of the ions following photo-ionization by the ultra-violet light shortward of the appropriate series limits, from the high-temperature central star. The statistical equilibrium governing captures into the ground state and a finite number of excited states, with subsequent cascades, in a field of dilute radiation, was formulated and computed by BAKER and MENZEL (1938). Extension to an infinite number of levels is due to PENGELLY (1964). The strength of a Balmer emission line is given by the number of atoms in the upper level and the transition probability. The former is

$$N_{nl} = N_e N_p (2l+1)\left[\frac{2\pi mkT}{h^2}\right]^{-\frac{3}{2}} \exp[I_{nl}/kT]\, b_{nl},$$

where N_e, N_p are the numbers of electrons and protons per cm^3, I_{nl} is the ionization energy for level nl, and b_{nl} measures the departure of the populations from those that would obtain in thermodynamic equilibrium and the values have been computed by PENGELLY.

Ionization of the other elements is also caused by the diluted high-temperature radiation from the central star. Forbidden lines are then produced by the following mechanism. Atoms and ions are excited by electron collision from the ground state to fairly low-lying metastable levels, transitions which are radiatively forbidden; they stay a relatively long time in these levels unless the electron density is high enough to cause collisional de-excitation, and then finally they decay to the ground state with the emission of forbidden lines. Determination of the electron density and temperature, N_e and T_e, from forbidden-line intensities is discussed by SEATON (1954) and SEATON and OSTERBROCK (1957). The energy $I(n, m)$ radiated per cm^3 per s in the transition $n \rightarrow m$ is given by

$$I(n, m) = E_{nm} A_{nm} E_n ,$$

where E_{nm} is the energy released per transition, A is the transition probability and N_n is the number of atoms or ions per cm^3 in the upper state. The N_n are governed by statistical equilibrium, *i.e.*, by equating the number of populations of a given level per s with the number of depopulations; the cross-sections for excitation and de-excitation are expressed in terms of dimensionless parameters $\Omega(m, n)$, $\Omega(n, m)$ which have been computed for cases of interest by several people, particularly SEATON and colleagues in recent years. The upper states of the [O II] $\lambda\lambda$3726, 3729 lines, with a long lifetime against radiative de-excitation, are particularly sensitive to collisional de-excitation and their intensities are therefore a good indicator of electron densities.

4. – General description of optical spectra of QSRS.

The QSRS have been found in general to show the same kind of emission lines in their spectra as the radio galaxies and indeed other galaxies and planetary nebulae. The two main differences are:

1) Because of the large red-shifts of the QSRS, we see a spectral region in the ultra-violet that is normally inaccessible to ground-based observation for galaxies and planetaries.

2) The emission lines are very broad (here they resemble the spectra of the nuclei of Seyfert galaxies, which we describe in Sect. 6). We shall come later to a detailed discussion of the spectra of these objects; here we merely note that the emission lines obviously lend themselves to the same kind of

discussion of the physical conditions in the objects that we have outlined in Sect. 3, *i.e.*, we can derive electron temperatures and densities, mode of ionization, and, if need be, abundances of the elements.

5. – Kinematic information from spectra.

Let us now turn to the information that optical spectra will yield on the kinematics of gas in radio galaxies and quasi-stellar radio sources. Turning for a moment to nearby normal galaxies, we can study the line-of-sight velocities of the gaseous component very efficiently by using a spectrograph with a *long slit* which can be set in any derived position angle in the plane of the sky.

The rotations of a number of nearby galaxies have been studied in this way by setting the slit along the *major axis* of the galaxy. For every point of the galaxy that lies on the slit we then obtain, perpendicularly to the slice of the galaxy observed (in the direction of the dispersion), a spectrum, and these add up to a continuous series of spectra. A spectral line appearing all the way along the slit, or at intervals along it wherever the slit crosses emitting gas, can have its wavelength measured at as many points as the spectral and photographic resolution and the atmospheric seeing warrant; these wavelengths will then yield Doppler shifts and hence line-of-sight velocities of the corres-ponding part of the galaxy. For example, a galaxy that is rotating *a*) as a solid body or *b*) with an angular velocity that decreases outward and yields a maximum linear velocity at a certain point will show spectral lines as indicated in Fig. 1.

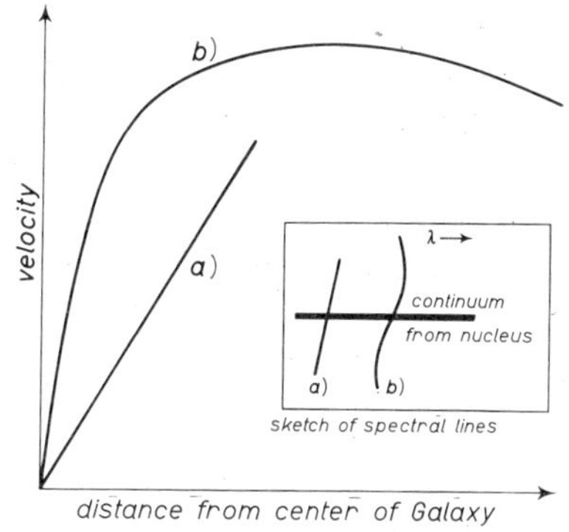

Fig. 1. – Schematic representation of two types of rotation curve for a galaxy: *a*) constant angular velocity, as from a uniform density distribution, and *b*) normal type of rotation curve, with density maximum at center of galaxy. Spectral lines giving these types of curve are also sketched.

This method can be used to explore a velocity field that is more complicated than simple rotation, by repeating the procedure described above in many different position angles; *e.g.*, we can look for expansion velocities in the gas away from the center of the galaxy, as was found by MÜNCH (1960) in M31 and more recently by BURBIDGE and BURBIDGE (1964*a*) in M51, by setting the slit along or near the direction of the minor axis, where the line-of sight component due to rotation should be zero.

Another technique that can be used is to observe complete images of galaxies with narrow interferometric filters or with Fabry-Pérot étalons; this has been developed by COURTÈS and his colleagues, mainly at L'Observatoire de Haute Provence.

Of particular interest to us is the application of the long-slit technique to build up, by a series of spectra in many position angles, a systematic picture of the velocity field in the gas of a radio galaxy. We can then deduce, for example, whether the gas shows the aftermath of a violent event in the galaxy. We shall discuss some examples of this application later.

For the QSRS, unfortunately, no such detailed source of information is available because, by their very definition, these objects appear as point sources of light with no extension and all their light enters the spectrograph slit at one point. What we do see, in general, is that the emission lines in these objects are quite broad, $\sim(20\div50)$ Å, and, while we shall return to this point later on, it should be mentioned here that this has been interpreted as being due to a velocity dispersion in the emitting gas. It is by no means certain, however, that this is the correct explanation.

In considering which radio galaxies should be studied kinematically, we are faced with a problem. It would obviously be most interesting to study the strongest radio emitters, but objects like *Cyg* A are rare in space and *Cyg* A itself, the nearest of them, is so far away that little detail can be discerned. For detailed study, we have to choose galaxies which are not such strong radio emitters, but which are spatially more common so that we can choose nearby examples. In the next few Sections, we shall describe studies of a selection of objects, which will cover quite a range of emission-line intensities, from those with strong emission lines like M82 and NGC 1275, to those with none at all like NGC 4782-3. We shall finish up with a more detailed discussion of the spectra of QSRS.

6. – Seyfert galaxies.

In a paper discussing violent events in the nuclei of galaxies as the origin of the phenomenon of radio emission from galaxies, BURBIDGE, BURBIDGE, and SANDAGE (1963) paid a good deal of attention to the category of galaxies that were singled out and discussed originally by SEYFERT (1943). Our reason for doing this was, firstly, that two of the objects in Seyfert's original list, NGC 1068 and NGC 1275, are radio emitters, the former (3C 71) at a level of 10^{40} erg/s and the latter (3C 84) at 10^{42} erg/s (MATTHEWS, MORGAN, and SCHMIDT, 1964). Secondly, the interpretation of the optical spectrum suggests a violent energy release in the nucleus.

The galaxies originally listed by SEYFERT were: NGC 1068, 1275, 2782, 3077, 3227, 3516, 4051, 4151, 4258, 5548, 6814, and 7469. The objects he studied himself were: NGC 1068, 1275, 3516, 4051, 4151, and 7469. Using the criteria discussed by SEYFERT, we should remove the galaxies: NGC 2782, 3077, 4258, and 6814 from this category, as they do not show the characteristic which we take to define the category. These characteristics are:

1) The galaxies have small, very bright nuclei.

2) The spectra of the nuclei may contain emission features not normally seen in the spectra of galaxies, indicating a very high degree of ionization, *e.g.*, lines of [Fe VII].

3) The emission lines, particularly the hydrogen lines, have very large widths, which, if interpreted as Doppler motions, correspond to velocities in the range ± 500 to ± 4250 km/s, according to SEYFERT.

Most of the 8 galaxies retained in the list show spiral structure; in NGC 4151 it is so much less bright than the intense stellar image that forms the nucleus that the Seyfert galaxies may be looked upon as forming some kind of a link between normal galaxies, on the one hand, and, on the other, the *N*-type galaxies (defined by MATTHEWS, MORGAN, and SCHMIDT, 1964) and the strong radio galaxies. The absolute magnitudes of Seyfert galaxies cover quite a range, from about -18 to -22. It will be remembered from Dr. Sandage's lectures that the morphological types of galaxy that comprise the strongest radio emitters, apart from the QSRS, are principally elliptical (*E*) or *SO* and *D*-type galaxies (elliptical-type central region surrounded by a much more extended stellar distribution), double ellipticals, and, lastly, *N*-type galaxies, which have a small bright nucleus surrounded by a faint wispy envelope. The connection between Seyfert galaxies, *N*-type galaxies, and the « compact galaxies » being studied by ZWICKY (1965) should be a very fruitful field of study.

The list of 8 Seyfert galaxies may be supplemented by some more distant objects: VV 144 (VORONTSOV-VELYAMINOV, 1959; BURBIDGE and BURBIDGE, 1964*b*), which was also listed as a « compact galaxy » by ZWICKY, a member of the group VV 150 (VORONTSOV-VELYAMINOV, 1959; BURBIDGE and BURBIDGE, 1961), and other compact galaxies being studied by ZWICKY.

The most interesting features of NGC 1275 do not pertain to its Seyfert characteristics, but to its velocity field; consequently it will be considered separately later. NGC 1068 also has a section to itself, because a detailed spectroscopic study has been made of it.

a) *NGC* 4151. Several years ago O. WILSON at the Mt. Wilson and Palomar Observatories noted that the very broad nuclear hydrogen emission-features are not smooth and uniform, but, when looked at with a coudé spectrograph with high resolution, break up into separate clumps, suggesting that the nucleus consists of separate cloud complexes moving about with velocities of some thousands of km/s; the forbidden lines and helium lines are considerably narrower. The object has a slightly smaller red shift than NGC 1068 which has a radio flux of about 145 f.u. at 178 MHz; thus NGC 4151 is at a similar or slightly smaller distance than NGC 1068, yet it has not been detected as a radio source. Consequently its radio luminosity must be less than $\sim 1/15$ that of NGC 1068. The faint « arms » of NGC 4151 (see BURBIDGE, BURBIDGE, and SANDAGE, 1963) are curiously distorted, and there are some very faint outer arms which may be seen in the Palomar Sky Survey prints. The nucleus has a diameter $< \frac{1}{2}''$, corresponding at a distance of 10 Mparsec to < 25 parsec.

b) *NGC* 7469. This has been studied by BURBIDGE, BURBIDGE, and PRENDERGAST (1963), where a photograph is published. A member of a double system, it has inner spiral arms around the very bright nucleus, and faint outer arms. Some kind of faint outer ringlike structure or spiral arms appear to be a rather characteristic feature of Seyfert galaxies. From a rotation curve observed for the inner arms of NGC 7469, a mass of $1.1 \cdot 10^{10} M_{\odot}$ within a radius of 3600 parsec was determined. Like NGC 4151, it also has not been observed as a radio source, but its red-shift is about 4.5 times as large as that of NGC 1068, so it could be emitting at the same power level without having been detected. The companion galaxy is a peculiar irregular object.

c) *NGC* 3227. This is also a member of a double system; its companion is an elliptical. As in NGC 7469, it has two broad rather smooth faint outer structures, but the spiral arms of its main body are of normal brightness and fairly regular in appearance. The only unusual morhopological feature is a jetlike streak of dust some way outside the nucleus.

d) *VV* 144. The red-shift of this is 6230 km/s, so that, with a Hubble constant of 75 km/s per Mparsec, its distance is 83 Mparsec. It consists of a main body with a magnitude of about 17^m, smooth with no discernible structure, and a long jet extending $45''$ or 18 parsec out of the main body on one side. The total brightness, according to VORONTOV-VELYAMINOV, is about 16^m, corresponding to an absolute magnitude of $M_{pg} = -18.6$ for the whole object and $M_{pg} = -17.6$ for the main body. The luminous jet naturally reminds us of the jet associated wtih the QSRS 3C 273. The width of the H_{α} emission line, if due to Doppler broadening, gives random motions of ± 1500 km/s.

7. – NGC 1068 (3C 71).

We shall discuss in some detail the physical conditions in this Seyfert galaxy which is also a radio galaxy, $\sim 10^2$ times more powerful an emitter than our galaxy. The outer spiral structure is of fairly normal brightness and appearance; study of a rotation curve derived from velocity measures in this outer part (BURBIDGE, BURBIDGE, and PRENDERGAST, 1959) yielded a mass of $3 \cdot 10^{10} M_\odot$. Like the objects discussed in Sect. 6, it has an outer ring of low luminosity with a diameter of order 30 kparsec.

The nucleus has the characteristic broad strong emission lines of Seyfert galaxies. WALKER, using the image-tube spectrograph at the coudé focus of the Lick 120-inch telescope, has found a very interesting structure in these lines: the emission region seems to be formed of a number of discrete clouds with velocities ranging from -2500 to $+2500$ km/s with respect to the center (similar to that found by WILSON in NGC 4151).

OSTERBROCK and PARKER (1965) have measured the intensities of the emission lines in the nucleus and, by the methods outlined in Sect. 3, have studied the physical conditions in the nucleus. We will go through their analysis.

a) Electron temperature T_e. The forbidden [O III] lines at 5007 Å, 4959 Å and 4363 Å have relative intensities that are sensitive to T_e, the value of which determines the kinetic energy of the exciting electrons, because the energy of the upper state of the 4363 Å line is 5.33 eV while that of the other two lines is only 2.50 eV. The collisional de-excitation cross-sections for all three lines are small enough that this process of depopulation of the upper states can be neglected unless the electron density N_e is very large. Consequently, these lines can be used to derive a good value of T_e; OSTERBROCK and PARKER found $T_e = 10\,200°$.

b) Electron density N_e. The upper states of the [O II] 3727 Å lines and the [S II] lines at 6717 Å, 6731 Å will suffer appreciable collisional de-excitation; consequently, once T_e is known, the ratio of the lines [O II] (3727/7330) and [S II] (6717+6731)/(4068+4076) gives N_e. OSTERBROCK and PARKER found $N_e > 4 \cdot 10^3/\text{cm}^3$ from [O II] and $N_e > 4 \cdot 10^4/\text{cm}^3$ from [S II]; the former is the more reliable estimate because the de-excitation cross-sections are better known.

Now the measured flux in H_α was found to be $2.3 \cdot 10^{41}$ erg/s. Let us suppose that the ionized hydrogen fills a sphere of radius 1″ (*i.e.* $r = 50$ parsec) which is the observed size of the small bright nucleus in this galaxy. The luminosity in H_α is given by

$$L(H_\alpha) = \frac{4\pi r^3}{3} j ,$$

where the emission coefficient per unit volume, j, is given by

$$j = N_e N_p \alpha_{32} h\nu ,$$

α_{32} being the effective recombination coefficient for the production of H_α and ν the frequency of H_α. Assuming $N_e = N_p$, and having $L(H_\alpha)$ measured as

$2.3 \cdot 10^{41}$ erg/s, we find $N_e = 1.6 \cdot 10^2/\text{cm}^3$. This density, with the radius given above, yields a mass $2 \cdot 10^6 M_\odot$ of ionized gas in the nucleus.

The discrepancy between this value of N_e and that from the forbidden lines suggests that the ionized material is located in discrete clouds occupying about 10^{-3} of the total volume of the nucleus, separated by a much lower density medium; on this picture the mass of ionized gas is about $3 \cdot 10^4 M_\odot$.

c) Source of ionization. OSTERBROCK and PARKER discussed various possible energy sources for the observed ionization. Let us consider first *collision by thermal electrons.* Now emission lines are observed from ions of various ionization potentials, from neutral atoms giving [O I] to ([Ne V] and [Fe VII] (with a ionization potential ~100 eV), but [Fe X] is absent so the maximum ionization potential found is < 235 eV. To get Ne^{+4} and Fe^{+6} ions by collisional ionization with thermal electrons, the electron temperature would have to be ~150 000°, and we have seen that $T_e = 10\,200°$. Consequently, this mechanism can be ruled out.

Secondly, one might consider *ionization by a central source of ultraviolet radiation,* as in planetary nebulae. In the latter objects, we observe the permitted lines of OIII at 3133 Å and 3444 Å. These lines are downward transitions from a particular upper level which is populated by the fortuitous coincidence of the HeII line at 304 Å, converted to energy units, with the excitation energy of the OIII level (BOWEN, 1935). These O III lines are not observed in NGC 1068; thus the radiation of the He II 304 Å line must all be absorbed before these photons can excite the O^{++} ions. These photons must be absorbed by neutral hydrogen or helium, and the neutral material must consequently be intimately mixed with the ionized material. In the case of ionization by a single central source, as in a Strömgren sphere, a completely ionized central sphere is surrounded by neutral hydrogen with a very thin transition zone, and no such mingling of ionized and neutral matter is possible. Consequently, ionization by a single central ultraviolet source cannot be the mechanism at work here.

Thirdly, since NGC 1068 is a nonthermal radio source, we should consider *ionization by ultraviolet synchrotron emission,* as was discussed by Dr. SANDAGE for M82. One finds, on extrapolating the radio spectrum beyond the Lyman limit, that there is not enough energy to cause the observed hydrogen recombination as evidenced by the observed flux in H_α. It is not, of course, impossible that there is present another synchrotron source, more intense in the visible and ultra-violet parts of the spectrum than the extrapolation of the observed radio spectrum, but with a cut-off in the infra-red. However, OSTERBROCK and PARKER have measured the continuum flux in the visible and near ultra-violet and found that this flux can all be explained by 2-photon conversion of Lyman α radiation. In that process, electrons in the $2p$ level of hydrogen can jump through electron collision to the $2s$ level which has the same energy. The $2s$-$1s$ transition is forbidden if accompanied by emission of a Ly-α photon, but can occur with the emission of two photons. The sum of the energies of these two photons is equal to the difference of energy between the $2s$ and $1s$ levels; the continuous spectrum so obtained obviously has a cut-off at Ly-α ($=1216$ Å).

Finally, OSTERBROK and PARKER discussed what appears to be the most likely mechanism for ionization, *i.e.*, collisions with fast protons. If bodies of electrically neutral gas that is mainly hydrogen are moving with large velocities, the protons will carry most energy. There are not many data on collisional ionization cross-sections σ_{ion}, but OSTERBROCK and PARKER supplemented what there was with approximate calculations, and assumed two different forms for the energy distribution of the photons—a power-law spectrum $F(E) = \text{const}\cdot E^{-\gamma}$, with $\gamma = 2$, and a flat spectrum up to a maximum energy E_0 and no photons with $E > E_0$. The form of the variation of σ_{ion} with E showed that σ_{ion} is small below a threshold E_t, and then has a very flat maximum. Thus all ions with $E_t < E_0$ will appear, and none with $E_t > E_0$. Since ionization potentials up to 100 eV occur, but not as high as 235 eV, it appears that $(20\div30)\text{ keV} < E_0 < 50\text{ keV}$.

Now the kinetic energies of protons moving at the speeds observed in the ionized gas (2 000 km/s) are just in the required range. A 2 000 km/s proton has energy 20 keV. Calculation of the ranges of such particles in an ambient medium with density $10^2/\text{cm}^3$ shows that it would need a 15 MeV particle to be able to cross the whole radius of the nucleus (50 parsec), and such high energies would not give us what is observed. Consequently, one may conclude that the ionization energy is produced in thin layers and comes from the kinetic energy of the clouds which are seen to be moving at the necessary speeds. We cannot answer the question: what is the source of the kinetic energy of the clouds? Presumably it comes from the explosion or violent event.

8. – M 82 and NGC 1275.

A detailed study of the radio galaxy M82 (3C 231) by LYNDS and SANDAGE has been described already by Dr. SANDAGE in his lectures. That work combined a kinematic study, photometry, spectroscopy, and polarization measures. The only thing I would like to add is the results of a recent more detailed kinematic study (BURBIDGE, BURBIDGE, and RUBIN, 1964). From spectra in many position angles, the diagram shown in Fig. 2 emerged as the most likely representation of the ejection geometry; the length of time elapsed since the violent event was also judged to be more like $(2\cdot10^6\div3\cdot10^6)$ years instead of 10^6 years.

NGC 1275 is a Seyfert galaxy and a strong radio source (3C 84; *Per* A) and it is the brightest member of the Perseus cluster of galaxies, having an absolute photographic magnitude of −22.2 (correcting for an absorption of 0.95 mag. in our own Galaxy, since the object has a galactic latitude of only—12°). No detailed spectrophotometric work has been done since that by SEYFERT, and it is the kinematics of the object that are particularly interesting.

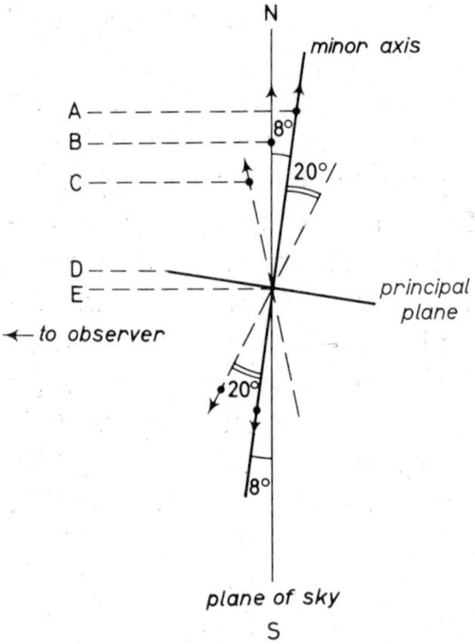

Fig. 2. – Schematic representation of geometry of explosive ejection in M 82, after BURBIDGE, BURBIDGE and RUBIN (1964).

MINKOWSKI (1957) discovered that the ionized gas exhibits two fairly discrete sets of velocities in one half of the galaxy—one near +5200 km/s and one near +8200 km/s; the mean recession velocity of the cluster is about +5200 km/s. He suggested that the object showed a collision between an Sa and an Sc galaxy, this collision explaining the radio emissivity. The « Sc galaxy » was formed by the filaments with the velocity of 8200 km/s, which indeed have some kind of spiral structure. The fact that no nucleus was found for this « spiral galaxy » was one argument for abandoning the assumption that a collision had occurred; other arguments depended on observations of other radio galaxies and theoretical considerations.

The red-shift of the object leads to a distance $D = 72$ Mparsec (with a Hubble constant of 75 km s^{-1} $Mparsec^{-1}$); at this distance, $1'' = 350$ parsec. Despite the small scale, a considerable amount of information has been obtained from a study made with the long-slit spectrograph on the 120-inch Lick telescope (BURBIDGE and BURBIDGE, 1965). The main body (*i.e.* the component with $v = 5200$ km/s) shows a dispersion of velocity of a few hundreds of kilometers per second and a maximum velocity with respect to the center of −540 km/s. Figure 3 shows a schematic polar diagram in which the velocities with respect to the center are plotted; it suggests that fairly narrow jets or bursts of gas are continuously emerging from the center in various directions. Radial filaments in a picture taken in H_α light also suggest this kind of asymmetrical jetlike activity.

The displaced component ($v = 8200$ km/s) shows a remarkably small spread in velocity of only ~360 km/s; this component may be due to continuous ejection of gas that is now seen behind the galaxy, the ejection

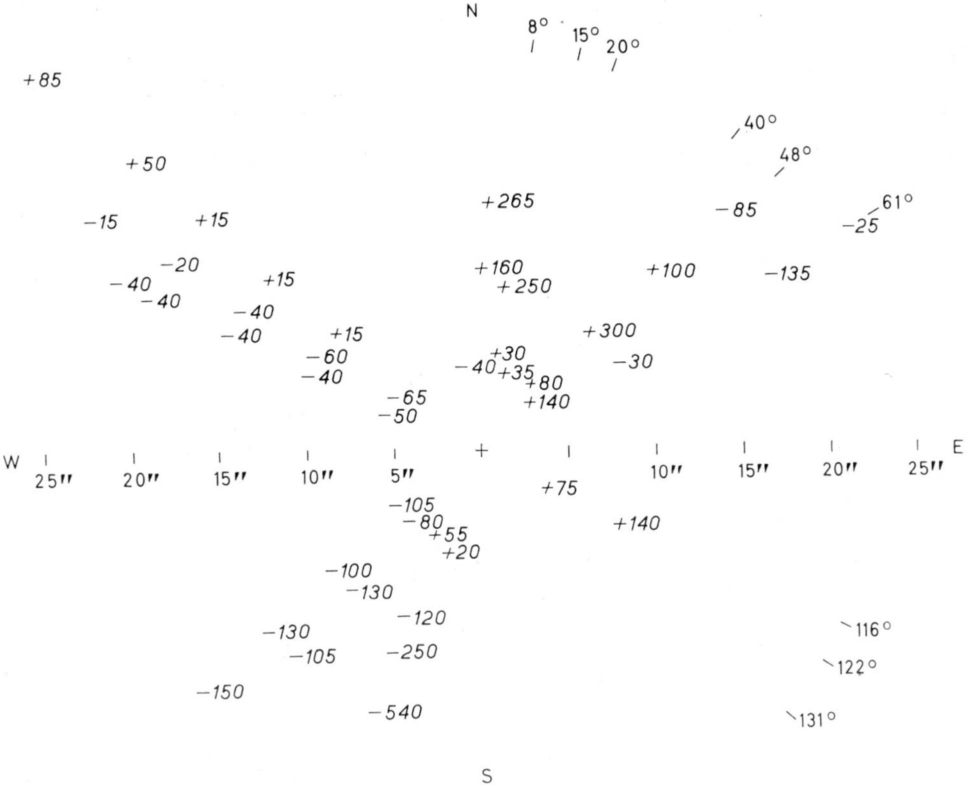

Fig. 3. – Polar diagram showing velocities in km/s of gas associated with main body of NGC 1275, relative to central velocity (numbers in italics). Cross in center of figure represents center of galaxy; scale in seconds of arc is marked along West-East line through center in roman numbers. Position angles of slit are marked around edge of diagram (Burbidge and Burbidge, 1965).

having begun $5 \cdot 10^6$ years ago, or else to gas ejected at that time which has not spread away laterally from the center of the galaxy as seen projected on the plane of the sky.

The radio structure is very complicated. A central source has a diameter of about 10″ with a composite spectrum, which is flat at high frequency and can therefore perhaps give an ultra-violet synchrotron source of radiation for ionization; no spectrophotometric or polarimetric measurements have yet been made, however, to check this possibility.

Two other fainter radio sources were found near NGC 1275; one of them is at the position of NGC 1265, another member of the Perseus cluster, about 30′ NW of NGC 1275. If this source is not actually produced by the galaxy NGC 1265, it might be due to fast electrons (moving near the velocity of light) having been ejected from the nucleus of NGC 1275 some $3 \cdot 10^6$ years ago; this length of time is of the order of the kinematical age found for the displaced component ($v = 8200$ km/s) of the ionized gas.

The other radio source is about 20′ South of NGC 1275 in the direction of the position angle for which a velocity of -540 km/s with respect to the center was measured. The directions to these two radio sources, and the po-

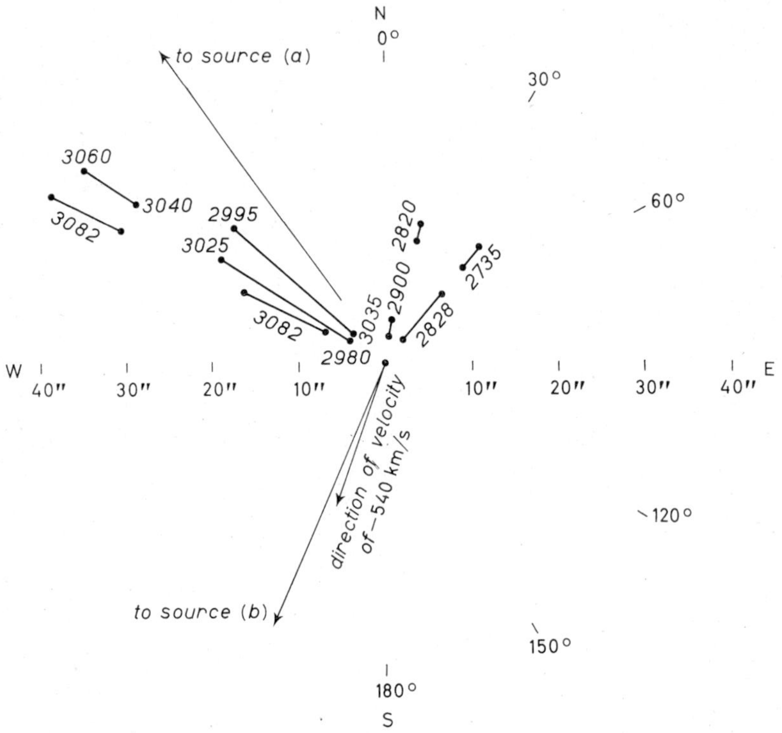

Fig. 4. – Polar diagram of NGC 1275 showing velocities in km/s of displaced component of gas, relative to center of galaxy (numbers in italics). Extent over which displaced component was measured in various position angles is indicated by lines ending in dots; either mean velocity at both ends or one mean velocity is shown. Scale in seconds of arc is marked along West-East line through center in roman numbers. Position angles are marked at 30° intervals around edge of diagram. Arrows in P.A. 324° and 204° indicate directions to radio source components (*a*) and (*b*); arrow in P.A. 200° indicates direction of large approach velocity (BURBIDGE and BURBIDGE, 1965).

sition angles and amount of the velocity of the displaced component, together with the position angle of the direction in which -540 km/s was measured, are shown in Fig. 4. This radio galaxy would repay more work, in particular work on the radio structure in relation to the optical details.

9. – NGC 5128, NGC 1316 and 3C 33: relation between optical and radio structure and axis of rotation.

We now turn to two nearby galaxies that are strong radio emitters but do not show strong emission lines in their optical spectra—NGC 5128 and NGC 1316.

NGC 5128 is a bright, nearby object which MATTHEWS, MORGAN, and SCHMIDT (1964) classified as of *ED*-type. It is associated with a complex radio source (*Centaurus* A) of very large extent and power level some $7 \cdot 10^{41}$ erg/s. In the North-South direction the source extends about 9° or 770 kparsec (BOLTON and CLARK, 1960), with two maxima at a separation of about 240 kparsec, *i.e.*, a similar separation to that found in those more distant radio sources whose interference fringes reveal them to be double (see Dr. Sandage's lectures). The very large size leads to a low volume emissivity for this source, despite its intrinsic great strength. In the center is another double radio source, suggesting that multiple violent events can occur in galaxies and lead to complex structure of this sort.

The optical extent of the galaxy along the major axis of its luminosity (in P.A. $\sim 30°$) is very great—some 80 kparsec over-all (JOHNSON, 1963)—and there is a very prominent well-known thick dust lane crossing the galaxy at right angles to this direction. The object is close enough for a detailed spectroscopic study to be made, but unfortunately it is at a very southerly declination and hard to work on from the northern hemisphere. BURBIDGE and BURBIDGE (1959) found that emission lines of moderate strength, characteristic of normal H II regions in spiral galaxies, are present in and near the dust lane, and the gaseous component responsible for these is rotating about an axis parallel to the major axis of the main luminosity distribution, *i.e.*, about an axis at right angles to the dark lane and at about 30° to the major axis of the radio emission. The velocity difference from one edge to the other of the dark lane is about 600 km/s; there are irregularities or « bumps » in the velocity curve which would repay further study and correlation with structural details.

NGC 1316 shows some structural resemblance to NGC 5128, in that it has dust lanes superimposed on a galaxy that is mainly composed of stars, of *SO* or *D* type. It is associated with the *Fornax* A source, which is radiating at a radio power level of about $5 \cdot 10^{41}$ erg/s. Like NGC 5128, it has an outer luminous structure of large dimensions (ARP, 1964) extending more than 30 kparsec from the center and jutting into the two areas of radio emission (the source is double). The structure of the dust lanes near the center is interesting; they resemble the bar and arms in a barred spiral and can be seen on a short-exposure photograph to be centered a little away from the center of the luminous distribution (BURBIDGE, BURBIDGE, and SANDAGE, 1963). Those authors found that emission lines are very weak in NGC 1316; they occur only in the center of the galaxy; in fact, only the [N II] λ 6583 line was detected, and that only in the center of the galaxy. SEARLE (1965) has observed rotation of the stellar component, by means of the absorption lines, about an axis lying in the projected direction of the *minor* axis of the luminosity distribution (contrary to what was found in NGC 5128); zero differential velocity was found when the spectrograph slit was aligned along the minor axis.

In one other more distant galaxy, 3C 33, which has fairly strong emission lines, Schmidt found inclined spectral lines suggesting that the object is rotating about an axis roughly North-South in direction (MATTHEWS, MORGAN and SCHMIDT, 1964). The galaxy has an elongated shape, $3''.3\times8''.4$, with its minor axis in position angle 163°, but there is also a faint outer envelope, which has diameters $9''.4\times22''$, with the long axis lying along the *minor* axis of the inner luminous structure. Thus, as in NGC 5128, the major axis of the outer luminous envelope lies close to the axis of rotation, and, further, the radio source is double in 3C 33, with the separation lying in P.A. 18° or about 35° to the major axis of the outer luminous envelope.

It will be important to ascertain the relationship between the axis of rotation or any other axis to which velocities can be referred and the radio brightness distribution in other objects; it is interesting that contrary results have been found in the first two nearby *E*, *D*, or *SO* galaxies in which this has been done.

10. – M 87.

The giant elliptical galaxy M87 was identified as the radio source *Virgo* A (3C 274) by BOLTON, STANLEY, and SLEE in 1951. CURTIS (1918) had pointed out that this galaxy has a straight jet extending from the nucleus in position angle 290°, a feature which can be plainly seen by visual inspection through a telescope. The jet is blue in color, relative to the galaxy, and shows only a continuous spectrum with no lines, either emission or absorption. The light from it, however, is strongly polarized (BAADE, 1956) and these observations provided confirmation of the synchrotron theory of radio emission which had been established by observations of polarization in the Crab Nebula.

Spectroscopically, M87 ranks as rather a weak-emission-line object, since the only line which has been detected is [O II] λ 3727 and this is seen only in the nucleus. However, the angular extent over which this emission feature is seen is very small—only about 1″—and over this extent it is actually very strong, broad, and asymmetrical to the extent that it can be called double

(OSTERBROCK, 1960). The main component has the same velocity as that given by the absorption lines in the nucleus, while the secondary or weaker component is shifted some 11 Å towards shorter wavelengths, indicating a velocity of approach, relative to the center of mass of the galaxy, of about 900 km/s. This suggests the ejection of gas from the nucleus of the galaxy.

11. – Multiple elliptical or *D*-type galaxies NGC 4782-3, NGC 6166, NGC 7236-7, and *Her* A.

The radio sources 3C 278 (power level $= 2.3 \cdot 10^{41}$ erg/s), 3C 338 (power level $= 5.0 \cdot 10^{41}$ erg/s), 3C 442 (power level $= 3.2 \cdot 10^{41}$ erg/s), and 3C 348 (*Her* A; power level $= 1.6 \cdot 10^{44}$ erg/s) are all strong radio emitters, and the first three are definitely identified with the double or multiple elliptical or *D*-type galaxies NGC 4782-3, NGC 6166, and NGC 7236-7, respectively. *Her* A is identified with an 18.5 mag. *D*-type galaxy with a fainter close companion that is either a compact companion galaxy or a 19.5 mag. superposed foreground star (GREENSTEIN 1962). The only emission line seen in any of these spectra is [OII] λ 3727, and in NGC 4782-3, no emission lines at all are seen.

a) NGC 4782-3. This object is a double elliptical or dumb-bell; the radio source is single and not of very large extent; however, it encircles both members of the pair so it is not possible from the radio distribution to see which galaxy is the one responsible for the radio emission.

The light distribution in NGC 4782-3 was studied by BURBIDGE, BURBIDGE, and CRAMPIN (1964) and it shows some very interesting features. First we note that, since no emission lines are seen, there is no evidence for any ionized gas in the system, and the luminosity must be wholly due to the stars of which it is composed, so that any unusual features in the light distribution have to be accounted for in terms of stellar dynamics and the star orbits, under the action of gravitational forces alone. Four exposures ranging from 45 minutes to 2 minutes were taken with the Lick 120-inch telescope, and they show *a*) the outer isophotes are unsymmetrical, with bulges out at the side of each galaxy on opposite sides, *b*) the degree of concentration in the nucleus is quite different in the two galaxies—one (NGC 4783) has a small concentrated nucleus and the other has a diffuse nuclear region of lower central intensity. These features are shown in Fig. 5.

From the velocity difference between the two centers, which was measured by THORNTON PAGE and later by GREENSTEIN, one can estimate a minimum mass by assuming that the galaxies are describing orbits about the center of mass, and that the line of sight lies in the orbital plane perpendicular to the line joining the two galaxies in space. Since the velocity difference is large, namely, 650 km/s, this minimum mass for the total system is large, *i.e.*, $M_1 + M_2 \geqslant 5.3 \cdot 10^{11} M_\odot$. Almost certainly the various orbital projection factors will differ from unity, and thus the combined mass may well be an order of magnitude larger than the minimum value. Thus this system is composed of two very massive ellipticals. They are also very luminous: $M_{pg} = -21.5$ (NGC 4782) and $M_{pg} = -21.1$ (NGC 4783).

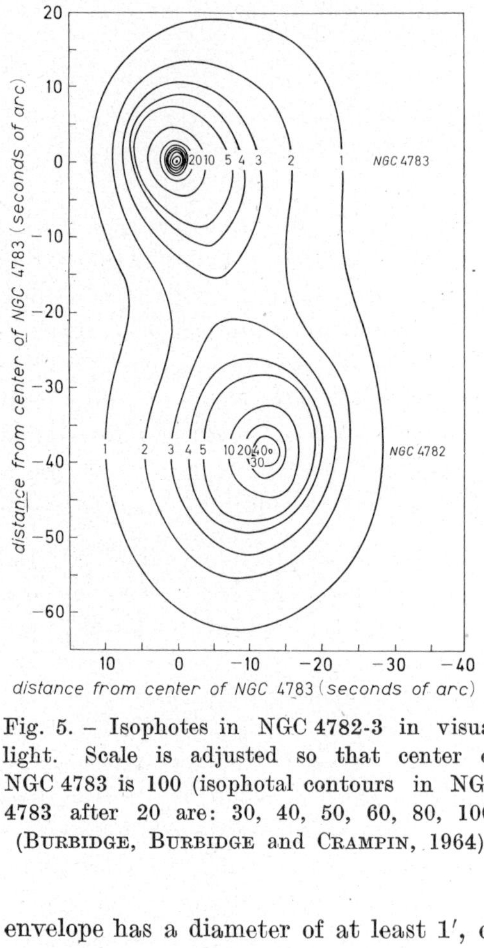

Fig. 5. – Isophotes in NGC 4782-3 in visual light. Scale is adjusted so that center of NGC 4783 is 100 (isophotal contours in NGC 4783 after 20 are: 30, 40, 50, 60, 80, 100) (BURBIDGE, BURBIDGE and CRAMPIN, 1964).

b) NGC 6166. This object consists of 4 galxies in a very extended common envelope (MINKOWSKI, 1958); it is the brightest member in the rich cluster of galaxies Abell 2199. The brightest of the 4 condensations (which are named A, B, C, D) is the object that is responsible for the very extended envelope; it has been classified as a *cD* (supergiant *D*-type) system by MATTHEWS, MORGAN, and SCHMIDT (1964), who printed photographs showing the object and the location of the (single) radio source with respect to the object; its center is displaced from all the optical components but lies closest to the center of the component A, the brightest one. The easily visible part of the envelope has a diameter of at least 1′, corresponding to 26.4 kparsec; on the Palomar Sky Survey it can be seen to extend further and to have a faint asymmetrical extension passing through and well beyond the half-intensity radio contour.

The three brightest condensations (A, B, and C) have velocities which show a considerable dispersion (MINKOWSKI, 1961), and indicate a very large mass for the system—the minimum mass is $3.8 \cdot 10^{12} M_\odot$. It is also very luminous; the combined absolute magnitude is $M_{pg} = -22.0$ and that of component A is $M_{pg} = -21.7$.

Component A is somewhat unusual in two other respects besides its great size and luminosity. First, there seems to be some dark absorbing material on the side toward the other components; this was noted by MINKOWSKI and may be seen in a Lick photograph by E. M. BURBIDGE (1962). Second, while a fairly short-exposure photograph in ordinary light shows no bright nucleus and only a low degree of central concentration in the component A (in this respect it is quite different from B and C and the other elliptical galaxies in the cluster), a photograph taken by BURBIDGE at Lick with a filter isolating a fairly narrow band-pass around the [O II] λ 3727 line shows a small bright center which thus seems to be constituted by ionized gas and not by stars. MINKOWSKI had earlier noted that this emission line was present in the spectrum of the center of component A.

c) NGC 7236-7. This double elliptical is very similar to NGC 4782-3, but at about twice the distance and so less detail can be discerned. However, in this pair also, one member (NGC 7237) has a much lower central concentration and a larger diameter than the other member. The absorption line spectra again indicate an old stellar population. The main difference between this pair and NGC 4782-3 lies in the fact that NGC 7237—the galaxy with the low central concentration—has [O II] λ 3727 emission occurring right in the center, and extending over only $1''.1$ on Greenstein's spectrum, *i.e.* within a radius of only 500 parsec. Another difference is that the line-of-sight velocities between these two galaxies are nearly the same. The [O II] line is rather broad, indicating velocities of ± 215 km/s, while the absorption lines are sharp.

As in NGC 4782-3, the radio source is simple but larger than the separation of the two galaxies, so that either one could be the origin of the emission. Probably NGC 7237 is responsible.

d) *Her* A. We have already referred to the earlier mis-identification of this source with a peculiar galaxy having strong emission lines. The object now believed to be the identification has only one emission line, strong and rather broad, which is presumed to be [OII] λ 3727 with $\Delta\lambda/\lambda_0 = 0.154$ (GREENSTEIN, 1962). Since the galaxy is rather distant, little detail can be seen on a direct photograph taken by MINKOWSKI, but one can see that the object has only a moderate central concentration and is rather extended, so that it is classified as of *D*-type. Minkowski's photographs also shows, by comparison with other stars in the field, that the companion object is more likely a galaxy rather than a foreground star. Because of the strength of [OII] λ3727, it is possible that other emission lines such as [OIII], H_α, and H_β, which would fall outside the range of wavelength photographed by GREENSTEIN, should be present in the spectrum.

12. – General discussion of radio galaxies: relation to theoretical work.

The large energies required in radio galaxies in the form of high-energy particles and magnetic fields have been a subject of discussion for many years. Dr. Sandage's lectures give the formulae for emission by the synchrotron mechanism, and calculations of total energy requirements may be found, *e.g.*, in BURBIDGE (1959). It is to explain these high energies, up to $\sim 10^{61}$ erg, that gravitational collapse of massive objects, as well as nuclear energy from the rapid evolution of massive objects, have been considered as possible energy sources. Let us collect some observational facts that have emerged from the preceding Sections, in order to see what a successful theory of radio galaxies has to explain:

1) In many cases, *single* galaxies are strong radio emitters, consequently it became necessary some years ago to discard the hypothesis that collisions between galaxies might be responsible.

2) All the evidence points to the *nuclei* of galaxies as the seat of what is producing the energy, and that a *violent event* has occurred there in radio galaxies.

3) These violent events can be *recurrent*; Dr. SANDAGE has discussed the lifetimes associated with the radio phenomen, and has shown that frequencies of radio galaxies then demand recurrent events. He has also shown that NGC 5128 is one of the best examples of a galaxy where we can see now the results of what must be more than one event. We may extend this recurrence argument to the Seyfert galaxies. From the masses that have been determined for NGC 1068 and NGC 7469, the escape velocity at the center can be computed; it is about 400 km/s in each case. Yet the broad emission lines in the nucleus yield velocities of the order of a few thousand km/s; we saw in NGC 1068 that actual cloud complexes with these velocities are seen. The gaseous material cannot, then, be contained by the gravitational potential at the center and must escape. The characteristic time for this excape must be given by simply dividing the dimension of the nucleus (~ 50 parsec) by the average velocity of the gas motions, and this time is $\sim 10^4$ years. The frequency of Seyfert galaxies among, say, the spiral galaxies contained in the Shapley-Ames Catalogue, about $(2 \div 3)\%$, then makes it plausible that the violent events must be recurrent, since otherwise, if we take the average age of galaxies to be the Hubble time or $\sim 10^{10}$ years, then the lifetime of the Seyfert phenomenon should be of the order of a few times 10^8 years.

4) The strong radio-emitting galaxies tend to be characteristically very massive stellar systems, with little uncondensed material in them, and with low angular momenta per unit mass. Assuming, as the absorption-line spectra

of M87 (*Virgo* A) and NGC 5128 indicate, that the stars giving most of the light are G8-K3 III normal giants, then, based on stellar evolution arguments, the objects must be $\sim 10^{10}$ years old. Consequently we can discard theories which require radio galaxies to be at a *young stage* in their evolution. For example, GINZBURG (1957) once suggested that high-energy particles might be produced in the early stages of formation of a galaxy when gravitational energy was released upon contraction. Theories such as that once suggested by HOYLE (1961), which relied on magnetic fields and large angular momenta, and involved gaseous discharges like giant flares, conflict with the observations because of the characteristic absence of much uncondensed gas and the fact that rotating spiral galaxies do not include the strongest radio emitters.

The annihilation of matter and antimatter, proposed by BURBIDGE (1956) and BURBIDGE and HOYLE (1956) has long been a tempting hypothesis. The general difficulty with this hypothesis is that one needs a mechanism for separating matter and antimatter, whatever cosmology one is working with, and with antigravity ruled out by the arguments of SCHIFF (1959), this does not appear to be possible. The attraction of the hypothesis, at the time it was proposed, was that it provided electrons and positrons directly, without the need for the large flux of high-energy protons, and hence, the energy requirements were reduced. Although an acceleration process was needed, which would necessarily accelerate protons as well as electrons and positrons, at least the latter would be injected into this process at energies above the low energies where electron acceleration is relatively inefficient.

Let us concentrate on the two facts that 1) the strongest radio galaxies tend to be *massive*, and 2) the phenomenon is connected with *events in nuclei of galaxies*. SHKLOVSKY (1962) suggested the accretion of intergalactic material and its infall into the nucleus as a possible mechanism. He specifically considered the case of M87, and argued that the material accreted by such a massive system would fall into the center. Energy would be released and material in the central region would be accelerated outward in the form of plasma jets. While the rate at which material falls in was estimated by SHKLOVSKY to be about 10 solar masses per year, and this is compatible with the normal accretion rate for a galaxy of mass of the order of 10^{12} solar masses in a medium of density $\sim 10^{-29}$ g/cm^3, the details of this process were never clear.

The places in the Universe where violent events are known to occur are supernova explosions. The observations of the Crab Nebula and other supernova remnants in our galaxy show that in, or following, stellar explosions the necessary condition for a synchrotron source to appear are produced. Also, only in stellar explosions (novae and supernovae) are velocities generated of the magnitude seen in the Seyfert nuclei. Thus, it is natural to suppose that the violent outbursts in galaxies might be the result of multiple supernova outbursts or their equivalent in energy output.

SHKLOVSKY (1960) argued simply that the supernova rate must have been very considerably enhanced so that some 10^6 or more supernovae have gone off at a rate of about 1 per year in an object like M87. However, he had no argument as to why this should occur. Since supernovae only occur at the end of a star's evolution it is not reasonable to take this view 1) unless it is supposed that the outbursts are causally connected, or, 2) unless stars of very great mass are continuously being formed and evolve very rapidly.

BURBIDGE (1961) proposed that a chain reaction of supernovae could be caused in the nucleus of a galaxy if one supernova went off naturally and the stellar density was sufficiently high so that other stars could be exploded. It was estimated that the star density required if such a mechanism were to work must be of the order of 10^6 to 10^7 stars per cubic parsec and it was pointed out that there was no observational argument against this, particularly for the elliptical galaxies. Even higher star densities might be acceptable. The difficulty lay in understanding how a detonation wave could propagate even if sufficient light nuclei were present. This problem has not been solved, partly because the geometry involved is exceedingly difficult to handle. Also modern ideas concerning supernova outbursts suggest that an integral part of the normal supernova process is a catastrophic collapse. The chain reaction mechanism would not lead to this.

It was the difficulties attendant on all the suggestions outlined here that led HOYLE and FOWLER to the idea that single massive objects, containing $(10^6 \div 10^8)\, M_\odot$, might be responsible for the great energy release required by the observations. The way in which such a « super-star » might form is still a puzzle, however. A deep potential well in the center of a very massive galaxy would tend to concentrate any uncondensed gas, or any accreted gas as suggested by SHKLOVSKY, into the center, where it might form a massive object.

One further possibility which has recently been considered is that a rapidly accelerating process of star collision might occur in the centers of galaxies where there is a high stellar density leading to what might be called a « phase change » of matter in the nuclei of galaxies, so that the aggregation of stars into one large mass might occur (ULAM and WALDEN, 1964; GOLD, AXFORD, and RAY, 1965). The star collisions themselves might provide a powerful energy source, as considered by GOLD. On these hypotheses, the phenomenon of *recurrence* of violent events remains a problem.

13. – Quasi-stellar radio sources.

DR. SANDAGE has described these objects in his lectures, and has spoken about their discovery, identification, colors and magnitudes, variations in energy output, and the exciting story of the identification of spectral features and the consequent measurement of red-shifts, up to values just greater than $z = \Delta\lambda/\lambda_0 = 2$.

I shall therefore discuss the two QSRS's for which detailed spectroscopic analyses have been made, and give an account of what has been found out about the physical conditions in these objects, using the methods outlined in Sect. **3** which can be applied to any emitting gaseous region. The optical spectra of 3C 273 and 3C 48 were analysed by GREENSTEIN and SCHMIDT (1964) and the continuum spectrum of 3C 273 was studied by OKE (1965).

We shall now follow the analysis of GREENSTEIN and SCHMIDT. The characteristic feature of QSRS's is that they show broad emission lines, similar in what features are seen and in the line breadths to the spectrum of, *e.g.*, the nucleus of NGC 1068. These lines, however, are much harder to study because the contrast between emission lines and the continuum is much lower, so that the broad emission lines are quite hard to see unless the spectra are considerably broadened by trailing the object along the slit.

a) The red-shifts. The red-shifts of $z = 0.158$ for 3C 273 and $z = 0.368$ for 3C 48 were determined from the lines shown in Table III, and are consequently well-determined. The question immediately arose: what are these red-shifts due to—are they Doppler shifts or gravitational shifts? GREENSTEIN and SCHMIDT used the following argument against their being gravitational in origin.

TABLE III. – *Emission lines found by* GREENSTEIN *and* SCHMIDT *in* 3C 48 *and* 3C 273.

3C 48	λ_0 (Å)	λ_{obs} (Å)	3C 273	λ_0 (Å)	λ_{obs} (Å)
H_β	4861	6646	H_α	6563	7590
H_γ	4340	5935	[O III]	5007	5792
[Ne III]	3869	5288	H_β	4861	5632
[O II]	3727	5097	H_γ	4340	5032
[Ne V]	3426	4685	H_δ	4102	4753
[Ne V]	3346	4575	H_ε	3970	4595
[Ne V]	2973	4066	Mg II	2798	3239
Mg II	2798	3832			

A body of radius R and mass M will produce, due to the gravitational field, a red-shift at the surface of the body that is given by

$$z = \frac{\Delta\lambda}{\lambda_0} = \frac{GM}{Rc^2} = 1.47\cdot 10^5 \frac{M}{M_\odot}\frac{1}{R}, \tag{1}$$

where G, c are the gravitational constant and the velocity of light, $M_\odot$ is the sun's mass, and R is in cm. Suppose a collapsed massive object is surrounded by a thin spherical shell, of thickness ΔR, in which the emission lines arise. There will be a gradient in gravitational potential across the thickness of the shell; let us assume that the resulting spread in the wavelength of line radiation leaving the object gives rise to the observed widths w of these lines. Then we have

$$\frac{\Delta R}{R} = \frac{w}{\Delta \lambda} = 0.07 \tag{2}$$

in 3C 273. We may now envisage two possibilities: *a*) the object consists of a collapsed star of about 1 solar mass, within our Galaxy, and *b*) the object is more massive, extragalactic but at only a moderate distance. The consequences of these two possibilities will be as follows:

i) The equation of state for collapsed stars leads to a radius of $R \sim 10^6\, M/M_\odot$ cm in order to yield a gravitational red-shift of $z = 0.158$, as observed in 3C 273. Now if $M/M_\odot \sim 1$, then $R \sim 10^6$ cm and thus $\Delta R \sim \sim 7 \cdot 10^4$ cm, so that the volume of the shell emitting the line radiation is determined. Now the volume emissivity in H_β is known from hydrogen recombination theory; for $T_e \sim 10^4$ it is $\sim 10^{-25} N_e^2$ erg s^{-1} cm^{-3}. The flux in H_β measured at the earth from 3C 273 is $3.4 \cdot 10^{-12}$ erg s^{-1} cm^{-2}. We can thus set up a relation between the volume emissivity in H_β, the volume of the emitting shell, and the measured H_β flux in which the distance to the object, d, is the only unknown. We have

$$10^{-25} R^2 \Delta R\, N_e^2 = 3.4 \cdot 10^{-12} d^2 \tag{3}$$

or, since ΔR and R are fixed,

$$N_e^2 = 5 \cdot 10^{-4} d^2 \,. \tag{4}$$

Now a search for a proper motion in 3C 273 has yielded negative results, consequently the object is unlikely to be very close to the sun. GREENSTEIN and SCHMIDT considered that d must be not less than 100 parsec, and this yields

$$N_e \geqslant 6 \cdot 10^{18}\ \text{cm}^{-3} \,. \tag{5}$$

Such a high density is quite incompatible with the appearance of the forbidden line [O III] $\lambda 5007$.

ii) Now let us suppose 3C 273 is a massive object, outside our Galaxy but not at a large distance. We can replace the above condition that the distance d should be <100 parsec by the condition that the mass should not be great enough nor the distance small enough for the object to produce detectable perturbations on the motions of stars in our galaxy. To set a number on this, GREENSTEIN and SCHMIDT postulated that such perturbations should be less than 10% of the gravitational acceleration due to the whole galaxy, so that

$$\frac{M}{M_\odot} \leqslant 10^{-35} d^2 . \tag{6}$$

Again using the measured flux in H_β and the volume emissivity in H_β, we find, combining equations (1) and (2) and the inequality (6),

$$\left| \begin{aligned} & d \geqslant 8 \cdot 10^6 N_e^{-\frac{1}{2}} \text{ parsec} \\ \text{and} & \\ & \frac{M}{M_\odot} \geqslant 7 \cdot 10^{15} N_e^{-1} . \end{aligned} \right. \tag{7}$$

As we shall see shortly, the emission-line spectrum in 3C 273 requires that $N_e \sim 10^7$ cm^{-3}, so that

$$d \geqslant 25\,00 \text{ parsec} \qquad \text{and} \qquad \frac{M}{M_\odot} \geqslant 7 \cdot 10^8 . \tag{8}$$

The same calculations for 3C 48 yield

$$d \geqslant 25\,000 \text{ parsec} \qquad \text{and} \qquad \frac{M}{M_\odot} > 7 \cdot 10^{10} . \tag{9}$$

Thus collapsed massive extragalactic objects on this scale could account for the observed red-shifts in these two objects. However, this becomes more unlikely when we consider objects with the very large red-shifts recently found by SCHMIDT, and indeed the conditions would be so extreme that we can rule this possibility out.

b) Physical conditions from emission lines. Table IV gives the energies

TABLE IV. – *Energies emitted in emission lines* (erg/s) *for distances given by red-shifts.*

	3C 48	3C 273
H_β	$6.4 \cdot 10^{42}$	$8.8 \cdot 10^{43}$
Mg II	$3.1 \cdot 10^{42}$	$4.0 \cdot 10^{43}$
[Ne V]	$1.7 \cdot 10^{42}$	—
[O II]	$3.3 \cdot 10^{42}$	—
[O III]	Present	$3.1 \cdot 10^{43}$

emitted in the emission lines in 3C 48 and 3C 273 assuming these objects to be at distance given by their red-shifts. In Sect. **7** we saw that the *electron density and temperature* N_e and T_e could be determined in the galaxy NGC 1068 by using pairs of emission lines from the same ion, so that uncertainties concerning the degree of ionization and abundances of the elements did not affect the results. For the quasi-stellar objects we cannot do this, because there is not enough observational information. GREENSTEIN and SCHMIDT assumed a reasonable value for T_e of 16 800° K and also assumed that the element abundances are similar to those found in planetary nebulae. They obtained:

$$N_e = 3 \cdot 10^4 \text{ cm}^{-3} \quad \text{for 3C 48},$$

$$N_e = 3 \cdot 10^6 \text{ cm}^{-3} \quad \text{for 3C 273},$$

with an uncertainty of about a factor 10 either way. The higher value of N_e is found for 3C 273 because of the absence of [O II] λ 3727, indicating that appreciable collisional de-excitation of its upper level must occur.

We now turn to the *volume and mass* of the objects. Recombination theory gives a volume emissivity for H_β of $10^{30} N_e^2$ erg s^{-1} parsec^{-3}, following the discussion given earlier. The total line emission is given in Table IV, consequently, having N_e we can obtain the volume and therefore the dimension, and the mass of the emitting gas. The results are:

$$\text{3C 48} \begin{cases} R = 11 \text{ parsec}, \\ M = 5 \cdot 10^6 M_\odot, \end{cases} \qquad \text{3C 273} \begin{cases} R = 1.2 \text{ parsec}, \\ M = 6 \cdot 10^5 M_\odot. \end{cases}$$

These results refer, of course, to the regions giving the emission lines.

An important feature of quasi-stellar radio sources, referred to by Dr. SANDAGE, is their *light variations*. The optical continuum from 3C 273 is variable with a time scale of $\frac{1}{3}$ year; this light travel time corresponds to 1/10 parsec; observations of the optical size of the stellar object give only an upper limit for its radius of 500 parsec. We have just seen that the emission lines come from a region of about 1.2 parsec radius, so emission lines and continuum cannot come from the same region. It will clearly be a very important observation to check on the constancy of the flux emitted in the lines; if the above arguments are correct, the lines should remain constant when the continuum varies in as short a time as $\frac{1}{3}$ year.

BIBLIOGRAPHY

Arp, H. C., 1964, *Ap. J.*, **139**, 1378.
Baade, W., 1956, *Ap. J.*, **123**, 550.
Baade, W. and R. Minkowski, 1954, *Ap. J.*, **119**, 206.
Baker, J. G. and D. H. Menzel, 1938, *Ap. J.*, **88**, 52.
Bolton, J. G. and B. G. Clark, 1960, *Pub. Astr. Soc. Pacific*, **72**, 29.
Bowen, I. S., 1935, *Ap. J.*, **81**, 1.
Burbidge, E. M., 1962, *Ap. J.*, **136**, 1134.
Burbidge, E. M. and G. R. Burbidge, 1959, *Ap. J.*, **129**, 271.
Burbidge, E. M. and G. R. Burbidge, 1961, *Astr. J.*, **66**, 541.
Burbidge, E. M. and G. R. Burbidge, 1964*a*, *Ap. J.*, **140**, 1445.
Burbidge, E. M. and G. R. Burbidge, 1964*b*, *Ap. J.*, **140**, 1307.
Burbidge, E. M. and G. R. Burbidge, 1965, *Ap. J.*, **142**, 1351.
Burbidge, E. M., G. R. Burbidge and D. J. Crampin, 1964, *Ap. J.*, **140**, 1462.
Burbidge, E. M., G. R. Burbidge and K. H. Prendergast, 1959, *Ap. J.*, **130**, 26.
Burbidge, E. M., G. R. Burbidge and K. H. Prendergast, 1963, *Ap. J.*, **137**, 1022.
Burbidge, E. M., G. R. Burbidge and V. C. Rubin, 1964, *Ap. J.*, **140**, 942.
Burbidge, E. M., G. R. Burbidge and A. R. Sandage, 1963, *Rev. Mod. Phys.*, **35**, 947.
Burbidge, G. R., 1956, *Phys. Rev.*, **103**, 264.
Burbidge, G. R., 1959, *Paris Symposium on Radio Astronomy*, ed. R. N. Bracewell, (Stanford), p. 541.
Burbidge, G. R., 1961, *Nature*, **190**, 1053.
Burbidge, G. R. and F. Hoyle, 1956, *Nuovo Cimento*, **4**, 558.
Curtis, H. D., 1918, *Pub. Lick Obs.*, **13**, 31.
Ginzburg, V. L., 1957, *Usp. Fiz. Nauk*, **51**, 343.
Gold, T., W. I. Axford and E. C. Ray, 1965, *Proc. Dallas Symposium on Quasi-Stellar Sources and Gravitational Collapse* (Chicago), p. 93.
Greenstein, J. L., 1962, *Ap. J.*, **135**, 679.
Greenstein, J. L. and M. Schmidt, 1964, *Ap. J.*, **140**, 1.
Hoyle, F., 1961, *Observatory*, **81**, 39.
Johnson, H. M., 1963, *Pub. Nat. Radio Astr. Obs.*, **1**, 251.
Matthews, T. A., W. W. Morgan and M. Schmidt, 1964, *Ap. J.*, **140**, 35.
Minkowski, R., 1957, *I.A.U. Symposium No. 4 on Radio Astronomy* (Cambridge), p. 107.
Minkowski, R., 1958, *Pub. Astr. Soc. Pacific*, **70**, 143.
Minkowski, R., 1960, *Ap. J.*, **132**, 908.
Minkowski, R., 1961, *Astr. J.*, **66**, 558.
Morgan, W. W. and N. U. Mayall, 1957, *Pub. Astr. Soc. Pacific*, **69**, 291.
Münch, G., 1960, *Ap. J.*, **131**, 250.
Oke, J. B., 1965, *Ap. J.*, **141**, 6.
Osterbrock, D. E., 1960, *Ap. J.*, **132**, 325.
Osterbrock, D. E. and R. A. R. Parker, 1965, *Ap. J.*, **141**, 892.
Pengelly, R. M., 1964, *Mon. Not. R.A.S.*, **127**, 145.
Schiff, L., 1959, *Proc. Nat. Acad. Sci.*, **45**, 69.
Schmidt, M., 1965, *Ap. J.*, **141**, 1.

SEARLE, L., 1965, *Nature*, **207**, 1282.
SEATON, M. J., 1954, *Mon. Not. R.A.S.*, **114**, 154.
SEATON, M. J. and D. E. OSTERBROCK, 1957, *Ap. J.*, **125**, 66.
SEYFERT, C. K., 1943, *Ap. J.*, **97**, 28.
SHKLOVSKY, I. S., 1960, *Astr. Žurn. U.S.S.R.*, **37**, 945; *Sov. Astr.*, **4**, 885.
SHKLOVSKY, I. S., 1962, *Astr. Žurn. U.S.S.R.*, **39**, 591.
ULAM, S. M. and W. E. WALDEN, 1964, *Nature*, **201**, 1202.
VORONTSOV-VELYAMINOV, B. A., 1959, *Atlas of Interacting Galaxies*, Moscow.
ZWICKY, F., 1964, Report Mt. Wilson and Palomar Obs., p. 33 in Carnegie Inst. of Washington Yearbook, 63, 1963-64; *Proc. Giornate Galileiane (Padova Conf.)*, in press.

Some Observational Aspects of X-Ray Astronomy (*).

R. Giacconi, H. Gursky and J. R. Waters
American Science and Engineering, Inc. - Cambridge, Mass.

B. Rossi, G. Clark, G. Garmire, M. Oda and M. Wada
Massachussetts Institute of Technology - Cambridge, Mass.

1. – Introduction.

The first totally unexpected result of space astronomy was the discovery of strong X-ray sources outside the solar system.

Because of atmospheric absorption, X-rays, of course, cannot be observed with land-based instruments. The altitude requirements for X-ray astronomy become clear from an examination of Fig. 1, showing the altitude where electromagnetic waves of different wavelengths arrive with different degrees of attenuation (1/2, 1/10, 1/100). One sees that X-rays with wavelength λ greater than about one Å (quantum energy E smaller than 12 keV) can be observed only at altitudes greater than 50 km, which can be reached only by rockets or space vehicles. X-rays with quantum energies E greater than about 15 keV, on the other hand, penetrate to altitudes of the order of 30 km, which are within the range of balloon flights.

Even beyond the atmosphere, X-ray astronomy is limited by the absorption in interstellar space. This is shown in Fig. 2; the curves represent the density of interstellar matter (in atoms per cm^3) times the distance (in light years) corresponding to various degrees of attenuation, plotted against wavelength. Since the average density of interstellar matter is of the order of 0.3 atoms per cm^3, we see that, for wavelengths less than about 6 Å, the whole Galaxy is essentially transparent; while X-rays with wavelengths greater than about

(*) The lectures were actually delivered by R. Giacconi (N. of the Ed.). This work was supported in part by National Aeronautics and Space Administration under Grant NsG-386 and Contract NAS w-898, and by the United States Atomic Energy Commission under Contract AT(30-1) 2098.

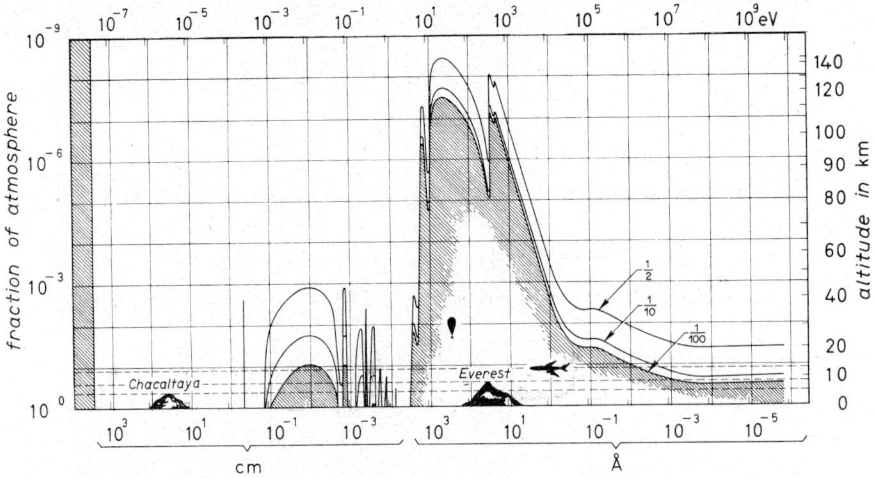

Fig. 1. – Attenuation of electromagnetic radiation in the atmosphere. Solid curves indicate altitude (and corresponding pressure expressed as a fraction of one atmosphere) at which a given attenuation occurs for a radiation of a given wavelength.

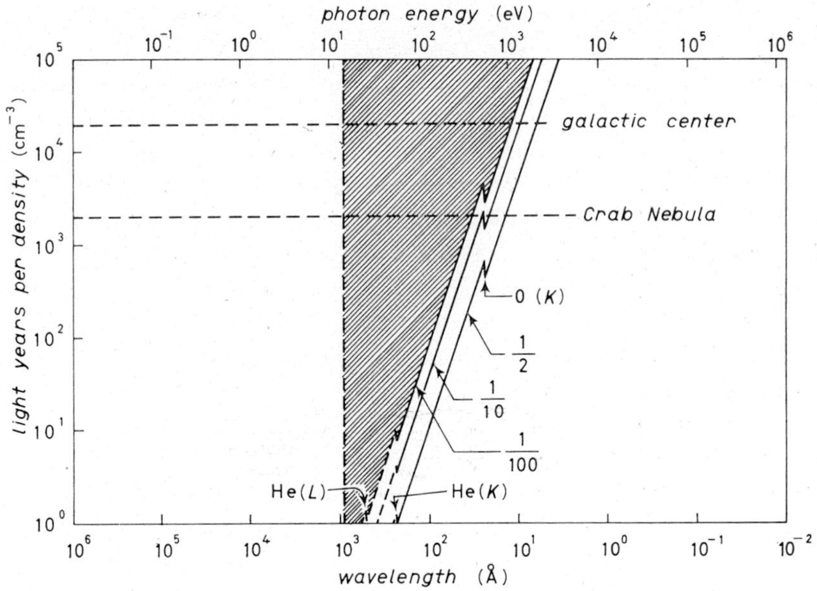

Fig. 2. – Attenuation of electromagnetic radiation in interstellar space. The ordinate represents the integrated particle density in terms of light years times the number of particles per cm³. The solid curves give the integrated density at which a given attenuation occurs for radiation of a given wavelength. O (K), He (K) and He (L) indicate the K absorption edges of O and He, and the L absorption edge of He. The ordinates corresponding to the Crab Nebula and the galactic center are calculated using the known distance to these objects and an assumed particle density of 0.3 atoms per cm³ and one atom per cm³ respectively.

100 Å can reach the earth only from sources closer than 100 light years.

Extrasolar X-rays were first detected by means of a rocket launched in June 1962 by GIACCONI, GURSKY, PAOLINI of AS & E and ROSSI of MIT [1]. The detectors were Geiger counters without a collimator and, therefore, with a wide field of view. The results revealed the existence of a strong source in the constellation Scorpius not far from the galactic center, of a possible secondary source in the constellation of Cygnus and of a diffuse X-ray background, apparently also of celestial origin. Two additional rocket experiments by the same group (October 1962 and June 1963) [2], with similar instrumentation, confirmed these results and gave a slight indication of another source in the general direction of the Crab Nebula. In the meantime (April 1963) a collimated counter, flown by a group at the Naval Research Laboratory under FRIEDMAN, again detected the Scorpio source [3]. The improved resolution made it possible to place an upper limit of 5° to its angular diameter and to determine its location with an accuracy of about 2°. Since the galactic center was below the horizon at the time of this flight, the X-ray source was certainly not coincident with the galactic center. The same flight provided clear evidence for another weaker source in Taurus, within about 2° of the Crab Nebula, and also confirmed the existence of the diffuse background.

In July 1964, the NRL group, using a pointing rocket, succeeded in

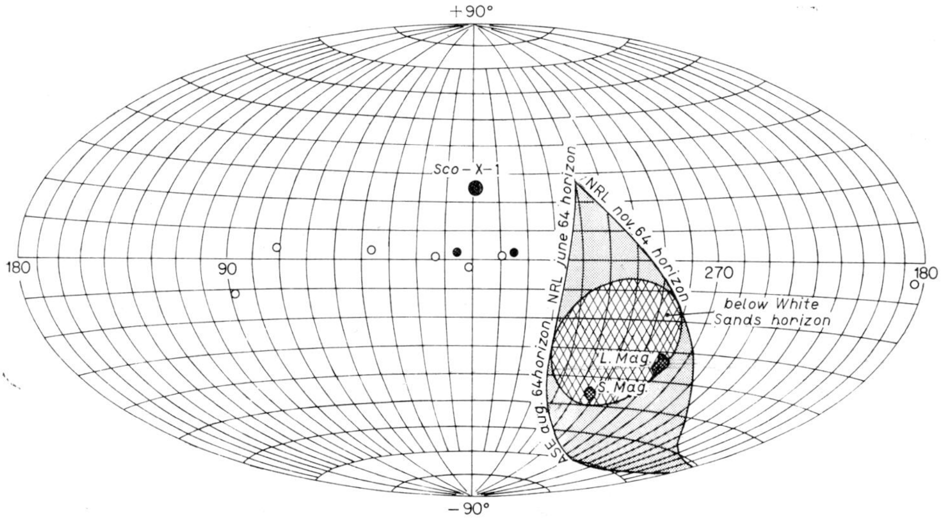

Fig. 3. – X-ray source locations in the galactic co-ordinate system (l^{II}, b^{II}). Cross-hatched region is not observable at the White Sands Missile Range. Shaded region is accessible but was not scanned in the rocket flights performed so far. This region includes the Large Magellanic Cloud (L. Mag.) and the Small Magellanic Cloud (S. Mag.). The minimum detectable source intensity in the surveyed region is about 0.05 of the intensity of *Sco* X-1. • ASE-MIT; ○ NRL (June 1965).

observing the occultation of the Crab Nebula by the Moon [4]. This remarkable experiment showed that the X-ray source in Taurus was indeed coincident with the Crab Nebula.

In addition to this flight, five other rocket flights were carried out in 1964, two by the NRL group, two by the AS & E-MIT group, and one by a group at Lockheed headed by FISHER. These flights reconfirmed the source in Scorpius. They also detected a complex of sources in the galactic plane, clustered within about 20° of the galactic center, and some additional sources in the constellations of Cygnus and Serpens.

The year 1964 saw also the first successful attempt to observe X-rays from celestial objects by means of balloon-borne instruments [5].

Figure 3 shows the region of the sky that has been explored thus far, and the approximate locations of the X-ray sources that have been detected.

2. – Instrumentation.

2·1. X-*ray detectors.* – A necessary requirement of the detectors for X-ray astronomy is high efficiency and large effective area because the flux of X-rays from celestial sources, although stronger than had been anticipated, is quite small.

The detectors used so far belong to three different categories.

2·1.1. G a s c o u n t e r s (G e i g e r c o u n t e r s a n d p r o p o r t i o n a l c o u n t e r s). These instruments may be made in a variety of sizes and shapes. Figure 4 shows a typical design. Their operation as X-ray detectors is based primarily on the production of secondary electrons by the photoelectric effect of the photons in the gas, and on the cascade multiplication of the ions produced by these electrons. The counters must be provided with windows thin enough to let X-rays through, yet sufficiently strong to withstand the gas pressure. The efficiency of a counter, ε, is the product of the probability for an X-ray photon to traverse the window, times the

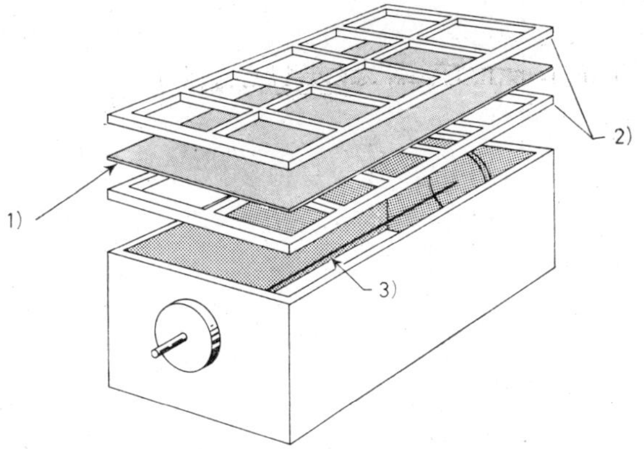

Fig. 4. – Schematic drawing of a thin-window gas counter used for the detection of soft X-rays: 1) Be window, 9.0 mg/cm^2; 2) window supports; 3) anode.

probability for the photon to be absorbed in the gas. It is thus given by the equation

$$\varepsilon(\lambda) = \exp[-\mu_w x_w](1 - \exp[-\mu_g x_g]) \,, \tag{1}$$

where μ_w and μ_g are the absorption coefficients of the window and the gas, x_w and x_g the respective thicknesses. Since μ_w and μ_g depend strongly on wavelength λ, ε is also a function of λ; in fact, ε is appreciably different from zero only within a certain range of wavelengths, which depends on the atomic number and on the thickness of the window and of the gas. The long wavelength limit of the sensitive region is determined by the window becoming opaque and the short wavelength limit by the gas becoming transparent. Thus, a thin, low-Z window and a low-Z gas filling will tend to make the counter preferentially sensitive to long wavelengths; with a comparatively thick window and a high-Z gas filling, on the other hand, the counter will discriminate in favor of short wavelengths. Examples of efficiency functions for gas counters with argon filling and different windows appear in Fig. 5.

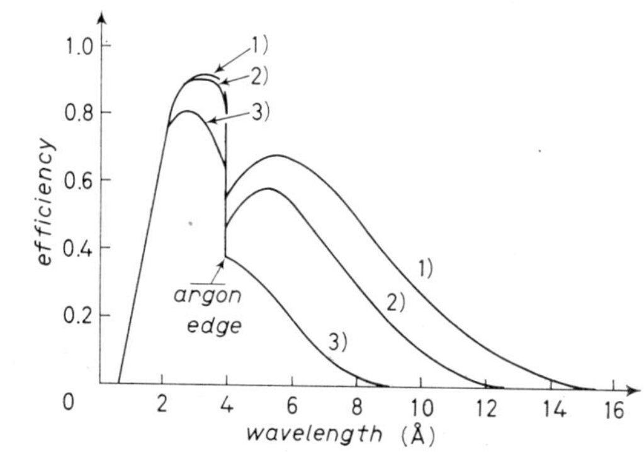

Fig. 5. – Calculated efficiency of gas counters with argon filling and different windows: 1) 0.88 mg/cm² mylar; 2) 9.1 mg/cm² beryllium; 3) 25 mg/cm² beryllium; gas: 5.4 mg/cm² argon.

The lower limit on the window thickness of a gas counter is set by the practical problem of achieving a gas-tight seal. If one insists on this requirement, it is difficult to extend the upper limit of the sensitivity range beyond about 10 Å, although the transmission curves of certain materials have « windows » at somewhat longer wavelengths (*e.g.*, aluminum has a « window » from 8 Å to about 15 Å).

The long-wavelength limit may be extended by relaxing the requirement that the window be gas tight. Although very thin windows (less than several hundred micrograms/cm²) invariably leak, a gas reservoir and pressure regulator may hold the gas pressure in the counter constant within a few percent for the short period of a rocket flight. This is essential because the gas multiplication factor is very sensitive to pressure.

By a suitable choice of voltage between the case and the wires, a gas counter may be operated as a Geiger counter or as a proportional counter (the first mode of operation requiring a higher voltage than the second).

As a Geiger counter, the detector gives pulses of uniform size, irrespective of the number of ion pairs N produced in the gas. In the proportional counter regime, the size of a pulse is proportional to N. The average value of N, N_{av}, is proportional to the energy dissipated in the gas. If the stopping power of the gas is sufficiently large, this energy may be taken as equal to the photon energy E (*) so that we can write

$$N_{av} = E/E_0 , \tag{2}$$

where E_0 is a characteristic energy dependent on the gas (*e.g.*, $E_0 = 27$ eV for argon). Thus, the pulse-height distribution of a proportional counter is directly related to the spectrum of the observed radiation. The counter, however, has a limited spectral resolution, for two separate reasons. In the first place, there may be cases where not all of the energy of the photon which has undergone photoelectric absorption is dissipated in the gas (this effect becomes increasingly important with increasing photon energy). In the second place, the actual value of N corresponding to a given energy dissipation undergoes statistical fluctuations around N_{av} (this effect becomes increasingly important as the photon energy decreases). Note that only if the counter is carefully designed will the multiplication factor remain essentially constant over its sensitive volume.

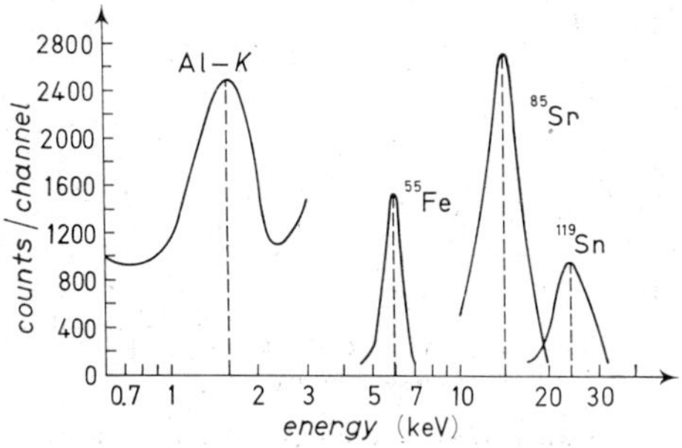

Fig. 6. – Pulse-height distributions obtained with a proportional counter exposed to monoenergetic X-rays generated by K-capture (*i.e.*, ^{85}Sr), isomeric transition (^{119}Sm) and K-X-rays induced by electron bombardment (Al). Window area $= (2 \times 6)$ in^2.; counter depth $= 2$ in.; Be window $= 2$ mg/cm^2; xenon gas at 1 atm.

Examples of actual pulse-height distributions obtained with a proportional counter exposed to monoenergetic X-rays of different energies appear in Fig. 6.

With detectors of the type described, ultra-violet rays, cosmic rays and other charged particles of lower energy are possible sources of background. It is easy to protect the detector against ultra-violet rays by a proper choice

---

(*) When a photon undergoes photoelectric absorption, the photoelectron acquires a kinetic energy equal to the photon energy minus the atomic binding energy which may be a substantial fraction of the photon energy. However, most of the binding energy will appear promptly in the form of de-excitation radiation or of kinetic energy of an Auger electron. If the stopping power of the gas is sufficient to absorb all of the electrons and photons emitted subsequent to the process of photoelectric absorption, the energy dissipated in the gas will be practically equal to that of the photon.

of the window. In order to reduce the cosmic-ray background, the counters are often set into a well-type scintillation counter whose output pulses are placed in anticoincidence with those of the X-ray counter. Low-energy charged particles, particularly electrons, whose energy is sufficient to traverse the window but not to penetrate the anticoincidence counter cannot be eliminated, and, therefore, represent a source of background that must be taken into consideration.

2·1.2. Scintillation counters. Figure 7 shows, as an example, the design of a scintillation counter used in several rocket experiments. X-ray quanta, incident on the thin slab of scintillating material (*e.g.* NaI crystal) produce secondary electrons by photoelectric effect. Practically all of these come to rest in the scintillator, giving light pulses proportional to their energy. Some of the photons thus produced reach the photocathode of the photomultiplier, releasing a certain number N of photoelectrons. The photomultiplier output is closely proportional to N.

The efficiency of the detector is the product of two terms. The first is the probability for the X-ray photon to produce a photoelectron in the scintillating material; this probability depends on the thickness and on the atomic number of the scintillator, being high for a high-Z scintillator (such as NaI), and low for a low-Z scintillator (such as anthracene). The second term is the probability that at least one photoelectron be released from the photocathode by the light pulse ($N > 1$). The average pulse height is proportional to the average value of N. It is therefore a linear function of the energy of the X-ray photon, and may be represented by an equation of the type of eq. (2). In typical situations, the average energy per photoelectron E_0 is of the order of 1000 eV. Comparing this number with the average energy for the production of a ion pair in a gas counter we see that, for a given E, N is smaller for a scintillation counter than for a gas counter. Thus, the smallest detectable photon energy is higher for a scintillation counter than for a gas counter.

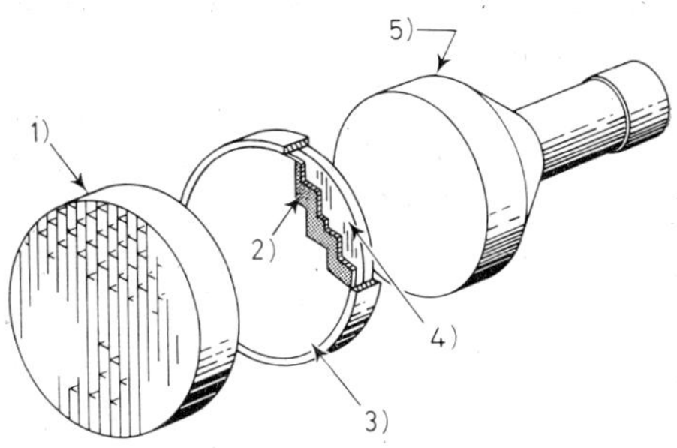

Fig. 7. – Schematic drawing of a scintillation counter used for the detection of soft X-rays: 1) collimator; 2) NaI crystal (1 mm); 3) aluminum window (6.7 mg/cm^2); 4) glass backing; 5) photomultiplier.

The spectral resolution is limited by the fluctuations in the pulse-height corresponding to a given photon energy, which is a decreasing function of N. Therefore, for small values of E, a scintillation counter will not yield as good an energy resolution as may be obtained with a proportional gas counter. For sufficiently high photon energies, on the other hand, scintillation counters have both better efficiency and higher energy resolution than gas counters because of the relatively higher stopping power of the sensitive medium.

A further limitation to the efficiency of scintillation counters for low-energy photons arises from photomultiplier noise. Under optimum conditions, scintillation counters can detect photons down to about 1 keV energy. Because of additional difficulties arising from the requirement of a large sensitive area, until now scintillation counters have been used in X-ray astronomy only in the energy region above 10 keV.

Scintillation counters must be covered with thin films of opaque material to protect the photomultipliers from visible or ultra-violet light. Cosmic-rays and other high-energy particles produce pulses of greater size than X-ray photons, and, therefore, can be easily distinguished from them. Low-energy particles, in particular electrons, cannot be distinguished from X-ray photons on the same basis. However, it is possible to separate these particles from X-rays by comparing the counting rates of two detectors with scintillation crystals of the same mass per cm² but different Z (*e.g.*, NaI and anthracene). Such counters have nearly the same response for electrons, but the low-Z counter is practically insensitive to photons.

2·1.3. Photoelectric detectors. Gas counters cannot be operated in a vacuum without a window and each window places a low energy limit to the observable portion of the X-ray spectrum. The photoelectric detector does not need a window and can, therefore, be used to extend the measurements to lower photon energies than are accesible to gas counters.

The possibility of building a photoelectric detector for X-rays rests on the fact, discovered by a group of Russian scientists in 1960 [6], that several alkali halides have an anomalously high photoelectric yield for X-rays. The design of a photoelectric detector for X-ray astronomy built by the AS & E group is shown in Fig. 8. The photocathode is an evaporated layer of KCl or CsI deposited on a spherical surface. The electrons ejected from the photo-

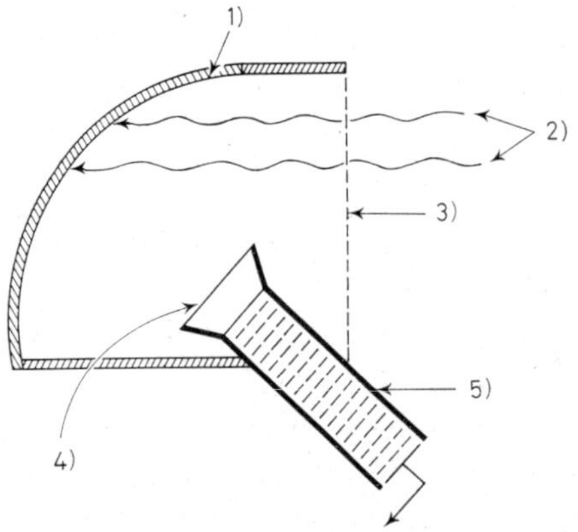

Fig. 8. – Schematic diagram of a photoelectric detector for soft X-rays: 1) photocathode; 2) incident X-rays; 3) entrance aperture; 4) electrostatic focusing element; 5) electron multiplier.

cathode are focused on the first dynode of an electron multiplier, whose output pulse is proportional to the number of these electrons. The sensitive area of this particular instrument is 40 cm². Its measured efficiency ranges from about 8% for 5 keV photons to about 25% for 0.8 keV photons. Although the instrument may be operated without a window in the high vacuum found at the altitudes where the measurements are made, a filter may be necessary to absorb ultra-violet light. Furthermore, such a window is needed to exclude ambient ionospheric electrons. Several hundred ångstrøms of aluminum evaporated on a thin organic film will achieve these purposes while allowing the transmission of X-rays well beyond the K-edge of carbon at 44 Å. Rejection of visible light does not present a serious problem because of the high work function of KCl or of CsI.

Detectors of this kind have already been flown. Although the results obtained so far are only of a preliminary character, they show that photoelectric detectors hold great promise for the future of X-ray astronomy.

2·2. *Collimators.*

2·2.1. Cellular collimators. In order to obtain accurate information on the location of the X-ray sources and on their angular sizes, it is necessary to limit the field of view of the detectors by means of suitable collimators. Because of the large area of the detectors and of the limited space available, cellular-type collimators have been used such as that shown in Fig. 9. With these collimators one can obtain fields of view of different shapes and different angular widths down to about two degrees. The transmission, of course, is a maximum for a beam parallel to the axis of the collimator (*i.e.*, the normal

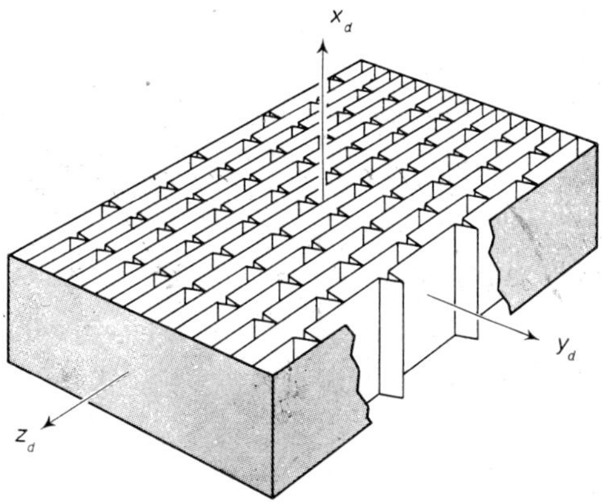

Fig. 9. – Schematic drawing of a cellular collimator.

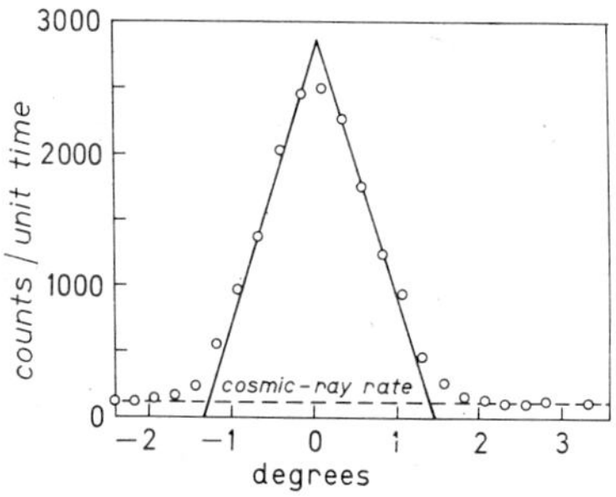

Fig. 10. – Experimental response curve of a cellular collimator to X-rays (circles) compared with its computed response function (solid line). The angular divergence of the X-ray beam was less than $\frac{1}{2}°$. The X-ray beam was in the $(\hat{x}_d, \hat{y}_d)$ plane (Fig. 9) and the abscissa represents the angle formed by this beam with the normal to the collimator $(\hat{x}_d)$.

x_d to its plane; see Fig. 9). The response curves (*i.e.* the curves giving transmission as a function of angle of incidence in planes containing the collimator axis) have typically nearly triangular shapes. As an example, Fig. 10 shows the computed and the experimental response curves in the plane $x_d y_d$ of a collimator of the type shown in Fig. 9.

2·2.2. Modulation collimators. In order to improve the angular resolution of a cellular collimator, it is necessary to decrease its field of view. In this manner, however, one also decreases the number of counts recorded when the X-ray source passes across the field of view, and therefore one reduces the statistical accuracy of the data. There is thus a practical limit to the resolution that may be obtained with these devices when used on spinning rockets.

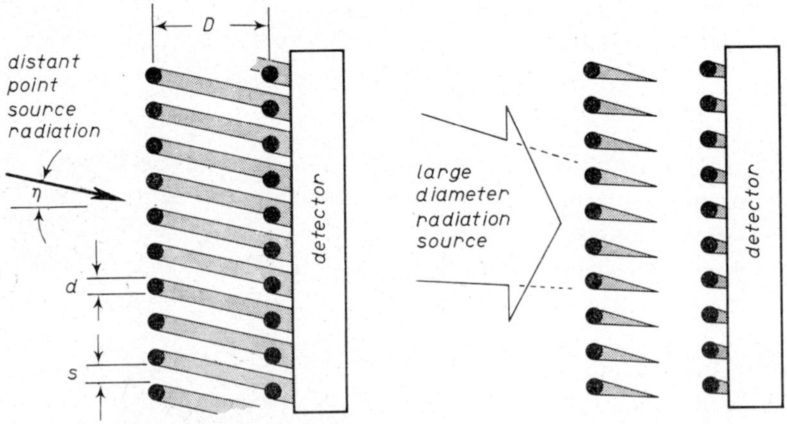

Fig. 11. – Illustrating the principle of operation of the modulation collimator. The drawing on the left indicates the shadowing that obtains with parallel radiation.

A collimator of a different type, which combines high resolution with wide field of view was conceived by ODA [7] and has been developed by the ASE-MIT group. Known as the « modulation collimator », it consists essentially of two plane grids of parallel wires placed one in front of the other at a suitable distance (Fig. 11). The diameter of the wires, *d*, is nearly equal to the spacing between adjacent wires, *s*. In a parallel beam of rays, the front grid casts a shadow on the rear grid. The shadow shifts as the orientation of the collimator relative to that of the incident beam changes, and the transmission of the collimator changes correspondingly, being a maximum when the shadow of the front wires falls exactly on the back wires, and a minimum when it is centered between adjacent wires.

Figure 12 shows the computed response curve of a modulation collimator in a plane perpendicular to the wires in the case of a parallel beam coming from a distant point source. The abscissa is the angle η between the beam and the collimator's axis (*i.e.* the normal to the planes of the grids; see Fig. 11). The ordinate is the transmission. The distance D between the grids is large compared with the distance $d + s$ between the axes of adjacent wires.

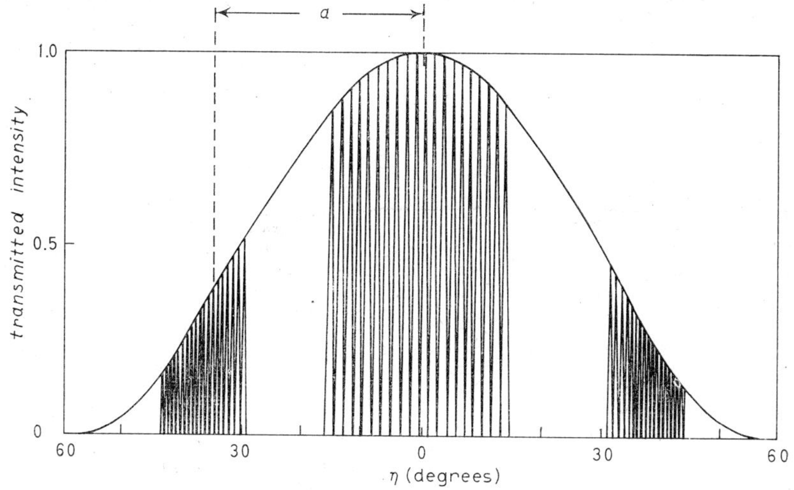

Fig. 12. – Calculated angular response of a modulation collimator. The X-ray beam lies in the plane perpendicular to the grids ($\hat{x}_d$, $\hat{y}_d$ plane), the abscissa is the angle η formed by the beam with the normal to the grids. Interval $a = \text{tg}^{-1}(k(s+d)/D)$ for k integer; continuous curve $= ((s+d)\cos\eta - d)/s$.

For small values of η the angular distance between maxima is

$$\Delta\eta = (d + s)/D .$$

It is clear that a distant source with angular dimensions δ small compared with $\Delta\eta$ will produce practically the same pattern of maxima and minima as a point source. If, on the other hand, the source has angular dimensions large compared with $\Delta\eta$ no « modulation » of the transmitted intensity will occur as the angle of incidence varies. With a source of angular dimensions comparable to $\Delta\eta$, a variation of the angle of incidence will produce a partial modulation, from which it may be possible to estimate the actual angular size of the source in the direction perpendicular to the wires. The minimum angular size of a source that can be distinguished from a point source depends on the mechanical precision achieved in the construction of the collimator, on the statistical accuracy of the data and on the contribution of the diffuse background radiation to the measured fluxes. The experience with the collimators that have been used has shown that this minimum size is about a quarter of $\Delta\eta$.

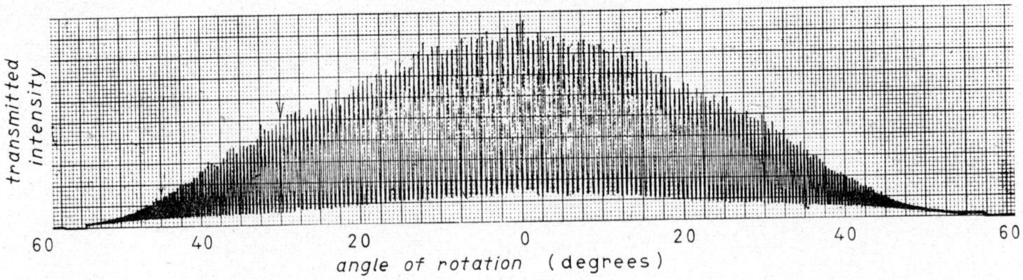

Fig. 13. – Angular response of modulation collimator measured with visible light. The abscissa is the angle η (Fig. 11). Dimensions of the collimator are shown.

Modulation collimators with $\Delta\eta$ as small as 8 arc minutes have been used. Figure 13 shows the response curve of a modulation collimator with $\Delta\eta$ of about 32 arc minutes, measured with visible light; Fig. 14 shows a similar curve for a modulation collimator having a $\Delta\eta$ of 2 degrees, measured with X-rays.

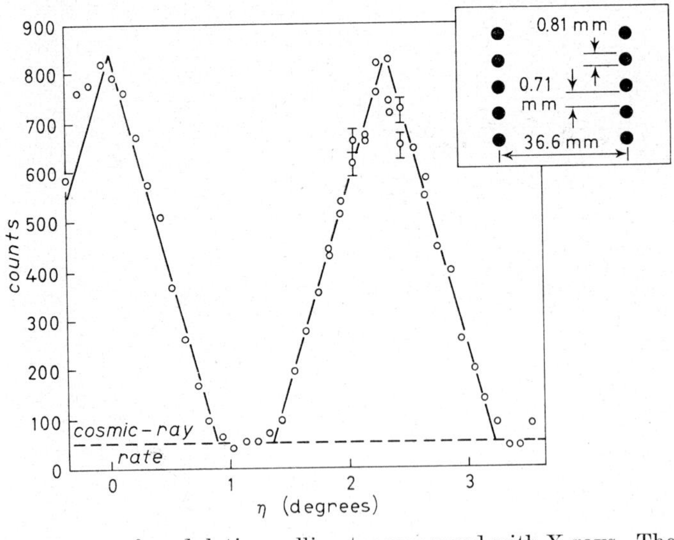

Fig. 14. – Angular response of modulation collimator measured with X-rays. The abscissa is the angle η (Fig. 11).

2·3. *Image-forming telescopes.* – It seems difficult to obtain resolving powers substantially better than several arc seconds by means of modulation collimators such as those described above. Moreover, these devices give ambiguous results when several sources are within their field of view. In order to improve the resolution further and to investigate the actual structure of an extended source, instruments of a different type are needed. The ideal instrument is an image-forming telescope. It is actually possible to build telescopes for

X-rays using the phenomenon of total external reflection of X-rays under grazing incidence [8,9]. It can be shown that two reflections are needed to obtain an image. The two reflecting surfaces may be a paraboloid and an hyperboloid with its external focal point at the focal point of the paraboloid, such as shown schematically in Fig. 15. Other combinations of surfaces, however, are possible.

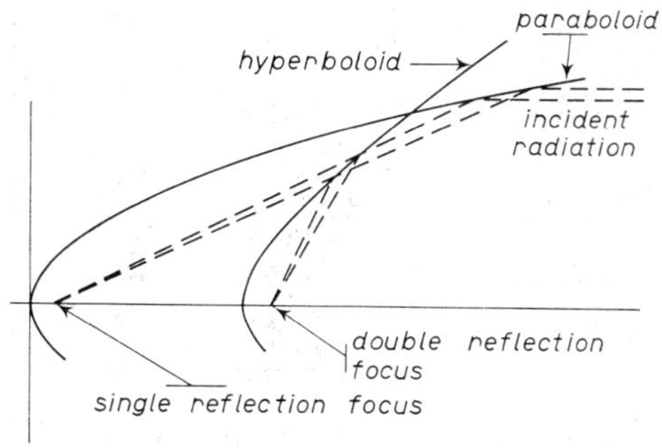

Fig. 15. – Ray tracing in a grazing-incidence X-ray telescope. The focus of the paraboloid coincides with the external focus of the hyperboloid.

Image-forming telescopes have been used so far only for solar X-ray astronomy. Figure 16 is the photograph of one such instrument. In Fig. 17 a picture of the Sun in X-rays obtained with this telescope from a rocket [10] is compared with a picture of the Sun in H_α obtained almost simultaneously with an ordinary telescope from the ground. The

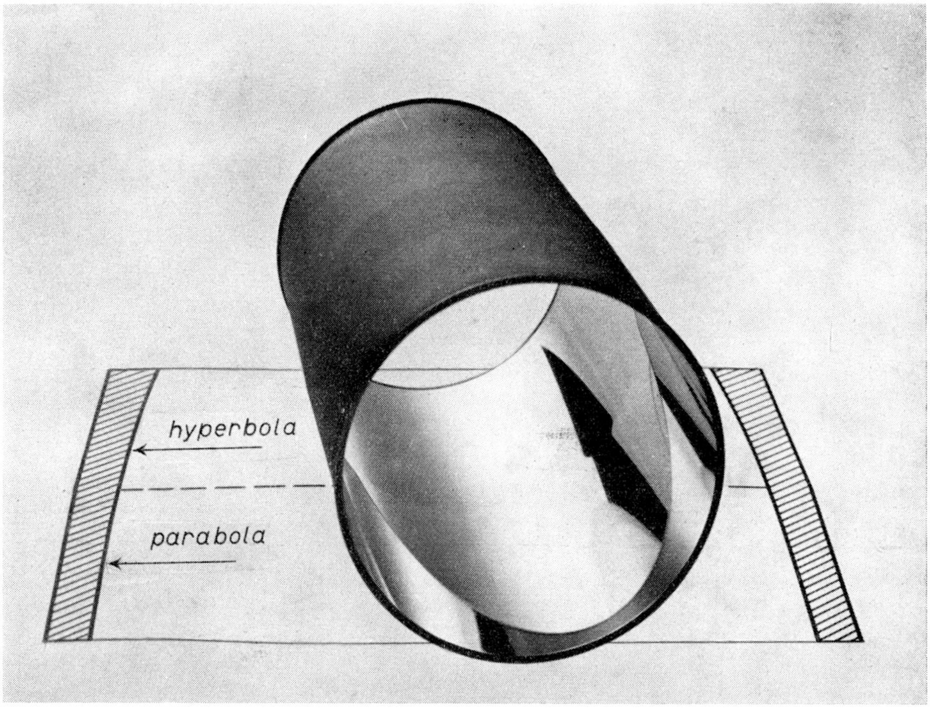

Fig. 16. – Photograph of a focusing X-ray telescope superimposed on the drawing of a section of the interior surfaces.

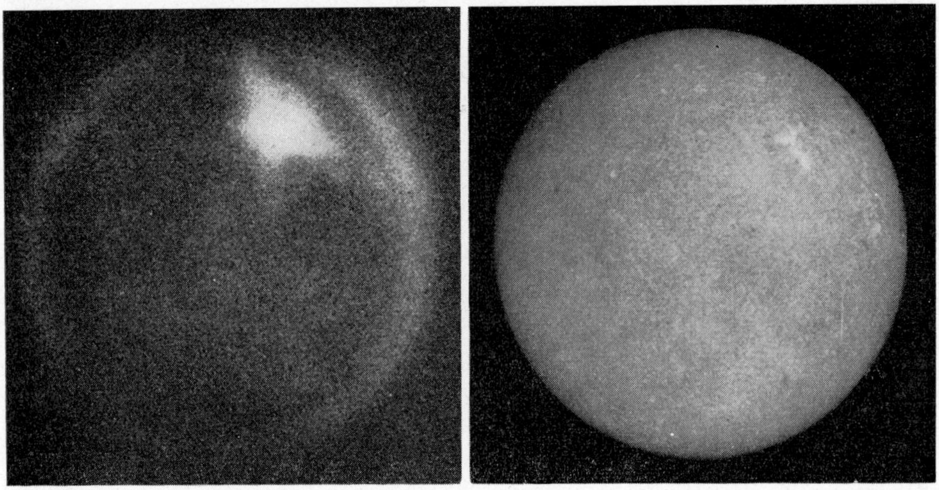

a) b)

Fig. 17. – Photographs of the Sun in X-rays and in H_α. X-ray photograph at left was taken during rocket flight, using the focusing telescope shown in Fig. 16. *a*) X-ray photograph, 17 March 1965, 1510-1515 h U.T. WSMR, 100 s exposure; 0.15 mil mylar filter (2200 Å Al), Ilford Industrial G Film; *b*) H_α photograph, 15 March 1965, 1520 h U.T. (by courtesy of Sacramento Peak Observatory, Air Force Cambridge Research Laboratory).

use of image-forming telescopes for the study of extra-solar sources shows great promise.

2·4. *Optical sensors.* – In order to determine the parameters of the vehicle's rotational motion during the period of observation, one generally uses optical sensors, capable of detecting celestial objects such as the Sun, the Moon and the stars. An example of such an instrument is shown in Fig. 18. It consists essentially of an objective lens with a rectangular slit in its focal plane and a photocell behind it. This arrangement provides a «rectangular» response function as defined by the slit in the focal plane.

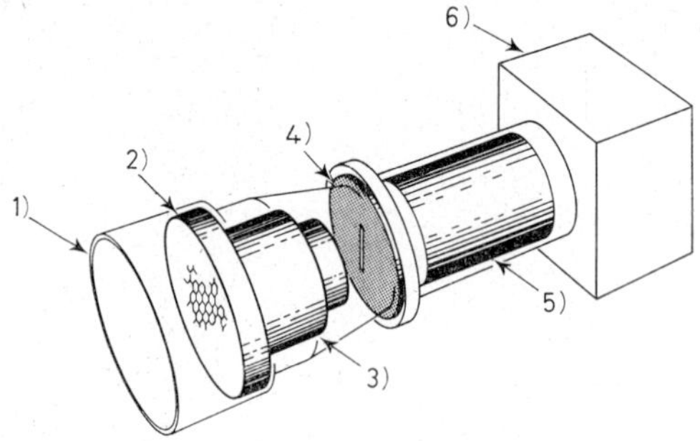

Fig. 18. – Schematic drawing of an optical aspect sensor: 1) lens shade; 2) collimator; 3) lens (*f*:2, 50 mm); 3) image plane; 4) photomultiplier; 5) electronics.

3. – Analysis problems relative to rocket observations.

Both freely spinning rockets and attitude-controlled rockets have been used for X-ray observations. In the first instance, if the rocket behaves like a rigid body and external torques are negligible, its rotational motion consists of a spin (with constant angular velocity ω_s) around the minor axis of inertia, accompanied by a precession (with constant angular velocity ω_p) of the spin axis around an axis fixed in space and parallel to the total angular momentum (precession axis). The minor axis of inertia is practically coincident with the longitudinal axis of the rocket whose momental ellipsoid may be regarded as a surface of revolution around this axis. The half-apex angle of the precession cone, α, is related to ω_s and ω_p by the equation

$$\cos\alpha = \frac{\omega_s}{\omega_p}\frac{I_1}{I_2 - I_1}, \tag{3}$$

where I_1 and I_2 are the moments of inertia relative to the spin axis and to a direction perpendicular to it. In the most accurate observations, it becomes necessary to take into account the possibility that the actual rotational motion of the rocket may differ slightly from that described above. The deviations occur mainly not because of the presence of external torques, but because the rocket does not behave exactly like a rigid body. Therefore, the direction of the precession axis remains fixed in space, but ω_s, ω_p and α may undergo small and gradual changes during the time of observation.

Useful X-ray observations may be made only above 80 km. The rockets that have been used (Aerobee) usually reach a maximum altitude somewhat in excess of 200 km, which gives an observation time of about 5 minutes. During boost the rocket is spun up to two revolutions per second for the purpose of stabilization. If it is not purposely despun, the rocket will maintain approximately this spin frequency until it re-enters the atmosphere (atmospheric friction during the ascent does not reduce the spin frequency substantially). With such high spin frequency, the apex angle of the precession cone is small and $\omega_p \ll \omega_s$.

In some experiments, the spin angular velocity of the rocket is reduced by means of gas jets or a yo-yo despin mechanism after the rocket has traversed the denser part of the atmosphere. The decrease of ω_s results in a widening of the precession cone and, in the extreme case, α may approach 90°.

Actively controlled rockets offer the possibility of exploring selectively predetermined regions of the sky. On the other hand, one cannot use rigid-body dynamics to predict the character of their motion. In the experiments carried out thus far, an attitude control system (or ACS), based on gyroscopes as sensing devices, is used to control the rocket orientation. By means of gas jets, it is possible to point the axis of any given detector to within several degrees of any given direction in the sky, or to sweep it at a prescribed speed over a prescribed angular interval.

3·1. *Frames of reference.* – In the analysis of the data and in the presentation of the results obtained with freely spinning rockets, it is convenient to consider a number of different frames of reference. Each shall be defined by a Cartesian co-ordinate system, specified by three mutually perpendicular unit vectors $\hat{x}$, $\hat{y}$, $\hat{z}$. We shall call x, y, z the three co-ordinates of the unit vector $\hat{r}$ specifying a given direction. To each Cartesian system, we shall associate a polar system of coordinates φ, λ, where φ is the azimuth and λ is the elevation. We take the polar axis in the direction of $\hat{z}$ and the plane $\varphi = 0$ coincident with the $(\hat{x}, \hat{z})$ plane.

Thus:

$$x = \cos\varphi \cos\lambda \,,$$

$$y = \sin\varphi \cos\lambda \,,$$

$$z = \sin\lambda \,.$$

A list of the various frames of reference appears below.

a) *Celestial frame of reference* $\hat{x}_c$, $\hat{y}_c$, $\hat{z}_c$; the $(\hat{x}_c, \hat{y}_c)$ plane coincides with the celestial equator (which coincides with the Earth's equator); $\hat{z}_c$ points toward the north pole and $\hat{x}_c$ toward the ascending node of the ecliptic. Thus φ_c is the right ascension and λ_c is the declination.

b) *Precession frame of reference* $\hat{x}_p$, $\hat{y}_p$, $\hat{z}_p$; $\hat{z}_p$ is parallel to $\boldsymbol{\omega}_p$, *i.e.* to the axis of the precession cone; $\hat{x}_p$ is parallel to the vector product $\hat{z}_c \times \hat{z}_p$; *i.e.* it lies in the $(\hat{x}_c, \hat{y}_c)$ plane, and points in the direction of the « ascending node of the precession equator ». With respect to the celestial frame of reference, the precession frame of reference is defined by the right ascension $\varphi_c^{(p)}$ and by the declination $\lambda_c^{(p)}$ of the precession axis $\hat{z}_p$. If angular momentum is conserved, the precession frame of reference is fixed with respect to the celestial frames of reference.

c) *The spin frame of reference* $\hat{x}_s$, $\hat{y}_s$, $\hat{z}_s$; $\hat{z}_s$ is parallel to $\boldsymbol{\omega}_s$, *i.e.* to the spin axis of the rocket; $\hat{x}_s$ lies in the direction of $\hat{z}_p \times \hat{z}_s$. With respect to the precession frame of reference, the spin frame of reference is defined by the angles $\lambda_p^{(s)}$ and $\varphi_p^{(s)}$, which are the elevation and the azimuth of $\hat{z}_s$ as measured in the precession frame of reference, as shown in Fig. 19. If momentum and energy are conserved, $\lambda_p^{(s)}$ is a constant and $\alpha = (\pi/2) - \lambda_p^{(s)}$ represents the semi-aperture of the precession cone, while $\varphi_p^{(s)}$ varies uniformly from 0 to 2π during one precession period.

d) The Rocket frame of reference $\hat{x}_r$, $\hat{y}_r$, $\hat{z}_r$; $\hat{z}_r$ coincides with the figure axis of the rocket and $\hat{x}_r$ is fixed with respect to the rocket. If the figure axis coincides with the spin axis then $\hat{z}_r$ coincides with $\hat{z}_s$. $\hat{x}_r$ rotates relative to $\hat{x}_s$ with angular velocity ω_s, and if ω_s is constant, the azimuth of $\hat{x}_r$ in the spin frame of reference is $\varphi_s^{(r)} = \omega_s(t - t_0)$ where t_0 is the time when $\hat{x}_r$ and $\hat{x}_s$ are coincident. In the ASE-MIT experiments so far it has not proven necessary to allow for the possible small discrepancy between the spin and figure axes.

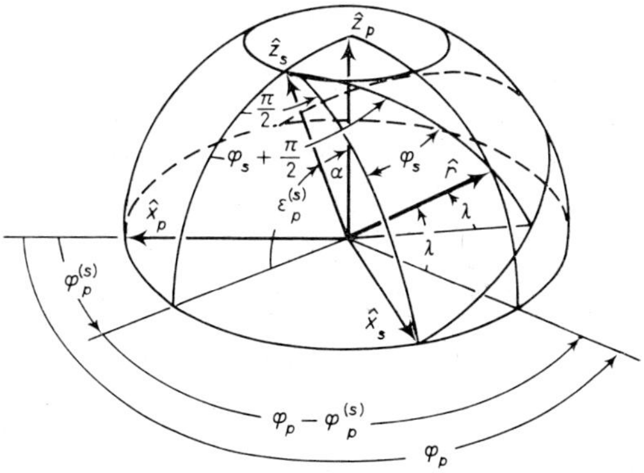

Fig. 19. – Precession and spin co-ordinate systems.

In what follows we shall have occasion to use the equation relating the elevation λ_r of a unit vector $\boldsymbol{r}$ in the rocket frame to the elevation λ_p of the same vector in the precession frame and to the relative azimuth, $\varphi_p - \varphi_p^{(s)}$, of the vector and of the spin axis in the precession frame. This equation may be derived from the vector identity $(\hat{z}_p \times \hat{z}_s)\cdot(\hat{z}_p \times \boldsymbol{r}) = \hat{z}_s \cdot \hat{r} - (\hat{z}_s \cdot \hat{z}_p)(\boldsymbol{r}\cdot\hat{z}_p)$ and reads

$$\sin\lambda_r = \sin\lambda_p \cos\alpha + \cos\lambda_p \sin\alpha \cos(\Phi_p - \Phi_p^{(s)}) \, . \tag{4}$$

The above equation shows that if $\boldsymbol{r}$ is fixed in the precession frame, λ_r varies from $\lambda_p + \alpha$ to $\lambda_p - \alpha$ during a precession cycle. Note that if λ_p and α are small angles, eq. (4) may be approximated by

$$\lambda = \lambda_p + \alpha \cos(\Phi_p - \Phi_p^{(s)}) \, . \tag{5}$$

3'2. *Freely spinning rockets.* – Consider now a freely spnining rocket carrying a detector (X-ray counter or optical sensor). Suppose that the detector's axis forms an angle $\lambda_r^{(d)} = \lambda_s^{(d)}$ with the equatorial plane of the rocket. Then its elevation in the precession frame will oscillate between $\lambda_r^{(d)} - \alpha$ and $\lambda_r^{(d)} + \alpha$ during each spin. On a rectangular grid (plate Carree projection) its representative point will describe a nearly sinusoidal curve with an amplitude equal to α and a phase that changes gradually from one spin to the next (see Fig. 20). Thus the region of the sky explored by the detector becomes wider as the apex angle of the precession axis increases.

In the rocket's frame of reference, on the other hand, the detector's axis is fixed, while the vector pointing to a celestial object moves in azimuth with slightly varying angular velocity, while changing its elevation between $\lambda_p^{(0)} - \alpha$

and $\lambda_r^{(0)}+\alpha$ during the precession cycle. On a rectangular grid, the representative point of the celestial object moves along a nearly horizontal line,

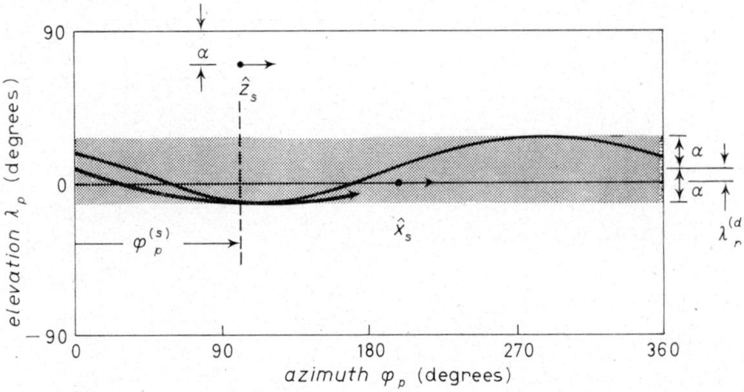

Fig. 20. – Motion of detector axis in the precession frame of reference. Shaded region represents the band covered by the detector axis during an entire precession cycle. The solid curve within the shaded region is the path of the detector axis during about 1.5 spin periods. The short arrow at z indicates the motion of the rocket axis during the same time. $\lambda_p^{(d)}$ is the elevation angle of the detector axis in the rocket frame of reference.

which oscillates up and down filling the band between $\lambda_p^{(0)}-\alpha$ and $\lambda_p^{(0)}+\alpha$ (see Fig. 21). The object will be seen by a given detector if the latter's field of view overlaps this band.

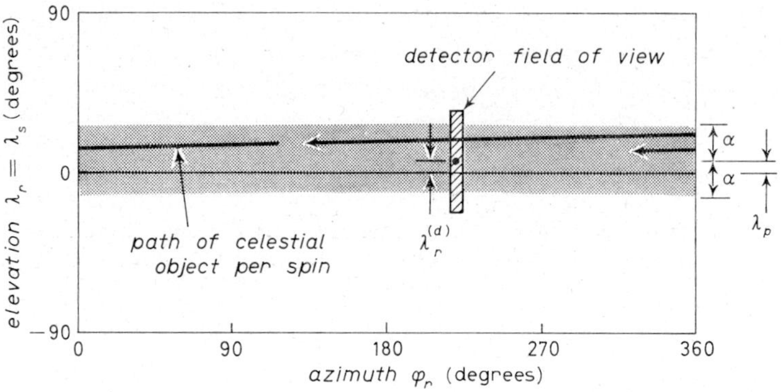

Fig. 21. – Motion of a celestial object in the rocket frame of reference. Shaded portion is the region traversed by a given celestial object during the precession cycle and the solid line is the motion of the object during slightly more than one spin period.

a) Despun rockets with long spin periods (~ 5 s), long precession periods (~ 300 s), and large precession cone angles ($\alpha \geqslant 60°$) have been employed in the NRL experiments. The nearly sinusoidal curve traced out by the representative point of the axis of a detector carried on such a flight changes in phase by a substantial amount during each spin. Thus any source within the large region of explored sky is detected on only a few successive spins out of the entire flight. In analysing the X-ray data from such an experiment, one searches for evidence of significant variations in the counting rate. These may show periodicities extending over several spins if the detector's field of view is large enough so that the regions swept out in successive spins overlap one another. The celestial orientations of the detector's axis when the maximum rates are recorded is, of course, established by reference to the data obtained by optical and magnetic sensors. If the field of view has a nearly circular shape, then it is possible to estimate a source's position making use of the fact that the number of counts produced by the source during one spin is a decreasing function of the minimum angular distance between the detector's axis and the source during that spin. By plotting the numbers of counts as a function of this distance, and comparing the curve thus obtained with the known angular response of the collimator, one can also evaluate the angular diameter of the source, or place an upper limit to it. Obviously the accuracy of both the position and size determinations will depend on the statistical accuracy of the data (and, therefore, on the area of the detector) as well as on the angular aperture of the collimator.

b) A situation of a somewhat different character occurs in experiments like those of the ASE-MIT group, which have employed rockets that retain their relatively high initial spin rates ($\sim 2\ \text{s}^{-1}$), have small precession cone angles ($\alpha \leqslant 10°$), and have precession periods that are sufficiently short so that several complete precession cycles occur during the period of observation. In these experiments a source within the relatively small region of sky scanned by a given detector is detected on many successive spins during those portions of the several precession cycles when the elevation of the source lies within the sensitive range of the detector. In order to exploit the information about a source which is potentially available in the data it is necessary to combine the data from many spins, taking proper account of the effect of the precession motion on the periodicity. A source too weak to have a statistically significant effect on the counting rate during one spin may be detected in the combined data from many spins. From such data it is possible to obtain precise information on the sizes and locations of sources.

In order to deal with the complications caused by precession motion in the analysis of data obtained from fast and freely spinning rockets, we have found it convenient to introduce a special angular variable ψ which we call the bearing. This angle is defined by the equation

$$\psi = \varphi_s + \varphi_p^{(s)} + \pi/2\ ,$$

where φ_s is the azimuth of a given direction in the spin frame, and $\varphi_p^{(s)}$ is the azimuth of the spin axis in the precession frame. If the given direction is fixed in the rocket frame, as are the directions of the axes of the various detectors, then we have $\dot{\varphi}_s + \dot{\varphi}_p^{(s)} = \omega_s + \omega_p$. Thus the bearing angle $\psi^{(d)}$ of a detector's axis at any given instant may be expressed as a function of time by the equation

$$\psi^{(d)} = \int_0^t (\omega_s + \omega_p)\,\mathrm{d}t + \psi_0^{(d)},$$

where $\psi_0^{(d)}$ is the bearing angle at $t = 0$. If the given direction is that of a celestial object (which is, of course, fixed in the precession frame) then during each precession cycle $\varphi_p^{(s)}$ increases uniformly by 2π while $\varphi_s^{(0)}$, the spin azimuth of the object, decreases nonuniformly by 2π. Thus the bearing angle of the object $\psi^{(0)}$ varies about an average value which is, in fact, the precession azimuth of the object, *i.e.*

$$\psi_{\text{av}}^{(0)} = \varphi_p^{(0)}.$$

This is obviously true in the limit $\alpha = 0$ where $\varphi_p^{(0)} = \varphi_p^{(s)} + \pi/2 + \varphi_s^{(0)}$ as can be seen in Fig. 19. In this case we have

$$\psi^{(0)} = \varphi_p^{(0)}.$$

In the general case when $\alpha \neq 0$, one can show that the difference $\psi^{(0)} - \varphi_p^{(0)}$ is an antisymmetric function of the difference $\varphi_p^{(0)} - \varphi_p^{(s)}$. Since $\psi^{(0)} = \varphi_p^{(0)}$ when this difference is zero (or π), the average value must be equal to $\varphi_p^{(0)}$ as previously stated.

Under the assumption of a rigid, freely-spinning rocket, $(\omega_s + \omega_p)$ is a constant so that the bearing angle of a detector's axis, $\psi^{(d)}$, increases linearly by 2π during a time interval equal to $2\pi/(\omega_s + \omega_p)$. The transit times of a celestial object through the meridian plane of a detector are determined by the intersections of the heavy solid curve, representing the time dependence of the bearing angle $\psi^{(0)}$ of a celestial object, with the sawtooth solid line representing the time variation of the bearing angle $\psi^{(d)}$ of the detector's axis (see Fig. 22).

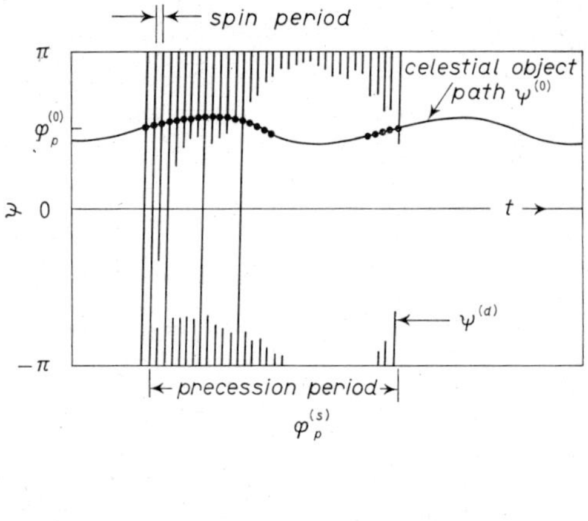

Fig. 22. – Time variation of the bearing angle of a celestial object (heavy solid line) and of the X-ray detector axis (light solid line) during several precession cycles. Average bearing angle of the object is its precession azimuth $\varphi_p^{(0)}$.

The explicit expression for the bearing angle of a given unit vector $\boldsymbol{r}$ fixed in the precession frame in terms of α and $\varphi_p^{(s)}$ is rather cumbersome. It may be expressed implicitly, however, in the following way which is particularly well suited to computer calculations. The components r_{si} in the spin frame are related to the components r_{pk} in the precession frame by the matrix equation

$$r_{si} = T_{ij}^{(2)} T_{jk}^{(1)} r_{pk} ,$$

where

$$r_{pk} = \begin{Vmatrix} (\cos\lambda_p \cos\varphi_p) \\ (\cos\lambda_p \sin\varphi_p) \\ (\sin\lambda_p) \end{Vmatrix} ,$$

$$T_{jk}^{(1)} = \begin{Vmatrix} [\cos(\varphi_p^{(s)} + \pi/2)] & [\sin(\varphi_p^{(s)} + \pi/2)] & 0 \\ [-\sin(\varphi_p^{(s)} + \pi/2)] & [\cos(\varphi_p^{(s)} + \pi/2)] & 0 \\ 0 & 0 & 1 \end{Vmatrix} ,$$

$$T_{ij}^{(2)} = \begin{Vmatrix} 1 & 0 & 0 \\ 0 & \cos\alpha & \sin\alpha \\ 0 & -\sin\alpha & \cos\alpha \end{Vmatrix} .$$

The orthogonal transformation matrices $T_{jk}^{(1)}$ and $T_{ij}^{(2)}$ correspond to the two rotations required to bring the precession frame into coincidence with the spin frame, namely, a positive rotation by the angle $\varphi_p + \pi/2$ about the $\hat{z}_p$ axis, followed by a positive rotation by the angle α about the $\hat{x}_s$ axis. The bearing angle can be expressed in terms of the transformed components of $\boldsymbol{r}$ by the equation

$$\psi^{(0)} = \frac{r_{s2}}{|r_{s2}|} \arccos\left(r_{s1}/\sqrt{r_{si}^2 + r_{s2}^2}\right) + \varphi_p^{(s)} + \pi/2 .$$

Turning now to the actual analysis of the data, the first step is to find an approximate value for $\omega_p + \omega_s$, the bearing angular velocity of the detector axes. To do this we search for a sequence of nearly periodic signals from one of the sensors (optical, X-ray or magnetic). The average value of the interval between successive signals in a sequence divided into 2π is then used as the first approximation to $\omega_p + \omega_s$.

The second step is the computation of the values of the bearing $\psi^{(d)}$ relative to the bearing $\psi_0^{(d)}$ at some given arbitrary time of the detector axis at the instants when signals were observed. This is done using the formula

$$\psi^{(d)} - \psi_0^{(d)} = \int_{t_0}^{t} (\omega_s + \omega_p)\, dt$$

with $\omega_s + \omega_p$ initially taken as constant and equal to the approximate value of this quantity determined as described above. In order to obtain a second approximation to $\omega_p + \omega_s$ we construct a plot in which each signal is indicated by a mark with the co-ordinates $(\psi^{(d)} - \psi_0^{(d)}, t)$. Recurrent signals from a celestial object give rise to a trail of marks advancing in t, and drifting gradually one way or another in $\psi^{(d)} - \psi_0^{(d)}$, depending on the error in $\omega_s + \omega_p$. From the trends revealed by this plot we determine an improved value of $\omega_s + \omega_p$ which reduces the long-term drift in the relative bearing. It turns out, however, that sounding rockets with liquid fuels are not perfectly rigid bodies after cut-off. Thus $\omega_s + \omega_p$ generally varies significantly during an experiment. To allow for this we express $\omega_s + \omega_p$ as a power series in t in the form

$$\omega_s + \omega_p = \omega_0 + At + Bt^2 + \dots .$$

In practice we have found it necessary to use only the first-order term in t in order to eliminate nearly all long-term drift.

Of course, even after correcting the computation of the relative bearing for the long-term drift of $\omega_s + \omega_p$, there remain the periodic variations in the relative bearing of a fixed source due to the precession motion. This motion, as we have seen, causes the bearing of the source to vary around its average value (which is its precession azimuth). A plot of the frequency of signals *vs.* the relative bearing of the detector's axis will therefore show a peak whose width is greater than the spread due to the azimuthal angular resolution of the detector and the angular width of the source itself. At this point the periodic precession variation of $\psi^{(0)}$ as well as any residual long-term drift in $\omega_s + \omega_p$ can be compensated by adding an empirically determined and smoothly varying quantity to the calculated values of $\psi^{(d)}$. A plot of this compensated quantity, which is essentially $\psi^{(d)} - \psi^{(0)}$, will now show a peak whose width is as narrow as the limit set by the resolution of the detector and the angular width of the object. When this method, which we call « self-synchronization », was applied to the *Sco* X-1 peak in Fig. 29, the width of the modified peak was found to be consistent with the assumption that the angular width of *Sco* X-1 is less than 20 arc minutes.

It is worth noting that the average over an integral number of precession cycles of the bearing of the signals in a peak is a correct measure of the precession azimuth of the corresponding celestial object even if the object passes in and out of the detector's elevation range. This is true because the deviation of $\psi^{(0)}$ from $\varphi_p^{(0)}$ when the object crosses a given rocket elevation in one direction is just the negative of the deviation when it crosses in the other direction. Thus the average relative bearing of the object during the time when it is within the detector's elevation range, plus the phase $\psi_0^{(d)}$, which is yet to be determined, is, in fact, the precession azimuth of the object.

The third step in the analysis is the determination of the precession motion and the orientation of the precession axis in the celestial frame of reference. The celestial orientation of the precession frame of reference is determined from the star sensor data. These data consist of the transit times of various stars whose identity is initially unknown. Selecting data from portions of the precession cycle when signals from several stars are observed in each rocket rotation, we determine the relative bearings of the unknown stars. With the aid of a star catalogue and an appropriate computer program we then search for a spin axis direction in the celestial frame which would cause the star sensor to sweep over a combination of stars with relative bearings that match the ones observed. In this way the stars which caused the observed signals are unambiguously identified, and first approximations to the spin orientations at several points around the precession cycle are obtained.

As the spin axis precesses, the rocket elevation of a given star varies so that the amplitude of its signal is modulated according to the response function of the star sensor. This modulation may be a prolonged appearance or disappearance of a periodic signal as the star crosses one boundary or the other of the elevation range of the sensor. It may be a momentary disappearance as it crosses a masked interval in the middle of the sensitive elevation range. In any event, the sequence of times at which significant modulation events occur in the amplitudes of the star signals is determined by the response function of the sensor and by the parameters of the precession motion: *i.e.* the celestial orientation of the precession axis, defined by $\alpha_c^{(p)}$ and $\delta_c^{(p)}$, the precession angular velocity ω_p, and the opening angle α of the precession cone. Only a particular combination of the precession parameters will lead to a predicted sequence of times of modulation events that matches the one observed. In practice we search for this combination with the aid of a computer. By successive approximations we obtain a set of parameters which minimizes the sum of the squared deviations between the predicted and observed times, and in this way we establish the celestial orientation of the precession frame and the precession cone angle. Any object whose precession azimuth and elevation is known can now be located in the celestial frame by a simple transformation.

The fourth step is the determination of the precession azimuths of the X-ray sources. Already, by comparing the bearing distribution plots for the X-ray detector and star sensor data described earlier, the relative average bearings (*i.e.* relative precession azimuths) of the X-ray sources and the various stars can be established. Now that the stars are identified, the absolute average bearings of the X-ray sources can be determined, and these are the precession azimuths.

The fifth step is the determination of the precession elevations of the sources. This can be accomplished, in principle, by measuring the variation of a source's bearing during the precession cycle, since, as previously noted, the amplitude of this variation depends on α and $\lambda_p^{(0)}$. This method amounts to a kind of « triangulation » of the source with a base line equal to twice the opening angle α of the precession cone. For the small values of α that occurred in the ASE-MIT experiments, the accuracy of this method is not very high.

A more accurate method for the determination of $\lambda_p^{(0)}$ is based on an analysis of the variation in the counting rate from a source which is caused by the periodic change in the elevation of the source in the rocket frame. By inspection of the bearing distribution we select an interval of bearing within which essentially all of the counts from the source occur. For each count recorded in this interval we compute the quantity

$$l = \lambda_r^{(d)} - \alpha \cos(\varphi_p^{(s)} - \varphi_p^{(0)})$$

where $\varphi_p^{(0)}$ is the precession azimuth of the source as previously determined, and $\lambda_r^{(d)}$ is the rocket elevation of the detector axis. If α and $\lambda_p^{(d)}$ are sufficiently small, then to a good approximation $l = \lambda_p^{(d)}$ when $\varphi_p^{(d)} = \varphi_p^{(0)}$; *i.e.* at the moment when the source transits the meridian plane of the detector in the precession frame (see eq. (5)). Moreover, if $\lambda_p^{(0)}$ lies with range from $\lambda_r^{(d)} - \alpha$ to $\lambda_r^{(d)} + \alpha$, then at some time during the precession cycle the detector axis sweeps across the source. At this time $\lambda_r^{(0)} = \lambda_r^{(d)}$, $l = \lambda_p^{(0)}$ (see eq. (5)), and therefore the counting rate plotted against l shows a maximum for a value of l equal to the precession elevation of the source. An example of such a distribution is shown in Fig. 30. When λ_p does not lie in the range from $\lambda_r^{(d)} - \alpha$ to $\lambda_r^{(d)} + \alpha$, one can still calculate the expected variation of the counting rate as a function of l from the known response function of the detector, and for any assumed value of $\lambda_p^{(0)}$. One can then adjust $\lambda_p^{(0)}$ to obtain the best fit of the computed variation to the observed one, and in this manner one can obtain an estimate of the precession elevation of the source.

In the case of a detector with a modulation collimator whose response maxima are separated by an angle smaller than 2α, the plot of counting *vs.* l will show several maxima at values of l given approximately by the equation

$$l_n = \lambda_p^{(0)} \pm \operatorname{arctg}(na) ,$$

where a is determined by the dimensions of the collimator. An example of such a distribution is shown in Fig. 31.

4. – Observational results.

4·1. *The Crab Nebula.* – The source whose co-ordinates and angular dimensions are best known is that coincident with the Crab Nebula. As already mentioned, the information concerning this source comes mainly from the observation of the occultation of the Crab Nebula by the Moon performed by

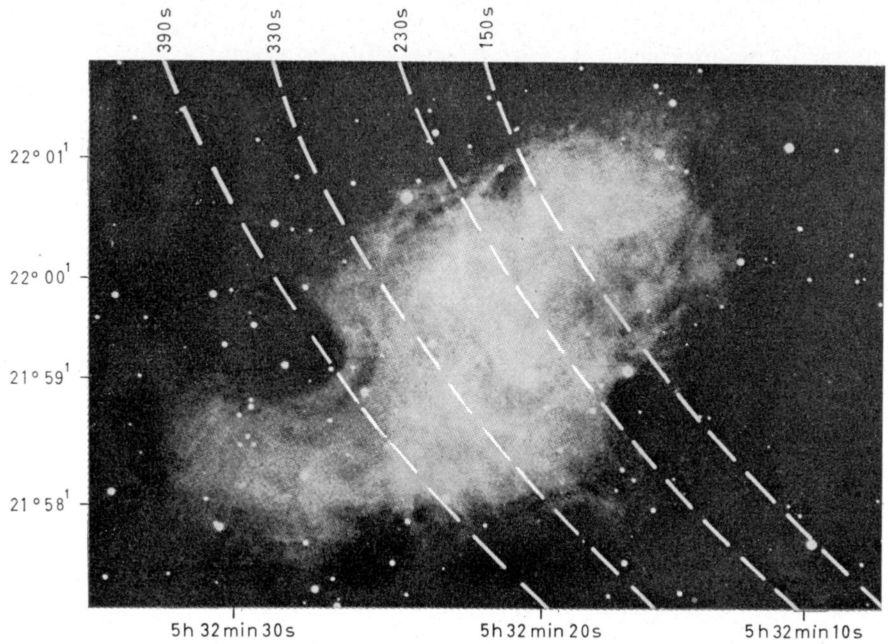

Fig. 23. – Position of the edge of the Moon superimposed on a photograph of the Crab Nebula during NRL rocket flight. The maximum rate of change of the observed counting rate from the X-ray detector occurred at 230 s; thus the centroid of the X-ray source distribution lies along the dashed line marked 230 s. (From ref. [4]).

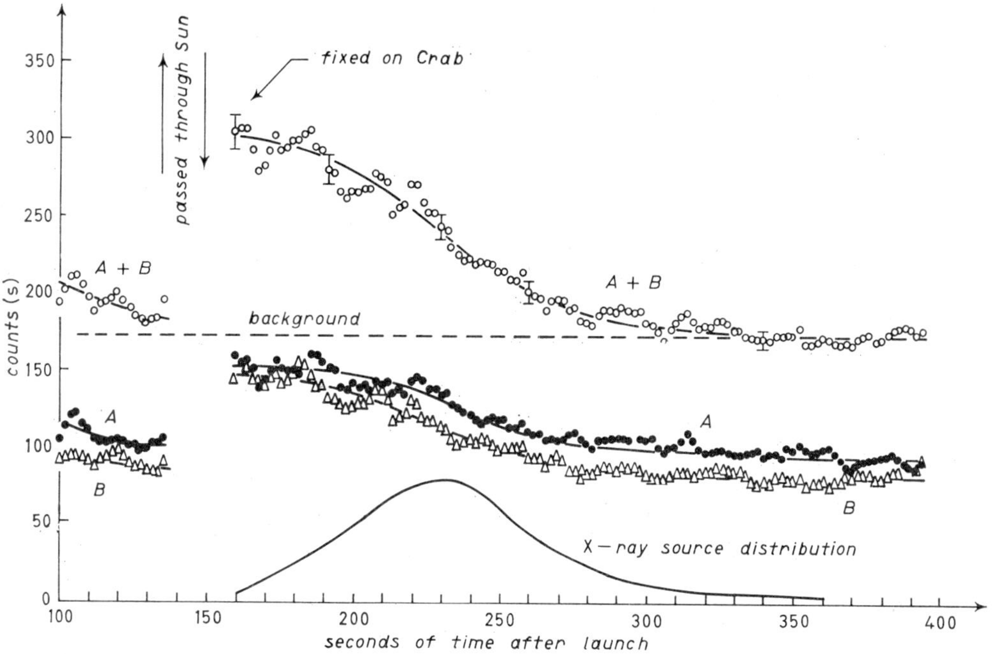

Fig. 24. – Counting rates of the X-ray detectors *A* and *B* during the NRL rocket flight observing the occultation of the Crab Nebula by the Moon. The solid curve at the bottom is minus the time derivative of the *A* and *B* counting rate. (From ref. [4].)

the NRL group (which named the source *Tau* XR-1) [4]. The rocket was attitude-controlled and carried two X-ray detectors which acquired the X-ray source 150 s after launch and observed it for 240 s thereafter, during which time the edge of the Moon swept across the Crab Nebula in the manner shown in Fig. 23. The counting rates of the two detectors, and their sum are plotted as functions of time in Fig. 24. Shown in the same figure is the time derivative of the total counting rate, which represents the distribution of the X-ray source in the direction perpendicular to the advancing edge of the Moon. From these results, the authors concluded that the angular diameter of the X-ray source was about 1 arc minute, and that its center was close to the center of the visible nebula.

42. *The sources near the galactic center.* – Let us consider next the complex of sources within 25° of the galactic center which includes the source in

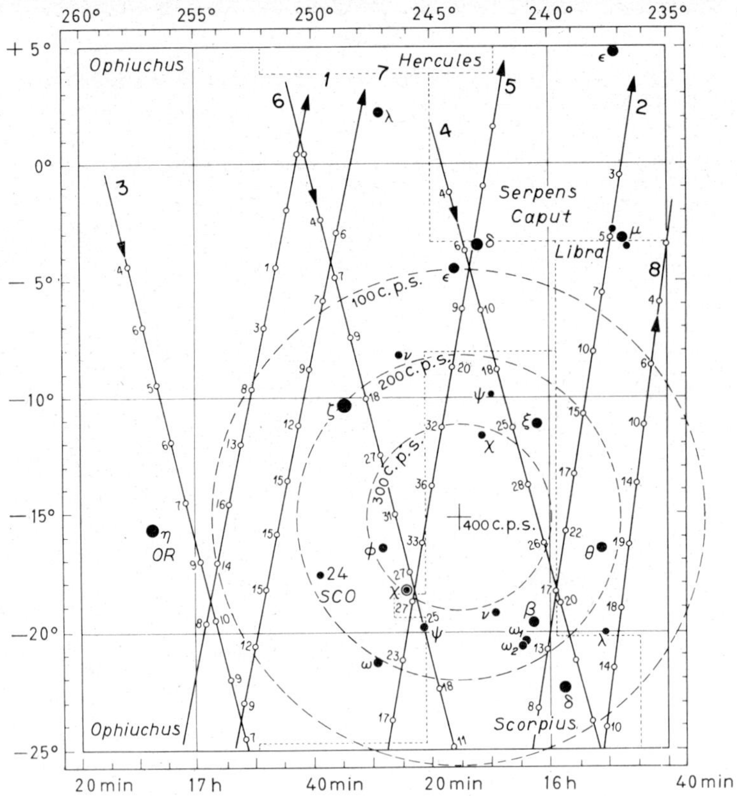

Fig. 25. – Observation of the X-ray source in *Scorpio* by the NRL group. Solid curves show motion of the detector axis during successive passes over the region of the sky containing the source. Dashed circles are contour of equal counting rates consistent with observed counting rates. The centroid of these contours gives the best location of the source. (From ref. [3].)

Scorpio, named *Sco* X-1 by the ASE-MIT group, the first X-ray source to be discovered and the strongest detected thus far.

Figure 25 illustrates the determination of the position of *Sco* X-1 performed by the NRL group by means of a slowly-spinning rocket in April 1963 [3]. The detector had a field of view about 10° full width at half maximum. The lines with arrows are traces of the detector's axis on the sky map during different spins; the numbers along these lines are counting rates. The circles are lines of equal counting rates, whose common center represents the source position.

Figure 26 shows the results of another flight carried out by the NRL

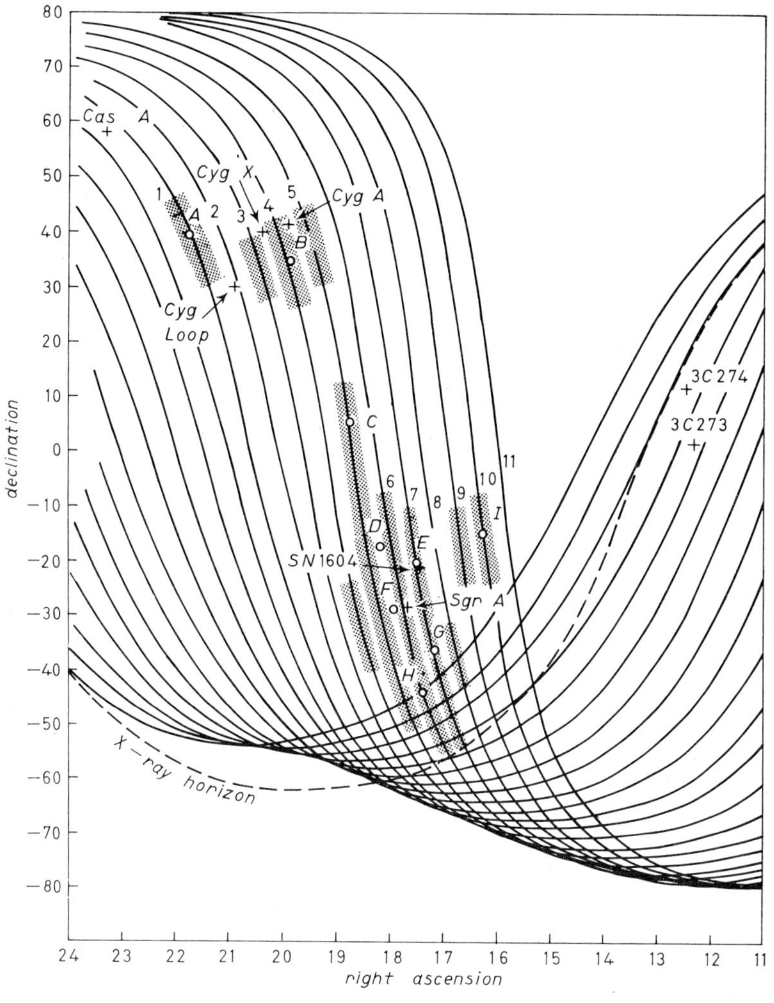

Fig. 26. – Locations of X-ray sources observed during an NRL rocket flight. Solid curves represent the path of the detector axis during the flight. Shaded regions indicate times when excess counting rates were observed and circles indicate estimates of source locations. (From ref. [11].)

group, with similar instrumentation, in June 1964 [11]. Shaded segments indicate portions of scan where the X-ray counting rate was clearly above background. Circles are positions assigned by the authors to the X-ray sources held responsible for these increases in counting rate. Of the sources near the galactic center, only *Sco* X-1 (indicated as I) gave a clearly separate peak. The other five were unresolved and, therefore, the results concerning these sources were somewhat tentative.

In addition to the sources near the galactic center, the instruments aboard the NRL rocket detected also two clearly resolved sources in *Cygnus* (*A* and *B* in Fig. 26), and one unresolved source in Serpens. We shall return to these observations later.

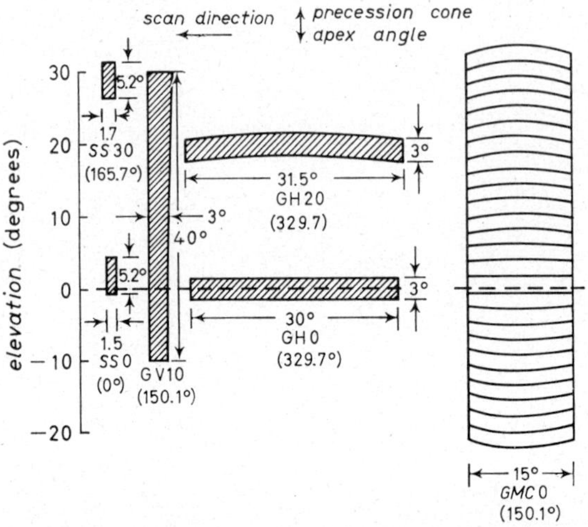

Fig. 27. – Fields of view of the detectors used by the ASE-MIT group in the October 1964 rocket flight, shown on a rectangular grid plot of the rocket frame of reference. The number in parentheses below the instrument designation is the rocket azimuth of the detector axis.

Accurate data for some of the X-ray sources appearing in the region of the sky near the galactic center were obtained by the ASE-MIT group with a rapidly spinning rocket flown in October 1964 [12]. The rocket carried three banks of Geiger counters provided with collimators having fields of view in the shape of narrow slits (GV 10, GH 0, GH 20) and one bank of Geiger counters provided with a modulation collimator. Figure 27 shows the fields of view

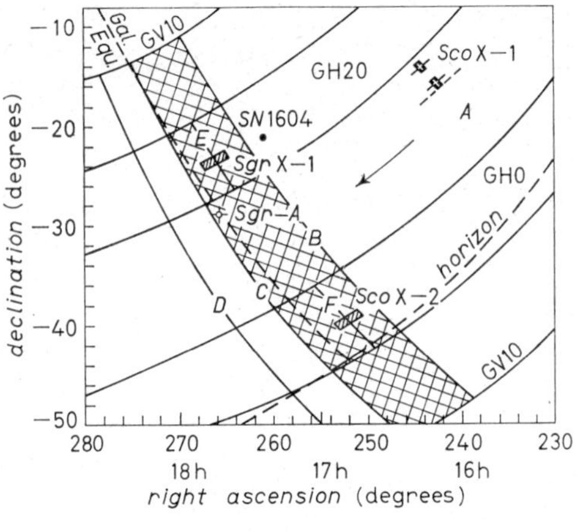

Fig. 28. – X-ray source locations determined during ASE-MIT rocket flight of October 1964. The region bounded by the arcs marked by GV10 has been scanned. Sources are found to lie along the solid curves marked *A*, *D*, *E* and *F*. The region between the curves marked *B* and *C* contains an unknown number of unresolved sources.

of these detectors and of the star sensors in the frame of reference of the spinning rocket. Figure 28 shows the regions of the sky explored by the three detectors with narrow-slit collimators, and the positions of three sources, clearly identified by these observations. One is *Sco* X-1; the second lies also in the constellation Scorpio and is denoted as *Sco* X-2; the third lies in Sagittarius and is denoted as *Sgr* X-1.

Let us discuss in more detail the observational evidence obtained in these experiments. Consider first the results of counter GV 10, whose direction of scan was perpendicular to the long side of the collimator's slit. Figure 29 shows the bearing angle distribution of the counts with respect to β *Ceti*. The sharp maximum at A is due to *Sco* X-1; it affords an accurate determination of the azimuth of this source in the precession frame of reference placing it on the arc A in Fig. 28. Moreover, the variation of the counting rate due to *Sco* X-1 during the precession cycle shows that the detector's axis came closest to *Sco* X-1 when its elevation in the precession frame was a maximum.

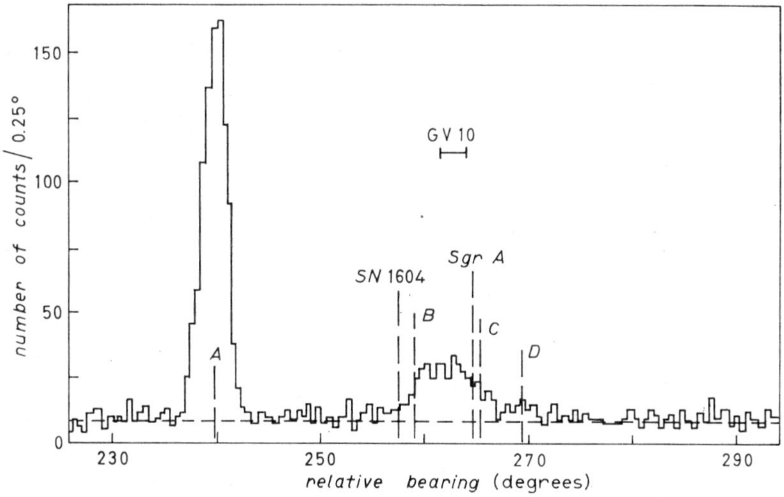

Fig. 29. – Bearing angle distribution of counts observed with detector GV10 during October 1964 rocket flight. The abscissa represents the bearing angle of the detector axis with respect to complete the average bearing angle of β Ceti. Full width of half maximum of detector response is indicated.

This observation places a lower bound to the elevation of *Sco* X-1, as indicated by the dotted line in Fig. 28. The smaller and broader maximum between B and C in Fig. 29 is due to a number of unresolved sources, including *Sgr* X-1, *Sco* X-2 and probably other sources near the galactic plane. These sources must lie in the cross-hatched region between the arcs of great circles marked B and C in Fig. 28. Still another small maximum in the bearing distribution suggests the existence of a weak source along the arc marked D, although it is not clear that D is separate from the source region between B and C.

Consider next the results of counter banks GH 0 and GH 20. Neither of these counters saw *Sco* X-1. The fact that this source never entered the field of view of GH 20 further restricts the possible range of elevation angles for *Sco* X-1, placing it below the region explored by the detector (see Fig. 28).

The curves giving the bearing angle distributions of counts recorded by both GH 0 and GH 20 had maxima, indicating the presence of sources lying within the bands scanned by the two detectors, and belonging to the source complex between the great circles B and C detected by GV 10. The positions of the maxima determine the azimuthal angles of the sources in the precession frame, placing the sources along the arcs of great circle marked E and F in Fig. 28. Because the long dimensions of the slits representing the fields of view are in the direction of the scan, the maxima are rather flat and the azimuth determinations provided by counters GH 0 and GH 20 are not as precise as those provided by counter GV 10. On the other hand, the narrow dimensions of the slits in the direction perpendicular to the scan affords an accurate determination of the elevation angles of the two sources in the precession frame. To obtain this information, appropriate « windows » were chosen around the azimuths of the sources, and the counts recorded within these windows, at various phases of the precession cycle, were plotted against the quantity $l-\lambda_r^{(d)}$ (see Sect. **3**.2) which is approximately the relative elevation of the detector's axis at the center of the window. The results for counters GH 0 and GH 20 are shown by the graphs in Fig. 30. In both graphs, the counting rate is a maximum near the middle of the precession cycle, *i.e.*, when the elevation of the detector's axis in the precession frame is nearly equal to its elevation in the rocket's frame. Thus, *Sgr* X-1 lies near the center of the band scanned by GH 20 and *Sco* X-2 lies near the center of the band scanned by GH 0.

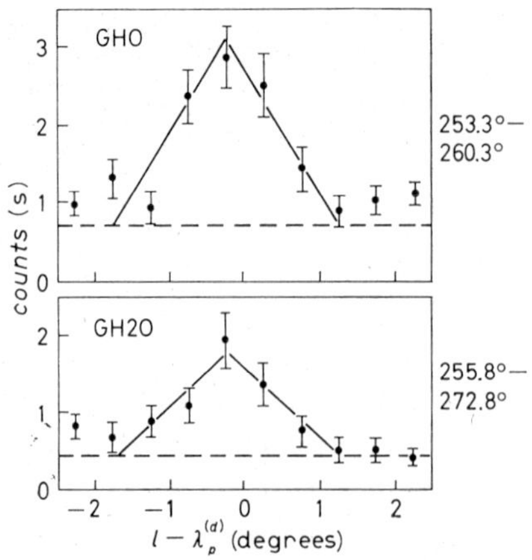

Fig. 30. – The distribution in relative elevation of counting rates observed with detectors GH0 and GH20 during October 1964 rocket flight. Superimposed on the observational points are the theoretical angular responses of the detectors. The abscissa is the elevation of the detector axis in the precession frame at the moment of closest approach to the source minus the (fixed) elevation of the detector axis in the rocket frame. The bearing angle range with respect to β *Ceti* is indicated at the right side of each curve.

Consider, finally, the results of counter bank GMC 0 provided with a modulation collimator of about 30 arc minutes resolution. Figure 31 shows the variation of its counting rate due to *Sco* X-1 during the precession cycle. A previous experiment with a modulation collimator of higher resolution had shown that the angular dimension of *Sco* X-1 was less than 7 arc minutes [13]. The completeness of the modulation observed with the present detector is entirely consistent with this result. Moreover, the position of the maxima makes it possible to place *Sco* X-1 on one of the circles of constant elevation corresponding to the transmission maxima of the modulation collimator at the time when a maximum of the counting rate is observed. Two of these circles fall between the limits of elevation previously determined, thus giving for *Sco* X-1 the two possible locations shown in Fig. 28.

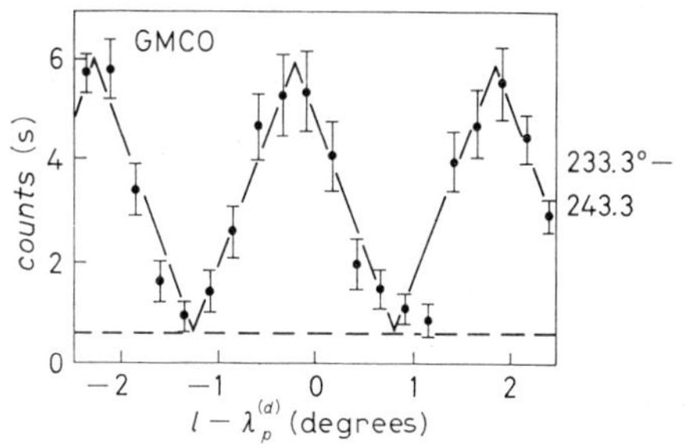

Fig. 31. – Distribution in relative elevation of the counting rates from *Sco* X-1 observed with detector GMCO which was provided with a modulation collimator. Superimposed on the observational points is the theoretical angular response of the collimator.

Table I lists the most likely positions of *Sco* X-1, *Sco* X-2 and *Sgr* X-1, as obtained from the observations just described.

TABLE I. – *X-ray source locations determined during October 1964 rocket flight.*

Source	Right ascension	Declination
Sco X-1	16 h 12 min ± 2 min 16 h 19 min ± 2 min	— (15.6 ± 0.5)° — (14.0 ± 0.5)°
Sco X-2	16 h 50 min ± 7 min	— (39.6 ± 0.9)°
Sgr X-1	17 h 44 min ± 7 min	— (23.2 ± 0 .9)°

Data relative to the same region of the sky were also obtained by the Lockheed group, by means of an attitude-controlled rocket flown in October 1964 [14]. The rocket carried three detectors with collimators having fields of view in the shape of narrow slits, whose long dimensions were arranged at different angles to the rocket's axis. Thus, from the relative delay between the transit times of a given source through these fields of view, it was possible to obtain information concerning the elevation of the source in the rocket's frame of reference. The rocket was programmed to execute four different scans during its flight. Figure 32 shows the arcs traced on the sky by the normals to the detectors during these scans; the rectangles at the beginning of scan 1 show the fields of view of the three detectors, denoted as T (top), C (center), B (bottom). The shaded areas indicate the bands scanned by detector C.

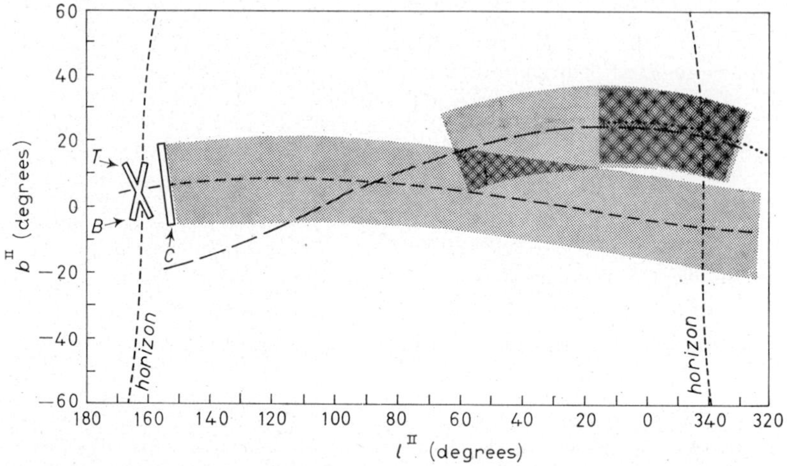

Fig. 32. – Traces of detector axes during Lockheed rocket flight (NASA Aerobee 4.120). Rocket was provided with attitude control. Scan information: – – – scan 1, rate 2.0°/s, direction →; · · · scan 2, rate 7.6°/s, direction ← ; ——— scan 3, rate 2.1°/s, direction →; — — — scan 4, rate 2.4°/s, direction ←. (From ref. [14].)

Sco X-1 was detected during scans no. 2, 3, 4. All three counters T, C, and B gave useful data during the two slower scans (no. 3 and 4). They provided the following determination for the position of this source:

right ascension: 16 h 14 min $\pm$ 1 min; declination: $-15° 36' \pm 15'$.

Only counter C provided useful data during scan no. 1, which ran along the galactic equator. The counting rate went through several max-

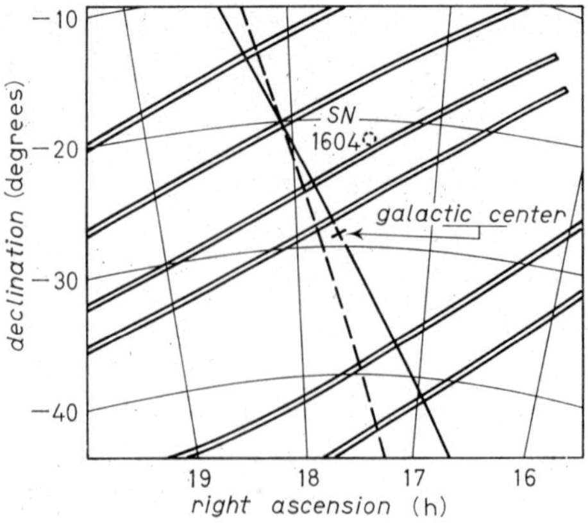

Fig. 33. – X-ray source locations in the vicinity of the galactic center determined during Lockheed rocket flight. Dashed line is the path of the detector axis and the narrow bands normal to this line represent regions of the sky containing X-ray sources.

ima, indicating the existence of a number of sources. However, only the azimuthal angles of these sources in the rocket's frame of reference could be determined. The arcs of great circle corresponding to the sources near the galactic center are shown in Fig. 33 as narrow bands having a width equal to the experimental uncertainty in the angular measurement.

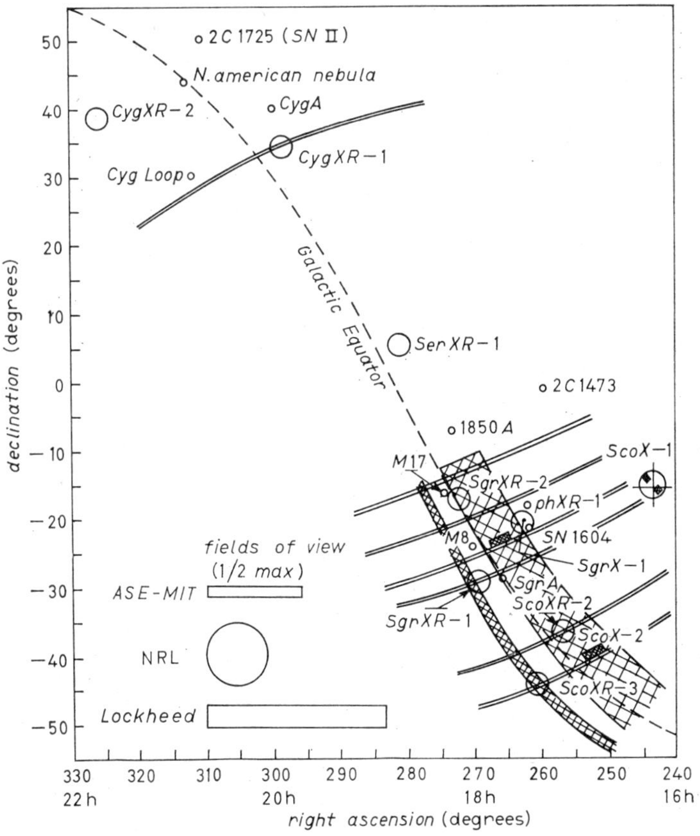

Fig. 34. – X-ray source locations as determined during three 1964 rocket flights. ASE-MIT locations have been given in Fig. 29: NRL locations have been given in Fig. 23, and Lockheed locations have been given in Fig. 34.

In Fig. 34 the results of the NRL group, the ASE-MIT group and the Lockheed group are summarized and compared. Concerning the sources near the Galactic center, we note the following:

a) Both alternate positions for *Sco* X-1 found by the ASE-MIT group fall within the circle of uncertainty of the determination made by the NRL group. One of them is consistent with the position given by the Lockheed group. As already noted, we know from the results of the ASE-MIT group that the angular size of *Sco* X-1 is less than 7 arc minutes.

b) The position for *Sgr* X-1, as determined by the ASE-MIT group, is about 1° from the arc of the great circle corresponding to one of the sources found by the Lockheed group. This discrepancy may be accounted for by experimental errors; thus, the sources observed by the two groups may be the same. However, *Sgr* X-1 does not lie within the circle of uncertainty of any of the sources found by the NRL group. The closest NRL source is *Oph* XR-1 whose center lies 5° from the ASE-MIT position of *Sgr* X-1. The existence of a source in this position is not consistent with the ASE-MIT data.

c) *Sgr* X-1 is 5° from the Kepler supernova remnant SN 1604. Thus, the ASE-MIT observation rules out the existence of a detectable X-ray source in this position, and the tentative identification by the NRL group of their *Oph* XR-1 source with SN 1604 [11] does not seem to be correct.

d) The position for *Sco* X-2, as determined by the ASE-MIT group, is about 1° from the arc of great circle corresponding to one of the sources seen by the Lockheed group. Again, the discrepancy may be due to experimental errors, and the sources seen by the two groups may be the same. On the other hand, *Sco* X-2 lies about 5° from the nearest source reported by the NRL group (*Sco* XR-2); the ASE-MIT results are consistent with the existence of this nearest source *Sco* XR-2, since the region containing it was not scanned. However, the region containing the other nearby NRL source *Sco* XR-3 was scanned by the same detectors which observed *Sco* X-2. The NRL and ASE-MIT results can be reconciled only if *Sco* XR-3 and *Sco* X-2 are two separate sources lying within the same 4° band of galactic longitude and *Sco* XR-3 is substantially weaker than *Sco* X-2. But, then the question remains as to why no evidence of a source at the position of *Sco* X-2 was found in the NRL data.

e) The NRL source *Sgr* XR-2 lies half-way between the arcs of great circle about 12° apart, on which the Lockheed group located two separate sources. Possibly the peak of counting rate in the NRL observations resulted from the combined effects of these two sources.

f) In addition to these two sources and to the ASE-MIT sources *Sgr* X-1 and *Sco* X-2, the Lockheed results indicate the existence of at least two other sources near the galactic center. One of them may coincide with NRL source *Sgr* XR-1. It appears difficult to identify the other with any of the NRL sources, unless there is a sizeable error in the position of *Sco* XR-2 quoted by NRL.

g) *Sgr* A, the radio center of the Galaxy, is at most a weak X-ray source compared with the other sources nearby.

4·3. *Other sources.* – Early observations by the ASE-MIT group suggested the presence of X-ray sources in the general region of Cygnus [1, 2]. As noted previously, the NRL group detected two sources, *Cyg* XR-1 and *Cyg* XR-2 in this region (see Fig. 34). One of them (*Cyg* XR-2) lies near the arc of great circle where also the Lockheed group located an X-ray source. *Cyg* XR-2 was not scanned by the Lockheed group. Neither *Cyg* XR-1 nor *Cyg* XR-2 coincides with the Cygnus loop or with *Cyg* A.

Lastly, the NRL observations indicate the existence of a source in Serpens; a small maximum in the counting rate observed by the Lockheed group in scan no. 1 may be due to the same source.

4·4. *Spectral information and flux estimates.* – Some information on the spectra of the X-ray sources has been obtained from absorption measurements as well as from the pulse-height distributions observed with proportional counters and with scintillation counters. Partly because of the nature of the measurements, partly because of the limited statistical accuracy, none of the available results affords a direct determination of the spectral distribution, *i.e.*, of the function $j(E)\,\mathrm{d}E$ giving the energy flux of X-rays with photon energy between E and $E+\mathrm{d}E$. Rather certain *a priori* assumptions had to be made on the form of the spectral function $j(E)$; the experimental results could then be used to compute the free parameters entering in the expressions for $j(E)$, and, in some cases, to rule out certain types of spectral functions.

The spectral functions usually considered are:

Power law:

$$j(E)\,\mathrm{d}E = \mathrm{const}\,\frac{\mathrm{d}E}{E^{\alpha}}\,. \tag{9}$$

Synchrotron radiation and inverse Compton effect are likely to produce spectra of this kind.

Exponential law:

$$j(E)\,\mathrm{d}E = \mathrm{const}\,\exp[-E/kT]\,\mathrm{d}E\,. \tag{10}$$

Spectra of this kind are characteristic of low-Z, fully ionized, optically thin, clouds containing electrons with a Maxwellian velocity distribution corresponding to a temperature T. In this case, the process responsible for the X-ray emission is bremsstrahlung. (In the presence of incompletely ionized matter with Z greater than about ten, there would be a substantial contribution from free-bound transitions, giving rise to characteristic discontinuities in the spectrum.)

Planck's law:

$$j(E)\,\mathrm{d}E = \mathrm{const}\,\frac{E^3\,\mathrm{d}E}{\exp[E/kT]-1}\,. \tag{11}$$

This law, characterizes the radiation from a black-body at a surface temperature T.

4·4.1. The Crab Nebula. The NRL group in their Nov. 1964 flight observed the Crab Nebula with two X-ray counters provided with mylar windows $\frac{1}{4}$ mil and $\frac{1}{2}$ mil thick respectively. The measured counting rates (2.7 and 1.6 per cm² s) were consistent with a power-law spectrum of the type

$$j(E)\,\mathrm{d}E = \mathrm{const}\,\frac{\mathrm{d}E}{E^{1.1}}\,.$$

The energy range to which this result applies extends from 1.2 to 4.0 keV.

The Crab Nebula was also observed by CLARK by means of a scintillation counter flown with a balloon in July 1964 [5]. The pulses were analysed in four channels corresponding to (nominal) energies from 15 to 28, from 28 to 42, from 42 to 62 and greater than 62 keV. The counting rates in the three lower channels (after subtraction of background and correction for atmospheric absorption) were consistent with a power-law spectrum of the type

$$j(E)\,\mathrm{d}E = \frac{\mathrm{const}}{E^2}\,\mathrm{d}E\,.$$

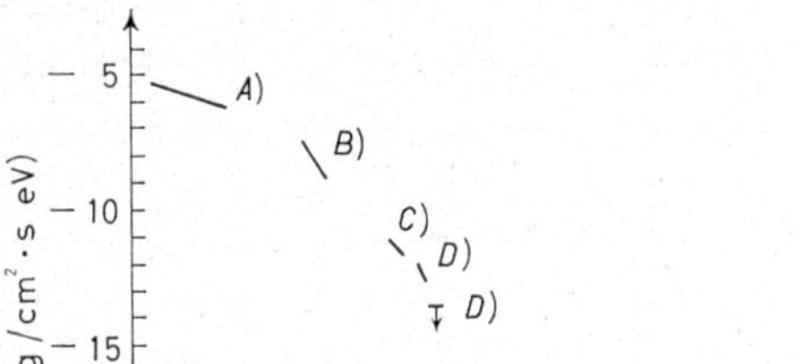

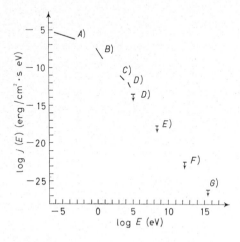

Fig. 35. – Summary of experimental data on the spectrum of electromagnetic radiation from the Crab Nebula: *A*) radio, ground based (C. R. O'DELL *Ap. J.*, **136**, 809 (1963)); *B*) infra-red and visible, ground based (O'DELL: cit.); *C*) X-ray, rocket (H. FRIEDMAN: unpublished); *D*) X-ray, balloon (G. CLARK: *Phys. Rev. Lett.*, **14**, 91 (1965)); *E*) γ-ray, satellite (W. KRAUSHAAR, G. CLARK, G. GARMIRE, H. HELMKEN, P. HIGBIE and M. AGOGINO: *Ap. J.*, **141**, 845 (1965)); *F*) γ-ray, ground based (Čerenkov light from air showers) (A. E. CHUDAKOV, V. I. ZATESPIN, N. M. NESTEROVA and D. L. DADIKEN: *Proc. of Fifth Interamerican Seminar on Cosmic Rays*, vol. V, p. XLIV-1(La Paz, 1962)); *G*) γ-ray, ground based (pure electromagnetic) air showers (K. SUGA, I. ESCOBAR, K. MURAKAMI, V. DOMINGO, Y. TOYODA, G. CLARK and M. LAPOINTE: *Proc. of the Intern. Conf. on Cosmic Rays*, Jaipur, 1963).

The higher channel did not contain any statistically significant signal, thus placing an upper limit to the flux. This upper limit indicated an increase in the logarithmic slope of the spectrum beyond 62 keV.

The experiments described above provided information not only on the shapes of the spectrum but also on the absolute values of the flux in the two regions explored. It is thus possible to combine their results into a single spectrum extending from about 1 to about 60 keV. It is also possible to compare the results relative to this range of energy with the flux measurements in the visible and in the radio regions of the electromagnetic spectrum, and with upper limits that have been obtained by various experimenters for the flux in the γ-ray region, from about 10^8 eV to about 10^{15} eV. The results of this comparison are summarized in Fig. 35. It appears that the spectrum of the Crab Nebula may be approximated by a single power law with exponent of about 1 from a few eV to a few 10 keV. For higher energies, however, the spectrum becomes considerably steeper. Moreover, interstellar absorption must produce a « gap » in the spectrum which has not yet been observed, but whose detailed experimental investigation promises to afford important information on the composition of interstellar gases.

4·4.2. The sources near the galactic center. Early results of the ASE-MIT group on the atmospheric attenuation of X-rays from these sources (as observed with Geiger counters) were found to be consistent with a black-body radiation corresponding to a temperature of about 10^7 °K, without, however, providing any evidence for or against the assumption that the shape of the spectrum was of this particular form. Later results for *Sco* X-1 by the NRL group (based again on atmospheric absorption) gave an effective temperature between 2 and $3 \cdot 10^6$ under the assumption of a black-body spectrum [11].

Additional data were obtained in 1964-1965 by the Lockheed group, the ASE-MIT groups and the NRL group. The results of the Lockheed group refer to *Sco* X-1 alone. They are based on observations made with the same three proportional counters that also provided the data on the location of this source [14] (T, C, and B in Fig. 32). Counters T and C had 5 mil thick Be windows, counter B had a 0.5 mil thick Al window. All counters were 4.0 cm deep and were filled to a pressure of 83 cm Hg with a mixture of 90 percent argon and 10 percent methane. From the computed efficiency curves, the estimated energy resolution of the counters and the associated circuitry, and the observed pulse-height distributions, they obtained the energy spectrum shown in Fig. 36. No significant signal was observed in the lowest channel so that only an upper limit could be placed to the flux in the $(2 \div 4)$ keV interval. This upper limit appears to indicate a sharp drop-off of the spectrum below 4 keV; however, it has been reported privately that the interpretation

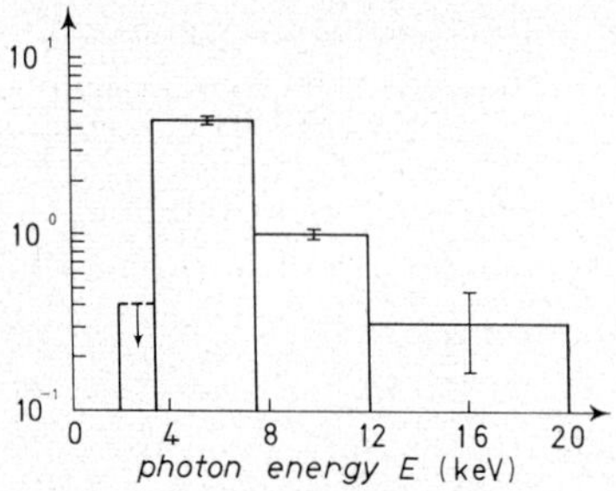

Fig. 36. – Spectral distribution of X-rays from *Sco* X-1 as obtained from pulse-height distribution of a proportional counter. (From ref. [14].)

of the measurements in the $(2 \div 4)$ keV channel is affected by considerable uncertainty.

The ASE group obtained spectral data in a rocket flight carried out in August 1964, as well as in the rocket flight of October 1964, mentioned previously [15]. The instrumentation of the August flight included a bank of Geiger counters with Be windows of 9.0 mg/cm² thickness, filled with argon to a gas thickness of 5.4 mg/cm². The computed efficiency curve of this counter was checked by means of the beam from a tungsten target, windowless X-ray tube operated at different voltages from 1.8 to 10 kV. The counter bank was provided with a collimator which made it possible to separate the signals received from *Sco* X-1 and from the sources near the galactic equator.

At launch two filters, one of 7.0 mg/cm² Be (*F*-1) and one of 1.72 mg/cm² Mylar (*F*-2) were placed in front of the counters. During the flight, first one then the other filter was removed so that the counting rates with *F*-1 and *F*-2, with *F*-1 alone and with no filter could be measured. Data relative to essentially a full precession cycle are available for each of the three situations; therefore, no correction is needed for a change in the average angle of incidence of the radiation during the three measurements.

The results are summarized in Table II. Note, in the first place, that the spectral information obtainable from these data refers to the energy region

TABLE II. – *Filter absorption data on X-ray sources.*

Filter condition	Source region	Counting rate measured counts/s	Attenuation relative to no filter
No filter	*Sco* X-1	620 ± 20	1
F1	*Sco* X-1	440 ± 18	0.71 ± 0.04
F1+F2	*Sco* X-1	350 ± 17	0.56 ± 0.03
No filter	Galactic center	350 ± 18	1
F1	Galactic center	240 ± 18	0.70 ± 0.06
F1+F2	Galactic center	210 ± 15	0.62 ± 0.05
Typical background rate		30	

for about 1 to about 10 keV. Note also that there is no stastically significant difference between the attenuations observed from *Sco* X-1 and for the sources near the galactic plane. It turns out that the experimental results do not permit a distinction between the three types of spectra represented by eqs. (6), (7), and (8). For each assumed type of spectrum, however, they provide a determination of the characteristic parameter, to wit:

Power law	$\alpha = 1.1 \pm 0.3$,
Exponential law	$T = (3.8 \pm 1.8) \cdot 10^7$ °K ,
Planck's law	$T = (9.1 \pm 0.9) \cdot 10^6$ °K .

The data are not consistent with the sharp drop-off of the spectrum below 4 keV tentatively indicated by the Lockheed results.

The instrumentation of the October flight included a NaI scintillation counter, provided with a suitable collimator. The pulse-height distributions observed in the two-source regions, with background subtracted, are shown in Fig. 37. The cut-off below 10 keV results from the electronic threshold. Above 10 keV, the three pulse-height distributions are significantly different. The distribution observed from *Sco* X-1 falls below the minimum detectable level at about 18 keV (a result consistent with a cut-off of the spectrum at about 15 keV). On the other hand, the combined spectrum of the sources near the galactic plane extends to higher energies.

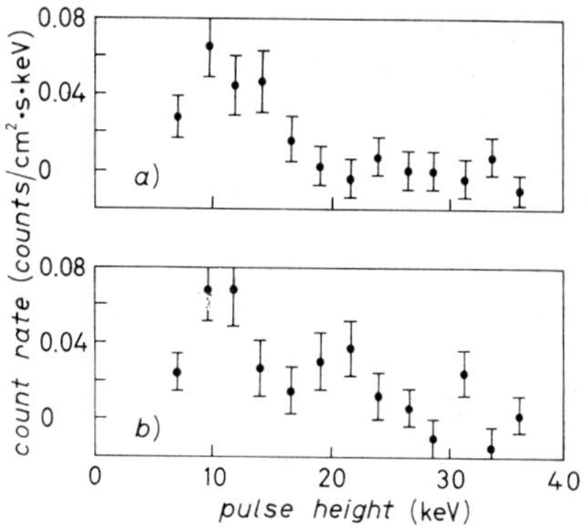

Fig. 37. – Pulse height distributions of a sodium iodide (NaI) scintillation detector, due to X-rays *a*) from *Sco* X-1 and *b*) from the galactic center region.

If we now compare the Geiger counter data obtained in the August flight with the scintillation counter data obtained in the October flight, we reach the following conclusions.

A black-body spectrum cannot fit both sets of data for either *Sco* X-1 or the sources near the galactic equator since such a spectrum falls off with increasing energy much more rapidly than the experimental results indicate. On the other hand, both a power law and an exponential law, with the appropriate values of the parameters mentioned previously, can account for the data obtained with the scintillation counter as well as with the Geiger counters. There is, however, evidence that the combined spectrum of the sources near the galactic equator is somewhat harder than that of *Sco* X-1.

The NRL group obtained spectral information on celestial X-ray sources both during the June 1964 flight, mentioned previously, and during a flight carried out in April 1965, whose results, so far, have been described only in a preliminary report.

In the June 1964 flight, *Sco* X-1 was observed at different altitudes during the descent of the rocket. From the measured atmospheric attenuation, it was concluded that of the flux detected at the highest altitude about $\frac{1}{3}$ was accounted for by photons with energies above 2 keV and $\frac{2}{3}$ by photons with energies between 1.2 and 2 keV.

In the April 1965 flight, the NRL group used four counters with the following characteristics: 1) argon filling, 1 mil mylar window; 2) argon filling, $\frac{1}{4}$ mil mylar window; 3) neon filling, $\frac{1}{4}$ mil mylar window; 4) helium filling, $\frac{1}{4}$ mil mylar window. The relative counting rates of these detectors, which had very different spectral response curves, were found to be significantly different for different X-ray sources. These differences indicate differences in the spectra, *Sco* X-1 being one of the sources which appeared to have the softest spectrum. The results concerning *Sco* X-1 could not be accounted for by a black body spectrum. They also provided evidence for a strong increment of flux at long wavelengths, in marked disagreement with the tentative results of the Lockheed group.

TABLE III. – *Integrated energy flux for various X-ray sources and two different ranges of photon energy.*

Source	Spectral range (keV)	Energy flux (erg/cm² s)	Remarks
Crab	1 to 10 20 to 30	$2\cdot10^{-8}$ $(6\pm2)\cdot10^{-9}$	NRL data G Clark balloon data
Sco X-1	1 to 10 20 to 30	$(1.6\pm0.4)\cdot10^{-7}$ $<6\cdot10^{-9}$ ([a])	ASE Geiger counter ([b]) data ASE scintillation counter data
Galactic equator (including *Sgr* X-1, *Sco* X-1 and probably several additional sources.)	1 to 10 20 to 30	$(0.4\pm0.1)\cdot10^{-7}$ $(16\pm5)\cdot10^{-9}$	ASE Geiger counter ([b]) data ASE scintillation counter data

([a]) Represents 2σ deviation above background; no significant excess was observed.
([b]) Assuming E^{-1} power spectrum.

To conclude this Section, we summarize in Table III some estimates for the X-ray fluxes in two different spectral regions from the Crab Nebula, from *Sco* X-1 and from the source complex along the galactic equator, within 20° of the galactic center. Note that these estimates depend, among other things, on the assumed shapes of the spectra which are still quite uncertain.

4.4.3. Background radiation. Since the earliest observations by the ASE-MIT group, the existence of an isotropic X-ray background has been indicated. Information on the background flux is summarized in Fig. 38. The ratios η, of the counting rate of the isotropic components to the peak Ω counting rate from *Sco* X-1 for various experiments are plotted *vs.* the solid angle corresponding to the field of view of the respective measurements. This ratio is insensitive to the experimental conditions provided the spectra of *Sco* X-1 and the background are essentially similar. The ratio is: $\varphi_B \cdot \Omega / \varphi_{Sco}$ where φ_B is the background flux per unit solid angle and φ_{Sco} is the flux density from *Sco* X-1. Results of the ASE-MIT measurements show that η is roughly proportional to Ω as is expected if the background consists of X-rays distributed isotropically, except for one result which is suspected to be in error because of a partial failure of the anticoincidence counter which rejected cosmic-ray particles. All other data were obtained without an anticoincidence counter and, hence, it is understandable that they show slightly higher background fluxes. The estimate of the flux by NRL is based on the difference of the counting rate when the detector was looking upwards and downwards. The lower limit of NRL values of η is consistent with ASE-MIT results. Thus, the background component, which is proportional to the field of view of the detector, is estimated as about 6 count/(cm² s sr) in the (2 ÷ 8) Å band. If we consider the spectral response of the detector and the energy spectrum, the flux may be as much as 10 quanta/(cm² s sr).

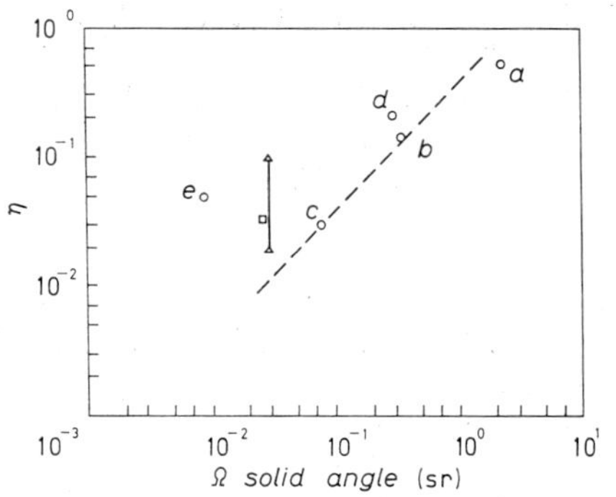

Fig. 38. – Comparison of observations of the X-ray background made by various experimenters. The quantity η is the ratio of the counting rate of the background to peak counting rate of *Sco* X-1 as observed in a given experiment. ○ ASE: *a*, 1962 and 1963; *b* and *c*, 1964 August; *d* and *e*, 1964 October; △ NRL; □ Lockheed.

There is no evidence for anisotropy for any specific direction of galactic co-ordinate: *e.g.* say the direction of the Milky Way. Also, there is no positive indication to show a bright atmospheric horizon or any preferential local azimuth. All information indicates that a background flux of extraterrestrial X-rays truly exists; however, it cannot yet be excluded that a portion of this background originates from the Earth's magnetosphere.

REFERENCES

[1] R. Giacconi, H. Gursky, F. Paolini and B. Rossi: *Phys. Rev. Letters*, **9**, 439 (1962).

[2] H. Gursky, R. Giacconi, F. Paolini and B. Rossi: *Phys. Rev. Letters*, **11**, 530 (1963).

[3] S. Bowyer, E. T. Byram, T. A. Chubb and H. Friedman: *Nature*, **201**, 1307 (1964).

[4] S. Bowyer, E. T. Byram, T. A. Chubb and H. Friedman: *Science*, **146**, 912 (1964).

[5] G. W. Clark: *Phys. Rev. Letters*, **14**, 91 (1965).

[6] A. P. Lukierskij, M. A. Rumsh and L. A. Smirnov: *Opt. i Spektroskopija*, **9**, 265, 353 (1960).

[7] M. Oda: *Applied Optics*, **4**, 143 (1965).

[8] R. Giacconi and B. Rossi: *Journ. Geophys. Res.*, **65**, 773 (1960).

[9] R. Giacconi, N. Harmon, R. F. Lacey and Z. Szilagyi: *J. Opt. Soc. Am.*, **55**, 345 (1965).

[10] R. Giacconi, W. P. Reidy, T. Zehnpfennig, J. C. Lindsay and W. A. Muney: *Astrophys. J.*, **142**, 1274 (1965).

[11] S. Bowyer, E. T. Byram, T. A. Chubb and H. Friedman: *Science*, **147**, 394 (1965).

[12] G. W. Clark, G. Garmire, M. Oda, M. Wada, R. Giacconi, H. Gursky and J. Waters: *Nature*, **207**, 584 (1965).

[13] M. Oda, G. W. Clark, G. Garmire, M. Wada, R. Giacconi, H. Gursky and J. Waters: *Nature*, **205**, 554 (1965).

[14] P. C. Fisher, H. M. Johnson, W. C. Jordan, A. J. Meyerott and L. W. Acton: submitted for publication to *Astrophys. J.* (1965).

[15] R. Giacconi, H. Gursky and J. R. Waters: *Nature*, **207**, 572 (1965).

X-Ray and γ-Ray Sources.

G. Burbidge
University of California - San Diego - Calif.

1. – Introduction.

At this summer school Dr. Giacconi has been concerned with the methods of detection of cosmic X-rays and γ rays. I shall be concerned with the theoretical side of X-ray and γ-ray astronomy. Thus I shall discuss first the basic processes which can be expected to give rise to X-ray and γ-ray fluxes, and then relate these to the observational results which have been described by Giacconi (*). The material that I shall describe is taken from an extensive discussion of X-ray and γ-ray astronomy prepared by R. J. Gould and myself which will appear in the *Handbuch der Physik*, 46, II.

From the theoretical standpoint it is clear that since a flux of charged particles is known to be present in the cosmos, fluxes of energetic quanta must always be present since there are many mechanisms which give rise to photons as secondary quanta. At present, many of the observations of high-energy photons are very preliminary and, in some cases, contradictory. However, it is clear that the interpretation of these observations can provide significant information on a large number of astronomical problems. Of special interest are questions of cosmology, and the early observational data were soon employed as a means of testing cosmological theories. Actually, further interpretation of the data already available may provide additional answers to cosmological questions. The data themselves are difficult to come by, because of the necessity of carrying photon detectors above the earth's absorbing atmosphere by means of balloons, rockets, or satellites. In these lectures we shall not attempt to describe the ingenious techniques developed for carrying out such observations since they have been discussed by Dr. Giacconi; we shall

(*) It is of some interest to point out that X-ray and γ-ray astronomy is the newest branch of high-energy astronomy. The first hard photons were detected from the sun as recently as 1957 [1].

concentrate on the problem of the *interpretation* of the results. However, on occasion we shall comment on the question of whether certain experimental results are suspect.

There are essentially three general sources of uncertainty involved in the interpretation of the observations on energetic photons: 1) experimental uncertainties or errors, 2) uncertainties in the calculations of the basic physical processes which produce the photons, and 3) uncertainties in the astronomical parameters employed in calculating the photon flux. Usually this last source of uncertainty is the most serious; for example, the mean gas density, (low energy) stellar photon density, magnetic field, and cosmic-ray (proton) intensity in the galaxy and intergalactic medium are known only approximately and in some cases may be different by several orders of magnitude. Moreover, the photon flux received from sources at great distances depends on the detailed structure of the universe.

The basic physical processes responsible for photon production may be summarized as follows: 1) Bremsstrahlung is emitted in the interaction of charged particles with matter. It results from e-p Coulomb scattering at nonrelativistic energies and from both e-p and e-e scatterings at relativistic energies. 2) The Compton scattering of a low-energy thermal photon by a high-energy electron produces a high-energy scattered photon, the energy being transferred from the electron. This process was first discussed by FEENBERG and PRIMAKOFF [2]. FERMI pointed out that this was probably the mechanism by which electrons were removed from the primary cosmic-ray flux. 3) Electrons moving in magnetic fields emit synchrotron radiation; this is the primary mechanism for radio emission in galaxies. Very high electron energies are required to produce high-energy photons by this process; cosmic synchrotron spectra probably extend at most to photon energies in the keV$\div$MeV range. 4) Gamma-rays result from the decay of π^0-mesons ($\pi^0 \rightarrow 2\gamma$) following the production of mesons in collisions between primary cosmic-ray particles and nuclei of the interstellar and intergalactic gas. Cosmic-ray nuclear collisions are also a source of high-energy electrons via charged-pion production and ($\pi \rightarrow \mu \rightarrow e$) decay, as was proposed by BURBIDGE and GINZBURG in the early attempts to understand radio sources. A recent discussion applying to galactic radiation has been given by POLLACK and FAZIO [3] and by GINZBURG and SYROVATSKY [4]. π^0-gammas are also produced following meson production in matter-antimatter annihilation. Some processes which produce line radiation are: 5) Characteristic X-rays are produced following the ejection of an atomic inner-shell electron by, for example, a high-energy particle or photon flux. The resulting cascade transitions give rise to the emission of K, L, etc.-series X-rays. 6) Gamma-rays are produced in the annihilation of electrons and positrons ($e^+ + e^- \rightarrow 2\gamma$). Energetic positrons in the interstellar (but not intergalactic) medium come essentially to rest by various energy loss processes (see Sect. 2) before annihilating, and the resulting γ-rays are essentially monoenergetic at about 0.51 MeV. 7) The formation of deuterium via $n+p\to d+\gamma$ (the inverse of photodisintegration) produces a photon of energy 2.23 MeV. This is the only low-energy nuclear reaction we have listed here which gives rise directly to γ-radiation. There are many low-energy reactions which give rise to γ-rays either directly or indirectly, but in general they will occur only in stellar interiors so that the γ-rays do not escape. However, there are some indications that nuclear reactions sometimes take place in stellar surfaces, so that these γ-rays may be observable. Both the 0.51 and 2.23 MeV lines were mentioned in an early paper by MORRISON [5] on the subject of gamma ray astronomy. 8) Finally, we mention the more general process called *inner bremsstrahlung* which really includes some of the processes mentioned above. If an electron is suddenly accelerated from rest to a velocity βc by *any* mechanism, the probability that in the acceleration process an additional *soft* photon of energy within $\hbar\,d\omega$ is emitted is given by the simple expression

$$(1.1)\qquad \begin{cases} dw = \dfrac{\alpha}{\pi}\left(\dfrac{1}{\beta}\ln\dfrac{1+\beta}{1-\beta}-2\right)\dfrac{d\omega}{\omega} \\ \qquad\to \dfrac{2\alpha}{3\pi}\,\beta^2\,\dfrac{d\omega}{\omega}\,, \quad \text{if } \beta\ll 1\,, \end{cases}$$

where α is the fine-structure constant.

Most of the photon-producing processes are treated in Sect. **2** of these notes where the effects of the high-energy electrons produced in cosmic-ray nuclear collisions are considered. Section **3** is devoted to the problem of discrete sources of X-rays and the possibility of observing extragalactic sources of high-energy photons. As we have already emphasized, the presently available data on both the photon fluxes and astronomical parameters are very rough; for this reason, we feel that in attempting interpretation no elaborate calculations are warranted. We have tried to give as simple a treatment of the physical processes as is possible while still doing justice to the data.

2. – Production in the interstellar gas, the galactic halo, and the intergalactic medium.

In this Section we consider the general background flux of cosmic photons produced in electromagnetic interactions involving *nonthermal* particles. A source of high-energy particles is provided by the ordinary cosmic rays, in particular the cosmic-ray protons, whose energy spectrum is known and extends up to $\sim 10^{20}$ eV. The protons themselves are not efficient at producing photons in direct electromagnetic interactions, due to their large mass. However, high-energy electrons can result from nuclear collisions of cosmic rays in which a shower of pions is produced; the charged pions then decay into electrons via $\pi \to \mu \to e$. The energetic « secondary » electrons which result can produce high-energy photons by a number of processes, and these will be considered later in this Section. The photon spectrum produced by a specific process is determined (among other things) by the electron spectrum, which in turn is determined by the cosmic-ray proton spectrum. We shall assume a *universal* cosmic-ray spectrum, that is, except near local sources of cosmic rays, the cosmic ray flux at any place in the universe is assumed to be the same as that measured at the earth. There is some difference of opinion as to whether the primary cosmic rays are predominantly of galactic or extragalactic origin. For a discussion of two extreme schools of thought on this point the reader is referred to the work of GINZBURG and SYROVATSKY [6] and BURBIDGE and HOYLE [7]. However, to make the calculations described here we have made the assumption that a universal cosmic-ray flux with the same energy density inside and outside galaxies is present. We take no position on the validity of this hypothesis in this article, as this has been done simply to facilitate the computations. The results are easily adjusted for other assumptions. GINZBURG and SYROVATSKY have argued against a universal cosmic-ray flux and estimate that the intergalactic cosmic-ray density is smaller than the local (galactic) value by a factor $\sim 10^{-3}$. However, their reasoning is based on equipartition arguments and is, in our opinion, not convincing. Of course, it may be that there exists a « primary » cosmic-ray electron component, where by primary electrons we mean those which may have been accelerated by the same process and in the same sources that produced the cosmic-ray protons. This question is open. Recent experiments by DE SHONG, HILDEBRAND, and MEYER [8] measuring the electron/positron ratio in the local cosmic-ray flux are certainly relevant to this problem, but the experiments still do not allow a definite conclusion regarding the primary or secondary origin of these electrons and positrons. We shall consider only the contribution from secondary electrons. It might be remarked that the acceleration of protons without an accompanying acceleration of electrons can be envisaged easily, since the electrons, with their smaller mass, lose energy by electromagnetic processes more readily.

We shall take a universal differential cosmic ray flux given by

$$\mathrm{d}J_{\mathrm{p}} = K_{\mathrm{p}}\gamma_{\mathrm{p}}^{-\Gamma_{\mathrm{p}}}\,\mathrm{d}\gamma_{\mathrm{p}}\,, \tag{2.1}$$

where $\mathrm{d}J_{\mathrm{p}}$ is the number of incident protons per cm^2 per second having Lorentz factors $\gamma_{\mathrm{p}}(=E_{\mathrm{p}}/m_{\mathrm{p}}c^2)$ within $\mathrm{d}\gamma_{\mathrm{p}}$ (centered at γ_{p}); here K_{p} and Γ_{p} are constants. By appropriate choice of K_{p} and Γ_{p} the power law (2.1) can be used to describe the observed flux for any range of γ_{p}. The choice $\Gamma_{\mathrm{p}} = 2.6$,

$K_p = 100\ \text{cm}^{-2}\ \text{s}^{-1}$ fits the observations [9] over many orders of magnitude of γ_p in the *high*-energy range. At lower energies the actual flux is smaller than that described by this choice of Γ_p, K_p. The extrapolation from high energies is too large by a factor ~ 2 at $\gamma_p \sim 100$ and by a factor ~ 4 at $\gamma_p = 10$. Since we are interested in the effects of the high-energy cosmic rays we shall adopt the above values for the parameters Γ_p, K_p in the calculations outlined in this Section. Given the astronomical parameters (gas density, magnetic field, etc.), the cosmic photon fluxes from various processes (synchrotron radiation, bremsstrahlung, Compton effect, etc.) are essentially determined by the cosmic-ray spectrum. However, due to uncertainties in our knowledge of the physics of certain processes, in particular that of meson production in high-energy nuclear collisions, the calculated photon fluxes must be considered at best only order-of-magnitude estimates. Uncertainties in the astronomical parameters further complicate the interpretation of the results. In view of this, a number of simplifying assumptions and approximations are made in the calculation of the physical processes.

After discussing meson production in cosmic-ray collisions (Sect. 2·1) the electron production spectrum is derived in Sect. 2·2. Electron energy losses in the galaxy and intergalactic medium are treated in Sects. 2·3 and 2·4 and the resulting electron spectra are derived in Sect. 2·5. The photon fluxes are calculated in Sect. 2·6 and a discussion and comparison with the observational results follows. Some cosmological considerations of photon production in the intergalactic medium are given in Sect. 2·8.

2·1. *Meson production in cosmic-ray nuclear collisions.* – All of the laboratory results on meson production are for incident-proton energies less than 10 GeV at which it is possible energetically to produce only a few relatively low-energy pions per inelastic collision. Our knowledge of meson production by high-energy protons is based primarily on theory, and the theories of meson production are very crude; of course, an accurate theoretical treatment of the problem would be extremely difficult, probably beyond our present knowledge of elementary-particle interactions. The simplest theory of meson production in high-energy nuclear collisions is that of Fermi [10] and is outlined briefly below. The theory predicts the correct shape for the spectrum of high-energy γ-rays resulting from π^0's produced in cosmic-ray collisions.

2·1.1. Fermi theory of meson production. Consider the collision of a proton of (lab) energy $\gamma_p m_p c^2$ incident on a proton at rest. In the center-of-mass (c.m.) system the total energy of the two protons is $2\bar{\gamma}_p m_p c^2 = [2(\gamma_p + 1)]^{\frac{1}{2}} m_p c^2$, where $\bar{\gamma}_p$ is the Lorentz factor of the protons in the c.m. system. Each proton carries a cloud of virtual pions; in the proton's rest frame the radius of this cloud is approximately $\Lambda_\pi = \hbar/m_\pi c$, where m_π is the pion mass. The interaction cross-section is then $\sigma \sim \pi \Lambda_\pi^2$. In the c.m. system each cloud is contracted in the direction of motion by a factor $\bar{\gamma}_D$, and when the protons collide the maximum common volume of the meson clouds (which, presumably, is when the interaction is strongest) is

$$\Delta V = \frac{4\pi}{3} \Lambda_\pi^3 \frac{1}{\bar{\gamma}_D} \,. \tag{2.2}$$

For high proton energies it is possible energetically to produce many pions in an inelastic collision and FERMI made the assumption that the interaction in the volume (2.2) was strong enough to produce a distribution of pion energies corresponding to *thermal equilibrium* with most of the initial-proton kinetic energy having been fed into the pion gas. Also, the pions are predominantly highly relativistic and thus have a Planckian distribution. The « temperature » for this distribution is easily shown to be $kT \approx \gamma_D^{\frac{1}{4}} m_\pi c^2$, so that in the c.m. system the mean pion energy corresponds to

$$\langle \bar{\gamma}_\pi \rangle \approx \gamma_D^{\frac{1}{4}} \,, \tag{2.3}$$

and in the laboratory system (where one of the protons is initially at rest)

$$\langle \gamma_\pi \rangle \approx \bar{\gamma}_D \gamma_D^{\frac{1}{4}} \approx \gamma_D^{\frac{3}{4}} \,. \tag{2.4}$$

FERMI assumed that the distribution arising when the pion clouds of the colliding protons overlap is « frozen in », so that eq. (2.4) would apply to the pions produced in the collision. Equation (2.4) also implies that the *multiplicity* of pions produced is proportional to (and is, in fact, roughly given by) $\gamma_D^{\frac{1}{4}}$.

A number of attempts have been made to improve the Fermi theory and some authors have taken a quite different approach to the problem. However, these alternative theories usually predict a pion production spectrum not radically different from that of the Fermi theory. The assumption of thermal equilibrium in the Fermi theory has been questioned by LANDAU [11], who has developed his own theory of meson production. Another defect in the simple Fermi theory is that the effects of the production of other unstable particles (for example, K-mesons), which eventually decay into pions, has not been taken into account. Nevertheless, for our purposes essentially the only result which need be specified is the relation between multiplicity (and mean pion energy) and γ_D. The detailed shape of the pion energy spectrum produced by an incident proton of given energy need not concern us.

2·1.2. Pion production spectrum. The number of pions produced per second per cm³ within the energy range $d\gamma_\pi$ in p-p collisions would be computed from

$$q_\pi(\gamma_\pi)\,\mathrm{d}\gamma_\pi = \int \mathrm{d}J_\mathrm{p}\, n_\mathrm{H}\,\sigma f(\gamma_\pi;\gamma_\mathrm{p})\,\mathrm{d}\gamma_\pi\,, \tag{2.5}$$

where $\mathrm{d}J_\mathrm{p}$ is the differential incident cosmic-ray proton flux, n_H the local density of hydrogen nuclei, σ ($\approx \pi\Lambda_\pi^2$) the total (excluding the multiplicity factor) cross-section for the event, and $f(\gamma_\pi;\gamma_\mathrm{p})$ the distribution function for the pion production spectrum. We approximate the spectrum $f(\gamma_\pi;\gamma_\mathrm{p})$ by a product of the multiplicity ($\approx \gamma_\mathrm{p}^{\frac{1}{4}}$) and a δ-function at the mean energy ($\approx \gamma_\mathrm{p}^{\frac{3}{4}}$) of the pion spectrum for given γ_p:

$$f(\gamma_\pi;\gamma_\mathrm{p}) \approx \gamma_\mathrm{p}^{\frac{1}{4}}\,\delta(\gamma_\pi - \gamma_\mathrm{p}^{\frac{3}{4}})\,. \tag{2.6}$$

With a cosmic-ray spectrum given by the power law (2.1) we then obtain

$$q_\pi(\gamma_\pi) \approx (4\pi/3)\,\Lambda_\pi^2 K_\mathrm{p} n_\mathrm{H} \gamma_\pi^{-\Gamma_\pi}\,, \qquad \Gamma_\pi = \tfrac{4}{3}(\Gamma_\mathrm{p} - \tfrac{1}{2})\,. \tag{2.7}$$

The δ-function approximation (2.6) does not introduce appreciable error. For example, if one computes $q_\pi(\gamma_\pi;\gamma_\mathrm{p})$, using the Wien approximation to the Planck thermal distribution, one obtains a slowly varying function of γ_π times γ_π to the power $-\frac{4}{3}(\Gamma_\mathrm{p} - \frac{1}{2})$, that is, essentially the same result as eq. (2.7). Moreover, the exponent in the spectrum (2.7) will be the same for the case where the mass of the incident cosmic-ray particle is different from that of the « target » nucleus. In such a case the analysis follows analogously, since the Lorentz factors in the c.m. system are still proportional to $\gamma^{\frac{1}{2}}$ (when γ is large), where γ is the Lorentz factor of the incident particle in the rest frame of the target particle.

2·1.3. An experimental test for $q_\pi\gamma(_\pi)$. For nuclear collisions at high energy the number of π^+, π^-, and π^0 mesons produced are the same, as is their energy distribution. The π^0 decays via $\pi^0 \to 2\gamma$, with the mean (lab) γ-ray energy being roughly $E_\pi/2$. Thus, a measurement of the γ-ray spectrum from π^0-mesons produced in primary cosmic-ray events would give the pion source spectrum $q_\pi(\gamma_\pi)$. Recently, KIDD [12] has measured the spectrum of high-energy γ's from π^0-mesons produced by cosmic rays at the top of the atmosphere. By performing the experiment at high altitudes he was able to observe γ's from π^0's produced predominantly in primary jets. KIDD found for the differential energy spectrum of the γ-ray flux a power law with exponent $\Gamma_0 = 2.9^{+0.3}_{-0.2}$. The γ-ray energy range observed by KIDD was $0.7\cdot 10^{11}\,\mathrm{eV} < E_0 < 10^{12}\,\mathrm{eV}$, corresponding to $10^3 < \gamma_\pi < 10^4$ and $10^4 < \gamma_\mathrm{p} < 2\cdot 10^5$. At these proton energies the cosmic-ray spectrum is described by the high-energy fit with $\Gamma_\mathrm{p} = 2.6$. The corresponding Γ_π from eq. (2.7) is 2.8 and is consistent with the value (Γ_0) measured by KIDD. We should like to emphasize that Kidd's experiment confirms the *results* of the Fermi theory, but not the fundamentals of the theory itself.

2·2. *The electron production spectrum.* – In the charged-pion decay ($\pi^\pm \to \mu^\pm + \nu$) most of the center-of-mass kinetic energy released to the products μ, ν is carried away by the neutrino whose energy is small compared with $m_\pi c^2$. The resulting laboratory energy of the muon is then approximately $(m_\mu/m_\pi)E_\pi$, where E_π is the laboratory energy of the pion before decay. The electron resulting from the muon decay ($\mu^\pm \to e^\pm + 2\nu$) is highly relativistic and behaves kinematically like the two neutrinos in the decay products. Thus, the mean energy in the spectrum of electron energies is about $\frac{1}{3}m_\mu c^2$ in the rest frame of the μ, and the mean laboratory energy $\langle E_e \rangle$ of the electron resulting from the $\pi \to \mu \to e$ decay is roughly $\frac{1}{3}(m_\mu/m_\pi)E_\pi \approx \frac{1}{4}E_\pi$; thus, $\langle \gamma_e \rangle \approx \frac{1}{4}(m_\pi/m_e)\langle \gamma_\pi \rangle$. Approximating the electron spectrum $f(\gamma_e; \gamma_\pi)$ by a δ-function at this energy we get, for the electron source spectrum,

$$q_e(\gamma_e)\,d\gamma_e \approx \frac{2}{3}\int q_\pi(\gamma_\pi)\,d\gamma_\pi\,\delta\left(\gamma_e - \frac{m_\pi}{4m_e}\gamma_\pi\right)d\gamma_e = \frac{8m_e}{3m_\pi}q_\pi\left(\frac{4m_e}{m_\pi}\gamma_e\right)d\gamma_e; \tag{2.8}$$

a factor $\frac{2}{3}$ has been introduced because only charged pions decay into electrons.

We shall consider production and energy losses of electrons with $10^2 \leqslant \gamma_e \leqslant 10^{10}$ corresponding to $1 \leqslant \gamma_\pi \leqslant 10^8$ and to $1 \leqslant \gamma_p \leqslant 10^{11}$.

2·3. *Electron energy losses in the galaxy.* – Here we consider the various processes tending to decrease the energy of high-energy electrons in the galaxy. We calculate the *average* rate of energy loss in the galaxy which we consider as the region within the galactic halo of radius $R_h \sim 5 \cdot 10^{22}$ cm. Actually, energy losses involving interactions with the galactic gas occur predominantly near the plane of the galaxy where most of the gas lies and where the gas is predominantly unionized. The volume of this disk of galactic interstellar gas is $\sim 10^{-2}$ of the volume of the galactic halo.

2·3.1. Ionization losses. The energy loss due to ionization and excitation of the interstellar gas may be computed from Bethe's formula for the stopping power. For high-energy electrons this formula is

$$-\left(\frac{dE_e}{dx}\right)_I = \frac{2\pi ne^4}{m_e c^2}\ln\frac{\gamma_e^3 m_e^2 c^4}{2I_0^2}, \tag{2.9}$$

where I_0 is the mean excitation energy of the stopping material (hydrogen), and n is the number density of atoms of the material. The argument of the logarithm in eq. (2.9) is very large and I_0 may be set equal to the Rydberg energy $\frac{1}{2}\alpha^2 m_e c^2$ ($\alpha^{-1} \approx 137$). We then have for the ionization loss in a hydrogen gas of mean density $\langle n \rangle$

$$-\langle d\gamma_e/dt \rangle_I = 2\pi c r_0^2 \langle n \rangle \ln (2\gamma_e^3/\alpha^4) . \tag{2.10}$$

Here r_0 $(= e^2/m_e c^2)$ is the classical electron radius. The energy loss computed from eq. (2.10) is shown as a function of γ_e in Fig. 1 for a mean gas density $\langle n \rangle = 0.03\ \text{cm}^{-3}$. This mean galactic gas density corresponds to a meandensity near the plane of the galaxy of $3\ \text{cm}^{-3}$. This value ($3\ \text{cm}^{-3}$) is about three times the observed density of atomic hydrogen. The higher value may be more appropriate if there is a high abundance of interstellar molecular hydrogen [13].

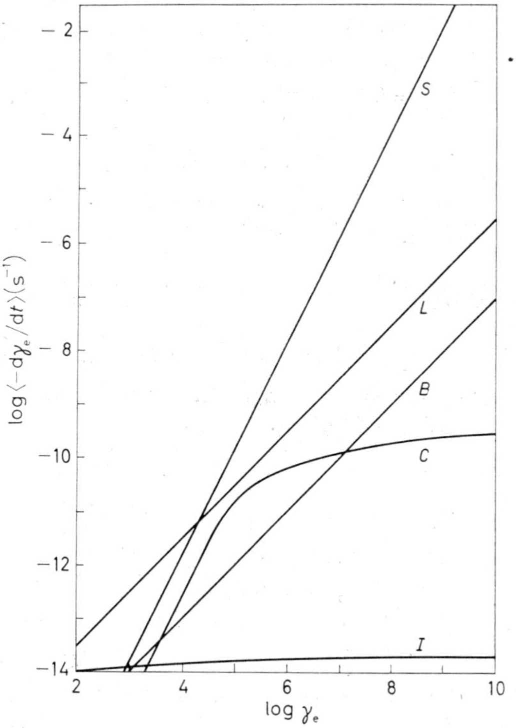

Fig. 1. – Electron energy loss rate in the galaxy by synchrotron emission (S), leakage out of the halo (L), bremsstrahlung (B), Compton scattering (C), and ionization (I).

2'3.2. Bremsstrahlung. The energy loss rate by bremsstrahlung emission would be computed from

$$-(dE/dt)_B = nc \int \hbar\omega \, d\sigma_B , \tag{2.11}$$

where n is the density of hydrogen nuclei and $d\sigma_B$ is the differential cross-section for the emission of a bremsstrahlung photon of energy within $\hbar\, d\omega$; in eq. (2.11) the integral is over ω from 0 to $\gamma_e m_e c^2/\hbar$. For $d\sigma_B$ we take the approximate simplified expression [14] $d\sigma_B \approx 4\alpha r_0^2 \omega^{-1} d\omega \ln 2\gamma_e$ and calculate the mean bremsstrahlung loss rate:

$$-\langle d\gamma_e/dt \rangle_B \approx 4c\alpha r_0^2 \langle n \rangle \gamma_e \ln \gamma_e . \tag{2.12}$$

This is the bremsstrahlung loss rate for interaction of electrons with *protons* and would be appropriate for calculating the energy loss in regions of ionized hydrogen. Actually, most of the galactic bremsstrahlung is likely to be produced near the galactic plane where the gas is predominantly atomic or molecular, and a correction for the associated shielding effects of the atomic electrons must be made. In fact, for the electron energies of interest the *strong shielding* expression would be more appropriate. In this case the argument of the logarithm in eq. (2.12) should be replaced by ~ 137 (see HEITLER [15]). Using this corrected expression the bremsstrahlung loss rate was computed for $\langle n \rangle = 0.03\ \text{cm}^{-3}$ and is shown in Fig. 1.

2·3.3. Synchrotron losses. It is well known that a highly relativistic electron of energy E_e in a magnetic field H moves in a circle with a Larmor radius $r_L = E_e/eH$ and radiates energy by the synchrotron process at a rate

$$-\langle dE_e/dt \rangle_S = \tfrac{2}{3} c r_0^2 \langle H^2 \rangle \gamma_e^2 . \tag{2.13}$$

The frequency spectrum of the radiation consists of a continuum with a maximum around $\nu_L \gamma_e^2$, ν_L $(= eH/2\pi m_e c)$ being the Larmor frequency. The loss rate $-\langle d\gamma_e/dt \rangle_S$ is shown in Fig. 1 for a magnetic field $H = 3 \cdot 10^{-6}$ gauss corresponding to the galactic halo.

2·3.4. Compton scattering by stellar photons. The Compton process, whereby a high-energy electron makes an elastic collision with a thermal stellar photon, and transfers some of its kinetic energy to the photon, has been considered in some detail by FEENBERG and PRIMAKOFF [2] and by DONAHUE [16]. More recently, FELTEN and MORRISON [17] have suggested this process as a mechanism for producing energetic photons. Consider the collision between an electron of energy $\gamma_e m_e c^2$ and a thermal photon of the galactic radiation field of initial energy ε_r. Let ε_r' denote the photon energy after scattering; let ε_r^* denote the initial energy of the photon in the rest frame of the electron; $\varepsilon_r^* \approx \gamma_e \varepsilon_r$. For $\varepsilon_r^* \ll m_e c^2$ the cross-section for the scattering process is given by the Thompson limit

$$\sigma_I \to \frac{8\pi}{3} r_0^2 , \tag{2.14}$$

while the mean energy loss per scattering may easily be shown, by the kinematics of the problem, to be

$$(\bar{\varepsilon}_r')_I \approx \gamma_e^2 \varepsilon_r . \tag{2.15}$$

For collisions with very-high-energy electrons in which $\varepsilon_r^* \ll m_e c^2$, the Klein-Nishina formula must be used to compute the scattering cross-section. For high energies this formula approaches

$$\sigma_{\text{II}} \to \pi r_0^2 \frac{m_e c^2}{\varepsilon_r^*} \ln \frac{2\varepsilon_r^*}{m_e c^2}, \tag{2.16}$$

while the mean energy loss per scattering is now comparable to the initial energy of the electron:

$$(\bar{\varepsilon}_r')_{\text{II}} \approx \gamma_e m_e c^2 . \tag{2.17}$$

The electron energy loss is computed from

$$-\langle \mathrm{d}E_e/\mathrm{d}t\rangle_{\mathrm{C}} = c\left\langle \int \sigma n_r(\varepsilon_r)\bar{\varepsilon}_r' \,\mathrm{d}\varepsilon_r \right\rangle, \tag{2.18}$$

where $n_r(\varepsilon_r)\,\mathrm{d}\varepsilon_r$ is the number density of photons of energy within $\mathrm{d}\varepsilon_r$ in the radiation field. We shall lump the stellar radiation field into one mean photon energy $\bar{\varepsilon}_r$. Then $\int n_r(\varepsilon_r)\,\mathrm{d}\varepsilon_r \equiv n_r \to \varrho_r/\bar{\varepsilon}_r$, where ϱ_r is the radiation energy density and n_r the number density of photons. For a thermal (black-body) radiation field ε_r is approximately $3kT_0$, where T_0 is the temperature of the thermal distribution. By employing the expressions for σ and $\bar{\varepsilon}_r'$ for the low-energy region (I) where $\gamma_e \ll m_e c^2/\bar{\varepsilon}_r$ and the high-energy region (II) where $\gamma_e \gg m_e c^2/\bar{\varepsilon}_r$ we get for the energy loss rates

$$-\left\langle \frac{\mathrm{d}\gamma_e}{\mathrm{d}t}\right\rangle_{\mathrm{CI}} = \frac{8\pi}{3}\frac{r_0^2}{m_e c}\langle\varrho_r\rangle\gamma_e^2, \tag{2.19 I}$$

$$-\left\langle \frac{\mathrm{d}\gamma_e}{\mathrm{d}t}\right\rangle_{\mathrm{CII}} = \pi r_0^2 m_e c^3 \frac{\langle\varrho_r\rangle}{\bar{\varepsilon}_r^2} \ln \frac{2\gamma_e\bar{\varepsilon}_r}{m_e c^2} . \tag{2.19 II}$$

It is interesting to note that at low energies the energy loss rate is proportional to the radiation energy density $\langle\varrho_r\rangle$ while at high energies it is essentially proportional to $\langle n_r\rangle/\bar{\varepsilon}_r$. Most of the contribution to the radiation field in the galactic halo comes from the relatively cool stars in the nuclear region of the galaxy. We shall take $\bar{\varepsilon}_r = 3$ eV and $\langle\varrho_r\rangle = 10^{-13}$ erg/cm³ as representative values for the radiation field in the halo. The corresponding energy loss rate is shown in Fig. 1. The curves for regions I and II were joined smoothly.

2'3.5. Leakage out of the galactic halo. Even for electron energies as high as $\gamma_e \sim 10^{10}$ the Larmor radii are only ~ 1 parsec, which, presumably is much less than the scale of « magnetic-field condensations » in the halo. For this reason the high-energy electrons moving in the halo are likely to penetrate only the outer edges of the magnetic field regions, and the paths of the electrons would resemble that of *Brownian motion.* The mean free path would correspond to motion between magnetic-field condensations and, because of the smallness of the electrons' Larmor radii, would be independent of energy if the magnetic fields between the condensations were very small. The mean leakage time τ_L for escape from the halo would be roughly

$$\tau_L \sim R_h^2/\lambda c \,, \tag{2.20}$$

where R_h ($\approx 5\cdot 10^{22}$ cm) is the radius of the halo and λ is the mean free path for the Brownian motion. The appropriate value of λ to be used to calculate τ_L is very uncertain. In the galactic disk the mean distance between gas clouds is ~ 100 parsec; λ for the halo is probably larger than this. Taking $\lambda = 1$ kparsec we calculate $\tau_L \sim 3\cdot 10^{15}$ s.

In a leakage process the energy of the electron is not lost gradually; instead essentially the *total* energy of the particle is lost (to the intergalactic medium) instantaneously. The *equivalent* loss rate is then

$$-\langle \mathrm{d}\gamma_e/\mathrm{d}t\rangle_L = \gamma_e/\tau_L \,, \tag{2.21}$$

and this quantity is plotted in Fig. 1 for $\tau_L = 3\cdot 10^{15}$ s.

2·4. *Electron production and energy losses in the intergalactic medium.*

2·4.1. The calculation of processes in the intergalactic medium is made difficult by our lack of knowledge of the astronomical parameters such as the gas density and magnetic field. Here we shall present results for *assumed* values of the parameters. The calculated production rates and energy losses are simply related to the parameters and can be easily revised when better astronomical data are available. Actually, it may be that some additional knowledge of these poorly known data may be gained from further interpretation of the high-energy cosmic-photon experiments.

As mentioned earlier, we assume a universal cosmic-ray flux. The pion and electron production rates are then proportional to the intergalactic gas density and this gas is very likely to be predominantly hydrogen. Observationally, the upper limit to the intergalactic density of *atomic* hydrogen is [18] $\sim 10^{-5}$ cm^{-3}; the amount of *ionized* hydrogen is unknown. The usually *assumed* total density of intergalactic hydrogen is $\langle n_H\rangle \sim 10^{-5}$ cm^{-3}; this is the so-called cosmological (*) value and is the figure which we shall adopt. Also, we shall

(*) Several cosmological theories, including HOYLE's formulation of the steady-state theory, lead to values of this order for the mean density in the universe. One can arrive at this result by simply setting $E_0 + V = 0$, where E_0 ($= Mc^2$; M is the « mass of the universe ») is the rest energy of the universe, and V ($\sim -GM^2/R$; R is the « radius of the universe » or Hubble radius) is the gravitational energy. The resulting mean density is about two orders of magnitude greater than the observed smeared out density ($\sim 3\cdot 10^{-31}$ g/cm^3) from galaxies. The bulk of the matter in the universe is then attributed to the uncondensed intergalactic gas.

assume that the intergalactic hydrogen is fully ionized. We adopt 10^{-7} gauss for the mean intergalactic magnetic field. Certainly the intergalactic medium must have some, if only random, magnetic field. The intergalactic radiation field can be estimated with some reliability. The contribution from all galaxies in the universe results in a radiation field similar to the galactic (halo) field but diluted by about a factor of ten. Thus we take $\langle \varrho_r \rangle = 10^{-14}$ erg/cm³ and, again, $\bar{\varepsilon}_r = 3$ eV.

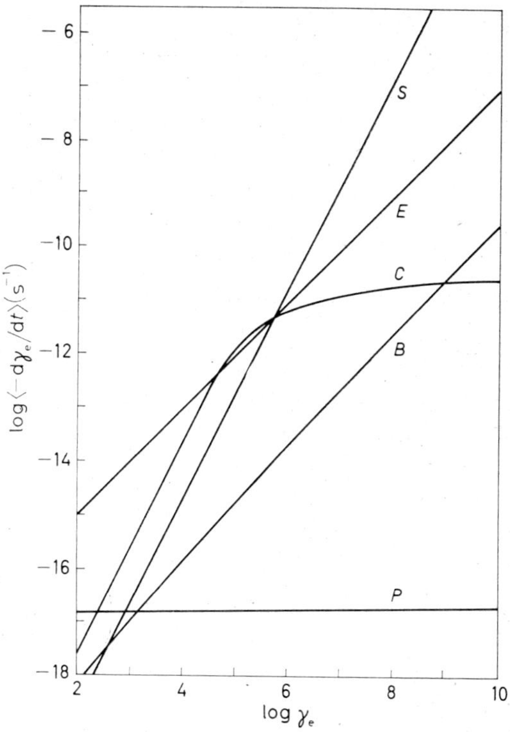

Fig. 2. – Electron energy loss rate in the intergalactic medium by synchrotron emission (S), cosmic expansion (E), Compton scattering (C), bremsstrahlung (B), and excitation of plasma oscillations (P).

Assuming the above values for the gas density, magnetic field, and radiation density in the intergalactic medium the various processes can be calculated readily by employing the relations given in Sect. 2·3 for galactic processes. However, for the bremsstrahlung contribution one must include the effects of *electron-electron* bremsstrahlung B_{ee} [14] as well as the contribution from B_{ep}. Since the cross-section for high-energy B_{ee} is approximately equal to that for B_{ep}, and since $n_e = n_p$ for the assumed fully ionized intergalactic medium, the total bremsstrahlung loss $-\langle d\gamma_e/dt \rangle_B$ is given by simply twice the expression (2.12) with $\langle n \rangle = 10^{-5}$ cm⁻³ (*). The « ionization losses » for the fully ionized intergalactic medium actually correspond to production of plasma oscillations. The associated expression for the electron energy loss at high energies reduces to [19]:

$$-\left\langle \frac{d\gamma_e}{dt} \right\rangle_P = 4\pi r_0^2 c \langle n \rangle \ln \frac{2 m_e c^2 \gamma_e}{\hbar \omega_p}, \tag{2.22}$$

(*) Although $B_{ee} \approx B_{ep}$ for high *relativistic* electrons, for *nonrelativistic* electrons $B_{ee} \ll B_{ep}$. Essentially, this is because the photon emission by the nonrelativistic system results from the dipole moment formed by the e-p system.

where $\omega_p(=[4\pi e^2\langle n\rangle/m_e]^{\frac{1}{2}})$ is the plasma frequency. The result is plotted in Fig. 2.

For the intergalactic medium one should consider another « effective » energy loss process. The expansion of the universe results in an effective energy loss for the electrons in a given volume of

$$-\langle \mathrm{d}\gamma_e/\mathrm{d}t\rangle = \gamma_e/\tau_E\,, \tag{2.23}$$

where τ_E is the characteristic expansion time given by $\frac{1}{3}H^{-1}\sim 10^{17}$ s ($H=$ Hubble constant). The factor $\frac{1}{3}$ takes into account the fact that the expansion is three-dimensional, that is, H^{-1} is the characteristic time for the one-dimensional expansion. The effective energy loss due to expansion is plotted in Fig. 2 for $\tau_E=10^{17}$ s, along with the energy losses due to bremsstrahlung, synchrotron radiation, and Compton scattering.

2·5. *The electron energy spectrum in the halo and intergalactic medium.* – Here we consider the electron spectrum which results from production (via π-μ-e decay) in nuclear collisions of cosmic rays and from the various loss processes. Let $n_e(\gamma_e)\,\mathrm{d}\gamma_e$ denote the number of electrons per cm³ with energies within $m_e c^2\,\mathrm{d}\gamma_e$. The spectral electron density $n_e(\gamma_e)$ satisfies a continuity equation in γ_e (energy) space:

$$\frac{\partial n_e(\gamma_e)}{\partial t}+\frac{\partial}{\partial\gamma_e}\left(n_e(\gamma_e)\,\frac{\mathrm{d}\gamma_e}{\mathrm{d}t}\right)=\sum_i q_i(\gamma_e)\,. \tag{2.24}$$

In eq. (2.24) the terms on the right-hand side (r.h.s.) represent *sources* and *sinks* of high-energy electrons corresponding to production, annihilation, and to processes leading to a sudden loss of a large fraction of the energy of the electron; terms representing leakage out of the halo or the expansion of the universe would also be included on the r.h.s. The factor $\mathrm{d}\gamma_e/\mathrm{d}t$ represents the *total* gradual energy loss from processes described earlier. We shall consider steady-state conditions, so that $\partial n_e(\gamma_e)/\partial t=0$.

2·5.1. Electron spectrum in the galactic halo. From Fig. 1 we see that for $\gamma_e\leqslant 10^4$ (region I) the effective energy loss is primarily by leakage from the halo and the continuity equation reduces to

$$0=q_e(\gamma_e)-n_e(\gamma_e)/\tau_L\,, \tag{2.25}$$

where $q_e(\gamma_e)$ is the production spectrum given by eq. (2.8) and is of the form $k_e\gamma_e^{-\Gamma_\pi}$, and τ_L is the leakage time. Thus, for $\gamma_e\leqslant 10^4$, $n_e(\gamma_e)$ is of the form

$$n_e^{(\mathrm{I})}(\gamma_e)=K_e^{(\mathrm{I})}\gamma_e^{-\Gamma_\pi}\,,\qquad K_e^{(\mathrm{I})}=\tau_L k_e\,. \tag{2.26}$$

The electron spectrum in region I is essentially the same as the production spectrum, that is, the electrons escape from the galaxy without losing an appreciable amount of their original production energy.

For $\gamma_e \gg 10^5$ (region II) the electrons lose their energy primarily by synchrotron radiation for which $d\gamma_e/dt = -b\gamma_e^2$, and the continuity equation reduces to

$$-b\frac{\partial}{\partial\gamma_e}\left(\gamma_e^2 n_e(\gamma_e)\right) = q_e(\gamma_e) = k_e\gamma_e^{-\Gamma_\pi}. \tag{2.27}$$

The solution is then

$$n_e^{(II)}(\gamma_e) = K_e^{(II)}\gamma_e^{-(\Gamma_\pi+1)}, \qquad K_e^{(II)} = k_e/b(\Gamma_\pi - 1). \tag{2.28}$$

With the assumed values for the parameters and with k_e computed from eqs. (2.7) and (2.8) the calculated spectral electron density is shown in Fig. 3. The solutions for $n_e(\gamma_e)$ in regions I and II were joined smoothly.

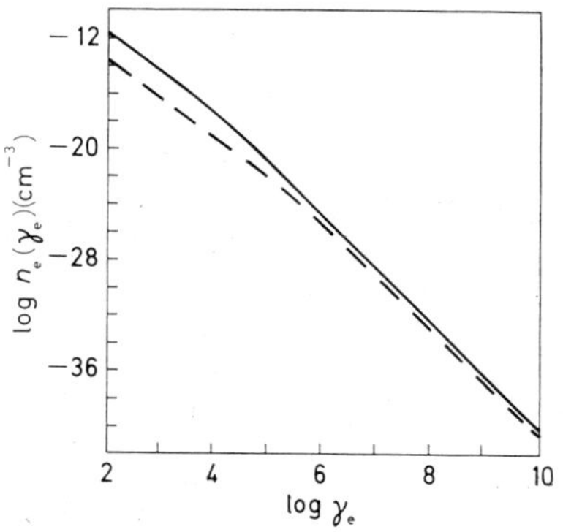

Fig. 3. – Calculated energy spectrum of relativistic electrons in the galactic halo (———) and in the intergalactic medium (— — —).

2'5.2. Electron spectrum in the intergalactic medium. The approximate spectrum of the intergalactic electrons is calculated by similar procedures. We approximate the effective energy loss for $\gamma_e \ll 10^5$ (region I, see Fig. 1) by the expansion loss and for $\gamma_e \gg 10^6$ (region II) by synchrotron losses. The electron spectrum in the two regions is then given by expressions similar to eqs. (2.25) and (2.26) for the halo, essentially with τ_L replaced by τ_E. The calculated spectrum, with the curves for the two regions joined smoothly, is shown in Fig. 3 for the previously stated assumed values of the astronomical parameters.

2'6. *High-energy photon flux from various processes.*

2'6.1. Absorption of high-energy photons. The *absorption* of cosmic photons is important in certain energy ranges. For X-ray photons traversing matter in the plane of the galaxy absorption by the photoelectric effect in various elements is appreciable at the longer wavelengths. In Fig. 4 we give the optical thickness as a function of wavelength for a path of 1 kparsec in neutral atomic gaseous matter of « cosmic » composition with $n(H) = 1\ cm^{-3}$.

The curve with the total contribution from all elements is given as well as that including only hydrogen and helium. The discontinuity in the total at 23 Å is due to the onset of K-shell photoionization of oxygen. The curves have a slope of approximately 3 due to the (approximate) λ^3 dependence of photoelectric absorption, and are taken from the results of STROM and STROM [20].

Except for the pronounced edge due to oxygen, we have smoothed over the data which show several other small jumps due to the onset of photoionization edges. Since the distance to the galactic center is ~ 10 kparsec, and over this distance $\langle n(\mathrm{H})\rangle \sim 1\ \mathrm{cm}^{-3}$, we see that $\tau > 1$ for $\lambda \geqslant 5$ Å. For photons traversing intergalactic matter the path length is $\sim 5\cdot 10^{27}$ cm, so that $\tau > 1$ for $\lambda > 10$ Å if $\langle n(\mathrm{H})\rangle > 10^{-6}\ \mathrm{cm}^{-3}$ (here a similar « cosmic » abundance has been assumed). A density of $\langle n(\mathrm{H})\rangle \sim \sim 10^{-5}\ \mathrm{cm}^{-3}$ is a reasonable value to assume for intergalactic space; however, this material is also likely to be composed essentially of pure hydrogen, or perhaps hydrogen and helium; material with this composition would be ionized if the temperature of intergalactic matter were $\geqslant 1.5\cdot 10^4$ °K (hydrogen), and $\geqslant 6\cdot 10^4$ °K (helium). The absorption by the ionized matter would be negligible.

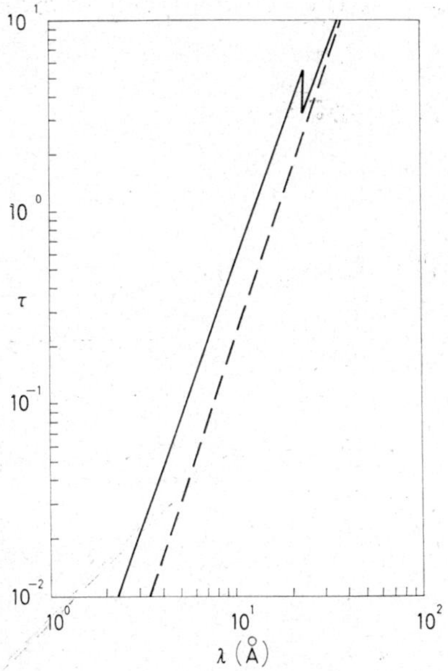

Fig. 4. – Optical thickness τ as a function of wavelength λ in the X-ray range for photons traversing a distance of 1 kparsec in which the matter is gaseous and atomic at a cosmic abundance with $n(\mathrm{H}) = 1\ \mathrm{cm}^{-3}$: —— total; – – – H+He.

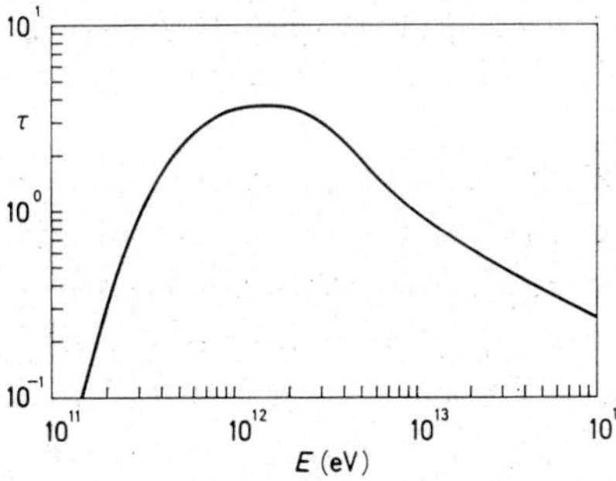

Fig. 5. – Optical thickness τ as a function of photon energy E at very high energies for photons traversing $5\cdot 10^{27}$ cm of intergalactic matter in which the radiation field is Planckian with $kT = 0.5$ eV with a total energy density of 0.01 eV/cm³.

The only other instance where absorption of high-energy cosmic photons is appreciable is when very-high-energy photons travel distances comparable with the classical radius of the universe. As NIKISHOV [21] has shown, absorption by pair production in photon-photon collisions ($\gamma+\gamma \to e^+ + e^-$) prevents us from seeing to the « outer edge » of the universe in photons of energy $\sim (10^{12} \div 10^{13})$ eV. For photons of this energy the cross-section for pair production in collisions with the thermal stellar photons in the intergalactic radiation field has a maximum. The intergalactic radiation field in the thermal stellar range ($\sim$ eV) is due to emission from galaxies. NIKISHOV calculated the optical thickness for a black-body radiation field of temperature $kT = 0.5$ eVand total energy density $0.1\ \text{eV/cm}^3$ out to the distance of *Cyg* A ($R_C = 6.6 \cdot 10^{26}$ cm). We feel that the energy density which he employed may be on the high side and shall give the results for a radiation field one-tenth as large but for a distance of $R = 5 \cdot 10^{27}$ cm (the « cosmological cut-off »). The associated optical thickness is shown in Fig. 5 as a function of photon energy. We should like to emphasize again the uncertainty in the intergalactic radiation field and thus in the magnitude of the effect. Because of this and other uncertainties we shall ignore absorption in the remainder of this lecture; however, it should still be kept in mind that it could be appreciable for certain photon energies and could affect the high-energy cosmic-photon spectrum.

2·6.2. Photon spectra. The photon production spectrum by a given process may be computed from the electron (energy) spectrum $n_e(\gamma_e)$ and the expression for the photon emission spectrum by this process as a function of γ_e. Denote the photon energy by ε. The energy loss by an electron of energy E_e in time dt due to the emission of dN photons of energy within $d\varepsilon$ is

$$-\,dE_e \equiv \varepsilon\, dN = f(E_e, \varepsilon)\, d\varepsilon\, dt\,, \tag{2.29}$$

where $f(E_e, \varepsilon)$ is the emission spectrum. The number of photons emitted per cm³ per second per interval of ε by an electron spectrum $n_e(\gamma_e)$ would then be

$$\frac{dn}{dt\, d\varepsilon} \equiv \frac{dn(\varepsilon)}{dt} = \int d\gamma_e\, n_e(\gamma_e)\, \frac{dN}{d\varepsilon\, dt}\,. \tag{2.30}$$

We now approximate the emission spectrum by a δ-function at the characteristic photon energy ε_c:

$$\frac{dN}{d\varepsilon\, dt} = \frac{1}{\varepsilon}\, f(E_e, \varepsilon) \to -\,\frac{m_e c^2}{\varepsilon}\, \frac{d\gamma_e}{dt}\, \delta(\varepsilon - \varepsilon_c)\,, \tag{2.31}$$

where $\varepsilon_c = \varepsilon_c(\gamma_e)$. The photon spectral *flux* due to emission along a line of sight of path $\int ds = R$ would be

$$j(\varepsilon) = \frac{dJ}{d\varepsilon} = \int \frac{dn(\varepsilon)}{dt}\, ds = \left\langle \frac{dn(\varepsilon)}{dt} \right\rangle R\,. \tag{2.32}$$

The incident-photon spectra from both the galaxy and the intergalactic medium are readily calculated from the eqs. (2.30), (2.31), and (2.32) using the derived electron spectra $n_e(\gamma_e)$ and the expressions for the energy losses $-\langle d\gamma_e/dt\rangle$. For synchrotron emission $\varepsilon_c \approx \hbar\omega_L\gamma_e^2$; for bremsstrahlung $\varepsilon_c \approx m_e c^2\gamma_e$; for the Compton process from electrons with $\gamma_e \ll m_e c^2/\bar{\varepsilon}_r$, $\varepsilon_c \approx \bar{\varepsilon}_r\gamma_e^2$; for the Compton process from electrons with $\gamma_e \gg m_e c^2/\bar{\varepsilon}_r$, $\varepsilon_c \approx m_e c^2\gamma_e$.

Taking a path length $R = 5\cdot10^{22}$ cm (the radius of the galactic halo) for the galaxy and a path length $R = 5\cdot10^{27}$ cm (half the Hubble radius) for the intergalactic medium, the resulting photon spectra are shown in Fig. 6.

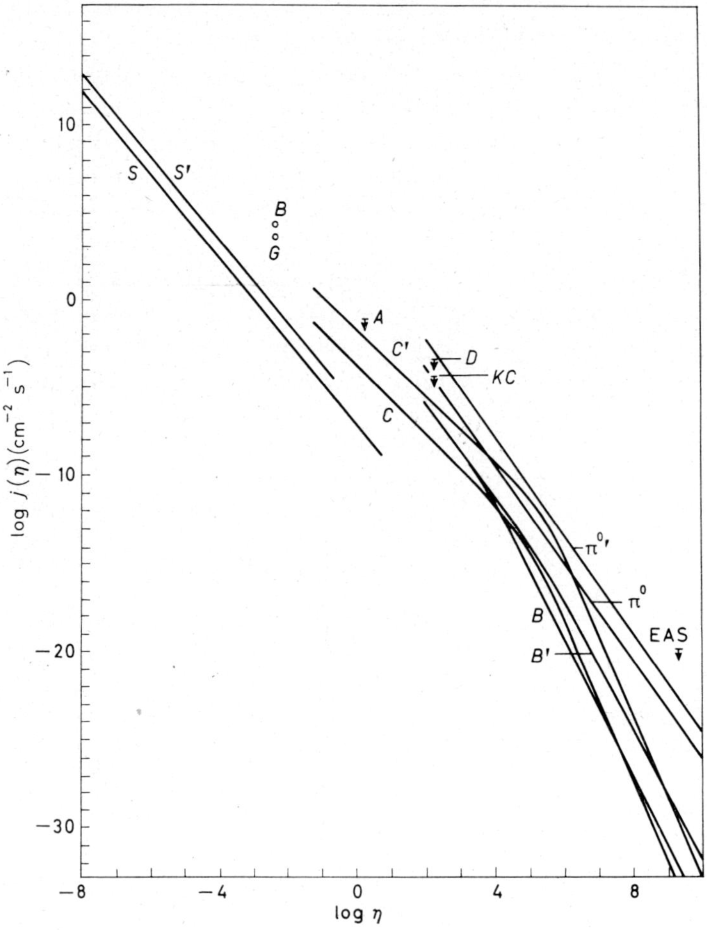

Fig. 6. – Calculated high-energy photon background fluxes from synchrotron radiation, Compton scattering, bremsstrahlung, and π^0-decay. The unprimed-designated spectra represent the galactic contributions and the primed denote the spectra from the intergalactic medium. Observational points are denoted by circles and arrows (limits). The letters next to the points refer to the observers (see Table I).

The photon energy η is in units of $m_e c^2$, that is, $\eta = \varepsilon/m_e c^2$, $j(\eta) = dj/d\eta$. The spectra are for synchrotron radiation, bremsstrahlung, Compton scattering, and π^0-decay. The spectra from π^0-decay are calculated directly from the pion production spectrum which is of the form $q_\pi(\gamma_\pi) = k_\pi \gamma_\pi^{-\Gamma_\pi}$ [eq. (2.7)]. One-third of the pions produced are π^0's, and each π^0 gives two photons of mean energy $\frac{1}{2}\gamma_\pi m_\pi c^2$. The π^0-decay photon production spectrum is then approximately

$$dn^0/d\eta\, dt \approx \tfrac{2}{3} k_\pi (2m_e/m_\pi)^{-(\Gamma_\pi - 1)} \eta^{-\Gamma_\pi}\,. \tag{2.33}$$

The galactic photon fluxes plotted in Fig. 6 are averaged over all directions; the average magnitude of the flux *per steradian* is $1/4\pi$ times the flux in Fig. 6. Actually, the photon flux per steradian from bresstrahlung and π^0-decay would be greatest in the direction along the galactic plane where the production and interaction with the gas takes place. The synchrotron radiation and Compton photons would also show a moderate anisotropy due, at least, to our off-center position in the galaxy. We have not computed the spectrum from positron annihilation. The cross-section for direct positron (energy: $\gamma_e m_e c^2$) annihilation with an electron at rest is, at high energies [14]

$$\sigma_a \approx \pi r_0^2 \frac{\ln 2\gamma_e}{\gamma_e}\,, \tag{2.34}$$

so that the bremsstrahlung spectrum dominates the annihilation spectrum by a factor $\sim \alpha\gamma_e$ for $\gamma_e \geq 10^2$. At lower positron energies ($\gamma_e < 10^2$) ionization losses are dominant (see Fig. 1) and the positron comes essentially to rest before annihilating, giving two photons each of energy $\eta \approx 1$.

To calculate the photon flux from the intergalactic medium we have taken essentially a static Euclidean universe cut-off at $R = 5 \cdot 10^{27}$ cm. It is natural to inquire into the effects of the expansion (differential red shift) and detailed structure of the universe on the resulting photon spectra. It can be shown that only if the photon production spectrum is a *power law*, will the observed flux show the same shape spectrum (power law with the same index), independent of the structure (including expansion) of the universe. This results essentially because the Doppler-shifted photon energy is *proportional* to the unshifted energy. As a result, our calculated spectra, which are of the power-law type in different energy regions, depend on the detailed structure of the universe only as far as the energy at which the spectra change their slope is concerned (at $\eta \sim 10^5$ for B and C, Fig. 6). However, the shift in this critical energy is likely to be less than an order of magnitude.

We should like to emphasize again that the calculated photon fluxes are only approximate, and this should be kept in mind when we attempt possible interpretations of the observations. In particular, our treatment of meson production in cosmic-ray collisions is very rough, especially at low energies where the Fermi theory should be invalid. Moreover, as mentioned earlier, our assumed cosmic-ray spectrum is too large at the low-energy end; this effect alone would produce a bend in the calculated photon fluxes at low energies such that the low-energy ends of the curves in Fig. 6 should be reduced by about an order of magnitude.

2·7. *Comparison with observations.*

2·7.1. General discussion. The experimental points exhibited in Fig. 6 correspond to the observed cosmic-background photon fluxes as summarized in Table I below (*). The observations are in essentially four energy regions and are over ranges such that $\Delta\eta/\bar{\eta} \sim 1$. There is, of course, another

TABLE I. – *The observed high-energy cosmic-photon spectrum.*

Author	Designation in Fig. 6	Energy	$\bar{\eta}$	$j(\bar{\eta})$ ($cm^{-2}\,s^{-1}$)
GIACCONI *et al.* [22]	*G*	$\sim(2\div3)$ keV	$5\cdot10^{-3}$	$4\cdot10^{3}$
BOWYER *et al.* [23]	*B*	$\sim(2\div3)$ keV	$5\cdot10^{-3}$	$2\cdot10^{4}$
ARNOLD *et al.* [24]	*A*	~1 MeV	2	$\leqslant0.08$
KRAUSHAAR and CLARK [25]	*K-C*	~100 MeV	200	$\leqslant4\cdot10^{-5}$
DUTHIE *et al.* [26]	*D*	~100 MeV	200	$\leqslant3\cdot10^{-4}$
FIRKOWSKI *et al.* [27] SUGA *et al.* [28]	EAS	$\sim10^{15}$ eV	$2\cdot10^{9}$	$\leqslant10^{-20}$

range of energies where cosmic photons are observed, namely, the radio range. The radio spectrum is represented fairly well by the low-energy range (not included in Fig. 6) of the calculated synchrotron radiation spectrum. We shall return to this question of the radio spectrum shortly.

We now consider the possibilities of interpreting any of the observed photon

(*) In this discussion we have taken the observational values given in Table I at their face value. However, it appears now that, while the background X-ray fluxes have been detected at the levels quoted, the γ-ray results are more uncertain and should all be treated as upper limits to the fluxes which may be present. That we are, therefore, only discussing possible explanations of hypothetical γ-ray fluxes in this section is to be emphasized.

fluxes in terms of the various calculated spectra represented in Fig. 6. First consider the X-ray observations. The flux $j(\eta)$ for point X (Fig. 6) is five orders of magnitude above the curve S' and six orders of magnitude above S. This discrepancy is, in our opinion, sufficient to rule out the interpretation of the point X as due to synchrotron radiation, at least if the high-energy electrons are of a secondary origin. The curves C and C' do not extend to lower energies because we have considered electrons with $\gamma_e \geqslant 10^2$, and in our approximate calculations have assumed that $\langle\varepsilon\rangle_C = \gamma_e^2\bar{\varepsilon}_r$, giving $\langle\varepsilon\rangle_C \geqslant 30$ keV However, due to the distribution of thermal photon energies there is, of course, a *distribution* of photon energies which can be produced by an electron of given energy. Moreover, for a pion decaying at rest there is still an appreciable probability for a low-energy (say, $\gamma_e \sim 30$) electron being produced. Therefore, the Compton spectra C and C' certainly do extend to the X-ray region. In spite of this, we do not believe that the X-ray point can be due to the Compton process, if the electrons responsible for the scattering have a secondary origin. For, as previously mentioned, the actual cosmic-ray spectrum which produces the low-energy pions and finally electrons is smaller by about a factor of 10 than the power-law spectrum used to compute the curves in Fig. 6. A realistic extrapolation of, for example, the curve C' to the X-ray region would still fall about three orders of magnitude below the observational point B.

FELTEN and MORRISON [17] suggested that not only the X-ray flux, but also the photon fluxes at ~ 1 MeV and ~ 100 MeV (see Table I), are due to the Compton process in the intergalactic medium. They suggested that the sources of the high-energy intergalactic electrons are the strong radio sources. We can see from the curve C' in Fig. 6 that the intergalactic spectral density $n_e(\gamma_e)$ required to explain the results is about $(20 \div 30)$ times as large as the density which we estimated to result from secondary production in intergalactic space. The Compton spectrum must, of course, extrapolate to the X-ray region and this precludes a secondary origin for the electrons, unless they are produced by a cosmic-ray spectrum which has a much higher intensity at low energies than that for cosmic-rays observed at the earth. We cannot rule out the Felten-Morrison hypothesis; in fact, elementary considerations of the necessary number of sources (radio galaxies) of high-energy electrons in the universe suggest that the hypothesis is reasonable quantitatively. As we have shown, for our galaxy this relatively low-energy part of the electron spectrum, that is, the radio electrons, does escape from the galaxy into the intergalactic medium before losing an appreciable amount of its initial energy. We shall show presently that, if the Felten-Morrison idea is correct, the amount of synchrotron radiation which these electrons would produce places an upper limit to the intergalactic magnetic field.

Regarding the possible interpretation of the observations at 1 MeV (A, Fig. 6), we see that the observed flux is about an order of magnitude above the calculated curve C'. In view of the inaccuracies involved this «agreement» within an order of magnitude indicates that Compton scattering by secondary-produced intergalactic electrons provides a possible explanation for the observed photon flux at 1 MeV. Of the calculated processes represented in Fig. 6 this appears to be the only possible association with the observations at 1 MeV. The spectrum from π^0-decay certainly does not extend below $\log \eta = 2$ ($E \approx 50$ MeV), and the bremsstrahlung spectra B and B' must be less steep below $\log \eta = 2$ since, although the energetic secondary electrons can emit a bremsstrahlung spectrum extending to the lower energies, the corresponding bremsstrahlung photon would then carry away only a small fraction of the electron's energy, and the photon production process would be less efficient.

It would appear from Fig. 6 that the ~ 100 MeV photon flux which KRAUSHAAR and CLARK first reported could be accounted for by π^0's produced in the galaxy or in the intergalactic medium. However, our calculated π^0 spectrum, based on the Fermi theory, is very unsatisfactory at the low-energy end. For low-energy p-p collisions it is primarily π^+ mesons that are produced and a more accurate treatment of meson production than our extrapolation of the Fermi theory must be employed. Now, in the Kraushaar-Clark observation the photon flux observed included essentially the whole spectrum from decays of π^0's of all energies, and most of the π^0's produced are of low energy. By employing the available data on meson production by incident protons of energy less than 10 GeV and the observed low-energy cosmic-ray spectrum, POLLACK and FAZIO [3] have computed the rate of production of pions by p-p, p-α, and α-p collisions per hydrogen nucleus as the rate of production of π^0 decay and positron annihilation (after $\pi^+ \to \mu^+ \to e^+$ decay) photons:

$$\pi^0\text{-decay: } q^0 \approx 1\cdot 10^{-26}\ \text{photons/s}\cdot\text{sr}\,,$$

$$\text{positron annihilation: } q^+ \approx 2\cdot 10^{-26}\ \text{photons/s}\cdot\text{sr}\,.$$

The π^0-decay photons have energies above about 70 MeV and the galactic positrons annihilation photons have energies of about 0.5 MeV, since the positrons come essentially to rest before annihilating. The π^0-decay photon flux from a region of density $\langle n_{\text{H}}\rangle$ of extent R would then be $4\pi q^0 \langle n_{\text{H}}\rangle R$ and in this manner we estimate fluxes of $2\cdot 10^{-4}$ photons/cm$^2\cdot$s and $6\cdot 10^{-3}$ photons/cm$^2\cdot$s from the galaxy and intergalactic medium respectively; the galactic flux is a directional average. The Kraushaar and Clark flux is roughly the same as the calculated contribution from the intergalactic medium while the flux observed by DUTHIE *et al.* is an order of magnitude larger. The origin of the discrepancy between the Kraushaar-Clark and Duthie *et al.* observations may lie in the latter's extrapolation of their balloon observations to zero atmospheric depth. At any rate, it is clear that an upper limit to essentially the product of the intergalactic cosmic-ray flux and gas density is established by these observations. The calculated intensity of the positron annihilation line using Pollack and Fazio's value of q^+ and again the « standard » intergalactic gas density (10^{-5} cm^{-3}) is $1\cdot10^{-2}$ photons/cm$^2\cdot$s which is just below the upper limit of $1.5\cdot10^{-2}$ photons/cm$^2\cdot$s established by ARNOLD *et al.* However, *intergalactic* relativistic positrons do not slow down before annihilating (see Fig. 2) and would not produce a 0.51 MeV line but rather an annihilation *continuum* extending to higher energies.

The point denoted by EAS in Fig. 6 results from observations of *extensive air showers* [27], [28] in which an abnormally low number of muons was observed, indicating possibly that the shower was initiated by electromagnetic processes rather than by a nuclear collision. If these showers result from primary photons the flux of these photons would be $\sim10^{-3}$ times the flux of cosmic-ray protons at the same energy. The results of these experiments are questionable and may only represent an *upper limit* to the primary cosmic-photon flux at these high energies. In Fig. 6 we see that the EAS point lies 2 or 3 orders of magnitude above the curve corresponding to the decay of high-energy secondary-produced π^0-mesons in the intergalactic medium.

As was mentioned in the footnote at the beginning of this Section, it is necessary to emphasize the preliminary nature of all of these observations of high-energy photons. While the existence of cosmic X-ray sources seems well established, the existence of positive fluxes at higher energies (the $\sim$MeV, 100 MeV, and 10^{15} eV observations) is *not* established. The fluxes given for these higher-energy photons probably should all be taken as upper limits until the observational situation is clarified. For example, the $\sim$MeV observations may be plagued by radioactivity induced in the crystal of the scintillation detector [29].

2'7.2. X-rays from external galaxies. We should like to mention another possible explanation for the observed background flux of X-rays, which we proposed earlier [30]. About 10 discrete sources of X-rays have been observed, and because of their apparent concentration toward the plane of the galaxy, are assumed to be *galactic* and presumably at a galactic distance $R_g\sim10$ kparsec (see Sect. **3**). Since our galaxy is believed to be a normal « average » galaxy, one would expect that this is a general characteristic of galaxies, so that external galaxies have X-ray luminosities L_X not too different from that of our own galaxy. If the average X-ray luminosity for galaxies is $\langle L_X\rangle_g$, the isotropic background flux per steradian observed at the earth would be roughly

$$f_X \approx \langle L_X\rangle_g n_g R_c/4\pi \,, \tag{2.35}$$

where n_g ($\sim 3\cdot 10^{-75}$ cm^{-3}) is the number density of galaxies, and R_c ($\sim 5\cdot 10^{27}$ cm) is a cosmological cut-off distance. Neglecting absorption, the total flux received from sources in our Galaxy is

$$F_X = \sum_i L_X^{(i)}/4\pi r_i^2 \approx L_X/4\pi R_g^2 , \tag{2.36}$$

where L_X $(= \sum_i L_X^{(i)})$ is the total X-ray luminosity of the galaxy. Assuming $\langle L_X \rangle_G \approx L_X$, we find

$$f_X \approx F_X n_g R_g^2 R_c . \tag{2.37}$$

The total flux from all galactic sources is (see Sect. 3) about $F_X \approx 33$ photons/cm$^2\cdot$s, so that we estimate from eq. (2.37) $f_X \approx 0.5$ photons/cm$^2\cdot$s$\cdot$sr, which is about an order of magnitude smaller than the observed flux. In view of the uncertainties and the assumptions involved, agreement within an order of magnitude must be regarded as satisfactory. Clearly, we make no assumption as to the production mechanism of these X-rays, but only that our galaxy is « typical ».

2·7.3. Radio emission. We conclude our discussion here with a few remarks about the observed cosmic *radio* spectrum from the galactic halo, which is undoubtedly due to synchrotron radiation by relativistic electrons. We attempt to answer the question as to whether the electron spectrum can be accounted for by secondary production by cosmic rays. This problem has been considered by a number of authors in a manner similar to our treatment. However, our view differs somewhat in that we consider leakage from the halo as the primary loss process for the radio electrons (*).

If the energy radiated per second per interval of frequency by an electron of energy $\gamma_e m_e c^2$ is $P(\nu, \gamma_e)$, the spectral intensity (erg/s$\cdot$cm$^2\cdot$sr$\cdot$frequency interval) of radiation received from a direction $\boldsymbol{r}$ is

$$I_\nu = \mathrm{d}E/\mathrm{d}t\,\mathrm{d}A\,\mathrm{d}\Omega\,\mathrm{d}\nu = (4\pi)^{-1}\iint n_e(\gamma_e)\,P(\nu, \gamma_e)\,\mathrm{d}\gamma_e\,\mathrm{d}\boldsymbol{r} , \tag{2.38}$$

(*) Our conclusions also differ. We conclude that the spectrum of radio electrons in the galactic halo can be accounted for by the production (via π-μ-e decay) by cosmic-ray nuclear collisions in the galactic plane and subsequent diffusion to the halo. However, GINZBURG and SYROVATSKY [31] conclude, by a similar analysis, that the halo radio electrons *cannot* be explained in this manner, and that the expected secondary electron spectrum is smaller by one or two orders of magnitude than the value derived from radio observations. We feel that the astronomical data are not known sufficiently accurately to *expect* agreement within an order of magnitude. Moreover, we do not understand the results given in Fig. 5 and 6 of the paper by GINZBURG and SYROVATSKY; it appears to us that the electron spectra computed for the higher assumed mean galactic gas density n should be proportionally *larger*, offsetting the small effect of increased collisional energy loss.

where $n_e(\gamma_e)\,d\gamma_e$ is the differential electron density. For an electron spectrum $n_e(\gamma_e) = K_e \gamma_e^{-\Gamma_e}$ the intensity I_ν may be computed approximately by taking $P(\nu, \gamma_e)$ to be equal to the expression (2.13) for dE_e/dt times a δ-function $\delta(\nu - \nu_L \gamma_e^2)$ at frequency where $P(\nu, \gamma_e)$ is a maximum. Assuming a constant magnetic field H and a path length $\int dr = R_h$, the halo radius, we obtain a familiar result:

$$I_\nu \approx (12\pi)^{-1} c r_0^2 K_e R_h H^2 \nu_L^{(\Gamma_e-3)/2} \nu^{-(\Gamma_e-1)/2}; \tag{2.39}$$

a power law spectrum with exponent $\alpha \equiv (\Gamma_e - 1)/2$ is also obtained using the exact expression for $P(\nu, \gamma_e)$. The constant K_e may be determined by the observed value (500 °K) of the radio brightness temperature $T_b = I_\nu \lambda^2/2k$ at 100 MHz in the direction of the galactic pole. Employing eq. (2.39) with $H = 3 \cdot 10^{-6}$ gauss, $R_h = 5 \cdot 10^{22}$ cm, $\Gamma_e = 2.8$ ($\alpha = 0.9$), we obtain $K_e = 1 \cdot 10^{-6}$ cm^{-3}. This number is to be compared with the value calculated from the production and loss process. By eqs. (2.7), (2.8), and (2.25) we get for the calculated K_e:

$$K_e \approx (8\pi/9) A_\pi^2 (m_\pi/4m_e)^{\Gamma_e-1} K_p \langle n_H \rangle \tau_L \,. \tag{2.40}$$

Using the previously assumed values $K_p = 100$ cm^{-2} s^{-1}, $\langle n_H \rangle = 0.03$ cm^{-3}, $\tau_L = 3 \cdot 10^{15}$ s we calculate $K_e = 1 \cdot 10^{-6}$ cm^{-3}; the agreement with the radio value is fortuitous. Actually, the observed radio spectrum has an index $\alpha \approx 0.7 \div 0.8$, and we have adopted the «theoretical» value 0.9. This discrepancy may not be serious; the observed slightly flatter spectrum could be accounted for by a slight variation with γ_e of the effective value of τ_L. For example, if τ_L were slightly shorter for the low-energy electrons (caused, perhaps by another energy-loss process at low energy) the smaller value of α and Γ_e could be understood. A more accurate treatment of the production spectrum could also indicate a smaller value for α and Γ_e. Further, we might mention that with our assumed values of the parameters (density, magnetic field, etc.) for the intergalactic medium, the calculated synchrotron intensity in the radio region from the intergalactic medium is comparable to that from the halo, while, as is seen from Fig. 6, the calculated intergalactic synchrotron radiation is actually greater by ~ 10 at the high-energy end. Admittedly, our calculations are based on many assumptions, but these assumptions may well be valid, and much of the observed nonthermal radio background radiation may be coming from the intergalactic medium (*).

It is of interest to consider the requirements on the intergalactic magnetic field if the Felten-Morrison idea is correct. From Fig. 6 we see that for the

(*) Recently this view has also been expressed by some radio astronomers, for example, J. E. Baldwin at the *Second Texas Symposium on Relativistic Astrophysics* (proceedings to the published by the University of Chicago Press).

curve C' to pass near the points X, A, and K-C, the value of K_e must be larger by a factor ~ 30, or must be $\approx 3 \cdot 10^{-7}$ cm^{-3}. One can then compute the intergalactic magnetic field, by eq. (2.39) with $R_h \to 5 \cdot 10^{27}$ cm, $\frac{1}{2}$ the Hubble radius, necessary to produce a brightness temperature of 500 °K at 100 MHz. One then finds $1 \cdot 10^{-8}$ gauss for this magnetic field. Thus, if the Felten-Morrison idea is correct, the intergalactic magnetic field must be less than $1 \cdot 10^{-8}$ gauss.

Finally, we should like to mention some further checks on the calculated spectrum of the halo electrons. Recently the French-Italian group (AGRINIER *et al.* [8]) has reported the measurement of a primary cosmic-ray electron flux of $6.6 \cdot 10^{-4}$ particles/cm$^2 \cdot$s$\cdot$sr for $E_e > 4.5$ GeV, corresponding also to an electron/proton cosmic-ray ratio of $1 \cdot 10^{-2}$. This measurement of the primary electron flux at fairly high energies is probably more reliable than results of measurements at lower energies which are influenced by solar activity. The measured flux is to be compared with that from the calculated spectra above 4.5 GeV$(\gamma_e > \gamma_0 = 4.5\ \text{GeV}/m_e c^2)$. One finds, with $K_e = 1 \cdot 10^{-6}$ cm^{-3}, $\Gamma_e = 2.8$, a flux

$$f_e = (4\pi)^{-1} \int_{\gamma_0}^{\infty} c K_e \gamma_e^{-\Gamma_e} \mathrm{d}\gamma_e \approx 1 \cdot 10^{-4}\ \text{particles/cm}^2 \cdot \text{s} \cdot \text{sr}. \tag{2.41}$$

This flux is somewhat smaller than the observed one, but in view of the uncertainties involved in the calculations, agreement within an order of magnitude is all that one could hope for.

Another check on whether the observed cosmic-ray electrons result from secondary production can be made by a measurement of the positron/electron ratio. This has been done by the group at the University of Chicago [8], who conclude that their measurements are inconsistent with the assumption that the bulk of the electron and positron spectrum is a result of secondary production. If indeed electrons and positrons of galactic origin are being observed, this would settle the question. Again, we take the conservative view that the question is still open, since the measured ratio is only off by a factor ~ 2 from the ratio expected on the basis of secondary production.

2'8. *Test of cosmological theories.*

2'8.1. The hot-universe model: bremsstrahlung from the intergalactic medium. GOLD and HOYLE [32] have suggested a cosmological model in which the intergalactic medium is at a very high temperature ($\sim 10^9$ °K). The high temperature is supposed to arise from the ~ 1 MeV electrons which would result after the decay of spontaneously created neutrons as envisioned by the steady-state theory. Galaxy formation within the framework of this model was considered by BURBIDGE, BURBIDGE, and HOYLE [33]. An observational test of this model can be made, since such a hot intergalactic medium would emit thermal bremsstrahlung photons in the X-ray region where observations have been made [23]. For a mean thermal electron energy $\langle E_e \rangle = 50$ keV, and a density $n_e = n_p = 1.2 \cdot 10^{-5}$ cm^{-3} the rate of production of bremsstrahlung photons within the energy range of the observations is about $r_b = 1.17 \cdot 10^{-25}$ photons/cm$^3 \cdot$s [30]. Taking a cut-off radius $R = 5 \cdot 10^{27}$ cm for the universe, one calculates a flux $f_b = r_b R/4\pi \sim 50$ photons/cm$^2 \cdot$s$\cdot$sr to be expected at the earth. This flux is ~ 10 times the observed X-ray background flux and is evidence against the hot-universe model (and the steady-state theory with spontaneous creation of *neutrons*). Actually, if the appropriate intergalactic density to be used is four times the usually adopted $2 \cdot 10^{-29}$ g/cm^3, as suggested by SCIAMA [34], the disagreement with observations is even more violent. In any case it appears that the X-ray observations have established an upper limit of 10^7 °K for the temperature of the intergalactic medium.

2'8.2. Matter and antimatter and the steady-state cosmological theory. The attractive feature of the steady-state theory is its simplicity. The unique feature is a spontaneous creation rate of « new » matter $\mathrm{d}n/\mathrm{d}t \sim 3Hn$, where $n \sim 10^{-5}$ cm^{-3} is the mean matter density in the universe (taken to be the mean hydrogen density in the intergalactic medium) and H is the Hubble constant ($3H \sim 10^{-17}$ s^{-1}). One might expect that in the spontaneous creation process, to conserve baryon and lepton number, particles and antiparticles are created. Since the expansion rate constant $3H$ is about two orders of magnitude greater than the annihilation rate (see below), BURBIDGE and HOYLE [35] suggested the possibility of an appreciable abundance of antimatter in the universe. This idea can be put to a test, since the end products of matter and antimatter annihilation are observable high-energy γ-rays.

Let us suppose that (p, e$^-$) and ($\bar{\mathrm{p}}$, e$^+$) are spontaneously produced and have a steady-state mean number density $n = 10^{-5}$ cm^{-3} and $\bar{\alpha}n$ respectively, where $\bar{\alpha}$ denotes the mean ratio of antimatter to matter (or vice-versa). The electron-positron annihilation cross-section at nonrelativistic energies is [14] $\sigma_a = \pi r_0^2/\beta$, where r_0 is the classical electron radius and $\beta = v/c$. The annihilation rate is then $\mathrm{d}n_a/\mathrm{d}t = \bar{\alpha}n^2\pi r_0^2 c \sim \bar{\alpha} \cdot 10^{-24}$ cm^{-3} s^{-1}, and the expected flux of 0.51 MeV photons from the intergalactic medium out to a distance $R \sim 5 \cdot 10^{27}$ cm is $2R\,\mathrm{d}n_a/\mathrm{d}t \sim \bar{\alpha} \cdot 10^4$ photons/cm$^2 \cdot$s. This can be reconciled with the upper limit of 10^{-2} photons/cm$^2 \cdot$s suggested by ARNOLD *et al.* [24] only if $\bar{\alpha} < 10^{-6}$. This means that if there is appreciable antimatter in the universe, it must be *separated* from matter, so that it cannot annihilate and produce observable γ-radiation.

A limit on the amount of antimatter in the universe can also be provided from an analysis of the γ-ray experiments at higher energies which can detect π^0-decay γ's. In the proton-antiproton annihilation ~ 5 pions are produced, some of which are π^0's which produce γ-rays of energy ~ 100 MeV in their decay. In each p-$\bar{p}$ annihilation about $m_\gamma = 4$ γ-rays are produced. The cross-section for p-$\bar{p}$ annihilation is $\sigma_a' = \sigma_0/\beta$, where $\sigma_0 = 5\cdot 10^{-26}$ cm^2 and βc is the relative velocity [36]. Again setting $n(=10^{-5}$ cm$^{-3})$ and $\bar{\alpha}n$ equal to the matter and antimatter densities respectively, the mean number of γ's produced in the universe per cm^3 is $m_\gamma \bar{\alpha} n^2 \sigma_0 c \sim \bar{\alpha}\cdot 6\cdot 10^{-25}$ cm^{-3} s^{-1}. If this production occurred in the universe out to a distance $R = 5\cdot 10^{27}$ cm, the resulting flux of γ-rays would be consistent with the Kraushaar-Clark experiment only if $\bar{\alpha} < 10^{-6}$—the same limit established from the observed upper limit for the intensity of the cosmic-positron annihilation line. Thus, it appears that in the steady-state cosmology matter and antimatter cannot be treated in comparable amounts in the same region.

Finally, regarding cosmological tests, we should like to mention the recent discussion by GOULD and SCIAMA [37]. They indicate how the measurement of the shape of an emission line, smeared into a continuum by the cosmic differential red shift, would provide information about the structure of the universe at great distances.

3. – Discrete sources of high-energy photons.

It has now been demonstrated quite conclusively by the NRL [23], [38], [39], MIT [22], [40], [41], and Lockheed [42], [43], [44] groups that there exist discrete sources of cosmic X-rays. About 10 such sources have been found and their properties are described below. The problem of the types of astronomical object and the mechanisms of emission which give rise to these sources is as yet unsolved, although it appears that there are only a few possible explanations. While the basic mechanism by which the X-rays are produced is not known, the present indication is that the X-ray sources are *galactic* and, in fact, are supernova remnants. This viewpoint is advanced here where supernova remnants, as sources of X- and γ-rays, are discussed in some detail; the Crab Nebula in particular receives considerable attention. We also discuss the X-ray source at the galactic center. However, before considering these specific objects, we give a general review of possible galactic sources and then discuss the possible physical mechanisms for high-energy photon production in discrete sources.

3·1. *General summary of the observations.* – The positions and intensities of the discrete X-ray sources as they are known at present are given in Table II which is taken from the paper by BOWYER *et al.* [38]. Results reported by

TABLE II. – *X-Ray sources* (*) (after BOWYER *et al.* [38]).

Source	R.A.	(1950) Dec.	Flux ([a]) counts/(cm²·s)	Flux ([a]) (10^{-8} erg/cm²·s) ([b])	Flux ([a]) (10^{-8} erg/cm²·s) ([c])
Tau XR-1	05 h 31.5 min	22.0°	2.7	5.5	1.1
Sco XR-1	16 h 15 min	−15.2°	18.7	38	7.9
Sco XR-2	17 h 8 min	−36.4°	1.4	2.9	0.6
Sco XR-3	17 h 23 min	−44.3°	1.1	2.3	0.5
Oph XR-1	17 h 32 min	−20.7°	1.3	2.7	0.6
Sgr XR-1	17 h 55 min	−29.2°	1.6	3.3	0.7
Sgr XR-2	18 h 10 min	−17.1°	1.5	3.0	0.6
Ser XR-1	18 h 45 min	5.3°	0.7	1.5	0.3
Cyg XR-1	19 h 53 min	34.6°	3.6	7.3	1.5
Cyg XR-2	21 h 43 min	38.8°	0.8	1.7	0.4

([a]) Uncorrected for atmospheric absorption. Measured 1/4-mil Mylar window.
([b]) Computed for $2\cdot10^{7}$ °K black-body (1.5÷8) Å.
([c]) Computed for $5\cdot10^{6}$ °K black-body (1.5÷8) Å.
(*) This table is included for completeness. A more recent discussion of the observations is given in the lectures of Dr. GIACCONI.

the other experimental groups (MIT and Lockheed) are in essential agreement with these in regard to both the positions (*) and intensities of the sources. The uncertainty in the positions of the sources is given as 1.5°, while the *Tau* XR-1 source has been localized to within 1′ of the optical center of the Crab Nebula. The observational results on the Crab source will be summarized in more detail later (Sect. **3**·4). The discrete sources appear to have a spatial distribution showing a concentration toward the plane of the galaxy, indicating that the sources are probably *galactic* and at characteristic distances of $\sim(1\div10)$ kparsec. The most intense of the X-ray sources is that in the constellation *Scorpius* (*Sco* XR-1) from which an X-ray flux of about $F_X \sim 10^{-7}$ erg/cm²·s is detected. The flux from most of the other sources is about one-tenth as large as that from *Sco* XR-1. With the exception of *Tau* XR-1, none of the sources have been identified with a reasonable degree of certainty with any radio or optical objects, although there have been some tentative identifications.

Attempts have been made [45] to identify the *Scorpius* X-ray source with the so-called spur of radio emission which some have argued is a comparatively

(*) Recent unpublished work by the Lockheed group has given a more accurate position for the *Sco* XR-1 source: $\alpha = 16$ h 14 min, $\delta = -15°\,36'$, with an expected error of $\pm 20'$.

nearby supernova remnant. However, it has been pointed out [46] that this positional identification is very poor since even with the uncertainties quoted for the position the center of the radio source component is some 27° away. Thus the situation here is uncertain.

Of the other X-ray sources, it is of interest to note that *Oph* XR-1 is 1.1° away from the position of Kepler's 1604 supernova and that *Sgr* XR-1 is 2.3° from the galactic center.

The size of *Sco* XR-1 has been established to be less than about 0.2° by both the NRL and MIT groups. With the exception of *Tau* XR-1, all that is known about the sizes of the other sources is that they are less than about 10° in extent. Little is known at present about the spectra of the X-ray sources. From the change in the counting rate from *Sco* XR-1 as the rocket was passing through the upper atmosphere (in which absoprtion is wavelength-dependent) the NRL group [38] has concluded that $\frac{1}{3}$ of the observed flux from the strong *Scorpius* source is emitted in the $(1 \div 6)$ Å band and $\frac{2}{3}$ of the flux is emitted in the $(6 \div 10)$ Å band. Such a spectrum is compatible with emission from a black body having a temperature of 2 or $3 \cdot 10^6$ degrees. However, these results on the spectra of X-ray sources are suspect; the Lockheed group [44] has found an effective black-body temperature of $\sim 2 \cdot 10^7$ °K for the *Scorpius* source—an order of magnitude higher than that reported by the NRL group.

3˙2. *Possible galactic sources*. – If an X-ray source at 10 kparsec is to produce an X-ray flux of 10^{-8} erg/cm²·s, its X-ray luminosity must be 10^{38} erg/s. Clearly, no individual *normal* star could produce such a luminosity in X-rays. For, although there are stars which have a *total* luminosity this large, the atmospheric conditions in these stars are such that most of the radiation emitted is at much lower energies (~, say, 10 eV). The sun emits X-rays from its corona and from flares, but at a much smaller rate (10^{21} to 10^{26} erg/s). Only the cumulative effect of very populous clusters or the integrated effect of the stars in the galactic bulge could possibly produce a significant X-ray flux. This possibility will be discussed later (Sect. 3˙5); suffice it to say for the moment that these combined effects of stellar coronae appear likely to be unimportant. However, there is an *abnormal* type of star which, at least for part of its evolutionary phase, emits a spectrum peaked on the X-ray region; this is the *neutron star*. We prefer to discuss neutron stars after first considering supernovae, which are known sources of large amounts of energy and high luminosity.

3˙2.1. Supernovae. Although much of the energy released in a supernova is emitted soon after the outburst, the remnants still possess a large amount of energy and could possibly maintain an X-ray luminosity of 10^{38} erg/s for much longer times. The required characteristic loss time τ_l for X-ray emission can be determined approximately as follows. Let us suppose that the $N_X \sim 10$ X-ray sources are galactic and resulted from supernova outbursts. Since the rate of supernova outbursts and formation of X-ray sources in the galaxy is $dN_s/dt \sim 1/100$ y, we must have

$$\begin{cases} (dN_s/dt)\,\tau_l = N_X\,, \\ \qquad \tau_l \sim 1000\ \text{y}\,. \end{cases} \tag{3.1}$$

Clearly, this result must hold for whatever type of mechanism is to produce the X-rays, as long as the origin of the X-ray sources is to be supernovae outbursts. Moreover, if a characteristic time for X-ray emission by some process is computed to be much shorter than 1000 y, then without regeneration that process cannot account for the X-ray sources. It is of interest to compare τ_l with the expected lifetime of *total* emission from the Crab Nebula (see Sect. 3·4), for which $E_{tot} \sim 10^{48}$ erg and $L_{tot} \sim 10^{37}$ erg/s. Then $E_{tot}/L_{tot} \sim \sim 3000\ \text{y} \sim 3\tau_l$.

Supernova remanants can emit high-energy photons through a variety of processes and at very different power levels. After the initial outburst, emission can occur by the synchrotron process, by bremsstrahlung in the high temperature gas produced by the expanding ejecta, and by the radioactivity produced. The initial outburst is more spectacular, however, and we shall now consider what can be expected during this very early, violent stage.

3·2.2. Early phases of supernova outbursts. At this phase two processes may be important. These are:

a) Nuclear γ-rays emitted in the process of nucleosynthesis at the time of the outburst.

b) γ-rays emitted through the early interaction of a cloud of relativistic particles with the magnetic field and material in the expanding shell.

If, in a supernova outburst, the inner part implodes and the outer part is suddenly heated so that hydrogen burning takes place very rapidly, we can suppose that the bulk of the energy released is degraded by its passage through the material, but some fraction, perhaps the energy released in burning $0.01\,M_\odot$ of hydrogen, will be emitted as γ-rays in the MeV range. Thus we might suppose that 10^{50} erg are emitted in ~ 1000 s. For a galactic supernova at assumed distances of 1 and 10 kparsec this gives fluxes at the earth of 10^3 and 10^5 erg/cm$^2\cdot$s^{-1}, fantastic rates. However, the appearance of a galactic supernova is highly improbable. From extragalactic supernovae at characteristic distances of 10 and 100 Mparsec the fluxes would be 10^{-5} and 10^{-7} erg/cm^2 s^{-1}, respectively. These rates are obviously uncertain by several powers of 10. It might also be expected that some part of the flux is degraded to the energies of a few kilovolt and is emitted as X-rays. As an upper limit we might suppose that this flux is of comparable intensity for a few days with the flux at maximum light from the supernova. If we suppose that it reaches a value of $M_v = -18$ this corresponds to 10^{43} erg/s and at distances of 1 kparsec and 10 kparsec (galactic) and 10 Mparsec and 100 Mparsec (extragalactic) fluxes at earth of 10^{-1} and 10^{-3} erg/cm² s^{-1} (galactic) and 10^{-9} and 10^{-11} erg/cm² s^{-1} (extragalactic) may be expected.

A large flux of relativistic electrons is currently present in many supernova remnants, and it is possible that this in part is the remnant of a much larger flux of relativistic particles which was produced at the time of the outburst. Let us suppose that some 10^{50} erg of particles, largely protons, was generated in the explosion. If they are originally confined in an expanding shell containing a magnetic field (they are the relativistic plasma component), then because of the high density in the shell in the first hours they will largely be destroyed, and their energy will be dissipated in the form of neutrinos, γ-rays, and electrons and positrons which radiate in the magnetic field. A large flux of high-energy ($\geqslant$100 MeV) γ-rays will thus be generated and we might expect fluxes to escape over this period at a rate of perhaps ($10^{44} \div 10^{45}$) erg/s. For reasonable magnetic field values the synchrotron radiation will not lie in the X-ray or γ-range. However, it is possible that some part of the electron-positron flux will be dissipated by Compton collisions with thermal photons in which γ-rays are emitted. It is obvious that these suggestions are highly speculative. However, it is clear that detection of a supernova explosion by X-ray and γ-ray telescopes would give much information on the conditions at the early phases. For example, if there are no high-energy γ-rays emitted this might be interpreted as meaning that there was no early generation of a large flux of relativistic protons.

3·2.3. Hard radiation emitted through radioactivity. It has been suggested that in a supernova outburst considerable nucleosynthesis takes place [47]. In this a large flux of neutrons is added very rapidly to seed nuclei (r-process) building up to nuclei with $A \simeq 270$ and giving rise to large numbers of neutron-rich nuclei wich subsequently decay. It is still not clear what fraction of the supernovae goes through this process but in connection with the possibility of checking this theory CLAYTON and CRADDOCK [48] have made calculations of the fluxes of γ-rays to be expected following such a process. The γ-ray line spectrum is calculated from the production curve for the r-process isotopes [49]. Using these abundances the best estimates are made of the prompt γ-ray spectrum using the nuclear energy levels. Also, an estimate has been made of the γ-ray flux which is emitted in spontaneous fission in such isotopes as ^{252}Cf. The fluxes to be expected for a supernova remnant at the distance of the Crab (∼1000 parsec) are shown in Fig. 7 taken from the calculations of CLAYTON and CRADDOCK. The strongest line (390 keV line from ^{249}Cf) radiates at a rate 10^{39} photon/s at the source. The calculations have been normalized for the assumption that in a supernova remnant $1.5\cdot10^{-4} M_{\odot}(3\cdot10^{29}\,g)$ of ^{254}Cf are produced. This is adequate to explain the light curve of a Type I supernova on the assumption [47] that this is due to ^{254}Cf. Detection of such a flux is being attempted at the time of writing. This will give a direct observational test of this hypothesis of *r*-process isotope synthesis in Type I supernovae.

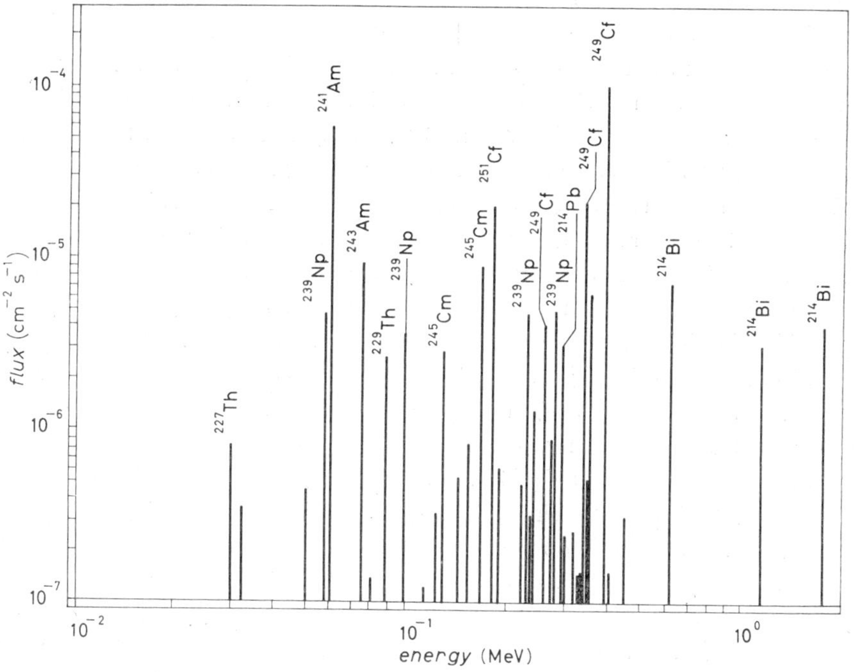

Fig. 7. – The spectrum of the line fluxes anticipated from the Crab Nebula as calculated by CLAYTON and CRADDOCK [48].

3.2.4. Neutron stars. It has been pointed out by CHIU [50] and FINZI [51] that, since it is possible that neutron configurations may be reached as an end phase of stellar evolution by processes which leave the star extremely hot, such configurations may, for rather a short period, be thermal X-ray emitters. However, from the theoretical standpoint it must be conceded that at the present time we cannot demonstrate conclusively that stable neutron configurations are ever formed or can exist if formed. The presumption of these authors is that the neutron configurations are formed during a supernova outburst, as was first proposed by BAADE and ZWICKY [52] many years ago. There are many theoretical uncertainties associated with neutron configurations which we mention briefly.

It is well known that there is a critical mass for a degenerate neutron configuration above which no stable equilibrium is possible. This result was first derived by LANDAU [53] and calculations by OPPENHEIMER and VOLKOFF [54] gave a value of about $0.7 M_\odot$ for this observable mass limit. While in later calculations this mass limit has been slightly revised, it is clear that the mass limit lies near $1 M_\odot$. Even the doubtful assumption of a hard-core nuclear potential, which is known to be incorrect from relativistic considerations, only extends the maximum mass to about $3 M_\odot$. In fact it is clear from the earliest considerations [53] that the maximum mass is very insensitive to the equation of state at nuclear densities and above. For masses above the critical mass it appears that implosion must occur [55]. For a modern review see HOYLE, FOWLER, BURBIDGE, and BURBIDGE [56]. Thus, if neutron configurations which can exist long enough to be detected as sources of X-rays come from supernova outbursts, it is required that in the supernova outburst sufficient mass is ejected so that the resulting configuration falls below the limit for support by a degenerate neutron configuration. None of the attempts to unravel the processes of supernova outbursts have yet given any real indication that such conditions can be achieved. The attempts by the California-Cambridge group [47], [57] have not been able to answer this question. Even the range of masses of stars which become supernovae is in doubt, but it appears highly probable that the Type II supernovae are stars of quite large mass $\sim 30 M_\odot$ [57]. All of the discussions of the supernova outburst as it applies to the last phases of nucleosynthesis, and neutrino emission, etc. have been carried out by neglecting the effects of rotation. However, as has been shown by HOYLE *et al.* [56] this *may* have the effect of allowing a massive star to fragment, either into white dwarf, or into neutron configurations (cf. eq. (45) of that paper [56]). In the work of CHIU [50] no conclusion as to whether a degenerate neutron configuration with a mass below the critical mass is left has been reached. The only attempt at a hydrodynamical calculation of the implosion of a supernova before relativistic effects become important is that by COLGATE and his colleagues [58]. This calculation follows the collapse until nuclear densities are reached, but then it is supposed that a bounce occurs and the outer envelope is ejected. The calculation is not able to determine what fraction of the mass is left as a degenerate neutron configuration.

The only supernova remnant which can be studied in any detail is the Crab Nebula. While there are uncertainties in the mass of the nebula, analysis shows that it is only [59] $\sim 0.64 M_\odot$ so that if the outburst originated from a star with a mass in excess of about $3 M_\odot$ (and the type of supernova involved is still uncertain, as is the relation of type with mass) it must be concluded either that a large remnant has imploded or else that it is fragmented into a number of neutron stars.

Finally, there is some question about the stability of neutron configurations. The question of their dynamical stability has recently been considered for a range of models by MISNER and ZAPOLSKY [60] who have concluded that dynamically stable solutions exist for stars below the maximum mass for cold static equilibrium.

There is thus considerable uncertainty as to whether neutron stars are ever formed. If they are, then detection of their X-rays emitted while the surfaces are still hot might provide the only direct observational test of their existence. Whether they are likely to be detected depends on the time that they may be expected to spend with their atmospheres hot enough to emit X-rays. The first calculations of the cooling rates [61], [62] suggested that such stars might emit for periods $\sim 10^3$ y. Thus if they were embedded in supernovae remnants such as the Crab which exploded in 1054 A.D. we might expect to detect them. The cooling is dominated by the neutrino production rate in the interior since the neutrinos escape from the stars with a negligible probability of being scattered or absorbed. A recent investigation by BAHCALL and WOLF [63] (see also FINZI [64]) takes into account the cooling reactions

$$n + n \rightarrow n' + p + e^- + \bar{\nu}_e$$

and

$$n + \pi^- \rightarrow n' + \mu^- + \bar{\nu}_\mu$$

and their inverses. If the first reaction alone is operating, the cooling rate is such that atmospheric temperatures only remain $\sim (2 \div 3) \cdot 10^6$ degrees for about 10 years. There is still some doubt as to whether the second process operates, but if it does the cooling times are very much shorter than this. In any case, because of the argument previously given [see eq. (3.1) and discussion], the short cooling time for neutron stars would rule them out as likely sources of X-rays.

From the observational side also there are very strong arguments against the neutron star hypothesis. The occultation observation of the NRL group [39] which shows that the source in the Crab has a diameter ~ 1 light year rules out its being a single neutron star and the existence of a cluster of such stars is improbable. Also, the observation of fluxes of $(10 \div 50)$ keV X-rays is not explicable in terms of a thermal source, since temperatures $\sim 10^8$ degrees are required, and these are far above that which the surface of a neutron star could attain for any significant time.

3·3. *Mechanisms for X-ray production in discrete sources.* – Apart from the mechanisms discussed earlier in this Section, there are three possible mechanisms for the X-ray production: 1) Compton scattering, 2) bremsstrahlung, and 3) synchrotron emission. When X-ray sources were first discovered, the possibility that they were neutron stars was discussed at length, but as was shown in the previous subsection this explanation now appears to be untenable. It has been suggested [65] that the X-rays from the Crab are due to Compton scattering of the radio-optical synchrotron photons by the associated synchrotron electrons; in this manner the synchrotron photon energy is amplified by a factor γ_e^2, where $\gamma_e m_e c^2$ is the energy of the (synchrotron) electron involved in the scattering. However, as has been emphasized recently [66], the intensity of this Compton-synchrotron radiation can be shown to be far too small to explain the observations. The effect is small essentially because the probability that a synchrotron photon undergoes such a Compton scattering before escaping from the nebula is very small. The Crab is one of the most intense galactic radio emitters and if the effect is small for it, one should not expect to observe the effect in other galactic objects. One might think that Compton scattering might produce a large X-ray flux from quasi-stellar radio sources in which the photon density and high-energy electron density are large. Again, however, simple calculations indicate a completely negligible and unobservable X-ray flux from this process. Consequently, we are led to rule out Compton scattering as an X-ray production mechanism in discrete sources [67]. This leaves only the synchrotron and bremsstrahlung processes as possible X-ray sources.

First we consider the possibility that the X-rays from discrete sources are synchrotron radiation. We shall assume that an X-ray flux $F_X = 10^{-8}$ erg/cm$^2\cdot$s comes from a galactic source at a distance $r = 10$ kparsec; the X-ray luminosity of the source is then $L_X = 4\pi r^2 F_X = 1\cdot 10^{38}$ erg/s. Further, we assume for simplicity that the X-ray flux is at an effective wavelength 3 Å and frequency $\nu = 10^{18}$ Hz, which is the characteristic synchrotron frequency $\nu_L \gamma_e^2$ emitted by electrons of energy $E_e = \gamma_e m_e c^2$. For a magnetic field $H = 10^{-4}$ gauss (the assumed value in the Crab Nebula) the electron energy required is $E_e(\propto H^{-\frac{1}{2}}) = 3\cdot 10^{13}$ eV. For such a high-energy electron the lifetime against energy loss by synchrotron emission is only $E_e(\mathrm{d}E_e/\mathrm{d}t)^{-1} = \tau_e(\propto H^{-\frac{3}{2}}) = 30$ y. The total energy in these electrons necessary to produce the flux F_X is $E_t(\propto F_X r^2 H^{-\frac{3}{2}}) = 1\cdot 10^{47}$ erg. We note that: 1) The electron energies required to produce synchrotron X-rays are extremely high, 2) their lifetime is very short, and 3) the total energy involved is comparable to the energy released in a supernova outburst. Actually, the energy E_t quoted above is really the minimum energy of the highly relativistic electrons, since it includes only the synchrotron electrons producing X-rays. The contribution of the lower-energy extension of the electron spectrum to the total energy would increase the value of the total energy by an amount depending on the index of the spectrum and the low-energy cut-off. For the case of the Crab Nebula (see Sect. **3**.4) the extension of the X-ray spectrum (which has an index of about 1.1) to the visible leads to a total electron energy which is not excessively large ($\sim 10^{48}$ erg). However, it is very significant that the lifetime of the high-energy electrons required to produce synchrotron X-rays is appreciably less then the age of the Crab Nebula and other supernova remnants, because it would mean that the electrons would have to be continuously or at least periodically produced. If they are spasmodically produced or accelerated, one might expect to observe variations in the X-ray intensity over time scales $\leqslant 10$ y.

Because of the difficulties associated with the hypothesis that the X-rays from discrete sources are produced by the synchrotron process, it is worth-while considering an alternative model in which it is supposed that an out-burst gives rise to a small very hot cloud which continues to emit X-rays as part of the thermal bremsstrahlung. We now discuss the properties associated with such a model. Earlier, we had suggested that the source at the galactic center resulted from bremsstrahlung. At the time we envisaged bremsstrahlung production by *nonthermal* electrons of energy greater than the energy of the X-ray photons. However, as was first pointed out by Rossi (*), about 10^5 times as much energy would be lost by these electrons in inelastic atomic collisions, so that if the X-ray luminosity of the source at the galactic center is 10^{38} erg/s, about 10^{43} erg/s must be supplied. This energy rate is excessively large on a galactic time scale (10^{10} y), although perhaps it may be supplied during shorter times.

In spite of this difficulty the conditions whereby X-rays are produced by nonthermal particles may still exist. If so, there will also be production of *characteristic* X-rays, as was pointed out by us [30] and by Hayakawa and Matsuoka [68]. These X-ray lines are produced in the radiative cascade following the ejection of K-shell electrons by the incident electrons or protons. Actually, most of the K-shell vacancies produced result in the emission of an Auger electron. The probability of X-ray emission by an element is given by the so-called *K-fluorescence yield* which is small for the light elements. The X-ray line emission, say of the K_α line, is approximately proportional to the product of the element abundance and K-fluorescence yield. One finds that the total intensity of the X-ray lines in the $(2\div 8)$ Å region should be $\sim 10\,\%$ of the intensity of the bremsstrahlung continuum in the same wave-length range. This result holds essentially *independent* of the spectrum of the incident suprathermal particles and holds whether the incident particles are

(*) Private communication.

protons or electrons. As HAYAKAWA and MATSUOKA have shown, the incident protons produce knock-on electrons and a radiation continuum by *inner bremsstrahlung* during the knock-on process. The observation of X-ray lines produced in this manner would be of great importance because, among other things (cf. [37]), the abundances of the elements producing X-ray lines could be determined in this manner. In Table III we list the K_α wave-legths of the elements from carbon to iron along with their abundance and K-fluorescence yield. It appears that the most intense lines would be from Si (7.1 Å) and S (5.4 Å).

TABLE III. – *Characteristic X-ray data* (after GOULD and BURBIDGE [30]).

Element	Logarithmic abundance	K-fluorescence yield	K_α wavelength (Å)
C	8.60	0.00126	45
N	8.05	0.00223	31
O	8.95	0.00397	24
F	6.0	0.00634	18
Ne	8.70	0.00963	15
Na	6.30	0.0140	12
Mg	7.40	0.0197	9.9
Al	6.22	0.0269	8.3
Si	7.50	0.0360	7.1
P	5.40	0.0468	6.1
S	7.35	0.0597	5.4
Cl	6.25	0.0748	4.7
Ar	6.88	0.0923	4.2
K	4.82	0.112	3.7
Ca	6.19	0.134	3.4
Sc	2.85	0.158	3.0
Ti	4.89	0.184	2.7
V	3.82	0.212	2.5
Cr	5.38	0.241	2.3
Mn	5.12	0.272	2.1
Fe	6.57	0.304	1.9

Energetically, bremsstrahlung X-ray production is more efficient in a high-temperature ($T \sim 10^7$ °K) and low-density gas where the bremsstrahlung is produced by *thermal* electrons and constitutes a major source of cooling and energy loss for the gas.

For the production of thermal bremsstrahlung the Gaunt approximation [69] to the bremsstrahlung cross-section provides an adequate simplification. The differential cross-section for the production of a bremsstrahlung photon of energy within $\hbar\, d\omega$ by an electron of velocity βc incident on a nucleus of charge Ze is

$$d\sigma_B(\beta, \omega; Z) = \frac{16\pi}{3\sqrt{3}} Z^2 \alpha r_0^2 \frac{1}{\beta^2} \frac{d\omega}{\omega}, \tag{3.2}$$

where α is the fine-structure constant and r_0 the classical electron radius. The bremsstrahlung energy spectrum emitted per unit volume by encounters with ions of charge Ze is then

$$\frac{dE_B(Z)}{dt\, dV\, d\omega} = n_e n_Z \int \frac{d\sigma_B(\beta, \omega; Z)}{d\omega} \hbar\omega v f(v)\, dv, \tag{3.3}$$

where $f(v)$ is the Maxwellian velocity distribution of the electrons; the integration in eq. (3.3) is over v from $(2\hbar\omega/m)^{\frac{1}{2}}$ to ∞. One obtains

$$\frac{dE_B(Z)}{dt\, dV\, d\omega} = n_e n_Z 2^4 3^{-\frac{3}{2}} \alpha r_0^2 \hbar c^2 Z^2 (2\pi m/kT_e)^{\frac{1}{2}} \exp[-\hbar\omega/kT_e], \tag{3.4}$$

and for the total emission between ω_1 and ω_2

$$\frac{dE_B(Z)}{dt\, dV} = n_e n_Z 2^4 3^{-\frac{3}{2}} \alpha r_0^2 mc^2 Z^2 (2\pi kT_e/m)^{\frac{1}{2}} \cdot \\ \cdot (\exp[-\hbar\omega_1/kT] - \exp[-\hbar\omega_2/kT_e]) \qquad (\omega_1 < \omega < \omega_2). \tag{3.5}$$

The total energy emitted per unit volume over all frequencies ($\omega_1 \to 0$, $\omega_2 \to \infty$) is

$$\Lambda_b = \sum_Z \frac{dE_B(Z)}{dt\, dV} = 1.43 \cdot 10^{-27}\, T_e^{\frac{1}{2}} n_e \sum_Z n_Z Z^2 \quad \text{c.g.s. units}. \tag{3.6}$$

It is noteworthy that the bremsstrahlung spectrum (eq. (3.4)) is significantly different from the spectrum of a black-body, so that from measurements of the X-ray spectrum it may be possible to establish that some sources are hot optically thin gases.

In addition to bremsstrahlung, there is also cooling and X-ray emission by electron-ion radiative recombination and by inelastic electron collisions with ions followed by radiative de-excitation (line emission). The line emission is due mainly to oxygen and neon in high stages of ionization and the calculation of the cooling and X-ray production involves a calculation of the ionization equilibrium. Equilibrium is established between ionization by electron collision and radiative and dielectronic recombination. Here we give only the results; the details will be published elsewhere. Preliminary results have already been published [66]. Figure 8 gives (*) the rate of loss Λ_e (erg/cm^3·s)

(*) The curve L in this figure differs from that given in [66] at lower temperatures. In our earlier work a rough estimate of the dielectronic recombination was used. More accurate calculations by W. TUCKER at UCSD give the curve in Fig. 8.

of the free electron kinetic-energy density by various processes in the temperature range between 10^6 and 10^8 °K. It is seen that bremsstrahlung dominates the cooling at higher temperatures. In Fig. 9 we give the rate of production of X-rays ($p_X = P_X/n_e^2$) in the $(1 \div 10)$ keV range as a function of temperature. In the calculation of these processes a general cosmic abundance of the elements has been assumed. The cooling time ($\tau_c \approx 3kT_e/n_e\Lambda_e$), density ($n_e$), and mass ($M$) of a volume V of gas required to produce the observed X-ray fluxes are of prime interest. We assume the source to be at a distance $r = 10$ kparsec and to produce an X-ray energy flux $F_X = 10^{-8}$ erg/cm²·s in the range $(1 \div 10)$ keV. Further, we assume the gas to be at a temperature of 10^7 °K; parameters for other values of the temperature may be determined readily from Fig. 8 and 9. Since

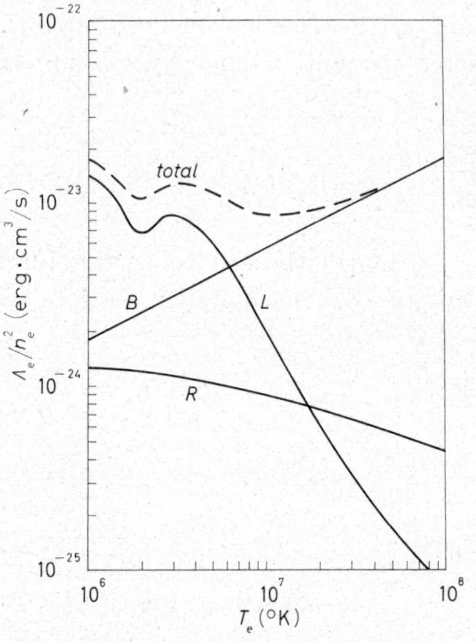

Fig. 8. – Cooling rate as a function of temperature. Λ_e denotes the rate of change of the free electron kinetic-energy density. Cooling by bremsstrahlung (B), line emission following inelastic electron collisions (L), and recombination (R) is shown. The ions of the following elements have been included: (B) H+He, (L) He+C+N+O+Ne+Mg and (R) H+He+O+Ne.

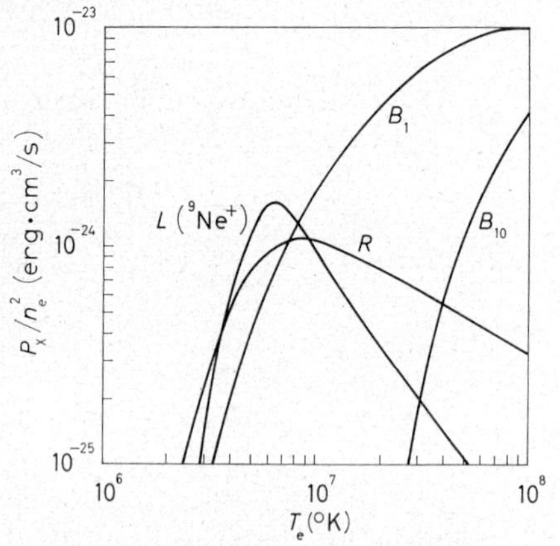

Fig. 9. – X-ray production rates in the $(1 \div 10)$ keV range by bremsstrahlung (B_1), recombination radiation (R) and the line emission (L). The bremsstrahlung rate (B_{10}) in the $(10 \div 20)$ keV range is also shown. Ions of the following elements have been included: (B_1, B_{10}) H+He, (L) Ne, and (R) H+He+H+O+Ne. The line emission is due to the $1s$ - $2p$ transition in ^{9}Ne$^+$ ($E = 1.02$ keV). This is the strongest line emitted in $(1 \div 10)$ keV range.

$$F_X = p_X n_e^2 V / 4\pi r^2 , \tag{3.7}$$

this choice of F_X, T, and r fixes the product $n_e^2 V$ at $4\cdot10^{61}$ cm^{-3}. Then for a range $n_e = 0.1$ to 10^4 cm^{-3}, $\tau_e \sim 10^8$ to 10^3 y, $V \sim 10^8$ to 10^{-2} parsec^3, and $M \sim 4\cdot10^5$ to 4 solar masses. The associated *optical* bremsstrahlung intensity is of interest and depends only on the choice of T. One finds that this intensity corresponds to a 12-th magnitude visual object which may be observable depending on the extent of the source.

3'4. *The Crab Nebula.* – The general observational data on the Crab are probably more extensive than for any other celestial object with the exception of the sun, although the general physical state of the Crab as derived from these observations is poorly known. Photon fluxes have been detected over a frequency range from 10^7 to 10^{19} Hz. In this Section we shall consider what can be inferred from the more recent observations in the high-energy end of the spectrum.

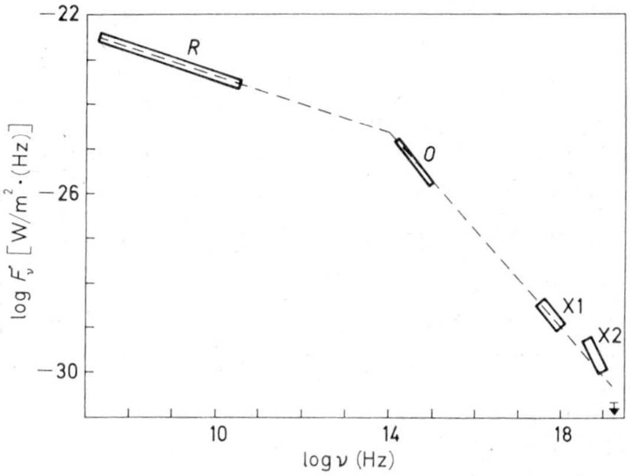

Fig. 10. – The observed emission continuum of the Crab Nebula in the radio (R), optical (O) and X-ray regions (X1, X2). The observational data are shown somewhat schematically, the rectangles showing errors in the observed fluxes. The point at the highest energy represents an upper limit [71].

Observations of continuum radiation emitted by the Crab have been made in essentially three frequency ranges: the radio range [70], the optical range [40], and the X-ray range [23], [71]; Fig. 10 summarizes the results. The radio spectral flux F_ν [watt/m$^2\cdot$Hz] is of the form $C_r\nu^{-\alpha}$, where $\alpha = 0.27$, and C_r can be determined by the value [70] ($1.23\cdot10^{-23}$ W/m$^2\cdot$Hz) of F_ν at $\nu = 400$ MHz. The synchrotron spectrum apparently retains this form up to a frequency $\nu_m = 10^{14}$ Hz at the beginning of the optical region. Designating this region $\nu < \nu_m$ as the radio range the radio *luminosity* L_r can then be computed from an assumed distance $d = 1030$ parsec to the Crab:

$$L_r = 4\pi d^2 \int_0^{\nu_m} C_r \nu^{-\alpha}\,d\nu = 4\pi d^2 C_r (1-\alpha)^{-1}\nu_m^{1-\alpha} \approx 7.4\cdot10^{36}\ \text{erg/s}\,. \tag{3.8}$$

The luminosity in, for example, the visible range ($\nu = (4 \div 8)\cdot10^{14}$ Hz) of the optical region is

$$L_v \approx 1.7\cdot10^{36}\ \text{erg/s}\,.$$

Assuming a spectrum $F_\nu \propto \nu^{-\alpha'}$ with $\alpha' = 1.1$ for the low-energy part of the X-ray region, the observations of the NRL group [23] in the range $3 \cdot 10^{17} < \nu < 10^{18}$ Hz indicate an X-ray luminosity

$$L_{X1} = 1.6 \cdot 10^{36} \text{ erg/s} .$$

The observations of Clark [71] in the higher-energy X-ray region between $5 \cdot 10^{18} < \nu < 10^{19}$ Hz suggest an index $\alpha'' = 2$ and an X-ray luminosity in this range of

$$L_{X2} = 1.6 \cdot 10^{36} \text{ erg/s} .$$

It should be noted that in the X-ray spectrum at the higher energies there is an apparent cut-off (see Fig. 10) or at least another change in slope.

When it was discovered that the Crab was an X-ray source, the suggestion was made that the X-rays were coming from a neutron star formed during the initial supernova outburst [23], [72]. An observation designed to test this hypothesis was carried out by the NRL group in July of 1964 during the lunar occultation of the Crab [39]. Since a neutron star would be essentially a point source of X-rays, as it would be occulted by the limb of the moon the observed counting rate would drop abruptly to zero. Had this effect been observed, it could have been taken as strong evidence for the existence of a neutron star. It was not observed. When the NRL group sent up a rocket during the time of the occultation (which lasted only a few minutes) with a detector system designed to look at the Crab, they found that the X-ray counting rate changed *continuously* during the occultation. This meant that the X-rays were coming from an *extended* source. The angular diameter of the X-ray source was found to be about 1′, compared with an optical diameter of 2′ and a radio diameter of 5′.

Assuming the radio spectrum $C_r \nu^{-\alpha}$ is due to synchrotron emission by relativistic electrons, an energy spectrum $n_e(\gamma_e) = K_e \gamma_e^{-\Gamma_e}$ with $\Gamma_e = 1 + 2\alpha = 1.54$ is implied. If the mean magnetic field in the Crab is $H = 10^{-4}$ gauss the Larmor frequency is $\nu_L = 280$ Hz, and the frequency $\nu_m = 10^{14}$ Hz would be emitted primarily by electrons with $(\gamma_e)_m = (\nu_m/\nu_L)^{\frac{1}{2}} \approx 6.0 \cdot 10^5$. The optical radiation from the Crab would be emitted by slightly higher-energy electrons. If the radio emission originates from a volume $\int dV = V_0$, the radio flux F_ν is related to V_0, d, K_e, H by [see eq. (2.38)]

$$F_\nu \approx (12\pi d^2)^{-1} V_0 K_e c r_0^2 H^2 \nu_L^{(\Gamma_e - 3)/2} \nu^{-(\Gamma_e - 1)/2} . \tag{3.9}$$

From the value of the product $V_0 K_e$ determined from the radio-brightness we can compute the total energy of the radio electrons in the Crab:

$$E_r = \int dV K_e m_e c^2 \int d\gamma_e \gamma_e^{-(\Gamma_e - 1)} = V_0 K_e m_e c^2 (2 - \Gamma_e)^{-1} (\gamma_e)_m^{2-\Gamma_e} \approx 1.0 \cdot 10^{48} \text{ erg} . \tag{3.10}$$

The age τ of the Crab is 910 years and we see that $E_r/\tau = 3.5\cdot 10^{37}$ erg/s $\gg$ $\gg L_r, L_v, L_X$.

For the assumed magnetic field 10^{-4} gauss the electrons lose energy at a rate [eq. (2.13)] $-\gamma_e^{-1}(d\gamma_e/dt) \approx \gamma_e\cdot 1.94\cdot 10^{-17}\ s^{-1}$; for $\gamma_e \leqslant 1.8\cdot 10^6$ ($\nu = \nu_L\gamma_e^2 \leqslant$ $\leqslant 9.0\cdot 10^{14}$ Hz), $-\gamma_e^{-1}(d\gamma_e/dt) < \tau^{-1}$. Thus, for the radio and optical electrons the characteristic time of energy loss by synchrotron emission is greater than the age of the nebula. The rough coincidence of the critical electron energy and synchrotron emission frequency with the value (Fig. 10) above which the spectrum is apparently reduced or perhaps cut off may be interpreted as an indication that the relativistic electrons in the Crab were produced in the initial supernova outburst. The absence of any continuous production of high-energy electrons would preclude any interpretation of the X-ray point in Fig. 10 as being due to electron synchrotron emission, since the lifetime against energy loss through synchrotron emission by the energetic electrons necessary to produce this synchrotron frequency is about 30 years $\ll \tau$. An important parameter in this discussion is the strength of the magnetic field in which the electrons radiate. We have chosen a value of $H = 10^{-4}$ gauss, for which the lifetimes of the radio and optical electrons are longer than 10^3 years. However, if the assumed value of H is increased perhaps to $5\cdot 10^{-4}$ gauss, the lifetimes of the electrons emitting the same synchrotron frequencies are decreased by a factor of $(5)^{\frac{3}{2}}(= 11.2)$, and the optical electrons have lifetimes less than the age of the nebula so that continuous injection of such electrons is required to explain the optical radiation. Since the magnetic-field strength is uncertain we shall consider the possibility of continuous injection of electrons in what follows. We also might mention that as GINZBURG, PIKELNER, and SHKLOVSKY [73] have shown, there might exist in the Crab an energy loss by scattering by magnetic-field condensations in the expanding nebula. These scatterings lead to a Fermi-type statistical *de*celeration of the electrons. The corresponding energy loss is approximately $-d\gamma_e/dt \approx \gamma_e V/r$, where V is the expansion velocity of the nebula and r its size; thus $r/V \approx \tau$, the age of the nebula. This energy loss process, if it is operative, dominates synchrotron losses for the radio and optical electrons but is negligible for higher energy electrons. With only this type of energy loss ($\propto \gamma_e$) the electron spectrum $n_e(\gamma_e)$ retains the power-law shape of its production spectrum $q_e(\gamma_e)$.

Consider the case where the radio electrons of the Crab are produced continuously and, for simplicity, at a constant rate since the origin of the nebula. Neglecting energy losses (*) the continuity equation (2.24) reduces to

$$\partial n_e(\gamma_e)/\partial t = q_e(\gamma_e) = k_e\gamma_e^{-\Gamma_e}, \tag{3.11}$$

(*) A similar result would be obtained if the Fermi-type statistical deceleration were operative since the characteristic loss time for this process is approximately τ, the age of the nebula.

and so the electron spectrum at the present time would have become

$$n_e(\gamma_e) = \tau q_e(\gamma_e) = K_e \gamma_e^{-\Gamma_e} . \tag{3.12}$$

If the continuous production is via meson production in nuclear collisions, as was proposed [74] by one of us, there will also be continuous production of π^0-decay photons, and it is of interest to compute the resulting π^0-photon flux. For a pion production spectrum $q_\pi(\gamma_\pi) = k_\pi \gamma_\pi^{-\Gamma_\pi}$ the π^0-decay photon production spectrum is approximately [eq. (2.33)]

$$\mathrm{d}n^0/\mathrm{d}\eta\,\mathrm{d}t \approx \tfrac{2}{3} k_\pi (2m_e/m_\pi)^{-(\Gamma_\pi - 1)}\, \eta^{-\Gamma_\pi} . \tag{3.13}$$

The observed spectral flux of π^0-photons would then be

$$j^0(\eta) = \mathrm{d}J/\mathrm{d}\eta = (4\pi d^2)^{-1} \int \mathrm{d}V (\mathrm{d}n^0/\mathrm{d}\eta\,\mathrm{d}t) . \tag{3.14}$$

Employing the relation (2.8) between k_π and k_e and eqs. (3.9) and (3.12) to determine k_π from the radio spectrum we find

$$j^0(\eta) = 1.0 \cdot 10^{-4} \cdot \eta^{-1.54} . \tag{3.15}$$

For photons of energy around $\eta = 200$ ($E \sim 100$ MeV) the integrated spectrum with $\Delta\eta/\eta \sim 1$ gives $\int j^0(\eta)\,\mathrm{d}\eta \sim 10^{-4} \eta^{-0.54} \sim 5.7 \cdot 10^{-6}$ photons/cm$^2\cdot$s. This photon flux is almost four orders of magnitude smaller than the upper limit established by KRAUSHAAR and CLARK [25].

One can also calculate the high-energy proton flux required to produce the pion production rate necessary to account for the secondary electron density and the radio spectrum. From this proton flux one can then compute the amount of K-series and inner bremsstrahlung X-rays in the wavelength range of the observations of BOWYER *et al.* [23]. The calculated X-ray flux for a low-energy proton cut-off $\gamma_p = 1$ is about 6 orders of magnitude smaller than the observed flux.

A more definite conclusion regarding secondary electron production in the Crab Nebula may be provided by an analysis of the observations of FRUIN *et al.* [75]. By employing Čerenkov-light detectors to observe light pulses from showers in the atmosphere they were able to set upper limits for the high-energy photon flux from the Crab Nebula and also from the quasi-stellar radio sources 3C147, 3C196, and 3C273. The threshold energy for their detection system was $5 \cdot 10^{12}$ eV ($\eta \approx 10^7$). The established upper limits to the photon fluxes are listed in Table IV.

If photons of energy $\eta = 10^7$ result from the decay of π^0's produced in nuclear collisions, the corresponding synchrotron emission frequency in the Crab's magnetic field by electrons resulting from the decay of charged pions of the same energy is about $\nu = 10^{16}$ Hz for $H = 10^{-4}$ gauss. This frequency is about midway (on the logarithmic scale) between the optical and X-ray frequencies at which the Crab has been observed (see Fig. 10). It is of interest

TABLE IV. – *Upper limits to the high-energy photon flux from various sources* (after FRUIN *et al.* [75]).

Source	Photon flux (photons/cm²·s)
Crab Nebula	$1\cdot10^{-10}$
3C147	$1\cdot10^{-10}$
3C196	$5\cdot10^{-11}$
3C273	$3\cdot10^{-10}$

to compute the π^0-photon flux at $\eta = 10^7$ from the Crab on the assumption that the optical–X-ray flux (if it exists) from the Crab is due to synchrotron emission by secondary-produced electrons.

In the region around $\nu = 10^{16}$ Hz the apparent index of the synchrotron spectrum is (Fig. 10) $\alpha = 1.1$, so that the electron spectrum in this region is of the form $n_e(\gamma_e) = K_e \gamma_e^{-\Gamma_e}$ with $\Gamma_e = 3.2$. Moreover, for these high-energy electrons the dominant energy loss process is synchrotron emission and K_e is related to the electron production spectrum $\varrho_e(\gamma_e) = k_e \gamma_e^{-\Gamma_\pi}$ $(\Gamma_\pi = \Gamma_e - 1)$ by eq. (2.28)

$$K_e = k_e / b(\Gamma_\pi - 1)\,, \tag{3.16}$$

with k_e related to k_π by eq. (2.8). Calculating the π^0-photon flux as in eqs. (3.12) and (3.13) and again determining the parameter $(4\pi d^2)^{-1} V_0 k_\pi$ from the supposed synchrotron emission rate $[F_\nu \approx 1.4_5 \cdot 10^{-27}$ w/m²·Hz at $\nu = 10^{16}$ Hz$]$ one calculates a π^0-photon spectrum given by

$$j^0(\eta) = 2.2_1 \eta^{-2.2}\,. \tag{3.17}$$

For photons of energy $\eta = 10^7$ we find the integrated spectrum with $\Delta\eta/\eta \sim 1$ gives $\int j^0(\eta)\,d\eta \sim 2.2_1 \eta^{-1.2} \sim 8\cdot 10^{-9}$ photons/cm²·s. This calculated photon flux is almost two orders of magnitude *above* the observational upper limit (Table IV). Thus, the present preliminary observations are inconsistent with the interpretation of the X-ray emission from the Crab as synchrotron radiation *if* the necessary continuous production of high-energy electrons is through secondary production via π-μ-e decay. If electrons are produced by secondary processes at a lower energy and then accelerated by Fermi processes to energies at which they will radiate synchrotron X-rays, it may be possible to explain the observed X-ray flux without coming into conflict with the results of FRUIN *et al.*

In summary, regarding synchrotron radiation and the relativistic electrons in the Crab, provided that the magnetic field is as weak as 10^{-4} gauss, the view that the energetic electrons responsible for the radio and optical radiation in the Crab were produced in the initial supernova outburst is quite consistent. In fact, the apparent reduction below the extrapolated radio spectrum $F_\nu = C_r \nu^{-\alpha}$ in the optical region may possibly be interpreted as a result of energy losses by the more energetic electrons; that is, higher-energy electrons would have already decayed in energy since the birth of the nebula. On the other hand, the electrons required to produce synchrotron radiation in the X-ray region would have to be continuously produced.

It should be pointed out that X-rays can also be emitted by the synchrotron process if electrons which are normally radiating in the optical range spiral into regions of much higher magnetic field. Since the critical frequency is proportional to H this means that the field must be increased by a factor of $(\nu_X/\nu_0) \sim 10^3$. Thus this would imply that there are regions in the Crab with magnetic field strengths as high as 10^{-1} gauss. There are many difficulties associated with such a model partly because it would require continuous production of particles which move into regions of high field, since the lifetimes are proportional to H^{-2}. Also, the mechanism by which such concentrations of magnetic flux can be maintained is difficult to understand.

Regarding the possibility that the X-rays from the Crab are from the bremsstrahlung process, we must emphasize again the difficulties of the energy requirement if the bremsstrahlung is by nonthermal electrons. On the other hand, as Clark [71] has emphasized, to explain his observations at 50 keV a temperature of about $2 \cdot 10^8$ °K would be required to produce such energetic thermal bremsstrahlung. This temperature is about an order of magnitude larger than the values predicted from theories of the heating of the gas by the shock front resulting from the expanding ejecta. In view of these difficulties, which seem very great, it would seem that the «least objectionable» explanation for the X-ray production in the Crab is that the synchrotron process is responsible. Such an explanation has also been suggested by SHKLOVSKY and WOLTJER [76]. This problem of the Crab X-ray source has not as yet received a thorough theoretical treatment, and present conclusions must be regarded as tentative.

3·5. *The galactic center.* – The X-ray source *Sgr* XR-1 at (or near) the galactic center is of special interest if it is indeed connected with processes in the nucleus of the galaxy. The first discrete X-ray source discovered [22] was identified with the galactic center, although apparently most of the observed counting rate was actually due to the stronger *Scorpius* source which, with the poor resolution, could not be distinguished from the galactic center. On the assumption that the X-ray source was the galactic center, we attempted to connect the effect with phenomena observed in the nuclei of external galaxies and with the radio observations of the galactic center [30]. As we mentioned earlier (Sect. **3**.3), our initial hypothesis of production by bremsstrahlung by nonthermal electrons meets with difficulties of energy requirements. A more plausible explanation is that the X-rays are due to thermal bremsstrahlung, in which case the characteristics (density, mass, etc.) of the source would correspond to those enumerated at the end of Sect. **3**.3.

Alternatively, the X-rays from the galactic center could be explained as synchrotron radiation. The energies of the synchrotron electrons would then have to be very large and their lifetime very short. However, it is interesting to plot [66] the X-ray observations of the galactic center along with radio observations [77] of the nonthermal source, as in Fig. 11. The lines are the extensions of the power law spectra derived for indices within limits (-0.72 ± 0.05) such as to fit the radio data. It is seen that the X-ray point lies within the limits defined by the extrapolated curves, although the extrapolation is over a factor 10^{10} in frequency. While this might be taken to mean that a single mechanism is responsible for both the radio and X-radiation, it must be remembered that the ratio of the lifetimes τ_r/τ_X of the electrons giving rise to synchrotron radiation in the two spectral regions ν_r and ν_X is $(\nu_r/\nu_X)^{\frac{1}{2}}$. Since the lifetimes of the X-ray synchrotron electrons must be very short (~ 30 y, see Sect. **3**.3), and there is apparently no change in spectral index over the radio to X-ray frequency range, this would mean that the radio synchrotron source was also formed recently.

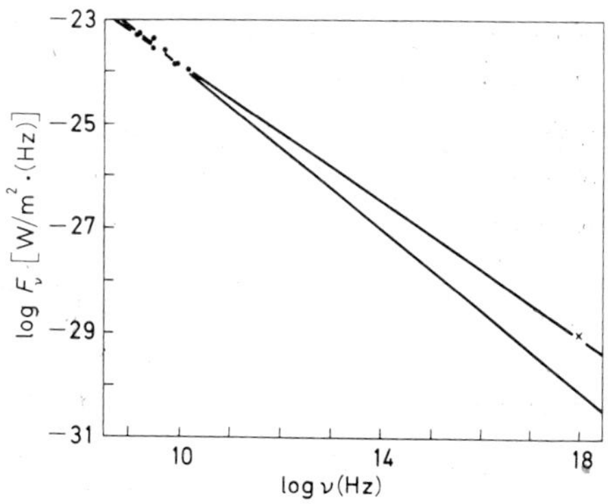

Fig. 11. – The observed radiation spectrum from the galactic center. Dots denote the radio observations; and X denotes the X-ray point, determined from an energy flux 10^{-8} erg/cm²·s and bandwidth $\Delta\nu/\nu = 1$ at $\nu = 10^{18}$ Hz.

3.6. *Extragalactic discrete sources.* – There is still the possibility that some of the sources are extragalactic, and we consider in particular the *Scorpius* source from which an energy flux of $J_E \sim 10^{-7}$ erg/cm²·s is observed in the X-ray region. If the *Scorpius* source were at a typical galactic distance (that is, within our own galaxy) $d_g \sim 10$ kparsec, its X-ray *luminosity* would be

$L_g = 4\pi d_g^2 J_E \sim 10^{39}$ erg/s. If it were at a typical *inter*-galactic distance (the distance to a nearby galaxy) $d_{i\text{-}g} \sim 1$ Mparsec, its luminosity would be $L_{i\text{-}g} \sim 10^{43}$ erg/s, while if it were at a cosmological distance (to a distant galaxy) $d_c \sim 1000$ Mparsec, its luminosity would be $L_c \sim 10^{49}$ erg/s. We now make several observations concerning the energetics of the problem of establishing the distance to and the nature of the *Scorpius* source. On a cosmic time scale (*) $\tau_c \sim 10^{10}$ y the energy $L_{i\text{-}g}\tau \sim 3 \cdot 10^{60}$ erg is small compared with the optical energy radiated by a normal galaxy ($\sim 10^{62}$ erg), but a normal galaxy would be expected to radiate a very much smaller amount of energy in X-rays. No unusual external galaxies are observed in the direction of the *Scorpius* source which is about 20° off the galactic center, although interstellar extinction of our own galaxy prevents observations at lower galactic latitudes (say $\leqslant 10°$). However, there are no strong radio sources in the direction of *Scorpius*. Regarding the possibility that the *Scorpius* source is a distant galaxy, we note that $L_c \tau_c \sim 3 \cdot 10^{66}$ erg, much greater even than the rest mass energy $M_g c^2$ of a galaxy. Moreover, in the matter-antimatter annihilation of a galactic mass which we might conceive took place in a time $\ll \tau_c$, the photon energies would be $\geqslant 0.5$ MeV, not X-ray (keV) energies. On the other hand, the size of a small radio source, for example a quasi-stellar object, is $s \sim 10$ kparsec, and the time τ_s for a light signal to propagate this distance is $s/c \sim 10^{12}$ s. The product $L_c \tau_s$ is then $\sim 10^{61}$ erg, roughly the energy E_r of strong radio sources which may be stored in the relativistic particles.

In summary, it appears that *normal* distant galaxies (including radio galaxies) are incapable of producing the observed energy flux J_E corresponding to the *Scorpius* source over evolutionary time scales $\sim 10^{10}$ y. However, an outburst over a shorter time might be capable energetically of producing the required X-ray luminosity. Let us consider further such a hypothetical outburst in a galaxy at a distance d involving the release of an amount E of energy, of which a fraction f_γ is emitted in high-energy photons of mean energy $\bar{E}_\gamma$. If the outburst occurs during a time τ, the observed resulting photon flux would be

$$J_\gamma = \frac{f_\gamma E/\bar{E}_\gamma}{4\pi d^2 \tau}\,. \tag{3.18}$$

For $E = 10^{60}$ erg, $d = 1000$ Mparsec, and with $\bar{E}_\gamma$ in MeV and τ in years we have

$$J_\gamma \approx 170\, f_\gamma/\bar{E}_\gamma \tau \text{ photons/cm}^2\cdot\text{s}\,,$$

(*) This time is also roughly the characteristic time for the evolution of a galaxy.

and for $\bar{E}_\gamma \sim 100$ MeV (mean energy from π^0-decay) and $\tau \sim 1000$ y (time scale for outburst), $J_\gamma \sim 10^{-3} f_\gamma$ photons/cm²·s. Unless f_γ is very small, a flux of this magnitude could be observable. The detection of such a discrete source of γ-rays (or X-rays) might then possibly be interpreted as the observation of the birth of a strong radio source. Finally, we might mention that DUTHIE *et al.* [26] report a possible (~ 100 MeV) γ-ray flux of ~ 0.002 photons/cm²·s from *Cygnus* A which is at a distance ~ 100 Mparsec.

REFERENCES

[1] T. A. CHUBB, H. FRIEDMAN, R. W. KREPLIN and J. E. KUPPERIAN jr.: *J. Geophys. Res.*, **62**, 389 (1957); see also H. FRIEDMAN: *Rep. Prog. Phys.*, **25**, 163 (1962).

[2] E. FEENBERG and H. PRIMAKOFF: *Phys. Rev.*, **73**, 449 (1948).

[3] J. B. POLLACK and G. G. FAZIO: *Phys. Rev.*, **131**, 2684 (1963); *Ap. J.*, **141**, 730 (1965).

[4] V. L. GINZBURG and S. I. SYROVATSKY: *Žur. Ėksp. Teor. Fiz.*, **45**, 353 (1963); *Soviet Phys.*, **18**, 245 (1964); *Žur. Ėksp. Teor. Fiz.*, **46**, 1865 (1964); *Soviet Phys.*, **19**, 1255 (1964).

[5] P. M. MORRISON: *Nuovo Cimento*, **7**, 858 (1958); see also M. P. SAVEDOFF: *Nuovo Cimento*, **7**, 1584 (1959).

[6] V. L. GINZBURG and S. I. SYROVATSKY: *Astr. Zhur.*, **40**, 466 (1963); *Soviet Astr.*, **7**, 356 (1963).

[7] G. R. BURBIDGE: *Progr. Theor. Phys.*, **27**, 999 (1962); G. R. BURBIDGE and F. HOYLE: *Proc. Phys. Soc.* (*London*), **84**, 141 (1964).

[8] J. A. DE SHONG, R. H. HILDEBRAND and P. MEYER: *Phys. Rev. Letters*, **12**, 3 (1964); B. AGRINIER, Y. KOECHLIN, B. PARLIER, G. BOELLA, G. DEGLI ANTONI, C. DILWORTH, L. SCARSI and G. SIRONI: *Phys. Rev. Letters*, **13**, 377 (1964).

[9] V. L. GINZBURG and S. I. SYROVATSKY: *Origin of Cosmic Rays* (London, 1964).

[10] See, for example, R. MARSHAK: *Meson Physics* (New York, 1952).

[11] L. LANDAU: *Izv. Akad. Nauk, SSSR*, **17**, 51 (1953).

[12] J. M. KIDD: *Nuovo Cimento*, **27**, 57 (1963).

[13] R. J. GOULD, T. GOLD and E. E. SALPETER: *Ap. J*, **138**, 408 (1963); J. DORSCHNER, J. GÜRTLER and K.-H. SCHMIDT: *Astron. Nachr.* (to be published).

[14] J. M. JAUCH and F. ROHRLICH: *Theory of Photons and Electrons* (Cambridge, 1955).

[15] W. HEITLER: *The Quantum Theory of Radiation* (London, 1954).

[16] T. M. DONAHUE: *Phys. Rev.*, **84**, 972 (1951).

[17] J. E. FELTEN and P. MORRISON: *Phys. Rev. Letters*, **10**, 453 (1963).

[18] G. FIELD: *Ap. J.*, **135**, 684 (1962); R. D. DAVIES and R. C. JENNISON: *M. N.*, **128**, 123 (1964); R. D. DAVIES: *M. N.*, **128**, 133 (1964).

[19] S. HAYAKAWA and K. KITAO: *Prog. Theor. Phys.*, **16**, 139 (1956).

[20] S. E. STROM and K. M. STROM: *Pub. Astron. Soc. Pacific*, **73**, 43 (1961).

[21] A. I. NIKISHOV: *Zhur. Eksp. Teor. Fiz.*, **41**, 549 (1961); *Soviet Phys.*, **14**, 393 (1962).

[22] R. GIACCONI, H. GURSKY, F. R. PAOLINI and B. ROSSI: *Phys. Rev. Letters*, **9**, 439 (1962); H. GURSKY, R. GIACCONI and F. R. PAOLINI: *Phys. Rev. Letters*, **11**, 530 (1963).

[23] S. BOWYER, E. T. BYRAN, T. A. CHUBB and H. FRIEDMAN: *Nature*, **201**, 1307 (1964).

[24] J. R. ARNOLD, A. E. METZGER, E. C. ANDERSON and M. A. VAN DILLA: *J. Geophys. Res.*, **67**, 4878 (1962); A. E. METZGER, E. C. ANDERSON, M. A. VAN DILLA and J. R. ARNOLD: *Nature*, **204**, 766 (1964).

[25] W. L. KRAUSHAAR and G. W. CLARK: *Phys. Rev. Letters*, **8**, 106 (1962); see also A. BRACCESI and M. CECCARELLI: *Nuovo Cimento*, **17**, 691 (1960).

[26] J. G. DUTHIE, E. M. HAFNER, M. F. KAPLON and G. G. FAZIO: *Phys. Rev. Letters*, **10**, 364 (1963).

[27] R. FIRKOWSKI, J. GAWIN, R. MAZE and A. ZAWADSKI: *J. Phys. Soc. Japan*, **17**, *Suppl. A-III*, 123 (1962).

[28] K. SUGA, J. ESCOBAR, G. W. CLARK, W. HAZAN, A. HENDEL and K. MURAKAMI: *J. Phys. Soc. Japan* **17**, *Suppl. A-III*, 128 (1962).

[29] L. E. PETERSON: *J. Geophys. Res.*, **65** (1965).

[30] R. J. GOULD and G. R. BURBIDGE: *Ap. J.*, **138**, 969 (1963); see also G. B. FIELD and R. C. HENRY: *Ap. J.*, **140**, 1002 (1964).

[31] V. L. GINZBURG and S. I. SYROVATSKY: *Astron. Žurn.*, **41**, 430 (1964); *Soviet Astron.*, **8**, 342 (1964).

[32] T. GOLD and F. HOYLE: *Paris Symposium on Radio Astronomy*, ed. by R. N. BRACEWELL (Stanford, 1958).

[33] E. M. BURBIDGE, G. R. BURBIDGE and F. HOYLE: *Ap. J.*, **138**, 873 (1963).

[34] D. W. SCIAMA: *Quart. J. R.A.S.*, **5**, 196 (1964).

[35] G. R. BURBIDGE and F. HOYLE: *Nuovo Cimento*, **4**, 1 (1956).

[36] C. A. COMBES, B. CORK, W. GALBRAITH, G. R. LAMBERTSON and W. A. WENZEL: *Phys. Rev.*, **112**, 1303 (1958).

[37] R. J. GOULD and D. W. SCIAMA: *Ap. J.*, **140**, 1634 (1964); regarding cosmological consideration, see also G. C. MCVITTIE: *Phys. Rev.*, **128**, 2871 (1962).

[38] S. BOWYER, E. T. BYRAM, T. A. CHUBB and H. FRIEDMAN: *Science*, **147**, 394 (1965).

[39] S. BOWYER, E. T. BYRAM, T. A. CHUBB and H. FRIEDMAN: *Science*, **146**, 912 (1964).

[40] H. GÜRSKY, R. GIACCONI and F. R. PAOLINI: *Phys. Rev. Letters*, **11**, 530 (1963).

[41] M. ODA, G. CLARK, G. GARMIRE, M. WADA, R. GIACCONI, H. GÜRSKY and J. WATERS: *Nature*, **205**, 554 (1965); R. GIACCONI, H. GÜRSKY, J. WATERS, G. CLARK and B. ROSSI: *Nature*, **204**, 981 (1964).

[42] P. C. FISHER and A. J. MEYEROTT: *Ap. J.* **139**, 123 (1964); *Ap. J.*, **140**, 821 (1964).

[43] P. C. FISHER, D. B. CLARK, A. J. MEYEROTT and K. L. SMITH: *Ann. d'Astrophys.*, **27**, 809 (1964).

[44] P. C. FISHER, D. B. CLARK, A. J. MEYEROTT and K. L. SMITH: private communication.

[45] I. S. SHKLOVSKY: private communication (1964).

[46] M. I. QUIGLEY and C. G. HASLAM: *Nature*, **203**, 1272 (1964).

[47] E. M. BURBIDGE, G. R. BURBIDGE, W. A. FOWLER and F. HOYLE: *Rev. Mod. Phys.*, **29**, 547 (1957).

[48] D. D. CLAYTON and D. D. CRADDOCK: *Ap. J.*, **142**, 189 (1965).

[49] D. D. CLAYTON, W. A. FOWLER and P. SEEGER: *Ap. J. Suppl.* (to be published).

[50] H. Y. Chiu: *Ann. Phys.*, **26**, 364 (1964).
[51] A. Finzi: *Ap. J.*, **139**, 774 (1964).
[52] W. Baade and F. Zwicky: *Ap. J.*, **88**, 411 (1938); F. Zwicky: *Ap. J.*, **88**, 522 (1938).
[53] L. Landau: *Physik. Zeit. Soviet Union*, **1**, 285 (1932).
[54] J. R. Oppenheimer and G. M. Volkoff: *Phys. Rev.*, **55**, 374 (1939).
[55] B. Datt: *Zeit. f. Ap.*, **108**, 314 (1938); J. R. Oppenheimer and H. Snyder: *Phys. Rev.*, **56**, 455 (1939).
[56] F. Hoyle, W. A. Fowler, G. R. Burbidge and E. M. Burbidge: *Ap. J.*, **139**, 909 (1964).
[57] W. A. Fowler and F. Hoyle: *Ann. Phys.*, **10**, 280 (1960); *Ap. J. Suppl.*, **9**, 201 (1964).
[58] S. Colgate: *Proc. of the Jaipur Conference* (in press).
[59] C. R. O'Dell: *Ap. J.*, **136**, 809 (1962).
[60] C. W. Misner and H. S. Zapolsky: *Phys. Rev. Letters*, **12**, 635 (1964).
[61] H. Y. Chiu and E. E. Salpeter: *Phys. Rev. Letters*, **12**, 413 (1964).
[62] D. C. Morton: *Ap. J.*, **140**, 460 (1964).
[63] J. N. Bahcall and R. A. Wolf: *Phys. Rev. Letters*, **14**, 343 (1965).
[64] A. Finzi: *Phys. Rev.*, **137**, B 472 (1965).
[65] P. Morrison: *Second Texas Symposium on Relativistic Astrophysics* (Chicago) in press.
[66] G. R. Burbidge, R. J. Gould and W. H. Tucker: *Phys. Rev. Letters*, **14**, 289 (1965).
[67] See, however, V. L. Ginzburg, L. M. Ozernoi and S. I. Syrovatsky: *Doklady Akad. Nauk SSSR*, **154**, 557 (1964), transl. *Soviet Physics-Doklady*, **9**, 3 (1964). They consider circumstances where one might be able to detect Compton-synchrotron photons of energy $\sim(10^7 \simeq 10^8)$ eV at a rate $\sim 10^{-5}$ photons/cm$^2\cdot$s from the quasi-stellar object 3C273-B which has a negative radio spectral index α. Because of the negative index, most of the Compton-synchrotron photon flux comes from the *high*-energy end of the spectrum. The expected number of X-ray photons is smaller and unobservable.
[68] S. Hayakawa and M. Matsuoka: *Prog. Theor. Phys.*, **29**, 612 (1963).
[69] See, for example, H. A. Bethe and E. E. Salpeter: *Quantum Mechanics of One- and Two-Electron Atoms* (New York, 1957).
[70] R. G. Conway, K. J. Kellermann and R. J. Long: *M. N.*, **125**, 261 (1963).
[71] G. W. Clark: *Phys. Rev. Letters*, **14**, 91 (1965).
[72] D. C. Morton: *Nature*, **201**, 1308 (1964).
[73] V. L. Ginzburg, S. B. Pikelner and I. S. Shklovsky: *Astr Žur.*, **32**, 503 (1955).
[74] G. R. Burbidge: *Suppl. Nuovo Cimento*, **8**, 403 (1958).
[75] J. H. Fruin, J. V. Jelley, C. D. Long, N. A. Porter and T. C. Weekes: *Phys. Letters*, **10**, 176 (1964).
[76] I. S. Shklovsky: private communication (1964); L. Woltjer: *Ap. J.*, **140**, 1309 (1964).
[77] A. Maxwell and B. Downes: *Nature*, **204**, 865 (1964).

The General-Relativistic Theory of Stellar Structure and Dynamics (*).

K. S. THORNE (**)

Palmer Physical Laboratory, Princeton University - Princeton, N. J.

1. – Introduction.

Astrophysics and general relativity influenced each other very little during the long period between the first few years of relativity theory and about 1963. In fact, during that period the absence of any extensive experimental or observational phenomena in which general relativistic effects might be important tended to insulate Einstein's theory from all other branches of physics.

However, during the last three years a marked change has begun to occur: The discovery and investigation of quasi-stellar radio sources (***), of explosions in galactic nuclei (*.*), and of X-ray emission from supernova remnants (.*.) have suggested to astrophysicists that strong gravitational fields might, after all, play an important role in astrophysical phenomena. At the same time, major advances in the techniques of radio and optical astronomy have enabled astronomers to begin to determine the cosmological structure of the universe (*..*)—which structure is believed to be governed by general relativity—; and the development of powerful new experimental techniques has made possible new and improved tests of Einstein's theory (.**.). Because of these developments, strong

(*) Supported in part by U. S. Air Force Office of Scientific Research.

(**) NSF Postdoctoral Fellow. Present address: California Institute of Technology, Pasadena, Cal.

(***) See, *e.g.*, ROBINSON *et al.* (1965) and the lectures in this volume by E. M. BURBIDGE and A. R. SANDAGE.

(*.*) See, *e.g.*, BURBIDGE, BURBIDGE and SANDAGE (1963); also the lectures in this volume by E. M. BURBIDGE and A. R. SANDAGE.

(.*.) See, *e.g.*, the lectures in this volume by GIACCONI *et al.*

(*..*) See, *e.g.*, the lectures in this volume by SANDAGE and by SCIAMA; also DICKE *et al.* (1965).

(.**.) See, *e.g.*, DICKE (1964), WEBER (1964), POUND and SNIDER (1964) and other references cited there, HILL and ZANONI (1966), SCHIFF (1960, 1966), FAIRBANK and EVERITT (1966), SHAPIRO (1964, 1966 *a*, *b*), ROSS and SCHIFF (1966).

gravitation physics as described by general relativity is rapidly becoming of interest to astrophysicists, and astrophysics is rapidly becoming of interest to relativists.

The present set of lectures is an attempt to facilitate the growing dialogue and co-operation between astrophysicists and relativists by presenting the general-relativistic theory of stellar structure and dynamics in a manner which, hopefully, will be intelligible to both, as well as to the uninitiated graduate student. As a result of this orientation neither a knowledge of the Newtonian theory of stellar structure, nor previous contact with general relativity are prerequisites for understanding these lectures—at least I hope they are not. All I have intended to assume of the reader is a strong background in the fundamentals of classical and modern physics, such as a student acquires in a four-year course of study at the university level.

The desire to not assume any general relativity as a prerequisite to reading these lectures has led me to employ a slightly novel—but, I believe, very powerful—approach to the derivation and discussion of the relativistic laws of stellar structure and dynamics. At no point in these lectures is tensor analysis or modern differential geometry used. Instead, the fundamental physical concepts of general relativity (*e.g.* the curvature of space-time), and a few basic results of the theory (*e.g.* red-shift in a static gravitational field) are introduced; and then these concepts and results are used, together with elementary considerations from theromodynamics and classical mechanics, as a complete basis for all further considerations. It must be emphasized that, although this « poor man's approach » to general relativity is extremely useful and powerful in the present context, it is so *only* because we restrict our attention to situations with spherical symmetry and thereby strongly limit the types of dynamical effects which are considered. (For example, spherically symmetric bodies cannot radiate gravitational waves.)

I make no apology to either the astrophysicist or the relativist for the omission of tensorial and differential-geometric tools from these lectures. The astrophysicist who is interested only in applying general relativity to stellar structure and dynamics has little or no need for the full formalism of relativity. On the other hand, this presentation of stellar theory will probably be clearer physically to a relativist who is familiar with differential geometry than would be a presentation couched in differential-geometric terms.

Throughout these lectures two distinct sets of physical units are employed: *standard* c.g.s. *units*, and *geometrized units*. Geometrized units are units in which Newton's gravitation constant, G, the speed of light, c, and Boltzmann's constant, k, are set equal to unity, and all quantities are expressed in terms of length. Quantities measured in geometrized units are distinguished from the corresponding cgs quantities by an asterisk; for example, the mass of the sun is $M_\odot = 1.989\cdot 10^{33}$ g in c.g.s. units, or $M^*_\odot = GM_\odot/c^2 = 1.476$ km in geometrized units. Table I shows how to convert quickly from one set of units to the other.

These lectures are divided into 6 major Sections: In Sect. **2** are presented the basic thermodynamic and gravitational concepts upon which the subsequent discussions are based. Section **3** contains a derivation and discussion of the general-relativistic equations of stellar structure, together with delineations and proofs of some fundamental properties of relativistic stellar models. Section **4** is a development of the theory of the dynamical stability of relativistic stellar models. In Sect. **5** the tools developed in Sect. **3** and **4** are applied to configurations of matter near the endpoint of thermonuclear evolution (white dwarfs, neutron stars, hyperon stars); while in Sect. **6** those tools are applied to a wide class of hot, nondegenerate stellar models. Finally, Sect. **7** is a brief introduction to the theory of gravitational collapse to zero volume and infinite density.

TABLE I. – *The conversion from* c.g.s. *units to geometrized units* (*).

Quantity	cgs units	Geometrized units
Length	l (cm)	l (cm)
Time	t (s)	t^* (cm) $= ct = 2.997\,925\cdot 10^{10}\,t$
Mass	M (g)	M^* (cm) $= GM/c^2 = 0.742\cdot 10^{-28}\,M$
Energy	E (erg)	E^* (cm) $= GE/c^4 = 0.826\cdot 10^{-49} E$
Density of mass	ϱ (g/cm³)	ϱ^* (cm⁻²) $= G\varrho/c^2 = 0.742\cdot 10^{-28}\varrho$
Density of energy	ε (erg/cm³)	ε^* (cm⁻²) $= G\varepsilon/c^4 = 0.825\cdot 10^{-49}\,\varepsilon$
Pressure	p (dyne/cm²)	p^* (cm⁻²) $= Gp/c^4 = 0.825\cdot 10^{-49} p$
Temperature	T (°K)	T^* (cm) $= GkT/c^4 = 1.140\cdot 10^{-65}\,T$
Entropy	S (erg/°K)	S^* (dimensionless) $= S/k = 7.243\,5\cdot 10^{15}\,S$
Luminosity	L (erg/s cm²)	L^* (cm⁻²) $= GL/c^5 = 2.755\cdot 10^{-60} L$
Mass of sun	$M_\odot = 1.989\cdot 10^{33}$ g	$M^*_\odot = GM_\odot/c^2 = 1.476$ km
Luminosity of sun	$L_\odot = 3.90\cdot 10^{33}$ erg/s	$L^*_\odot = GL_\odot/c^5 = 1.07\cdot 10^{-26}$ cm⁻²
Nuclear density	$\varrho_{nuc} = 2\cdot 10^{14}$ g/cm³	$\varrho^*_{nuc} = G\varrho_{nuc}/c^2 = 1.48\cdot 10^{-14}$ cm⁻²
Quantum of angular momentum	$\hbar = 1.0544\cdot 10^{-27}$ gcm²/s	$\hbar^* = G\hbar/c^3 = 2.610\cdot 10^{-66}$ cm²

(*) Adapted from HARRISON, THORNE, WAKANO and WHEELER (1965).

If this written version of my lectures seems to overemphasize hot, nondegenerate stars as compared to configurations at the endpoint of thermonuclear evolution, it is because there is already in print a comprehensive monograph on configurations at the endpoint of thermonuclear evolution. That monograph—HARRISON, THORNE, WAKANO, and WHEELER (1965); cited henceforth as HTWW—is in large measure a companion to these lectures. Also closely related to these lectures are the review articles by ZEL'DOVICH and NOVIKOV (1964, 1965), and the brief, semipopular article of THORNE (1965*c*).

The form of these lectures and my point of view on the topics treated here have been influenced by a large number of people, foremost among whom are J. M. BARDEEN, J. P. WRIGHT, and *above all* J. A. WHEELER. I thank them.

2. – Thermodynamic and gravitational preliminaries.

2·1. *Separation of short-range and long-range forces* (*). – The structure and dynamics of a star are governed by an interplay between nuclear forces, electromagnetic forces, and gravitational forces. If it were necessary to describe the interactions between these three fundamental forces in precise mathematical detail, so complex a problem as the structure of a star could never be studied. The basic simplification which makes stellar theory possible is the clean separation of the short-range nuclear and electromagnetic forces from the long-range gravitational forces. By the phrase « clean separation of forces » we mean the following. In astrophysical situations the characteristic distance over which the gravitational force changes is many orders of magnitude greater than the microscopic scale at which nuclear and electromagnetic forces act. Consequently, the thermodynamic properties of matter and radiation, which describe the statistically averaged, macroscopic effects of nuclear and electromagnetic forces, are unaffected by gravitation. Gravitation is important only at the macroscopic scale, where, in cooperation with the thermodynamic properties of matter, it fixes the thermodynamic state (pressure, density, temperature).

Let us verify that short-range and long-range forces are, indeed, separated in astrophysical situations. There are several fundamental short-range lengths over which gravitational forces must be homogeneous in order for ordinary, « flat-space » thermodynamics to be valid. One fundamental short-range length is the $\sim 10^{-13}$ cm which characterizes nuclear forces. Another is the characteristic distance of action of strong electric forces, which is usually less than or of the order of the separation between atomic nuclei (**).

$$l_{\text{s.r.}} \sim [(\text{density of total mass-energy})^*/(\text{nuclear rest mass})^*]^{-\frac{1}{3}} = (\varrho^*/\mu_{\text{N}}^*)^{-\frac{1}{3}} \tag{2.1a}$$

(macroscopic charge neutrality). A third short-range length is the size of a sample of matter containing $\sim 10^{21}$ atomic nuclei (**),

$$l_{\text{s.r.}} \sim 10^7 (\varrho^*/\mu_{\text{N}}^*)^{-\frac{1}{3}}\,. \tag{2.1b}$$

(*) For a more detailed exposition of these ideas see HTWW, p. 96.

(**) Formulae (2.1*a*), (2.1*b*) for the separation between nuclei and the size of a region containing 10^{21} nuclei break down at densities above $\sim 10^{14}$ g/cm³ because of large Fermi kinetic energies and nuclear interaction energies. However, these formulae remain sufficiently accurate for present purposes up to $\sim 10^{30}$ g/cm³.

(It is over such samples of matter that the statistical averaging which underlies thermodynamics takes place.) Finally, additional fundamental lengths are the characteristic «localizability distances»—the Compton wave lengths— of the particles which make up the matter. An upper limit on all of the short-range lengths is

$$(2.2)\qquad \begin{cases} l_{\text{s.r.}} \leqslant \begin{cases} 10^{7}(\varrho^*/\mu_{\text{N}}^*)^{-\frac{1}{3}} & \text{if } \varrho \leqslant 10^{27}\ \text{g/cm}^3 \\ \hbar/m_e c \sim 10^{-10}\ \text{cm} & \text{if } \varrho \geqslant 10^{27}\ \text{g/cm}^3 , \end{cases} \\ \sim \begin{cases} 10^4\ \text{km} & \text{if } \varrho \sim 10^{-29}\ \text{g/cm}^3 \ \text{(density of universe)}, \\ 0.1\ \text{cm} & \text{if } \varrho \sim 1\ \text{g/cm}^3 \ \text{(density of water)}, \\ 10^{-6}\ \text{cm} & \text{if } \varrho \sim 10^{15}\ \text{g/cm}^3 \ \text{(nuclear density)}, \\ 10^{-10}\ \text{cm} & \text{if } \varrho \geqslant 10^{27}\ \text{g/cm}^3 . \end{cases} \end{cases}$$

The characteristic size of inhomogeneities in a gravitational field is the radius of the space curvature which, according to general relativity, describes gravitation. In a region of space-time where the density of mass-energy is ϱ^*, this radius of curvature is (see, *e.g.* HTWW pp. 13 and 97)

$$(2.3)\qquad l_{\text{l.r.}} \sim \varrho^{*-\frac{1}{2}} \sim \begin{cases} \text{the Hubble radius} & \text{if } \varrho \sim 10^{-29}\ \text{g/cm}^3 \ \text{(density of universe)}, \\ 10^{14}\ \text{cm} & \text{if } \varrho \sim 1\ \text{g/cm}^3 \ \text{(density of water)}, \\ 10^{7}\ \text{cm} & \text{if } \varrho \sim 10^{15}\ \text{g/cm}^3 \ \text{(nuclear density)} \\ 10^{-10}\ \text{cm} & \text{if } \varrho \sim 10^{49}\ \text{g/cm}^3 . \end{cases}$$

So long as $l_{\text{l.r.}}$ is orders of magnitude greater than $l_{\text{s.r.}}$, *i.e.* so long as

$$(2.4)\qquad \varrho \ll 10^{49}\ \text{g/cm}^3 ,$$

long-range gravitational forces can be cleanly separated from short-range forces. Condition (2.4) is satisfied with more than 20 orders of magnitude to spare in all conceivable astrophysical situations except one: the endpoint of gravitational collapse to a «general-relativistic singularity» (see Sect. **7**). Hence, throughout our discussion (except in analysing the endpoint of collapse) we can place great confidence in the clean separation of gravitational forces from the short-range forces which determine the construction and thermodynamic properties of matter.

2'2. *Thermodynamics, the science of short-range forces.*

2'2.1. Fundamental thermodynamic quantities. The macroscopic effects of short-range forces on the constitution of matter are described by the thermodynamic properties of matter. Throughout our discussion we shall restrict ourselves to matter which has the properties of a *perfect* ! *uid—i.e.*, nonviscous matter in which all stresses are zero except for an isotropic pressure. The basic thermodynamic quantities of interest to us will be:

a) *Pressure*, p (dyne/cm^2) or p^* (cm^{-2}) $= Gp/c^4$, as measured in a reference frame comoving with the matter. We shall assume that the pressure is always isotropic (negligible shear).

b) *Number density of baryons*, n (cm^{-3}) or $n^* = n$, as measured in a reference frame comoving with the matter. We shall often make use of the law of conservation of baryons.

c) *Average rest mass of a baryon*, μ_B (g) or μ_B^* (cm) $= G\mu_B/c^2$. The quantity μ_B depends upon the nuclear state of the matter: for a hydrogen gas μ_B is the mass of a hydrogen atom in its ground state; for a sample of pure ^{56}Fe, μ_B is 1/56 times the mass of a ^{56}Fe atom in its ground state. For a mixture of relativistically degenerate electron, proton, and neutron gases containing 8 neutrons for each proton and electron, μ_B is $(\frac{8}{9})\times$(rest mass of neutron)+ $+(\frac{1}{9})\times$(mass of hydrogen atom in its ground state). Whenever nuclear reactions occur, μ_B changes.

d) *Internal energy density of the matter*, ε (erg/cm^3) or ε^* (cm^{-2}) $= G\varepsilon/c^4$, as measured in a reference frame comoving with the matter. The internal energy includes all forms of energy except the rest mass of the baryons. For example, it includes atomic excitation energies, thermal kinetic energies, « zero-point » energies of compression, and photon energies.

e) *Density of total mass-energy*, ϱ (g/cm^3) or ϱ^* (cm^{-2})$=G\varrho/c^2$, as measured in a reference frame comoving with the matter. This includes rest mass-energy and internal energy

$$\varrho^* = \mu_B^* n + \varepsilon^* . \tag{2.5}$$

f) *Thermodynamic temperature of the matter*, T(°K) or T^*(cm) $= G(kT)/c^4$, as measured in a reference frame comoving with the matter.

g) *Entropy per baryon*, s (erg/°K) or s^*(dimensionless)$= s/k$, as measured in a reference frame comoving with the matter. The density of entropy is clearly ns (erg/°K cm^3) or ns^* (cm^{-3}).

h) *Fractional nuclear abundances*, $Z_H, Z_{He}, Z_n, Z_\Lambda, \ldots$. Z_k is the fraction of all baryons in a given sample of matter which are in the form k. The nuclear abundances must satisfy

$$\sum_k Z_k = 1 , \qquad \sum_k \mu_k Z_k = \mu_B , \tag{2.6}$$

where μ_k is the rest mass per baryon of the nuclear species k, and μ_B is the average baryonic rest mass.

i) *Nuclear chemical potentials*, $\bar{\mu}_k(g)$ or $\bar{\mu}_k^*(\mathrm{cm}) = G\bar{\mu}_k/c^2$. Let one baryon of species k be inserted into a sample of matter, along with enough internal energy to keep the sample's total entropy and volume constant. The total mass-energy added in this process is equal to $\bar{\mu}_k$, the chemical potential for baryons of type k.

In almost all astrophysical situations to be considered in these lectures nuclear burning occurs sufficiently slowly that nuclear reactions are *not* in thermodynamic equilibrium with other types of thermodynamic energy exchange. Consequently, when a sample of matter is subjected to a thermodynamic change of state the quantities p^*, n, ε^*, ϱ^*, T^*, and s^* change, but the average baryonic rest mass, μ_{B}^*, and the nuclear abundances remain fixed. Of the 6 parameters p^*, n, ε^*, ϱ^*, T^*, s^* which describe the thermodynamic state only 5—p^*, n, ϱ^*, T^*, s^*—are fundamental; the internal energy ε^* can always be expressed in terms of the other parameters through eq. (2.5).

In addition to the above thermodynamic parameters we shall be interested in the *adiabatic indices*, defined by (*)

$$\Gamma_1 \equiv (\partial \ln p^*/\partial \ln n)_{s^*} = (\varrho^* + p^*)\,p^{*-1}(\partial p^*/\partial \varrho^*)_{s^*}\,, \tag{2.7}$$

$$\Gamma_2 \equiv [1 - (\partial \ln T^*/\partial \ln p^*)_{s^*}]^{-1}\,, \tag{2.8}$$

$$\Gamma_3 \equiv 1 + (\partial \ln T^*/\partial \ln n)_{s^*} = 1 + (\varrho^* + p^*)\,T^{*-1}(\partial T^*/\partial \varrho^*)_{s^*}\,, \tag{2.9}$$

and in the *velocity of sound* (*)

$$v_s^* = [\Gamma_1 p^*/(\varrho^* + p^*)]^{\frac{1}{2}} = [(\partial p^*/\partial \varrho^*)_{s^*}]^{\frac{1}{2}}\,. \tag{2.10}$$

Note that because the velocity of sound can never exceed the velocity of light ($v_s^* \leqslant 1$), the pressure, p^*, can never exceed the density of mass-energy, ϱ^*.

2.2.2. Effects of special relativity on the laws of thermodynamics. By virtue of the separation of short-range and long-range forces, we need not take general relativity into account when discussing the thermodynamic properties of matter. Furthermore, so long as we carry out our thermodynamic analysis in reference frames which comove with the matter, we need not consider special relativity effects—with one exception. We must be careful to take into account the equivalence of mass and energy and the consequent inclusion

(*) The second equality in eq. (2.7) and that in (2.9) are straightforward consequences of the first law of thermodynamics—see eq. (2.14). Expression (2.10) for the velocity of sound has been derived within the framework of special relativity by TAUB (1948) and in general relativity by CURTIS (1950). The partial derivatives in eqs. (2.7)-(2.10) must be taken, not only with entropy held constant, but also with nuclear abundances held constant.

of the internal energy density, ε^*, in the total density of mass-energy, ϱ^*. (Cf. equation (2.5).)

To gain some insight into the manner in which the equivalence of mass and energy affects the formulae of thermodynamics, let us state the relationship between heat and entropy, and the first and second laws of thermodynamics in their correct relativistic forms: 1) If a small amount of heat $đQ^*$ is added quasi-statically to a small sample of matter containing δA baryons, then the entropy of the sample is increased by

$$\mathrm{d}(s^*\,\delta A) = (\delta A)\,\mathrm{d}s^* = đQ^*/T^* \,. \tag{2.11}$$

This formula is the same in relativity theory as in ordinary thermodynamics.

ii) During any quasi-static change in the state of our sample in which the total number of baryons, δA, is held fixed, but nuclear reactions may occur, the volume may change, and heat may be added

$$\begin{aligned}\mathrm{d}(\text{total mass-energy}) &\equiv \mathrm{d}(\varrho^*\,\delta A/n) = \\ &= -\,p^*\,\mathrm{d}(\text{volume}) + T^*\,\mathrm{d}(s^*\,\delta A) + \sum_k \bar{\mu}_k^*\,\mathrm{d}(\delta A Z_k) = \\ &= -\,p^*\,\mathrm{d}(\delta A/n) + T^*\,\delta A\,\mathrm{d}s^* + \sum_k \bar{\mu}_k^*\,\delta A\,\mathrm{d}Z_k \,,\end{aligned}$$

or, equivalently,

$$\mathrm{d}\varrho^* = [(\varrho^* + p^*)/n]\,\mathrm{d}n + T^* n\,\mathrm{d}s^* + \sum_k \bar{\mu}_k^* n\,\mathrm{d}Z_k \,. \tag{2.12}$$

These formulae for the first law of thermodynamics differ from the more familiar Newtonian formula

$$\mathrm{d}(\text{internal energy}) = -\,p\,\mathrm{d}(\text{volume}) + đQ + \sum_k \bar{\mu}_k\,\mathrm{d}(\text{number of type } k) \,,$$

because in relativistic theory we must allow for the possibility of changes in the rest mass-energies of the baryons. 3) For any change in the state of our sample which occurs in isolation

$$\mathrm{d}(\text{total entropy}) = (\delta A)\,\mathrm{d}s^* \geqslant 0 \,; \tag{2.13}$$

and equality holds if and only if the change of state occurs reversibly. This formula for the second law of thermodynamics is the same as the corresponding nonrelativistic formula.

An important consequence of the relativistic first law (2.12) is an equation relating isentropic changes in the density of mass-energy to changes in baryon number density

$$(\partial\varrho^*/\partial n)_{s^*} = (\varrho^* + p^*)/n \,. \tag{2.14}$$

The more familiar nonrelativistic statement of this relation is the trivial formula

$$(\partial\varrho^*/\partial n)_{s^*} = \mu_B^* \qquad \text{(nonrelativistic limit).}$$

Additional examples of changes forced onto the formulae of thermodynamics by the equivalence of mass and energy can be found in expression (2.7) and (2.9) for the adiabatic indices Γ_1 and Γ_2 in terms of ϱ^* and p^*, and in expression (2.10) for the velocity of sound in terms of Γ_1, ϱ^*, and p^*. The new, relativistic forms of these expressions are quite easily traced back through eq. (2.14) to the effect of the equivalence of mass and energy on the first law of thermodynamics.

All other formulae of thermodynamics can be put into relativistic form by going back to the foundations of thermodynamics, adding the law of the equivalence of mass and energy, and rederiving the formulae desired by the usual, nonrelativistic method. (See, *e.g.*, TOLMAN (1934*a*) for a partial development of the theory.)

2·2.3. Equations of state. Let us focus our attention on a small sample of matter located inside a static or dynamic star. The thermodynamic properties of that sample can be specified in either of two equivalent ways; 1) by giving the *fundamental equation*

$$\varrho^* = f(n, s^*, Z_1, Z_2, ..., Z_N) \tag{2.15}$$

for the material of which the sample is made, or

2) by giving $2+N$ *equations of state* relating the «intrinsic variables», p^*, T^*, $\bar{\mu}_1^*, ..., \bar{\mu}_N^*$, to the «reduced extrinsic varables», ϱ^*, n, and s^*, and to the nuclear abundances, $Z_1, Z_2, ..., Z_N$ — *e.g.*

$$\left\{\begin{aligned} p^* &= g(\varrho^*, n, s^*, Z_1, ..., Z_N)\,, \\ T^* &= h(\varrho^*, n, s^*, Z_1, ..., Z_N)\,, \\ \bar{\mu}_k^* &= j_k(\varrho^*, n, s^*, Z_1, ..., Z_N)\,. \end{aligned}\right. \tag{2.16}$$

Once the fundamental equation or $2+N$ equations of state have been given, the machinery of thermodynamics enables one to calculate all other desired thermodynamic properties of the sample of matter (see, *e.g.* CALLEN [1960]).

Any sample of matter has $1+N$ thermodynamic degrees of freedom. From a knowledge of the equations of state of the sample, of the laws of thermodynamics, and of the nuclear abundances one can express any $4+N$ of the parameters $(\varrho^*, n, s^*, p^*, T^*, Z_1, ..., Z_N, \bar{\mu}_1^*, ..., \bar{\mu}_N^*)$ as functions of the other $1+N$ parameters.

2·2.4. Inertial mass per unit volume. In our analyses of stellar structure and dynamics we will need one more fundamental result from relativistic thermodynamics and mechanics; an expression for the inertial mass per unit volume of a perfect fluid in which p^*/ϱ^* is not small compared to unity. In order to obtain such an expression, consider in the framework of special relativity a perfect fluid which moves in the x-direction with velocity $v \ll c$ relative to an inertial observer. Focus attention on a fluid element of area A and thickness Δx. The momentum of this fluid element is the total mass-energy, m, which it carries past the observer multiplied by its velocity, v:

$$g = mv .$$

The mass m which passes the observer arises form *two* sources: the density of mass-energy, ϱ, of the fluid, and the work done on the rightward-moving fluid element by the pressure force acting on its left face

$$m = \varrho A\Delta x + \frac{1}{c^2}\times(\text{force on left face})\times$$
$$\times(\text{distance through which force acts as fluid passes observer}) =$$
$$= \varrho A\Delta x + pA\Delta x/c^2 = (\varrho + p/c^2)A\Delta x .$$

Consequently, the momentum is

$$g = (\varrho + p/c^2)(A\Delta x)v .$$

Next suppose that the fluid element is initially at rest and that the external observer applies a force, F, to accelerate it up to velocity $v \ll c$ without changing its proper density and pressure. Then

$$F = \mathrm{d}g/\mathrm{d}t = (\varrho + p/c^2)(A\Delta x)\,\mathrm{d}v/\mathrm{d}t .$$

Consequently, the inertial mass of the fluid element is $(\varrho + p/c^2)A\Delta x$; or, equivalently,

$$(2.17)\qquad \begin{pmatrix}\text{inertial mass per unit volume of a perfect}\\ \text{fluid momentarily at rest with respect to}\\ \text{the inertial observer who measures it}\end{pmatrix}^* = (\varrho^* + p^*).$$

At first sight this result might be disturbing since in Newtonian physics ϱ^* is *by definition* the inertial mass per unit volume. However, in relativity theory, as throughout modern physics, we define mass-energy *not* in terms of reaction to applied forces, but in terms of conservation laws. The density of mass-energy, ϱ^*, is that quantity which obeys the conservation law embodied in the first law of thermodynamics (2.12). In the Newtonian limit $(p/\varrho c^2 \ll 1)$

this quantity happens to be also the inertial mass per unit volume; but in relativity theory it is not.

We should note in passing that the inertial mass per unit volume is actually a tensorial quantity: For bodies in an anisotropic state of stress and with $v \ll c$, the acceleration, $\mathrm{d}\boldsymbol{v}/\mathrm{d}t$, produced by a force per unit volume, $\mathscr{F}$, which does not deform the body, satisfies (*)

$$\mathscr{F} = \varrho(\mathrm{d}\boldsymbol{v}/\mathrm{d}t) + \sum_{j,k=1}^{3} (T^{(0)}_{jk}/c^2)(\mathrm{d}v_j/\mathrm{d}t)\, \boldsymbol{e}_{[k]} . \tag{2.18}$$

Consequently, the inertial mass per unit volume, $\varrho + T^{(0)}_{xx}/c^2$, which resists acceleration in the x-direction differs from that, $\varrho + T^{(0)}_{yy}/c^2$, which resists acceleration in the y-direction. Only in the case of isotropic stresses is the inertial mass the same in all directions.

Although the inertial mass per unit volume is not equal to ϱ, the total inertial mass of any body of negligible self-gravitation (special-relativity limit) and zero velocity is given by

$$(\text{Total inertial mass}) = \int \varrho \, \mathrm{d}(\text{volume}) . \tag{2.19}$$

The stress gives no contribution to the total inertial mass because the equations of stress balance for a body not being deformed,

$$\sum_{j=1}^{3} \partial T^{(0)}_{kj} / \partial x^j = 0 ,$$

guarantee that the volume-integrated stress vanishes.

2·3. *General relativity, the science of long-range forces.*

2·3.1. Gravitation as geometry. According to general relativity the concepts of *gravitational field* and *curvature of space-time* are equivalent. From a knowledge of the curvature, or intrinsic geometry, of 4-dimensional space-time one can calculate the gravitational acceleration of any freely falling test particle as measured by an observer in an arbitrary state of motion near the test particle.

In our discussions of relativistic stellar models we shall find useful two quite different methods for describing the gravitational field. The first method is

(*) See, *e.g.*, the discussion of momentum density by Tolman (1934*a*), p. 65. Alternatively, this equation and the high-velocity generalization of it can be obtained by expressing the special-relativistic equations of motion $\sum_{\mu=0}^{3} (\partial T^{\mu}_{k}/\partial x^{\mu}) = 0$, in terms of the velocity, v^k, and the stresses $T^{(0)}_{jk}$ and density of mass-energy ϱ as measured in the rest frame of the body.

to construct a precisely-defined co-ordinate system in the stellar model, and to give the value relative to this co-ordinate system of the metric tensor, $g_{\mu\nu}$, as a function of the co-ordinates ($x^0 = t^*, x^1, x^2, x^3$). (The value of $g_{\mu\nu}$ is such that the squared proper length of the co-ordinate displacement $[dx^0, dx^1, dx^2, dx^3]$ is

$$ds^2 = \sum_{\mu,\nu} g_{\mu\nu}\, dx^\mu\, dx^\nu \,.) \tag{2.20}$$

The components of $g_{\mu\nu}$ play a role in relativity theory analogous to that of the gravitational potential, U, of Newtonian theory.

Although this first method of describing the gravitational field is very useful in mathematical analyses of stellar models, it has one serious deficiency: It is a co-ordinate-dependent description, whereas the gravitational field—or geometry of spacetime—is co-ordinate-independent. Our second method of describing the gravitational field avoids this deficiency by exhibiting the geometry of space-time pictorially. The pictorial tools of this method are « embedding diagrams », *i.e.* pictures of 3-dimensional spacelike hypersurfaces as they would look if extracted from the space-time manifold of the star and embedded, with one dimension suppressed, in our own 3-dimensional Euclidean space. By means of embedding diagrams we can describe the results of co-ordinate-dependent mathematical analyses in a co-ordinate-free manner. We shall first encounter embedding diagrams in Sect. **3**˙5.1.

2˙3.2. Energy and pressure as the sources of curvature. In Einstein's theory of gravitation the curvature of spacetime is produced by the nongravitational stress-energy which moves through space-time. The equation which links curvature to stress-energy—*i.e.* to density of mass-energy, ϱ^*, pressure, p^*, and velocity of fluid—is

$$(\text{Einstein curvature tensor}) = 8\pi(G/c^4)\times(\text{stress-energy tensor}). \tag{2.21}$$

This equation is the analogue of the Newtonian equation

$$\nabla^2(\text{gravitational potential}) = 4\pi G\times(\text{mass density})\,. \tag{2.22}$$

We shall be concerned here with eq. (2.21) only as it is applied in particular co-ordinate systems to particular situations.

2˙3.3. Proper reference frames. There is sometimes considerable confusion in general-relativistic situations over the reference frames in which such quantities as density of mass-energy, fluid velocity and acceleration, and photon energy are measured. In order to avoid such confusion, let us introduce the concept of *proper reference frame*.

Consider an observer who moves along some arbitrary path, or « world line », through space-time, Let such an observer use physical rods and clocks, which he carries with himself, to perform measurements in his own neighborhood (within a distance small compared to the radii of curvature of space-time (*)). The results of such measurements will be called the values of the measured quantities relative to the observer's proper reference frame.

In more mathematical terms, the observer's proper reference frame is formed by an orthonormal tetrad which keeps its time-leg tangent to the observer's world line and which, for definiteness, is Fermi-Walker transported along the world line (see SYNGE (1960), pp. 13-15).

The reference frame to which the thermodynamic quantities and laws of Sect. 2'2. are referred is the proper reference frame of an observer who comoves with the matter being studied. The laws of physics in this comoving proper frame are those of flat space-time (special relativity) as augmented by an inertial (or, according to the equivalence principle, gravitational; or, in more intuitive terms, centrifugal) acceleration. This inertial acceleration is caused by deviations of the motion of the origin of the comoving frame from a freely falling, or geodesic path.

2'3.4. The Newtonian approximation. In studying a particular astrophysical situation it would be a great waste of time and effort to use Einstein's geometric theory of gravitation if Newtonian theory would yield the same results. For this reason it is important to delineate those circumstances under which Newtonian theory is a good approximation to general relativity. We refer the reader to EINSTEIN (1965), pp. 85-90, for a beatiful and coincise demonstration that Newtonian theory and general relativity theory are equivalent if the following three conditions are satisfied throughout the system under study:

a) The system is small compared with the radii of curvature of space-time (*); or equivalently (cf. eq. (2.3)), the maximum density of mass-energy, $\varrho^*_{\max}$, and the linear dimensions, l, over which the density of mass-energy is large satisfy

$$l \ll (\varrho^*_{\max})^{-\frac{1}{2}}; \tag{2.23}$$

or, equivalently, the Newtonian gravitational potential, U, satisfies

$$U/c^2 \ll 1 \tag{2.24}$$

everywhere.

(*) By « radii of curvature of space-time » we mean (physical components of 4th rank Riemann curvature tensor as measured in the observer's proper frame)$^{-\frac{1}{2}}$.

b) The pressure and density of mass-energy satisfy

(2.25) $$p^*/\varrho^* = p/\varrho c^2 \ll 1$$

everywhere in the system.

c) The macroscopic velocity, v, of the matter relative to the Newtonian co-ordinate system is everywhere small compared to the speed of light

(2.26) $$(v/c)^2 \ll 1 .$$

When these conditions are satisfied the discrepancy between the results of a Newtonian analysis and a general-relativistic analysis is usually of the order of the maximum of the dimensionless quantities U/c^2, $p/\varrho c^2$, and v^2/c^2. However, there are exceptions to this «rule-of-thumb»: If a particular phenomenon depends critically, in Newtonian theory, upon the difference between two quantities; and if that difference is of order U/c^2 or $p/\varrho c^2$ or v^2/c^2 smaller than the two quantities, then general-relativistic effects can play a crucial role in the phenomenon. An important example of such a situation is the phenomenon of general-relativistic instabilities in hot stellar models (see Sect. **4**˙3.1).

2˙3.5. The post-Newtonian approximation. The Newtonian theory of gravitation is obtained from general relativity by expanding Einstein's equations in powers of U/c^2, $p/\varrho c^2$, $\varepsilon/\varrho c^2$, and v^2/c^2; and keeping only the zero-order terms. A more accurate approximation to general relativity—the *post-Newtonian approximation*—results from keeping both zero-order and first-order terms in the expansion. The resultant equations are very useful for studying general-relativistic effects in systems for which U/c^2, $p/\varrho c^2$, and v^2/c^2 are everywhere small.

The post-Newtonian approximation to general relativity has been developed in full generality for perfect fluids by CHANDRASEKHAR (1965*a*, *b*); and it has been independently developed in restricted form for application to problems of stellar structure, stability, and collapse by FOWLER (1964, 1966). We shall briefly describe Chandrasekhar's formulation since results obtained from it will play an important role in some of the later Sections.

To orient ourselves let us briefly review the Newtonian theory of perfect fluids. In Newtonian theory we describe the gravitational field by a single gravitational potential, $U(\boldsymbol{x})$; and we describe the fluid by (in the notation of CHANDRASEKHAR (1965*a*, *b*) except that our ϱ_0 is his ϱ) its density of rest mass,

(2.27) $$\varrho_0 \equiv \mu_B n ,$$

its pressure, p, its temperature, T, its internal energy per unit rest mass,

(2.28) $$\Pi \equiv \varepsilon/\varrho_0 ,$$

and its three components of velocity, v_x, v_y, v_z. These eight quantities (U, $\varrho_0, p, T, \Pi, v_x, v_y, v_z$) are tied together by eight relations: One gravitational source equation

$$\nabla^2 U = -4\pi G \varrho_0 , \tag{2.29}$$

one equation of continuity

$$\partial \varrho_0 / \partial t + \nabla \cdot (\varrho_0 \boldsymbol{v}) = 0, \tag{2.30}$$

three equations of motion

$$(\partial/\partial t)(\varrho_0 v_j) + \sum_k (\partial/x_k)(\varrho_0 v_k v_j) = -\partial p/\partial x_j + \varrho_0 \partial U/\partial x_j , \tag{2.31}$$

two thermodynamic equations of state, and the demand that the motion be adiabatic.

In Chandrasekhar's analogous post-Newtonian theory the gravitational field is described *not* by a single potential function, U, but by 3 scalar potentials (U, Φ, χ) and the three components (U_1, U_2, U_3) of a vector potential. The orders of magnitude of the five new potentials are

$$\left\{\begin{aligned} &\Phi/c^4 \lessapprox [\text{maximum}\,(U/c^2, v^2/c^2, p/\varrho_0 c^2)]^2 = O(1/c^4) , \\ &(\partial^2 \chi/\partial t \partial x_j)/c^3 \lessapprox [\text{maximum}\,(U/c^2, v^2/c^2, p/\varrho_0 c^2]^{\frac{3}{2}} = O(1/c^3) , \\ &U_j/c^3 \lessapprox [\text{maximum}\,(U/c^2, v^2/c^2, p/\varrho_0 c^2)]^{\frac{3}{2}} = O(1/c^3) . \end{aligned}\right. \tag{2.32}$$

The six post-Newtonian gravitational potentials are related to the metric tensor of general relativity by (*)

$$\left\{\begin{aligned} g_{00} &= 1 - 2U/c^2 + (2U^2 - 4\Phi)/c^4 + O(1/c^6) , \\ g_{0j} &= 4U_j/c^3 - (\partial^2 \chi/\partial t \partial x_j)/2c^3 + O(1/c^5) , \\ g_{jk} &= -(1 + 2U/c^2)\delta_{jk} + O(1/c^4) . \end{aligned}\right. \tag{2.33}$$

Why are some components of the metric (2.33) expanded in powers of « $1/c$ » to order 4, some to order 3, and some only to order 2? Why are we not consistent? Each component is expanded just far enough to guarantee that in the equations of motion of the fluid all terms of order « $1/c^2$ » are included.

(*) The arbitrariness in $g_{\mu\nu}$ associated with the arbitrariness of co-ordinate systems is here partially removed by the co-ordinate condition $\frac{1}{2}(\partial/\partial t)\left(\sum_\alpha h_\alpha^{\ \alpha}\right) - \sum_\alpha \partial h_0^{\ \alpha}/\partial x_\alpha = 0$, where $h_{\mu\nu}$ is the deviation of $g_{\mu\nu}$ from the Minkowskian metric: $h_{\mu\nu} = g_{\mu\nu} - \eta_{\mu\nu}$.

The physics of Chandrasekhar's post-Newtonian approximation is contained in 13 equations which relate the 6 gravitational quantities (U, Φ, χ, U_1, U_2, U_3) and the 7 fluid quantities (ϱ_0, p, T, Π, v_x, v_y, v_z) to each other. Of these 13 basic equations 6 are gravitational source equations analogous to the Newtonian eq. (2.29), one is an equation of continuity analogous to (2.30), three are equations of motion analogous to (2.31), two are the thermodynamic equations of state, and one is the demand that the motion be adiabatic. We refer the reader to CHANDRASEKHAR (1965*a*) (eqs. (6), (7), (9)–(12)) for the precise forms of these equations.

In general-relativity theory there is considerable difficulty with the definitions of energy, momentum, and angular momentum and with the corresponding conservation laws. Roughly speaking, the difficulty results from interchanges of energy and momentum between the gravitational field and the fluid, and from the nonlocalizability of the gravitational field energy-momentum. Such difficulties are *not* encountered in the post-Newtonian approximation because there cannot be gravitational radiation in this approximation. Gravitational radiation couples to the fluid only in higher orders of the expansion in « $1/c$ » than are included here. As a result, rest mass, total energy, momentum, and angular momentum are well defined in the post-Newtonian approximation and satisfy local as well as global conservation laws. Expressions for these 4 conserved quantities are given in CHANDRASEKHAR (1965*a*) (eqs. (13)–(16)), and the conservation laws are proved in CHANDRASEKHAR (1965*b*). CHANDRASEKHAR also gives post-Newtonian forms of the tensor and scalar virial theorems.

The post-Newtonian approximation as developed by CHANDRASEKHAR is sufficiently simple that any astrophysical problem ever solved numerically in Newtonian theory can now be solved without too much more effort in post-Newtonian theory. The results of several such post-Newtonian analyses will play important roles in later Sections (**3**.6.2, **4**.1, **4**.4).

2.4. *Summary.* – The principal results of Sect. **2** are these: 1) In all astrophysical situations except the endpoint of gravitational collapse long-range gravitational forces can be separated from the short-range forces which determine the structure and properties of matter. 2) The effect of short-range forces on the properties of matter can be described in a comoving proper reference frame by the parameters and laws of classical thermodynamics plus the law of the equivalence of mass and energy. 3) The gravitational field is described by the general-relativistic curvature of space-time. Alternatively, if U/c^2, v^2/c^2, and $p/\varrho c^2$ are all small compared to unity, Newtonian or post-Newtonian gravitational potentials can be used to describe the gravitational field. 4) The coupling between the long-range gravitational field and the matter whose thermodynamic properties are determined by short-range forces is described by Einstein's field equations (2.21) or, in the Newtonian and post-Newtonian approximations, by the source equations of the gravitational field plus the equations of motion of the fluid.

With these thermodynamic and gravitational preliminaries completed, we are now prepared to turn our attention to the structure of equilibrium stellar configurations.

3. – Equilibrium stellar configurations.

3·1. *Parameters describing the structure of nonrotating stellar models.*

3·1.1. Description of the gravitational field. To give an analytic description of the gravitational field of a nonrotating star, we must first construct a precisely defined co-ordinate system and then give, relative to that co-ordinate system, the metric tensor, $g_{\mu\nu}$, which determines the geometry of space-time (cf. Sect. **2**·3.1). Nonrotating, equilibrium stellar configurations are necessarily spherically symmetric. Consequently, we can use as our three space co-ordinates the familiar spherical co-ordinates (r, θ, φ); r being such that $4\pi r^2$ is the surface area of a sphere about the center of the star, and (θ, φ) being angular coordinates on that sphere. Our time co-ordinate, t, is chosen such that *a*) the geometry of space-time is independent of t; and *b*) very far from the star (at $r \to \infty$) co-ordinate time, t, is identical to the proper time measured by the clock of an observer at rest with respect to the star.

These conditions determine our co-ordinate system uniquely, except for trivial rotations about the center of the star. With respect to this co-ordinate system the metric tensor which describes the gravitational field can be put into the form

$$(3.1)\quad \mathrm{d}s^2 = \sum_{\mu,\nu} g_{\mu\nu}\,\mathrm{d}x^\mu \mathrm{d}x^\nu = e^{2\Phi}\,\mathrm{d}t^2 - (1 - 2m^*/r)^{-1}\,\mathrm{d}r^2 - r^2(\mathrm{d}\theta^2 + \sin^2\theta\,\mathrm{d}\varphi^2)\,.$$

(See, *e.g.*, Tolman (1934), Sect. **95**.) Hence the geometry of space-time depends upon two gravitational potentials, $\Phi(r)$ and $m^*(r)$. These potentials always satisfy $\Phi(\infty) = m^*(0) = 0$ (The gravitational potential Φ of eq. (3.1) is not to be confused with the potential Φ of post-Newtonian theory (Sect. **2**·3.5).)

We shall see in Sect. **3**·2.2 that $m^*(r)$ can be thought of as the mass inside a radius r. As for $\Phi(r)$, it plays in general relativity a role analogous to that of the gravitational potential, U, of Newtonian theory. In fact, a comparison of equation (2.33) with the expression

$$g_{00} = e^{2\Phi} \approx 1 + 2\Phi + O(\Phi^2)$$

reveals that $-U/c^2$ is the Newtonian limit of Φ. For this reason $\Phi(r)$ is sometimes called the « Newtonian potential » of general relativity.

3·1.2. $\Phi(r)$ as a governor of energy red-shift. Just as U provides us with an equation governing the rate of change of the kinetic energy of a particle moving in a Newtonian gravitational field

$$\tfrac{1}{2}m_0 v^2 - m_0 U = \text{const}\,, \tag{3.2}$$

so Φ is the basis for a general-relativity energy equation. At each point on the orbit of a particle (or photon) let an observer fixed with respect to the star $\big((r, \theta, \varphi) = \text{const}\big)$ measure the particle's total energy, E, in his own proper reference frame. (By total energy, E, we mean $E = h\nu$ for a photon, and $E = (\text{rest mass plus kinetic energy}) = m_0/(1-v^2)^{\frac{1}{2}}$ for a material particle.) Then the energies measured by observers at different points in the star are related by

$$Ee^{\Phi} = \text{const}\,. \tag{3.3}$$

This equation is valid for particles or photons falling freely inside the star as well as outside it. In fact, eq. (3.3) is valid for particles or photons falling in *any static gravitational field* of the form

$$\mathrm{d}s^2 = e^{2\Phi}\,\mathrm{d}t^2 + \sum_{i,j=1}^{3} g_{ij}\,\mathrm{d}x^i\,\mathrm{d}x^j\,. \tag{3.4}$$

(See *e.g.* LANDAU and LIFSHITZ (1962), Sect. **89.**)

Equation (3.2), which is the Newtonian limit of eq. (3.3), is usually called « the equation of energy conservation »; the energy which is conserved is the sum of the kinetic energy, $\frac{1}{2}m_0v^2$, and the potential energy, $-m_0U$. In general relativity, however, it is more convenient to avoid introducing the concept of potential energy and to regard eq. (3.3) as an « energy red-shift » equation. The energy which is red-shifted as a particle or photon climbs out of a gravitational field is E, and the amount by which this energy is red-shifted in moving from point A to point B is

$$[E(B) - E(A)]/E(A) = \exp[\Phi(A) - \Phi(B)] - 1\,. \tag{3.5}$$

3·1.3. Description of thermodynamic structure. The thermodynamic structure of an equilibrium stellar configuration will be described in these lectures by giving the radial distribution of the following thermodynamic parameters: density of mass-energy, ϱ^*; pressure, p^*; number density of baryons, n; internal energy density, ε^*; entropy per baryon, s^*, temperature, T^*; average baryonic rest mass, μ_{B}^*; nuclear abundances, $Z_1, \ldots, Z_N$; nuclear chemical potentials, $\bar{\mu}_1^*, \ldots, \bar{\mu}_N^*$; number of baryons inside a radius r, $a(r)$; total luminosity, L_r^*; neutrino luminosity, $L_r^{(\nu)*}$; radiative absorption coefficient,

$\varkappa_R^*$; thermal conductivity, λ_c^*; rate of change of nuclear abundances, $\alpha_1^*, \ldots, \alpha_N^*$; rate of thermonuclear energy generation, q^*; and rate of energy release into neutrinos, $q_{(\nu)}^*$. All of these quantities were defined in Sect. 2·2 except the following: *The number of baryons inside a radius r*, $a(r)$, is a very useful parameter for identifying shells of matter in successive configurations of an evolutionary sequence. In the language of hydrodynamics, a is a Lagrangian radial co-ordinate. We shall sometimes use a rather than r as the independent radial co-ordinate. *The radial luminosity*, L_r^*, is the total mass-energy carried by photons, by neutrinos, by conduction, and by convection outward across a sphere of co-ordinate radius r in unit time, as measured in the proper frame of an observer located at r and at rest with respect to the star. *The neutrino luminosity* $L_r^{(\nu)*}$ is that portion of L_r^* due to neutrinos. *The radiative absorption coefficient*, $\varkappa_R^*$, multiplied by the density of mass-energy, ϱ^*, is the fractional attenuation per unit proper distance of the intensity (watt/cm² s) of a beam of light in the absence of gravitational fields

$$\mathrm{d}I/I = -\varkappa_R^* \varrho^* \mathrm{d}(\text{proper distance}) \qquad \text{(no gravitation)}. \tag{3.6}$$

The light beam is assumed to have the average spectral distribution of the radiation at point r. *The thermal conductivity*, λ_c, is the proportionality constant which, in the absence of a gravitational field, relates the energy flux by heat conduction to the temperature gradient.

$$\boldsymbol{Q} = -\lambda_c \boldsymbol{\nabla} T \qquad \text{(no gravitation)}. \tag{3.7}$$

The rates of change of nuclear abundances, $\alpha_1^*, \ldots, \alpha_N^*$, are defined by

$$\alpha_k^* = \mathrm{d}Z_k/\mathrm{d}\,(\text{time as measured in proper frame of observer at rest in star}). \tag{3.8}$$

The nuclear abundances change as a result of nuclear reactions. Because $Z_1 + \ldots + Z_N = 1$, we always have

$$\alpha_1^* + \ldots + \alpha_N^* = 0\,. \tag{3.9}$$

The rate, q^*, *of thermonuclear energy generation* is the rate per baryon, as measured by an observer at rest in the star, at which rest mass-energy is converted into internal energy by thermonuclear reactions

$$q^* = -\mathrm{d}\mu_B^*/\mathrm{d}\,(\text{proper time}) = -\alpha_1^*\mu_1^* - \ldots - \alpha_N^*\mu_N^*\,. \tag{3.10}$$

The rate of energy release into neutrinos, $q_{(\nu)}^*$, is the rate per baryon at which internal energy is converted into outgoing neutrinos. (We view nuclear reactions as an exchange of energy between rest mass, $\mu^*_B n$, and internal energy, ε^*, followed by the conversion of some of the internal energy into neutrinos and photons.)

3·2. *Equations of stellar structure.* – The structure of a star which contains N different types of baryons can be described by the $16 + 3N$ functions of radius (Φ, m^*, a, ϱ^*, p^*, n, ε^*, s^*, T^*, L^*_r, $L^{(\nu)*}_r$, $\varkappa^*_R$, λ^*_c, q^*, $q^*_{(\nu)}$, μ^*_B, $Z_1, \ldots, Z_N$, $\bar{\mu}^*_1, \ldots, \bar{\mu}^*_N$, $\alpha^*_1, \ldots, \alpha^*_N$). These $16 + 3N$ functions are governed by $16 + 3N$ equations of stellar structure:

I) *Differential equations of stellar structure*:

a) Baryon number equation:

(3.11-1) $$\mathrm{d}a/\mathrm{d}r = 4\pi r^2(1 - 2m^*/r)^{-\frac{1}{2}} n\,, \qquad a(0) = 0\,,$$

b) Mass equation:

(3.11-2) $$\mathrm{d}m^*/\mathrm{d}r = 4\pi r^2 \varrho^*\,, \qquad m^*(0) = 0\,,$$

c) TOV equation of hydrostatic equilibrium:

(3.11-3) $$\frac{\mathrm{d}p^*}{\mathrm{d}r} = \frac{-(\varrho^* + p^*)(m^* + 4\pi r^3 p^*)}{r(r - 2m^*)}\,,$$

d) Source equation for Φ:

(3.11-4) $$\frac{\mathrm{d}\Phi}{\mathrm{d}r} = \frac{m^* + 4\pi r^3 p^*}{r(r - 2m^*)}\,; \qquad \Phi(\infty) = 0\,,$$

e) Equations of thermal equilibrium:

(3.11-5) $$\frac{\mathrm{d}(L^*_r e^{2\Phi})}{\mathrm{d}r} = \frac{4\pi r^2 n e^{2\Phi}}{(1 - 2m^*/r)^{\frac{1}{2}}}\left\{q^* - \left[e^{-\Phi}\frac{\mathrm{d}}{\mathrm{d}t}\left(\frac{\varepsilon^*}{n}\right) - \frac{p^*}{n^2}e^{-\Phi}\frac{\mathrm{d}n}{\mathrm{d}t}\right]_{a=\mathrm{constant}}\right\} =$$
$$= \frac{-4\pi r^2 n e^{\Phi}}{(1 - 2m^*/r)^{\frac{1}{2}}}\left\{T^*\left(\frac{\mathrm{d}s^*}{\mathrm{d}t}\right)_{a=\mathrm{constant}} + \sum_k \bar{\mu}^*_k\left(\frac{\mathrm{d}Z_k}{\mathrm{d}t}\right)_{a=\mathrm{constant}}\right\},$$

(3.11-6) $$\frac{\mathrm{d}(L^{(\nu)*}_r e^{2\Phi})}{\mathrm{d}r} = \frac{4\pi r^2 n e^{2\Phi}}{(1 - 2m^*/r)^{\frac{1}{2}}} q^*_{(\nu)}\,.$$

f) Equation of energy transport:

i) If convective transport is negligible beside conductive plus radiative transport (temperature gradient subadiabatic)

(3.11-7*a*) $$\begin{cases} \dfrac{\mathrm{d}(Te^{*\Phi})}{\mathrm{d}r} = -\dfrac{3}{16\sigma^*}\dfrac{\varkappa^*\varrho^*}{T^{*3}}\dfrac{(L^*_r - L^{(\nu)*}_r)e^{\Phi}}{4\pi r^2}\left(1 - \dfrac{2m^*}{r}\right)^{-\frac{1}{2}}, \\[2ex] \dfrac{1}{\varkappa^*} = \dfrac{1}{\varkappa^*_R} + \dfrac{1}{\varkappa^*_c}, \qquad \varkappa^*_c = \dfrac{16\sigma^* T^{*3}}{3\varrho^*\lambda^*_c}\,. \end{cases}$$

ii) If conductive and radiative transport are negligible beside convection, and if convection proceeds efficiently (adiabatic approximation)

(3.11-7b) $$\frac{dT^*}{dr} = \frac{\Gamma_2 - 1}{\Gamma_2}\frac{T^*}{p^*}\frac{dp^*}{dr}.$$

Procedure for choosing between (3.11-7a) and (3.11-7b): Calculate temperature gradient from (3.11-7a); if it is subadiabatic then the assumption of no convection was correct; but if it is superadiabatic then convection is important and (3.11-7b) should be used.

II) *Gas characteristic relations*:

a) Thermodynamic relations:

(3.11-8) → (3.11-11 + N) $4+N$ algebraic thermodynamic relations linking the fundamental thermodynamic quantities (ϱ^*, p^*, n, s^*, T^*, $Z_1, \ldots, Z_N$, $\bar{\mu}_1^*, \ldots, \bar{\mu}_N^*$).

(3.11-12 + N) $$\varrho^* = \mu_B^* n + \varepsilon^*,$$

(3.11-13 + N) $$\mu_B^* = \sum_k Z_k \mu_k^*.$$

b) Opacity relation:

(3.11-14 + N) $$\varkappa_R^* = \varkappa_R^*(\varrho^*, T^*, Z_1, \ldots, Z_N).$$

c) Conductivity relation:

(3.11-15 + N) $$\lambda_c^* = \lambda_c^*(\varrho^*, T^*, Z_1, \ldots, Z_N).$$

d) Equations of thermonuclear energy generation:

(3.11-16 + N) $$q^* = -\sum_k \alpha_k^* \mu_k^*,$$

(3.11-17 + N) $$q_{(\nu)}^* = q_{(\nu)}^*(\varrho^*, T^*, Z_1, \ldots, Z_N),$$

(3.11-18 + N) → (3.11-16 + $2N$) $$\alpha_k^* = \alpha_k^*(\varrho^*, T^*, Z_1, \ldots, Z_N), \quad k = 1, \ldots, N-1,$$

(3.11-17 + $2N$) → (3.11-16 + $3N$) $$(dZ_k/dt)_{a=\text{const}} = e^{\Phi}\alpha_k^* \qquad k = 1, \ldots, N.$$

Let us examine the origin, the significance, and the Newtonian limits of these equations.

3·2.1. Baryon number. The baryon number eq. (3.11-1) states that the number of baryons inside radius r is

(3.12) $$a(r) = \int_0^r (\text{baryon number density})\, d(\text{proper volume}) = \int_0^r n 4\pi r^2 (1 - 2m^*/r)^{-\frac{1}{2}} dr.$$

3·2.2. Mass equation. The mass eq. (3.11-1) arises from Einstein's field eq. (2.21) (see *e.g.* TOLMAN (1934*a*), Sect. **95**). Its form suggests that we interpret $m^*(r)$ as the *total mass–energy inside radius* r, including rest mass-energy, internal energy, and (negative) gravitational potential energy. $m^*(r)$ is split into its three parts as follows

$$(3.13)\qquad m^*(r) = (\text{rest mass-energy}) + (\text{internal energy}) + (\text{gravitational potential energy}) = \int_0^r \mu_B^* n \, d(\text{proper volume}) + \int_0^r \varepsilon^* \, d(\text{proper volume}) - \int_0^r \varrho^*[1-(1-2m^*/r)]^{\frac{1}{2}} \, d(\text{proper volume}) \,.$$

(To derive the second equality, combine the mass eq. (3.11-2) with the two-way split (2.5) of ϱ^* into rest mass plus internal energy, and with the expression

$$d(\text{proper volume}) = 4\pi r^2 (1 - 2m^*/r)^{-\frac{1}{2}} \, dr$$

for the proper volume of a spherical shell of co-ordinate thickness dr.) In the Newtonian limit the three-way split (3.13) takes the familiar form

$$(3.13')\qquad m(r)c^2 = \int_0^r \mu_B n c^2 \, d(\text{proper volume}) + \int_0^r \varepsilon \, 4\pi r^2 \, dr + \int_0^r \mu_B n(-Gm/r) 4\pi r^2 \, dr \,.$$

Although it is very useful to give the title «total mass-energy inside radius r» to $m^*(r)$ (*), and although the rest mass-energy, $\int \mu_B^* n \, d(\text{proper volume})$, is a useful quantity (**), the internal energy and gravitational potential energy of eq. (3.13) are *not particularly* useful except in the Newtonian and post-Newtonian approximations.

The value of m^* at the surface of the star,

$$(3.14)\qquad M^* \equiv m^*(R) = \int_0^R 4\pi r^2 \varrho^* \, dr \,,$$

is the total gravitating mass as measured by an observer who applies Kepler's

(*) See *e.g.* the remainder of Sect. **3**, as well as HTWW Chapters 2 and 3 and Appendix B; and THORNE (1965*b*), Chapter 5.

(**) See *e.g.* Sect. **3**·5.3 and **4**·2.4, as well as BARDEEN (1965) and TOOPER (1966).

laws to planets in large orbits about the star (cf. Sect. 3˙4.1). The difference between this total mass-energy and the total rest mass-energy,

$$M_0^* = \int_0^R \mu_B^* \, n 4\pi r^2 (1 - 2m^*/r)^{-\frac{1}{2}} \, dr \,, \tag{3.15}$$

is the negative of the binding energy, $-E_B^*$:

$$E_B^* = M_0^* - M^* \,. \tag{3.16}$$

Binding energy and rest mass play an important role in the supermassive stellar models of FOWLER (1964, 1966) and BARDEEN (1964, 1965, 1966).

3˙2.3. TOV equation of hydrostatic equilibrium. The TOV (TOLMAN [1934*a*], [1939], OPPENHEIMER and VOLKOFF (1939]) equation (3.11-3), like the mass equation (3.11-2), arises from Einstein's field equations. It expresses the fact that the buoyant force per unit volume, as measured in the proper reference frame of an observer fixed in the star,

$$\boldsymbol{F}^*_{\text{buoyant}} = - dp^*/d(\text{proper radial distance})\, \boldsymbol{e}_r = -(1 - 2m^*/r)^{\frac{1}{2}} (dp^*/dr) \boldsymbol{e}_r \,, \tag{3.17a}$$

precisely balances the gravitational force per unit volume,

$$\boldsymbol{F}^*_{\text{grav}} = \frac{-(\varrho^* + p^*)(m^* + 4\pi r^3 p^*)}{r^2 (1 - 2m^*/r)^{\frac{1}{2}}} \, \boldsymbol{e}_r \,. \tag{3.17b}$$

(Here $\boldsymbol{e}_r$ is a unit vector in the radial direction.)

The TOV equation of hydrostatic equilibrium (3.11-3) differs from its Newtonian counterpart

$$- F^*_{\text{buoy}} = dp^*/dr = F^*_{\text{grav}} = - \varrho^* m^*/r^2 \tag{3.18}$$

in several key ways: 1) In place of the density of mass-energy, ϱ^*, appears density plus pressure, $(\varrho^* + p^*)$. This is a consequence of the relativistic role of $(\varrho^* + p^*)$ as inertial mass per unit volume (cf. Sect. 2˙2.4), plus the equivalence of inertial and gravitational forces (Einstein's equivalence principle). 2) In place of the mass, m^*, appears the expression $m^* + 4\pi r^3 p^*$. The additional term proportional to p^* results in one of the most important of all nonlinear gravitational effects, *multiplicative regeneration of pressure* (see Sect. 3˙5.2). 3) In the denominator of the TOV equation (3.11-3) is a factor $(1 - 2m^*/r)$ which does not appear in the Newtonian equation (3.18). This factor prevents the mass inside a radius r, $m^*(r)$, from ever being as large as $r/2$ (cf. Sect. 3˙5.1);

and it is closely related to the evolution of an event horizon in gravitational collapse (cf. Sect. **7**).

3˙2.4. Source equation for Φ. The source equation (3.11-4), like eqs. (3.11-2)–(3.11-3) arises from Einstein's field equations (see, *e.g.*, TOLMAN [1943*a*] Sect. **95**); and like the TOV equation (3.11-3), it can be rewritten in a form which expresses the hydrostatic balance between gravitational force and pressure-buoyant force:

$$(3.19)\quad \boldsymbol{F}^*_{\text{grav}} = -(\varrho^* + p^*)(1-2m^*/r)^{\frac{1}{2}}(\mathrm{d}\Phi/\mathrm{d}r)\boldsymbol{e}_r = -\boldsymbol{F}^*_{\text{buoy}} = (1-2m^*/r)^{\frac{1}{2}}(\mathrm{d}p^*/\mathrm{d}r)\boldsymbol{e}_r .$$

Note that the relativistic expression (3.19) for the gravitational force per unit volume, when rewritten in words, takes a form familiar from Newtonian theory

$$(3.20)\quad \boldsymbol{F}^*_{\text{grav}} = -(\textit{inertial mass per unit volume}) \times \mathrm{d}\Phi/\mathrm{d}(\textit{proper radial distance})\boldsymbol{e}_r .$$

This is another aspect of the close analogy between the general-relativity potential Φ and the gravitational potential U of Newtonian theory (cf. Sect. **3**˙1.1 and **3**˙1.2).

3˙2.5. Thermal equilibrium. The energy which a star radiates is supplied from its rest mass by nuclear burning, from its gravitational and internal energy by quasistatic contraction, or from both sources by both processes. Equation of thermal equilibrium (3.11-5) expresses the energy balance which occurs during this conversion of mass-energy from one form to another.

To derive eq. (3.11-5) consider a spherical shell of the star inside of which there are a baryons and which itself contains δa baryons. During a co-ordinate time interval $\mathrm{d}t$ the internal energy of this shell changes by

(3.21) d(internal energy) =

= (rest mass-energy converted to internal energy by nuclear reactions) +

+ (work done on shell by gravitational forces to change its volume during quasistatic contraction) −

− (energy radiated away, conducted away, or convected away).

By virtue of definition (3.10) the amount of rest mass converted to internal energy is $q^*\,\delta a e^{\Phi}\,\mathrm{d}t$. During quasi-static contraction the shell under consideration changes its volume by an amount $\mathrm{d}(\delta a/n)$, and the work done on the shell to produce this change is $-p^*\,\mathrm{d}(\delta a/n)$. The rate, as measured by a clock fixed in the shell, at which the shell radiates, conducts and convects away energy is

$$(3.22)\quad L^*_r(r+\delta r)\exp\left[2[\Phi(r+\delta r)-\Phi(r)]\right] - L^*_r(r) = (\mathrm{d}L^*_r/\mathrm{d}r + 2L^*_r\,\mathrm{d}\Phi/\mathrm{d}r)\,\delta r .$$

One of the factors of $\exp[\Phi(r+\delta r)-\Phi(r)]$ accounts for the gravitational red-shift which the transported energy undergoes as it crosses the shell (cf. Sect. 3˙1.2.), while the other accounts for time dilation between the inner and outer surfaces of the shell. Consequently, the total energy carried away from the shell in co-ordinate time $\mathrm{d}t$ is

$$(\mathrm{d}L_r^*/\mathrm{d}r + 2L_r^*\,\mathrm{d}\Phi/\mathrm{d}r)\,\delta r e^{\Phi}\,\mathrm{d}t\,.$$

These results enable us to rewrite the equation of energy balance (3.21) as

$$\text{(3.23)}\quad \mathrm{d}(\varepsilon^*\,\delta a/n) = q^*\,\delta a e^{\Phi}\,\mathrm{d}t - p^*\,\mathrm{d}(\delta a/n) - (\mathrm{d}L_r^*/\mathrm{d}r + 2L_r^*\,\mathrm{d}\Phi/\mathrm{d}r)\,\delta r\, e^{\Phi}\,\mathrm{d}t\,.$$

When expanded and rearranged this becomes the equation of thermal equilibrium (3.11-5). The alternative form (second equality) of the equation of thermal equilibrium (3.11-5) follows from the relation

$$q^* - e^{-\Phi}(\mathrm{d}/\mathrm{d}t)(\varepsilon^*/n) - p^* e^{-\Phi}(\mathrm{d}/\mathrm{d}t)(1/n) = -\,e^{-\Phi}\,[(\mathrm{d}/\mathrm{d}t)(\varrho^*/n) + p^*(\mathrm{d}/\mathrm{d}t)(1/n)] =$$
$$= -\,e^{-\Phi}\,T^*\,(\mathrm{d}s^*/\mathrm{d}t) - \sum_k \bar{\mu}_k^*(\mathrm{d}Z_k/\mathrm{d}t)$$

(cf. the first law of thermodynamics, eq. (2.12)).

From the above derivation it is evident that *the time derivatives in the equation of thermal equilibium must be taken with baryon number, a, held fixed; not with radius, r, held fixed.* How these time derivatives are handled in practice will be discussed in Sect. 3˙4.3.

It should be mentioned that the equation of thermal equilibrium (3.11-5) can be derived directly from the general-relativity law of local energy conservation, $\sum_{\mu,\nu} u_\mu T^{\mu\nu}{}_{;\nu} = 0$ (see BARDEEN [1965], or MISNER and SHARP [1965, 1966]).

In addition to the general equation of thermal equilibrium (3.11-5), we have equation (3.11-6) which expresses the law of energy balance for neutrinos alone. Neutrinos have their own, separate equation of thermal equilibrium because once a neutrino is produced it escapes freely from the equilibrium configuration without ever being converted into any other form of energy. Equation (3.11-6) can be derived in the same way as was (3.11-5).

3˙2.6. Energy transport. In general, energy is transported from the hot interior of a star toward its cool surface by a combination of diffusing photons, escaping neutrinos, heat conduction in the stellar material, and convective motions of the stellar material. In any particular situation a careful analysis of the processes of energy transport yields three basic equations: the equations of thermal equilibrium (3.11-5, 6)—which are expressions for the gradient of the energy flux—; and the equation of energy transport (3.11-7), which is an expression for the temperature gradient.

The analysis of energy transport for stellar models in which convection contributes roughly the same energy flux as conduction plus photon diffusion is very difficult and has not yet been carried out in general relativity. Fortunately, in most situations of physical interest either convection is negligible beside conduction plus radiation, or conduction plus radiation is negligible beside convection. We consider these two cases below.

3.2.7. Energy transport by conduction, photon diffusion, and neutrino escape. When convective transport is absent or negligible, the equation of energy transport takes the form (3.11-7*a*). We will derive this equation in three steps: *First*, we will obtain a relation between temperature gradient and photon energy flux; *second*, we will obtain a similar relation between temperature gradient and conduction energy flux; *third*, we will combine these relations to obtain eq. (3.11-7*a*).

a) *Photon energy transport.* The theory of radiative transport in general relativity has been developed independently by BARDEEN (1965), by MISNER and SHARP (1965, 1966), by HÄMEEN-ANTTILA and ANTTILA (1966), and, in greatest detail, by LINDQUIST (1966). For the interior of a star, where photon transport is diffusive, this theory yields the following *equation of radiative transport*:

$$\frac{\mathrm{d}(T^* e^{\Phi})}{\mathrm{d}r} = -\frac{3}{16\sigma^*}\frac{\varkappa_R^* \varrho^*}{T^{*3}}\frac{L_r^{(R)*} e^{\Phi}}{4\pi r^2}\left(1-\frac{2m^*}{r}\right)^{-\frac{1}{2}}. \tag{3.24}$$

Here $L_r^{(R)*}$ is that portion of the luminosity, L_r^*, which is due to photon diffusion; σ^* is the Stefan-Boltzmann constant (cf. eq. (3.28)); and the other quantities have the meanings given in Sect. 3.1.

One can give a physical derivation of eq. (3.24) without going into the details of transport theory. At any point inside the star the electromagnetic radiation consists of two parts—a large, isotropic part; and a very much smaller, purely radial part which accounts for the photon luminosity $L_r^{(R)*}$. Consider the gradient in the radial component of the (almost isotropic) radiation pressure. It arises from two sources—gravitational attraction of the photon gas toward the center of the star; and interaction of the radiation with matter. The gravitational attraction must be balanced by a pressure gradient

d(radiation pressure)/d(proper radial distance) =

= − (inertial mass per unit volume of photon gas) dΦ/d(proper radial distance);

or, equivalently,

$$(\mathrm{d}p_R^*/\mathrm{d}r)_{\text{grav}} = -(\varrho_R^* + p_R^*)\,\mathrm{d}\Phi/\mathrm{d}r \tag{3.25}$$

(cf. Sect. 3·2.4). Of all interactions between matter and radiation only absorption of the excess radial component, $L_r^{(R)*}$, is anisotropic and can thus contribute to the radiation pressure gradient. The drop in radiation pressure over a co-ordinate interval dr due to absorption is the mass-energy absorbed from the radial beam per unit proper time and per unit area by the matter in the shell of thickness dr:

$$(3.26) \qquad (\mathrm{d}p_R^*)_{\text{absorption}} = -\varkappa_R^*\,\varrho^*(L_r^{(R)*}/4\pi r^2)(1-2m^*/r)^{-\frac{1}{2}}\mathrm{d}r.$$

Consequently, the total gradient of the radiation pressure (sum of (3.25) and (3.26)) is:

$$(3.27) \qquad \mathrm{d}p_R^*/\mathrm{d}r = -(\varrho_R^* + p_R^*)\,\mathrm{d}\Phi/\mathrm{d}r - \varkappa_R^*\,\varrho^*(L_r^{(R)*}/4\pi r^2)(1-2m^*/r)^{-\frac{1}{2}}\,.$$

Now, the (very nearly isotropic) radiation pressure, p_R^*, and the density of radiation energy, ϱ_R^*, are related to the temperature, T^*, of the matter by

$$(3.28) \qquad \varrho_R^* = 3p_R^* = 4\sigma^*\,T^{*4}\,,$$

where σ^* is the Stefan-Boltzmann constant. By combining equations (3.27) and (3.28), and rearranging, one obtains the equation of radiative energy transport (3.24).

b) Conductive energy transport. The portion, $L_r^{(c)*}$, of the total luminosity L_r^*, which is due solely to heat conduction is related to the temperature gradient by the equation of conductive energy transport

$$(3.29) \qquad \frac{\mathrm{d}(T^*e^{\Phi})}{\mathrm{d}r} = -\frac{L_r^{(c)*}e^{\Phi}}{4\pi r^2\,\lambda_c^*}\left(1-\frac{2m^*}{r}\right)^{-\frac{1}{2}}.$$

This equation can be derived from the following considerations: In the Newtonian approximation the conductive luminosity is related to the temperature gradient by the equation of conductive energy transport

$$(3.30) \qquad \mathrm{d}T^*/\mathrm{d}r = -\lambda_c^{*-1}\times(\text{energy flux}) = -L_r^{(c)*}/4\pi r^2\,\lambda_c^*\,.$$

The relativistic generalization of this equation must be obtainable by insertion of the general-relativity « correction factors » e^{Φ} and $(1-2m^*/r)^{\frac{1}{2}}$ in appropriate places. The factor $(1-2m^*/r)^{\frac{1}{2}}$ is always used to convert differential radial co-ordinate intervals, dr, to proper radial distances, $(1-2m^*/r)^{-\frac{1}{2}}\mathrm{d}r$. Hence, eq. (3.30) when corrected for the effects of $(1-2m^*/r)^{\frac{1}{2}}$ reads .

$$(3.30') \qquad \mathrm{d}T^*/\mathrm{d}(\text{proper radial distance}) \equiv (1-2m^*/r)^{\frac{1}{2}}\,\mathrm{d}T^*/\mathrm{d}r = -L_r^{(c)*}/4\pi r^2\,\lambda_c^*\,.$$

The second correction factor, e^{Φ}, must be inserted in such a manner as to account for the red-shift of the energy which is being conducted upward through the star. A factor of e^{Φ} to some power, k, will appear inside the radial derivative; and another factor, $e^{k'\Phi}$, will appear outside the radial derivative

$$(3.30'') \qquad (1-2m^*/r)^{\frac{1}{2}} e^{k'\Phi} \mathrm{d}(T^* e^{k\Phi})/\mathrm{d}r = - L_r^{(c)*}/4\pi r^2 \lambda_c^* .$$

We have chosen our normalization of Φ in such a manner that $\Phi(\infty)=0$. However, just as Newtonian gravitation theory is unaffected by the addition of a constant to the gravitational potential, $U \to U + \text{constant}$, so the laws of general relativity are unaffected by the corresponding transformation $\Phi \to \Phi + \text{const}$. Such a transformation merely corresponds to an expansion or contraction of the *co-ordinate* time scale (cf. eq. (3.1)). The demand that the equation of conductive transport (3.30″) be invariant under the transformation $\Phi \to \Phi + \text{const}$ tells us that $k' = -k$.

To determine the correct value of $k = -k'$, consider a hot star which is surrounded by an insulator that prevents energy from flowing into or out of it. Inside the star photon diffusion will attempt to create a temperature distribution of $T^* e^{\Phi} = \text{const}$ (cf. eq. (3.24)), while heat conduction will attempt to create the distribution $T^* e^{k\Phi} = \text{const}$. (cf. eq. (3.30″)). Consequently, if $k > 1$, photons will carry energy at a finite rate from the center of the star to the surface, and heat conduction will recycle the energy back to the center. The result will be a finite heat flow from a hot region to a cold region by one route and back by another with no increase in entropy—a violation of the second law of thermodynamics. Since $k<1$ would lead to a similar violation of the second law, k must be precisely 1, and k' must be -1 (*). By setting $k = -k' = 1$ in eq. (3.30′) and rearranging, we obtain the general-relativity equation (3.29) for heat conduction in a star.

c) *Combined photon, conduction, and neutrino transport.* We have now completed the first two steps in our derivation of the transport equation (3.11-7*a*). We have obtained the eqs. (3.24) and (3.29) which govern photon diffusion and heat conduction whenever there are no mass motions in the star (negligible convection). Before constructing the combined transport equation (3.11-7*a*), it is useful to rewrite the equation of conductive transport in a form identical to the equation of radiative transport

$$(3.29') \qquad \frac{\mathrm{d}(T^* e^{\Phi})}{\mathrm{d}r} = -\frac{3}{16\sigma^*}\frac{\varkappa_c^* \varrho^*}{T^{*3}}\frac{L_r^{(c)*} e^{\Phi}}{4\pi r^2}\left(1-\frac{2m^*}{r}\right)^{-\frac{1}{2}} .$$

Evidently the conductive absorption coefficient $\varkappa_c^*$ which appears here is related

(*) This proof that $k=1$ is due to P. J. E. PEEBLES (private communication).

to the thermal conductivity λ_c^* by

$$\varkappa_c^* = (16\sigma^* T^{*3})/(3\varrho^* \lambda_c^*) . \tag{3.31}$$

By combining the conduction eq. (3.29′) with the equation of radiative transport (3.24), and by noting that because convection is negligible

$$L_r^{(R)*} + L_r^{(c)*} = L_r^* - L_r^{(\nu)*} ,$$

we obtain the transport equation (3.11-7*a*).

3·2.8. Convective energy transport. In general relativity, as in Newtonian theory, a layer of a star is unstable against convection if and only if its temperature gradient is superadiabatic:

$$\text{Instability against convection} \Leftrightarrow \tag{3.32}$$

$$\Leftrightarrow (-\,\mathrm{d}T^*/\mathrm{d}r) - (1 - 1/\Gamma_2)(T^*/p^*)(-\,\mathrm{d}p^*/\mathrm{d}r) > 0 .$$

Here Γ_2 is the adiabatic index of eq. (2.8).

This condition for convective instability can be derived in general relativity theory by a physical argument analogous to the Newtonian argument of SCHWARZSCHILD (1958), pp. 44-46: (*)

Consider a particular configuration of hydrostatic and thermal equilibrium. Displace a small element of fluid at radius r_A upward through a small coordinate distance Δr, to $r_B = r_A + \Delta r$. As it is displaced let the fluid element expand adiabatically until it reaches the same pressure as its new surroundings. Then release the displaced fluid element and see in what direction the sum of the gravitational and buoyant forces acts. If the fluid falls back toward its original position, the star is stable against convection in the neighborhood of r_A; if it continues to rise, the star is unstable against convection. The forces per unit volume acting on the displaced fluid element, as seen by an observer at rest at r_B, are (cf. Sect. **3**·2.4)

$$\boldsymbol{F}^* = \boldsymbol{F}^*_{\text{grav}} + \boldsymbol{F}^*_{\text{buoyant}} = \tag{3.33}$$

$$= [-\,(\varrho^*_{fe} + p^*)(1 - 2m^*/r)^{\frac{1}{2}}(\mathrm{d}\Phi/\mathrm{d}r)\,\boldsymbol{e}_r]_B + [-\,(1 - 2m^*/r)^{\frac{1}{2}}(\mathrm{d}p^*/\mathrm{d}r)\,\boldsymbol{e}_r]_B .$$

(*) For a considerably more rigorous relativistic derivation of (3.32) see THORNE (1966). For a post-Newtonian discussion see CHANDRASEKHAR (1965*d*). BONDI (1964) seems to have been the first to notice that convective instability is unaffected by general relativity.

Here $\varrho^*_{\rm fe}$ is the density of mass-energy of the displaced fluid element,

$$\varrho^*_{\rm fe} = \varrho^*_A + [(\varrho^* + p^*)(\mathrm{d}p^*/\mathrm{d}r)/\Gamma_1 p^*]_A \Delta r; \tag{3.34}$$

and the subscripts « A » and « B » indicate quantities evaluated at r_A and r_B. By combining expressions (3.33), (3.34), and (3.19), we obtain for the proper acceleration of the displaced fluid element relative to the surrounding medium

$$\boldsymbol{a} = \frac{\boldsymbol{F}}{\varrho^*_{\rm fe} + p^*} = -\frac{(1-2m^*/r)^{\frac{1}{2}}}{(\varrho^* + p^*)\Gamma_1 p^*}\left(\frac{-\mathrm{d}p^*}{\mathrm{d}r}\right)\Delta r S(r)\boldsymbol{e}_r\,, \tag{3.35}$$

where $S(r)$, the relativistic Schwarzschild discriminant, is

$$S(r) = \mathrm{d}p^*/\mathrm{d}r - \Gamma_1 p^*(\varrho^* + p^*)^{-1}\mathrm{d}\varrho^*/\mathrm{d}r\,. \tag{3.36}$$

If $S(r)$ is positive (subadiabatic temperature gradient), the displaced fluid element is accelerated back toward r_A and the star is stable against convection; but if $S(r)$ is negative (superadiabatic temperature gradient), the displaced fluid element is accelerated on upward, away from r_A, and the star is unstable against convection. Hence, criterion (3.32) for convective instability, which is, equivalent to $S(r) < 0$, is proved.

It should not be surprising that the condition for convective instability is the same in general-relativity theory as in Newtonian theory. Convective instability is a purely local phenomenon; it occurs locally and it is governed entirely by the local values of the thermodynamic variables and their gradients. Consequently, it cannot be affected by nonlinearities in the gravitational field, which act only over finite distances.

Whenever photon, conduction, and neutrino energy transport alone would produce a superadiabatic temperature gradient, convection breaks out and drives the temperature gradient down to adiabatic or near-adiabatic (*). In the adiabatic approximation, which is usually valid, the temperature and pressure gradients are related by eq. (3.11-7b); and they are related to the density gradients by

$$\mathrm{d}\varrho^*/\mathrm{d}r = (\varrho^* + p^*)n^{-1}\mathrm{d}n/\mathrm{d}r\,, \tag{3.37a}$$

$$\mathrm{d}T^*/\mathrm{d}r = (\Gamma_3 - 1)(T^*/n)\mathrm{d}n/\mathrm{d}r = (\Gamma_3 - 1)(T^*/[\varrho^* + p^*])\mathrm{d}\varrho^*/\mathrm{d}r\,, \tag{3.37b}$$

$$\mathrm{d}p^*/\mathrm{d}r = \Gamma_1(p^*/n)\mathrm{d}n/\mathrm{d}r = \Gamma_1(p^*/[\varrho^* + p^*])\mathrm{d}\varrho^*/\mathrm{d}r\,. \tag{3.37c}$$

(*) See *e.g.*, SCHWARZSCHILD (1958), p. 47. For a Newtonian discussion of those rare circumstances in which convection does not produce an adiabatic temperature gradient, see KIPPENHAHN (1963).

Here Γ_1 and Γ_3 are the adiabatic indices of eqs. (2.7) and (2.9). A stellar model in which the gradients are adiabatic is often called *isentropic* because it has constant entropy per baryon,

$$\text{(3.37}d\text{)} \qquad \mathrm{d}s^*/\mathrm{d}r = 0\,.$$

This completes our discussion of energy transport in relativistic stellar models. We have considered transport only for the cases in which convective transport is negligible beside radiation plus conduction (eq. (3.11-7*a*)), and for the case in which radiation plus conduction is negligible beside convection, and convection proceeds efficiently (eq. (3.11-7*b*) or, equivalently, any one of eq. (3.37)). It is interesting to note that in neither case does the neutrino luminosity $L_r^{(\nu)*}$ have a direct influence on the temperature gradient. This is because once neutrinos are emitted they never interact again with the star.

3˙2.9. Thermodynamic relations. As was discussed in Sect. **2˙**2.3, once the equations of state of the stellar material have been specified, the laws of thermodynamics fix any $4+N$ of the quantities (ϱ^*, p^*, n, s^*, T^*, Z_1, ..., Z_N, $\bar{\mu}_1^*$, ..., $\bar{\mu}_N^*$) as algebraic functions of the other $1+N$. The stellar structure equations (3.11-8)-(3.11-11 $+N$), which include $Z_1+...+Z_N=1$, are these three algebraic relations. Equation (3.11-12 $+N$) is the split of the density of mass-energy into rest mass plus internal energy, which we discussed in Sect. **2˙**2.1. Equation (3.11-13 $+N$) is the expression for the average baryonic rest mass in terms of the nuclear abundances and rest masses.

3˙2.10. Opacity and conductivity relations. The radiative absorption coefficient, $\varkappa_R^*$, and the thermal conductivity, λ_c^*, depend upon local thermodynamic conditions, which are determined by two thermodynamic parameters (*e.g.* ϱ^* and T^*) and the nuclear aboundances, Z_1, ..., Z_N. The opacity and conductivity relations (3.11-14 $+N$) and (3.11-15 $+N$), which put this dependence in quantitative form, are discussed in all treatises on the Newtonian theory of stellar structure (see *e.g.*, SCHWARZSCHILD (1958), pp. 62-73; SCHATZMAN (1958), pp. 78-87; and COX (1965)).

For the purpose of computing stellar models the effects of opacity and conductivity are combined into the single absorption coefficient $\varkappa^*$ of eq. (3.11-7*a*). Perhaps the most accurate values of this combined absorption coefficient are those produced by a computer program which has been developed by COX and his collaborators at Los Alamos Scientific Laboratory (see *e.g.*, COX (1965)).

3˙2.11. Equations of thermonuclear energy generation. The reaction rates for thermonuclear transformations, like opacity and conductivity, depend upon local thermodynamic conditions. Equations (3.11-17 $+N$) through

(3.11-16 + $2N$) are embodiments of this dependence. (*) For discussions of the specific reaction rates which are needed to make these equations quantitative see *e.g* SCHWARZSCHILD (1958), pp. 73-88; BURBIDGE (1963); REEVES (1965); BAHCALL (1964); BAHCALL and WOLF (1965*a*, *c*).

The remaining equations of thermonuclear energy generation, (3.11-16 + N) and (3.11-17 + $2N$)–(3.11-16 + $3N$), follow from the definitions of q^* and α_k^* (cf. Sect. **3**.1.3).

This completes our discussion of the equations of stellar structure. We next turn our attention to the boundary conditions which must be imposed on the stellar-structure parameters at the center and surface of the star.

3.3. *Boundary conditions for stellar structure.* – Of the $16+3N$ equations of stellar structure (3.11), 7 are first-order differential equations with respect to the radial co-ordinate, r. Corresponding to these 7 differential equations are 7 boundary conditions on the stellar-structure parameters

$$a(0)=0\,,\qquad m^*(0)=0\,,\qquad L_r^*(0)=0\,,\qquad L_r^{*(\nu)}(0)=0\,, \tag{3.38a}$$

$$\Phi(\infty)=0\,, \tag{3.38b}$$

$$p^*(R)=0\,,\qquad T^*(R)=0\,. \tag{3.38c}$$

These boundary conditions can be understood as follows: a and m^* vanish at the center of the star by definition, since $a(r)$ is the number of baryons inside a sphere of area $4\pi r^2$ and $m^*(r)$ is the mass-energy inside that same sphere. The radial luminosities L_r^* and $L_r^{(\nu)*}$ vanish at the center because of spherical symmetry. The gravitational potential, Φ, is zero at radial infinity by definition—Φ is defined by the physics only up to an additive constant; the choice $\Phi(\infty)=0$ corresponds to the demand that

$$(\text{co-ordinate time}, t)=\begin{pmatrix}\text{proper time as measured by an observer at rest}\\ \text{with respect to the star but very far away from it}\end{pmatrix}. \tag{3.39}$$

The boundary conditions at the surface of the star ($r=R$) are not so straightforward as those at the center and at infinity. Any star not at zero temperature possesses an atmosphere in which originate most of the photons that escape from the star. Although the atmospheric temperatures and pressures are definitely not zero, they are generally very small by comparison with interior temperatures and pressures. For this reason one can describe accurately all regions of a star except its surface layers and all properties of a star except the spectrum of its radiation by imposing the « zero-boundary conditions »

(*) α_N^* is fixed in terms of $\alpha_1^*, \ldots, \alpha_{N-1}^*$ by the relations $\sum Z_k=1$ (one of eqs. [3.11-8]→→[3.11-11 + N]) and $\mathrm{d}Z_k/\mathrm{d}t=e^{\Phi}\alpha_k^*$ (eqs. 3.11-17 + $2N$]→[3.11-16 + 3N]).

(3.38c). Since a relativistic theory of stellar atmospheres has not yet been developed, we shall confine ourselves to the zero-boundary conditions throughout these lectures (*).

3·4. *Construction of stellar models.*

3·4.1. External gravitational field. The equations of stellar structure (3.11) are easily solved in the region outside the star, yielding

$$(3.40) \qquad \begin{cases} m^*(r) = M^* \equiv m^*(R) \\ \Phi(r) \;\; = \frac{1}{2}\ln(1-2M^*/r) \end{cases} \qquad \text{for } r < R\,.$$

Consequently, the geometry of space-time outside the star is that first discussed by SCHWARZSCHILD (1961):

$$(3.41) \qquad ds^2 = (1-2M^*/r)\,dt^2 - (1-2M^*/r)^{-1}\,dr^2 - r^2(d\theta^2 + \sin^2\theta\, d\varphi^2)\,.$$

At distances $r \gg M^*$ this geometry represents a gravitational field which can be described accurately by the Newtonian gravitational potential

$$(3.42) \qquad U = -\Phi c^2 = M^* c^2/r = GM/r.$$

Hence, the quantity $M \equiv m(R)$ is the mass of the star as measured gravitationally by a distant observer; it is the mass which governs the Keplerian motion of distant planets about the star.

3·4.2. Internal structure of noncontracting stars. As in Newtonian theory, so also in general relativity, one can obtain physically interesting interior solutions to the equations of stellar structure only by numerical integration. In the case of noncontracting configurations (configurations in which the energy flux, L_r, is precisely balanced by thermonuclear energy generation) the time derivatives of eq. (3.11-5) (first equality) vanish. The equations of stellar structure then become 7 ordinary first-order radial differential equations (3.11-1)–(3.11-7) coupled to $9+2N$ (N being the number of different nuclear species present) algebraic relations (3.11-8)–(3.11-16 $+\,2N$) and to N first-order, time differential equations (3.11–17 $+\,2N$)–(3.11-16 $+\,3N$). There, are in all $16+3N$ equations for the $16+3N$ structure parameters (Φ, m^* a, ϱ^*, p^*, n, ε^*, s^*, T^*, L_r^*, $L_r^{(\nu)*}$, $\varkappa_R^*$, λ_c^*, q^*, $q_{(\nu)}^*$, μ_B^*, Z_1, ..., Z_N, $\bar{\mu}_1^*$, ..., $\bar{\mu}_N^*$, α_1^*, ..., α_N^*).

(*) For Newtonian discussions of stellar atmospheres see, *e.g.*, SCHWARSCHILD (1958), p. 89, and GREENSTEIN (1960). The general-relativity treatment should differ from the Newtonian treatment only as a result of red-shift effects, which will often be of negligible importance.

In order to construct a noncontracting stellar model and follow its subsequent evolution one might proceed in a manner similar to that used in Newtonian theory (see *e.g.* SCHWARZSCHILD (1958), pp. 97-101): 1) Specify *ab initio* the total number of baryons in the star, $A = a(R)$, plus the initial nuclear abundances $Z_1, ..., Z_N$, as functions of the baryon-number co-ordinate, a. 2) Calculate the remaining $16 + 2N$ structure parameters by integrating the 7 differential equations (3.11-1)–(3.11-7) subject to the 7 boundary conditions (3.38) and coupled to the $9 + 2N$ algebraic relations (3.11-8)–(3.11-16 + $2N$). The solution will be uniquely determined—aside from cases of mathematical degeneracy (*)— by these equations and boundary conditions. 3) Having now constructed the initial stellar model at time $t = 0$, use eqs. (3.11-17 + $2N$)–(3.11-16 + $3N$) to determine the nuclear abundances at a later time Δt

$$(3.43) \qquad Z_k(a, \Delta t) = Z_k(a, 0) + \exp[\Phi(a, 0)]\alpha_k^*(a, 0)\Delta t\,, \qquad k = 1, ..., N\,.$$

In regions where convective transport occurs, correct (3.43) for convection by averaging over the convective zone the $Z_k(a, \Delta t)$ obtained from (3.43). 4) Next calculate the stellar configuration at time Δt by step 2). 5) Repeat steps 3) and 4).

In those phases of evolution characterized by rapid contraction or expansion of the star, this procedure must be replaced by that of the following Section in order to account for the internal energy changes caused by compression or expansion of the fluid.

3·4.3. Internal structure of stars in quasi-static contraction. Whenever the luminosity, L_r, is not precisely balanced by nuclear energy generation, the star must supply the required excess luminosity by quasi-static contraction and by changing its internal energy per baryon, ε^*/n. In order to construct a stellar model in quasi-static contraction (or expansion) and follow its evolution, one can proceed as follows: 1) Specify *ab initio* the total number of baryons, A, plus the initial nuclear abundances, $Z_1(a), ..., Z_N(a)$, plus the radial distribution of one thermodynamic variable—say $s^*(a)$ for definiteness. 2) Calculate the remaining $15 + 2N$ structure parameters by integrating the 6 radial differential equations (3.11-1, 2, 3, 4, 6, 7) subject to the 6 boundary conditions (3.38*a*, *b*) and $p^*(R)=0$, and coupled to the $9+2N$ algebraic relations (3.11-8)–(3.11-16 + $2N$). (The boundary condition $T^*(R) = 0$ should be guaranteed by the specified value of $s^*(A)$ and the condition $p^*(R) = 0$.) The solu-

(*) Such cases do occasionaly arise, particularly for stars at the end point of thermonuclear evolution (see *e.g.* Sect. 5·4.1). For a discussion of the mathematical structure of the initial-value problem—which is the same in general relativity as in Newtonian theory—and of the uniqueness of the solution, see *e.g.* SCHWARZSCHILD (1958), p. 97.

tion will be uniquely determined aside from cases of mathematical degeneracy (*). 3) Having now constructed the initial stellar model at time $t = 0$, use eqs. (3.11-5) and (3.11-17 + $2N$)–(3.11-16 + $3N$) to determine the nuclear abundances and the distribution of entropy at time $t = \Delta t$

$$(3.44a) \qquad Z_k(a, \Delta t) = Z_k(a, 0) + \exp[\Phi(a, 0)]\alpha_k^*(a, 0)\Delta t\,, \qquad k = 1, \ldots, N$$

$$(3.44b) \qquad s^*(a, \Delta T) = s^*(a, 0) - \frac{(1 - 2m^*/r)^{\frac{1}{2}}\, e^{-\Phi}}{4\pi r^2 n T^*}\frac{\mathrm{d}(L_r^*\, e^{2\Phi})}{\mathrm{d}r}\Delta t - \\ - T^{*-1}\sum \bar{\mu}_k^*(a, 0)\exp[\Phi(a, 0)]\alpha_k^*(a, 0)\Delta t\,.$$

4) Calculate the stellar configuration at time Δt by step 2) but with the initial condition $s^*(a) =$ (initial value of $s^*(a)$) replaced by (3.44b). 5) Repeat steps 3) and 4) until the assumption of quasi-static motion breaks down, *e.g.*, as the result of the onset of dynamical instabilities (cf. Sect. **4**), or until the star has cooled to zero temperature.

3'5. *Properties of nonrotating stars.* – We now turn our attention from procedures for constructing relativistic stellar models to some of the properties of such models. Our discussion will be based on the equations of stellar structure (3.11).

3'5.1. Geometry of space-time. For stars with mass M^* and radius R such that $2M^*/R \sim 1$, the geometry of space-time is far from Euclidean. Consequently, there is no *a priori* reason to expect that the surface area, $4\pi r^2$, of successive spheres about the center of such a star will be an always-increasing function of distance from the center. Indeed, in Sect. **7**'3.7, we shall see that $4\pi r^2$ can sometimes decrease (« bag of matter ») as one moves outward from the center of a gravitationally collapsing star. However, this peculiar radial decrease in $4\pi r^2$, and hence also in r, is limited to dynamical situations; *in any spherical configuration of hydrostatic equilibrium the radial co-ordinate, r, increases monotonically from 0 at the center of the star to ∞ at an infinite distance away.*

The monotonicity of r can be seen as follows: Introduce as a new radial co-ordinate proper distance, l, from the center of the star. By virtue of expression (3.1) for the geometry of space-time, l and r are related by

$$(3.45) \qquad \mathrm{d}r = \pm(1 - 2m^*/r)^{\frac{1}{2}}\,\mathrm{d}l\,.$$

Since r is zero at the center of the star and r is always nonnegative, r must at first increase with l as one moves outward from $l = 0$. $r(l)$ can later reach a maximum and start decreasing only at a point where $2m^*/r$ becomes unity

(*) See footnote (*) on p. 199.

(cf. eq. (3.45)). However, if $2m^*/r$ approaches unity in some region of the star, the pressure gradient (eq. (3.11-3)) becomes so large that the surface of the star, $p^* = 0$, is reached before $2m^*/r$ reaches one. After the surface of the star is passed, m^* remains constant and $2m^*/r$ decreases. Consequently, *$2m^*/r$ is always less than unity*; and $r(l)$ cannot have a maximum. QED. (For a more rigorous proof see BONDI (1964)).

The gravitational field of an equilibrium configuration is most easily visualized by means of an embedding diagram (Sect. 2·3.1.) of the hypersurfaces of constant time. The geometry of these hypersurfaces is given by

$$\mathrm{d}\sigma^2 = (1 - 2m^*/r)^{-1}\,\mathrm{d}r^2 + r^2(d\theta^2 + \sin^2\theta\,\mathrm{d}\varphi^2)\,. \tag{3.46}$$

In order to construct a surface with this geometry in Euclidean 3-space we must suppress one rotational degree of freedom; *i.e.* we must restrict ourselves to the 2-geometries

$$\mathrm{d}\sigma^2 = (1 - 2m^*/r)^{-1}\,\mathrm{d}r^2 + r^2\,\mathrm{d}\theta^2 \tag{3.47}$$

of constant t and φ.

An embedding of this 2-geometry is most conveniently obtained by introducing into the Euclidean 3-space cylindrical co-ordinates $(\bar{r}, \bar{\theta}, \bar{z})$ and by taking as the embedded 2-surface

$$\bar{r} = r\,, \qquad \bar{\theta} = \theta\,, \qquad \bar{z} = \int_0^r [2m^*/(r - 2m^*)]^{\frac{1}{2}}\,\mathrm{d}r\,. \tag{3.48}$$

That the intrinsic geometry of the 2-surface (3.48) in Euclidean 3-space is, indeed, identical to the geometry (3.47) of space around an equilibrium stellar configuration is easily verified as follows:

$$\begin{aligned}\mathrm{d}\bar{\sigma}^2 = \mathrm{d}\bar{z}^2 + \mathrm{d}\bar{r} + \bar{r}^2\,\mathrm{d}\bar{\theta}^2 &= [2m^*/(r - 2m^*)]\,\mathrm{d}r^2 + \mathrm{d}r^2 + r^2\,\mathrm{d}\theta^2 = \\ &= (1 - 2m^*/r)^{-1}\,\mathrm{d}r^2 + r^2\,\mathrm{d}\theta^2 = \mathrm{d}\sigma^2\,.\end{aligned} \tag{3.49}$$

The embedded stellar geometry (3.48) for a typical equilibrium configuration is shown in Fig. 1.

The embedding diagram for any equilibrium configuration necessarily has the following properties: 1) The interior region is a bowl with a smooth bottom which opens outward and upward. 2) The exterior region is a paraboloid of the form

$$\bar{r} = 2M^* + (\bar{z} - \bar{z}_0)^2/8M^*\,, \qquad \bar{z}_0 = \text{const} < \bar{z} \text{ at surface of star}\,. \tag{3.50}$$

3) The interior and exterior regions join together smoothly. 4) The geometry

nowhere contains a radial bulge or neck (« bag of matter »); *i.e.* r is a monotonic increasing function of z.

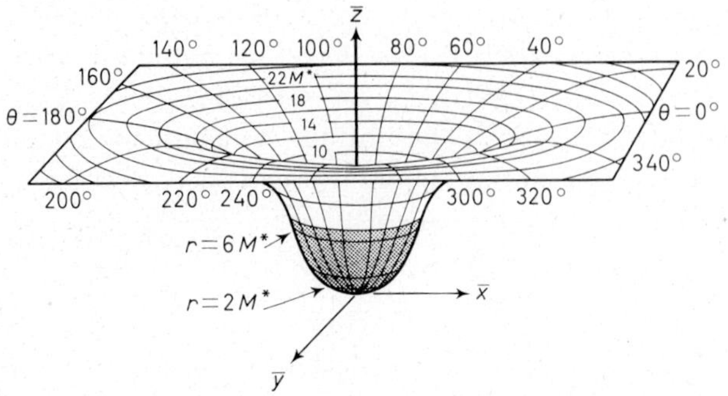

Fig. 1. – Embedding diagram for the geometry of the 2-surface $(t, \varphi) =$ constant of a nonrotating star in hydrostatic equilibrium. The co-ordinates (r, θ) intrinsic to this 2-surface are related to the co-ordinates $[\bar{r} = (\bar{x}^2 + \bar{y}^2)^{\frac{1}{2}}, \ \bar{\theta} = \text{tg}^{-1}(\bar{y}/\bar{x}), \ \bar{z}]$ of the Euclidean embedding space by eqs. (3.48). The interior of the star is distinguished from the exterior by stippling. Because the rotational degree of freedom associated with φ has been suppressed from the diagram, regions of constant radius, r, are here circles of circumference $2\pi r$ about the center, $r = 0$. The 3-geometry of space around the star at a particular moment of time, t, can be visualized by mentally replacing the circles of constant r in this diagram with spheres of area $4\pi r^2$.

It must be emphasized that only points lying on the embedded 2-surface have physical significance so far as the stellar geometry is concerned; the 3-dimensional regions inside and outside the bowl of Fig. 1 are physically meaningless, as are the co-ordinates $(\bar{r}, \bar{z}, \bar{\theta})$ of the Euclidean embedding space. They merely permit us to visualize the geometry of space around the star in a convenient manner.

From the embedding diagram of Fig. 1 and also from eq. (3.46) it is clear that *the area, $4\pi r^2$, of a sphere about the center of the star is always less than $4\pi l^2$, where l is the proper radius of the sphere*

$$l = \int_0^r (1 - 2m^*/r)^{-\frac{1}{2}} \mathrm{d}r \, . \tag{3.51}$$

3·5.2. Distribution of pressure. From the TOV equation (3.11-3) of hydrostatic equilibrium it is evident that *pressure, p^*, decreases monotonically from the center of an equilibrium configuration to its surface.* Also, a comparison of the TOV equation with its Newtonian counterpart (3.18) reveals this, that at a radius r, inside of which is a mass m^*, *the pressure gradient is steeper than would be expected from Newtonian theory.* An increased pressure gradient is necessary to counterbalance the relativistically enhanced gravitational acceleration (eq. (3.17)).

Two different types of relativistic nonlinearities enhance the gravitational acceleration, and hence the pressure gradient: 1) the « geometric » nonlinearity associated with the quantity $(1-2m^*/r)$ in the denominator of the TOV equation (3.11-3); and 2) « pressure-regenerative » nonlinearities associated with the two pressure terms in the numerator. In hot, supermassive stars, both geometric nonlinearities and pressure-regenerative nonlinearities are important; and they steepen the pressure gradient by $\lesssim 1\%$. Pressure-regenerative nonlinearities dominate and reach their extreme in (physically unrealistic) configurations of incompressible fluid—see, *e.g.*, HTWW Chapter 4, and WHEELER (1964*a*) pp. 222-225—where they enhance the pressure gradient by arbitrarily large amounts. In superdense stars near the endpoint of thermonuclear evolution (Sect. **5**) the two types of nonlinearities are equally important; they both enhance the pressure gradient by $\sim 10\%$.

3'5.3. Extremal mass-energy. A very important and intuitively satisfying property of equilibrium configurations is the following: Consider an arbitrary, momentarily static, spherical configuration of fluid which may or may not be in hydrostatic equilibrium. Adiabatically perturb this configuration in the radial direction by an amount $\xi(r) = \delta r$, and calculate the change, δM^*, in the total mass of the star which results from the perturbation. Then the original configuration was in hydrostatic equilibrium if and only if δM^* vanishes to first order in the amplitude of the perturbation, ξ. Put more briefly, *the total mass-energy, M^*, of an equilibrium configuration is an extremum with respect to adiabatic, radial perturbations* (*).

In SECT. **4**'2.1 we will see how this theorem of extremal mass-energy can be extended to determine the stability of an equilibrium configuration.

3'5.4. Orbits of freely falling bodies. The orbits of small bodies falling freely in the external gravitational field of a relativistic star have been studied in great detail by DARWIN (1959). We summarize here some of the most interesting results, assuming always that the surface of the star is inside the orbits under discussion.

(*) This theorem was first proved independently by COCKE (1965) and by THORNE and WHEELER (1965). (See also HTWW, p. 16 and 156). The proof in HTWW applies only to zero-temperature configurations, but it can be generalized to arbitrary configurations by simply replacing all ordinary derivatives ($dp^*/d\varrho^*$, $dn/d\varrho^*$, etc.) by isentropic partial derivatives [$(\partial p^*/\partial\varrho^*)_s$, $(\partial n/\partial\varrho^*)_s$, etc.]. COCKE actually proves the theorem, in an inverted but equivalent form; he shows that the total entropy, S, of an equilibrium configuration is extremized with respect to adiabatic, radial perturbations in which M^*—but not necessarily A—is kept fixed.

Orbits with perihelions at $r \gg M^*$ are Keplerian in form, except for the perihelion shift which is familiar in the case of Mercury. However, orbits which extend into the region $r \lesssim 10M^*$ have forms unexpected in Newtonian theory. For example, there is never a perihelion in the region $r < 3M^*$; any orbit which extends into this region necessarily hits the surface of the star. Circular orbits are allowed throughout the region $r \geqslant 3M^*$; but they are stable only for $r > 6M^*$. A particle in a circular orbit with $3M^* < r < 4M^*$, if perturbed, will escape to infinity or fall into the star. A circling particle with $4M^* < r < 6M^*$, if perturbed, will enter a spiraling orbit which eventually falls into the star. Circular orbits at $r = 3M^*$ are allowed only for photons or neutrinos since they can be maintained only by a particle moving with the speed of light.

The energy red-shift relation (3.3) plays a fundamental role in the study of particle and photon orbits.

3'5.5. Gravitational red-shift. The energy red-shift relation (3.3) when applied to photons yields an expression for the gravitational red-shift of the wavelength of light. Consider a photon which is emitted at a point $(r_0, \theta_0, \varphi_0)$ in the gravitational field of a star and received at a point $(r_1, \theta_1, \varphi_1)$. Let the energy and wave length of the photon, as measured in the proper frames of observers at rest with respect to the star, be E and $\lambda = hc/E$. Then

$$Ee^{\Phi} = \big(hc/\lambda(r)\big) \exp[\Phi(r)] = \text{const}\,, \tag{3.52}$$

so that the red-shift factor is

$$z \equiv (\lambda_1 - \lambda_0)/\lambda_0 = \exp[\Phi(r_1) - \Phi(r_0)] - 1\,. \tag{3.53}$$

For a photon emitted from the surface of the star ($r = R$) and received at infinity this becomes (cf. eq. (3.40))

$$z = (1 - 2M^*/R)^{-\frac{1}{2}} - 1\,. \tag{3.54}$$

We found in Sect. **3**'5.1 that $(1 - 2M^*/R)$ is necessarily greater than zero for a configuration of hydrostatic equilibrium. Consequently, the red-shift is never infinite. Bondi (1964, 1965), by a very careful and elegant analysis of the TOV equation of hydrostatic equilibrium, has put much more stringent limits on z. (See also Buchdahl (1959), a forerunner of Bondi's work.) For all configurations which are in principle physically realizable ($\varrho^* \geqslant p^* \geqslant 0$ everywhere; cf. end of Sect. **2**'2.1). Bondi finds

$$M^*/R \leqslant 0.432\,, \qquad z \leqslant 1.71\,. \tag{3.55}$$

If, in order to avoid Taylor instabilities (see *e.g.* CHANDRASEKHAR (1961)), one imposes the additional restriction that ϱ^* be monotonic decreasing from the center of the star to the surface, then one obtains (BONDI (1964, 1965))

$$M^*/R \leqslant 0.390\,, \qquad z \leqslant 1.14\,. \tag{3.56}$$

In most realistic situations one actually has $p^* \leqslant \frac{1}{3}\varrho^*$ (cf. HTWW, Chapter 10) and an adiabatic or subadiabatic temperature gradient (cf. Sect. 3˙2.8). When this is the case, Bondi's analysis yields the limits

$$M^*/R \leqslant 0.310\,, \qquad z \leqslant 0.63\,. \tag{3.57}$$

Although the red-shift of a photon originating at the *surface* of any equilibrium configuration is limited by $z < 1.63$, the red-shift of a photon—or, more realistically of a neutrino—which originates at the *center* can be arbitrarily large. An expression for the red-shift of such a neutrino is (cf. eqs. (3.53) and (3.11-3, 4))

$$z = (1 - 2M^*/R)^{-\frac{1}{2}} \exp\left[\int_0^R (\varrho^* + p^*)^{-1}(-\,\mathrm{d}p^*/\mathrm{d}r)\,\mathrm{d}r\right] - 1\,. \tag{3.58}$$

For configurations of arbitrarily high central pressure, this red-shift is arbitrarily large.

3˙5.6. Spectrum of the stellar radiation. Having forgone any attempt to describe the stellar atmosphere (cf. Sect. 3˙3), we have placed a barrier between ourselves and a *detailed* knowledge of the spectrum of the light radiated by a relativistic star. However, simple physical considerations, as well as astronomical observations, reveal that the spectrum is roughly that of a black body. By equating the total nonneutrino luminosity at the surface of the star, $L_r^*(R) - L_r^{(\nu)*}(R)$, to the integrated intensity, $4\pi R^2 \sigma^* T_e^{*4}$, of a black body of temperature T_e^* and surface area $4\pi R^2$, we obtain for the « effective temperature » which characterizes the star's black-body radiation

$$T_e^* = \{(L_r^* - L_r^{(\nu)*})_{r=R}/(4\pi R^2 \sigma^*)\}^{\frac{1}{4}}\,. \tag{3.59}$$

This is actually the effective temperature as seen by an observer near the surface of the star. For an observer very far away the light will be red-shifted by a factor

$$z \equiv \Delta\lambda/\lambda = \exp[-\,\Phi(R)] - 1 = (1 - 2M^*/R)^{-\frac{1}{2}} - 1\,. \tag{3.60}$$

This red-shift of wavelength preserves the (roughly) black-body form of the spectrum but lowers the temperature, which characterizes the spectrum, from

T_e to

$$(3.61)\quad \begin{pmatrix}\text{Black-body temperature}\\ \text{as seen at } r=\infty\end{pmatrix}^* = T_e^*\left(1-\frac{2M^*}{R}\right)^{\frac{1}{2}} = \left\{\left[\frac{L_r^* - L_r^{(\nu)*}}{4\pi r^2\sigma^*}\right]_{r=\infty}\right\}^{\frac{1}{4}}.$$

To verify this, combine eqs. (3.11-5, 6) and (3.59) with the Planck distribution law for black-body radiation.

3·5.7. Injection energy and convection (*). Let an astrophysicist far from a stellar equilibrium configuration create δA baryons and drop them, along with an additional mass-energy W_0^*, down an idealized pipe, which is inserted into the star, to a colleague situated at radius r. Require that the nuclear abundances of the δA baryons be the same as the abundances at radius r in the star. Have the colleague at r: 1) catch the falling baryons, thereby extracting their kinetic energy of fall, W_{kin}^*; 2) use the energy $W_0^* + W_{\text{kin}}^*$ to compress and heat the δA baryons to the local thermodynamic conditions, and to insert them from the pipe into the star; 3) throw the excess mass-energy back up the pipe to the astrophysicist far away. The total mass-energy used up in this process, as measured by the distant astrophysicist, is called *the injection energy at r* and is equal to the change, δM^*, in the total mass-energy of the star which results from the addition of the δA baryons at r (conservation of total mass-energy). Let us calculate δM^*:

The total mass-energy which the distant astrophysicist drops down the pipe is $\mu_0^*\,\delta A + W_0^*$, where μ_B^* is the average rest mass of the baryons created. When the colleague at r catches the δA baryons and excess mass W_0^*, they have a total energy of (cf. eq. (3.3))

$$W_{\text{total}}^* \equiv \mu_B^*\,\delta A + W_0^* + W_{\text{kin}}^* = (\mu_B^*\,\delta A + W_0^*)\exp[-\Phi(r)]\,.$$

Hence, the kinetic energy which he extracts is

$$W_{\text{kin}}^* = (\mu_B^*\,\delta A + W_0^*)(\exp[-\Phi]-1)\,.$$

The colleague at r uses $W_{\text{kin}}^* + W_0^*$ to heat and compress the baryons to local thermodynamic conditions and to push aside enough fluid in the star to make room for the new baryons. Heating and compression require

$$W_{\text{heat}}^* + W_{\text{compress}}^* = [\varrho^*(r)/n(r) - \mu_B^*]\,\delta A\,;$$

(*) The analysis of this Section is patterned after a similar analysis by WHEELER (HTWW, p. 20) for zero-temperature configurations.

while opening up a space in the star requires

$$W^*_{\text{open}} = p^*(r)[\delta A/n(r)]\,.$$

Hence, the excess energy which the colleague at r must throw back up the pipe is

$$W^*_{\text{excess at } r} = W^*_0 + W^*_{\text{kin}} - (W^*_{\text{heat}} + W^*_{\text{compress}} + W^*_{\text{open}}) = \\ = (W^*_0 + \mu^*_{\text{B}}\,\delta A)\,e^{-\Phi} - (\varrho^* + p^*)(\delta A/n)$$

According to the equation of energy red-shift (3.3) the colleague at r must convert a portion $(W^*_{\text{excess at } r})(1-\exp[\Phi(r)])$ of this excess mass-energy into the kinetic energy of his throw in order to get the rest of the excess mass-energy back up to the distant astrophysicist. Thus, the distant astrophysicist receives an excess mass-energy of only

$$W^*_{\text{excess at } \infty} = W^*_{\text{excess at } r}\exp[\Phi(r)] = W^*_0 + \mu^*_{\text{B}}\,\delta A - (\varrho^* + p^*)\,n^{-1}\,e^{\Phi}\,\delta A\,.$$

The total mass-energy required to create the δA baryons and perform the injection process is thus

$$\delta M^* = W^*_0 + \mu^*_{\text{B}}\,\delta A - W^*_{\text{excess at } \infty}$$

$$\delta M^* = [\varrho^*(r) + p^*(r)][n(r)]^{-1}\exp[\Phi(r)]\,\delta A = (\partial\varrho^*/\partial n)_{s^*}\exp[\Phi(r)]\,\delta A\,. \tag{3.62}$$

This result has a simple interpretation: $(\partial\varrho^*/\partial n)_{s^*}\delta A$ is the local increase in mass-energy at r which results from adding δA baryons; and $\exp[\Phi(r)]$ is the fraction by which this mass-energy at r is red-shifted when it is brought out to radial infinity, where δM^* is measured.

The injection energy, δM^*, generally depends upon the radius, r, at which the δA baryons are injected. From the way in which we calculated injection energy, it is clear that δM^* *will be independent of* r if and only if baryons can be moved about freely in the star without any expenditure or release of energy —*i.e. if and only if the star is in marginal convective equilibrium.*

Let us verify that the condition $\delta M^* = \text{const.}$ is, indeed, equivalent to the adiabatic-gradient criterion (Sect. **3**.2.8.) for marginal convective equilibrium:

$$\delta M^* = \text{const} \Leftrightarrow [(\varrho^* + p^*)/n]e^{\Phi} = \text{const} \Leftrightarrow \ln(\varrho^* + p^*) - \ln n + \Phi = \text{const}\,,$$

$$\Leftrightarrow (\varrho^* + p^*)^{-1}(\text{d}\varrho^*/\text{d}r + \text{d}p^*/\text{d}r) - n^{-1}\,\text{d}n/\text{d}r + \text{d}\Phi/\text{d}r = 0\,,$$

$$\Leftrightarrow (\varrho^* + p^*)^{-1}(\text{d}\varrho^*/\text{d}r + \text{d}p^*/\text{d}r) - n^{-1}\,\text{d}n/\text{d}r - (\varrho^* + p^*)^{-1}\,\text{d}p^*/\text{d}r = 0\,,$$

$$\Leftrightarrow \text{d}\varrho^*/\text{d}r = (\varrho^* + p^*)\,n^{-1}\,\text{d}n/\text{d}r \Leftrightarrow \text{d}\varrho^*/\text{d}r = (\partial\varrho^*/\partial n)_{s^*}\text{d}n/\text{d}r\,,$$

$\Leftrightarrow$ the thermodynamic gradients are adiabatic.

The value of the constant injection energy for a configuration which is everywhere isentropic (marginally convective) is most conveniently calculated at the star's surface

$$\delta M^* = \mu_B^*(R)[1-2M^*/R]^{\frac{1}{2}}\,\delta A\,. \tag{3.63}$$

This completes our discussion of general properties of nonrotating equilibrium configurations. Before moving on to a discussion of stellar stability (Sect. **4**) and of specific stellar models (Sect. **5** and **6**), we shall describe briefly the little which is known about rotating, relativistic equilibrium configurations.

3·6. *Rotating equilibrium configurations.*

3·6.1. Rotation in general relativity. The relativistic gravitational field of an axially-symmetric rotating equilibrium configuration is conveniently described in terms of four gravitational potentials $\gamma(r,\theta)$, $K(r,\theta)$, $\omega(r,\theta)$, $N(r,\theta)$, which determine the geometry of space-time through the line element

$$\mathrm{d}s^2 = (N^2-\omega^2K^2r^2\sin^2\theta)\,\mathrm{d}t^2 - e^{2\gamma}\,\mathrm{d}r^2 - \\ - r^2K^2(\mathrm{d}\theta^2+\sin^2\theta\,\mathrm{d}\varphi^2) - 2\omega K^2r^2\sin^2\theta\,\mathrm{d}\varphi\,\mathrm{d}t\,. \tag{3.64}$$

Here (t, r, θ, φ) are a particular, geometrically selected set of space-time co-ordinates which, for the special case of zero rotation, reduce to the spherical co-ordinates used to describe nonrotating equilibrium configurations.

The gravitational source equations and the equations of hydrostatic equilibrium for rotating configurations have been worked out by HARTLE and SHARP (1966) and by many others; but they are so complicated that no physically interesting solutions to them have yet been found.

Even the partial differential equations for the exterior gravitational field are almost unmanageable. Only one physically interesting solution to them is known—that of KERR (1963, 1965) (See also CARTER (1966) and BOYER and LINDQUIST (1966).) Kerr's solution is the external gravitational field for a limited class of rotating equilibrium configurations. BOYER (1965*a*, *b*) has studied some of the properties of those rigidly rotating equilibrium configurations which would generate Kerr's gravitational field, but the precise forms of the internal solutions are unknown (*). Other contributions to our understanding of the external gravitational fields of rotating configurations have come from PAPAPETROU (1953, 1966).

(*) DOROSHKEVICH, ZEL'DOVICH and NOVIKOV (1965) incorrectly argue that no rotating configuration could generate Kerr's gravitational field unless the fluid in its interior performed a circulatory motion in addition to rotating. Their argument is based upon the false belief that Kerr's metric contains nonremovable off-diagonal terms in addition to $g_{t\varphi}$. (Cf. BOYER and LINDQUIST (1966).)

Because the equations which govern rotating configurations are so intractable analytically, attempts to construct numerical solutions will soon be initiated. The construction of numerical solutions should not be too much more difficult in general relativity than in Newtonian theory because the number of independent variables is the same—two.

HARTLE and SHARP (1965, 1966) have recently constructed a mass-energy variational principle for rotating configurations, which is analogous to the variational principle of Sect. 3'5.3 for nonrotating configurations, and which may be of considerable value in the construction of numerical solutions to the equations of rotation. This variational principle states that *the equilibrium states of a uniformly rotating perfect fluid are those configurations which extremize the total mass-energy with respect to pertubations that a) are adiabatic, b) keep the total angular momentum fixed, and c) conserve the total number of baryons.*

As a special case of the Hartle-Sharp work on rotation, HARTLE (1966) has studied in some detail the effects of small amounts of rotation on relativistic configurations of hydrostatic equilibrium.

3'6.2. Rotation in the post-Newtonian approximation. The post-Newtonian approximation has been used frequently since 1925 to study the effects of rotation upon equilibrium configurations of perfect fluid and upon their external gravitational fields (see *e.g.* AKELEY (1931), CLARK (1947, 1948, 1950), CHANDRASEKHAR (1965*c*), FOWLER (1966), ROXBURGH (1965), DURNEY and ROXBURGH (1965)).

Those post-Newtonian studies which perhaps are most interesting from an astrophysical standpoint are the recent analyses by FOWLER (1966), by ROXBURGH (1965), and by DURNEY and ROXBURGH (1965) of the relationship between angular velocity, binding energy, and stability for rotating configurations; and the analysis by CHANDRASEKHAR (1965*c*) of the shapes of rotating configurations. Since Fowler's work is available in this volume, we shall describe only Chandrasekhar's results.

Consider a star with uniform density of mass-energy, ϱ^*, in uniform rotation about an axis of symmetry. Newtonian theory reveals that Maclaurin spheroids are possible equilibrium configurations for such a star. CHANDRASEKHAR has used his post-Newtonian tensor virial theorem to show that post-Newtonian gravitational forces will pull the equator of such a spheroid in toward its center. The order of magnitude of the reduction in eccentricity is indicated in Table II, where we compare the eccentricities expected from Newtonian theory with those predicted by post-Newtonian theory, for a spheroid with density of mass-energy ϱ, angular velocity ω, total mass-energy M, and equatorial radius R_{eq} (*). Note that the fractional post-Newtonian correction to the eccentricity

(*) For the precise physical meaning of the post-Newtonian quantities ω and R_{eq} (Ω and a_1 in Chandrasekhar's notation) see CHANDRASEKHAR (1965*b*, *c*).

is proportional to $2GM/c^2 R_{eq} = 2M^*/R_{eq}$. This is a particular case of a frequent phenomenon in post-Newtonian theory: fractional post-Newtonian corrections to the Newtonian stucture of a star are usually proportioned to $2M^*/R$.

TABLE II. – *The effects of post-Newtonian gravitational forces on the eccentricity of a Maclaurin spheriod* ([a]).

$\omega^2/\pi G\varrho$	$2GM/c^2 R_{eq}$	e_{Newton}	$e_{post\text{-}Newton}$
0.02146	0.01	0.20000	0.1996
0.02146	0.1	0.2000	0.196
0.27734	0.01	0.700	0.698
0.27734	0.1	0.70	0.68

([a]) Based on an exact formula due to CHANDRASEKHAR (1965c).

3.7. *Summary.* – The principal conclusions from our discussion of equilibrium stellar configurations are these: The structure of a nonrotating equilibrium configuration is determined by $16 + 3N$ quantities, where N is the number of different nuclear species present: the gravitational potential, Φ; the mass-energy inside radius r, m^*; the number of baryons inside radius r, a; the density of mass-energy, ϱ^*; the pressure, p^*; the number density of baryons, n; the density of internal energy, ε^*; the entropy per baryon s^*; the temperature, T^*; the total luminosity (energy flux), L_r^*; the neutrino luminosity, $L_r^{(\nu)*}$; the radiative absorption coefficient, $\varkappa_R^*$; the thermal conductivity, λ_c^*; the rate of thermonuclear energy generation, q^*; the rate of energy release into neutrinos, $q_{(\nu)}^*$; the average baryonic rest mass, μ_B^*; the nuclear abundances, $Z_1, \ldots, Z_N$; the nuclear chemical potentials, $\bar{\mu}_1^*, \ldots, \bar{\mu}_N^*$; and the rates of change of nuclear abundances, $\alpha_1^*, \ldots, \alpha_N^*$. These quantities are all functions of a radial co-ordinate, r, defined such that $4\pi r^2$ is the surface area of a sphere about the center of the star. Equations (3.11) are $16 + 3N$ equations of stellar structure which uniquely determine the distributions of the $16 + 3N$ structural parameters once sufficient initial data are given. These equations also govern the evolution of relativistic stars.

Some important properties of nonrotating equilibrium configurations are the following: 1) The geometry of space-time about an equilibrium configuration, as given by the line element (3.1), can be represented pictorially by the bowl-like embedding diagram of Fig. 1. 2) This geometry (or gravitational field) causes a red-shift of photons emitted from the surface of the star. The red-shift is greater the more compact the star; but for no equilibrium configuration can it ever exceed $(\Delta\lambda/\lambda) = 1.71$. 3) The total mass-energy of an equilibrium configuration is an extremum with respect to adiabatic, radial perturbations. 4) An equilibrium configuration has injection energy independent of radius if and only if it is in marginal convective equilibrium.

The relativistic theory of rotating equilibrium configurations has not yet been developed. However, it is known that 1) uniformly rotating configurations have extremal mass-energy; and 2) post-Newtonian gravitational forces tend to reduce the equatorial bulge of a rotating star.

4. – Stability of equilibrium configurations.

We now turn our attention from the theory of the structure of relativistic stellar models to the theory of their stability against small perturbations. We shall first discuss nonradial perturbations, about which very little is known; and then we shall review the extensively-developed theory of radial perturbations.

4·1. *Nonradial perturbations of nonrotating configurations.* – The analysis of small, nonradial motions of a star about its equilibrium configurations is so difficult that only recently has the Newtonian theory been developed into a fairly definitive form (LEDOUX and WALRAVEN (1958), CHANDRASEKHAR and LEBOVITZ (1964), CHANDRASEKHAR (1964*a*), and LEBOVITZ (1965*a*, *b*)); and the general relativity theory is as yet nonexistent. The relativistic theory, when it is developed, will be far more complicated than the Newtonian theory because, according to general relativity, a star in nonradial motion should emit gravitational waves.

One would like to gain some insight into the effects of general relativity on nonradial perturbations without becoming enmeshed in the complications of gravitational radiation theory. This can be done by going to the post-Newtonian approximation, where radiation is not present (cf. Sect. 2·3.5). CHANDRASEKHAR (1965*a*, *b*) has given a definitive post-Newtonian treatment of nonradial perturbations of equilibrium configurations. The most interesting and useful results of his analysis are these: As in Newtonian theory, so also in the post-Newtonian approximation 1) all of the nonradial normal modes of a star are stable if and only if the temperature gradient is everywhere subadiabatic; 2) there exist nonradial normal modes of zero frequency if and only if the temperature gradient is adiabatic over some finite region of the star; 3) there exists at least one unstable nonradial normal mode if and only if the temperature gradient is superadiabatic over some finite region; and when this is the case there is at least one unstable normal mode for each value, $l > 1$, of the spherical-harmonic index.

Because a superadiabatic temperature gradient is the criterion for convective instability, the above theorems state, in effect, that in post-Newtonian theory the instability of any nonradial normal mode of oscillation goes hand-in-hand with convective instability somewhere in the star. In most stars any convective instability which arises in the course of stellar evolution— and with it the associated dynamical instabilities— will be quickly removed by convective motions in the interior. Consequently, for most post-Newtonian configurations the only types of dynamical instability which are of any consequence are the radial instabilities discussed in the next Section.

Whether the remarkable Newtonian and post-Newtonian tie-up between dynamical, nonradial instabilities and convective instabilities holds also in general relativity is now unknown. It would not be surprising if this tie-up were to break down in the presence of very strong gravitational fields.

4·2. *Radial perturbations of nonrotating configurations* (*). – The theory of small radial motions of a star about its equilibrium configuration is unaffected by the complications of gravitational radiation because, just as a spherical charge distribution cannot radiate electromagnetically, so a spherical mass distribution cannot radiate gravitationally. The absence of gravitational waves has made possible a detailed development of the theory of radial perturbations of nonrotating, relativistic stellar models (ZEL'DOVICH (1963*b*), CHANDRASEKHAR (1964*b*, *c*), FOWLER (1964), WRIGHT (1964, 1965), HTWW (1965), BARDEEN (1965), COCKE (1965), BARDEEN, THORNE and MELTZER (1966)). We shall briefly describe that theory here.

There are two essentially different approaches to the study of the radial stability of relativistic configurations. There is a dynamical approach, which involves an analysis of the dynamics of radial oscillations; and there is a static approach, which requires only a comparison of the masses and radii of the members of a particular sequence of static, equilibrium configurations.

4·2.1. Dynamical approach to stability (**). Consider a star in small-amplitude, adiabatic, radial motion about its equilibrium configuration. Describe the motion by $\xi(r, t) \equiv \delta r(r, t)$, the radial co-ordinate displacement of the fluid element whose equilibrium radius is r, as a function of co-ordinate time, t. The total mass-energy of the perturbed star will differ from that of the equilibrium configuration by an amount δM^*, which can be divided into

---

(*) For a more detailed review of this topic see BARDEEN, THORNE and MELTZER (1966).

(**) Most of the results described in this section are due to CHANDRASEKHAR (1964*b*, *c*); but the present mass-energy derivation of them is due to THORNE (see HTWW, Appendix B). For a maximum-entropy derivation of these results see COCKE (1965).

a potential part, $\mathscr{P}^*$, plus a kinetic part, $\mathscr{K}^*$

$$\delta M^* = \mathscr{P}^*[\xi, \xi'] + \mathscr{K}^*[\dot{\xi}] . \tag{4.1}$$

A fairly straightforward calculation reveals (*)

$$\mathscr{P}^*[\xi, \xi'] = 2\pi \int_0^R \{P(r^2 e^{-\Phi} \xi)'^2 - Q(r^2 e^{-\Phi} \xi)^2\} \, dr , \tag{4.2a}$$

$$\mathscr{K}^*[\dot{\xi}] = 2\pi \int_0^R W(r^2 e^{-\Phi} \dot{\xi})^2 \, dr , \tag{4.2b}$$

where $X' \equiv \partial X/\partial r$, $\dot{X} \equiv \partial X/\partial t$, Φ is the gravitational potential of eq. (3.1) for the equilibrium configuration, and P, Q, W are functions of the equilibrium configuration defined by

$$\begin{cases} P = e^{3\Phi}(1 - 2m^*/r)^{-\frac{1}{2}} r^{-2} \Gamma_1 p^* , \\ Q = - 4e^{3\Phi}(1 - 2m^*/r)^{-\frac{1}{2}} r^{-3} p^{*\prime} - 8\pi e^{3\Phi}(1 - 2m^*/r)^{-\frac{3}{2}} r^{-2} p^*(\varrho^* + p^*) + \\ \qquad + e^{3\Phi}(1 - 2m^*/r)^{-\frac{1}{2}} r^{-2}(\varrho^* + p^*)^{-1} p^{*\prime 2} , \\ W = e^{\Phi}(1 - 2m^*/r)^{-\frac{3}{2}} r^{-2}(\varrho^* + p^*) . \end{cases} \tag{4.3}$$

Note that the mass-energy, δM^*, associated with the perturbation is quadratic in the amplitude of the perturbation. The vanishing of linear terms is in accordance with the theorem of extremal mass-energy for equilibrium configurations (Sect. **3**˙5.3). Note further that the expression for the kinetic energy can be rewritten

$$\mathscr{K}^*[\dot{\xi}] = \int_0^R \frac{1}{2} (\varrho^* + p^*)(\dot{\xi} e^{-\Phi}[1 - 2m^*/r]^{-\frac{1}{2}})^2 e^{\Phi}(4\pi r^2 [1 - 2m^*/r]^{-\frac{1}{2}} \, dr) = \tag{4.2b'}$$

$$= \int \frac{1}{2} \begin{pmatrix}\text{inertial mass} \\ \text{per unit volume}\end{pmatrix} \times \begin{pmatrix}\text{velocity measured in} \\ \text{proper reference frame}\end{pmatrix}^2 \times \\ \times \begin{pmatrix}\text{gravitational} \\ \text{red-shift factor}\end{pmatrix} \times d\begin{pmatrix}\text{proper} \\ \text{volume}\end{pmatrix} .$$

Expression (4.1) for δM^* can be taken as a foundation for the theory of small-amplitude, adiabatic, radial motions about equilibrium configurations. From

(*) See HTWW, Appendix B. The analysis in HTWW is for zero-temperature configurations, but it can be generalized to hot configurations by replacing all thermodynamic derivatives by the same derivatives at constant entropy $dp^*/d\varrho^* \to (\partial p^*/\partial \varrho^*)_{s^*}$, etc. Expressions (B.26) and (B.27) of HTWW for $\mathscr{P}^*$ and $\mathscr{K}^*$ contain an incorrect factor of $\exp[\nu_0(0)/2]$ ($\exp[\Phi(0)]$ in our notation).

it one can derive *a*) a potential-energy criterion for stability, *b*) the equation of motion which governs the time development of small, radial perturbations, and *c*) the frequencies and amplitudes of the normal models of radial motion.

a) *Potential-energy criterion for stability.* Because spherical motions cannot produce gravitational radiation, the total mass-energy of a radially perturbed configuration—and, hence, also δM^*—is a constant of its motion. Since the kinetic energy, $\mathscr{K}^*$, is positive definite and quadratic in the amplitude of the motion, the amplitude can grow large only for those $\xi(r, t)$ which make the potential energy negative. Hence, *an equilibrium configuration is stable against small radial perturbations if and only if the potential energy, $\mathscr{P}^*[\xi, \xi']$, associated with such perturbations is positive for all nonzero displacements, $\xi(r)$.* This criterion for stability is the analogue of the criterion that a particle in a potential $V(\boldsymbol{r})$ in is stable equilibrium if and only if it sits at a local minimum of V.

Although the potential-energy criterion for stability is conceptually simple, in numerical calculations it is considerably harder to apply and less reliable than the criteria which arise from the static analyses of Sect. **4**.2.2, **4**.2.3, and than the method of BARDEEN described near the end of this Section.

b) *Equation of motion for arbitrary perturbations.* – Consider an arbitrarily, but radially perturbed equilibrium configuration, the motion of which is described by $\xi = \xi(r, t)$. According to the Lagrangian formulation of mechanics, the difference between the kinetic and potential energies when integrated over time,

$$I^* = \int \{\mathscr{K}^*[\dot{\xi}] - \mathscr{P}^*[\xi, \xi']\} \, dt \,, \tag{4.4}$$

is extremized by the allowed modes of motion, ξ. The Euler-Lagrange equation

$$W r^2 e^{-\Phi} \ddot{\xi} = [P \cdot (r^2 e^{-\Phi} \xi)']' + Q r^2 e^{-\Phi} \xi \,, \tag{4.5}$$

which results from extremizing I^*, *is the equation of motion that governs the time-development of the arbitrary, adiabatic, radial perturbation.*

c) *Normal modes of radial oscillation.* An equilibrium configuration generally has a discrete set of normal modes of radial oscillation,

$$\xi(r, t) = \xi_n(r) \exp[i\omega_n^* t] \,, \tag{4.6}$$

which are distinguished from each other by the index $n = 0, 1, 2 \ldots$ (*). A par-

(*) Note that, because co-ordinate time, t, is measured in centimeters, the angular frequency, ω_n^*, which appears in eq. (4.6) is measured in cm^{-1}, *i.e.* it is « geometrized » as discussed in Sect. **1**.

ticular normal mode is stable (periodic oscillation) if its frequency, ω_n, is real, and unstable (exponential growth) if ω_n is imaginary. It is convenient to order the normal modes according to increasing squared frequency

$$\omega_0^2 < \omega_1^2 < \omega_2^2 < \ldots , \tag{4.7}$$

so that *a star is stable against small radial perturbations if and only if its fundamental squared frequency,* ω_0^2, *is positive.*

The normal-mode amplitudes ξ_n, are governed by an eigenvalue equation which can be obtained by inserting expression (4.6) into the equation of motion (4.5):

$$[P\cdot(r^2 e^{-\Phi}\xi_n)']' + (Q + \omega_n^{*2} W) r^2 e^{-\Phi}\xi_n = 0 . \tag{4.8}$$

The normal modes of radial motion are those solutions to eq. (4.8) *which satisfy the boundary conditions*

$$\xi_n(r=0) = 0 \tag{4.9a}$$

(center of star remains fixed during the motion), and

$$\Delta p^* = -e^{\Phi} r^{-2} \Gamma_1 p^* (r^2 e^{-\Phi}\xi_n)' \to 0 \text{ as } r \to R \tag{4.9b}$$

(pressure remains zero at the surface of the star during the motion). An equivalent formulation of the eigenproblem 4.8, 4.9), is the following variational principle due to CHANDRASEKAR (1964*b*, *c*): *Among all functions* $\xi(r)$ *which satisfy the boundary conditions* (4.9), *the normal-mode amplitudes are these that extremize the quantity*

$$\omega^{*2} \equiv \frac{\int_0^R [P(r^2 e^{-\Phi}\xi)'^2 - Q(r^2 e^{-\Phi}\xi)^2]\,dr}{\int_0^R W(r^2 e^{-\Phi}\xi)^2\,dr} = \frac{\mathscr{P}^*[\xi, \xi']}{\mathscr{K}^*[\xi]} ; \tag{4.10}$$

and the corresponding squared frequencies, ω_n^{*2}, *are the extremal values of* ω^{*2}.

The eigenvalue problem (4.8) (4.9) for the normal radiation modes is of the Sturm-Liouville type. Consequently, the powerful theorems of Sturm-Liouville theory (see *e.g.*, MORSE and FESHBACH (1953), pp. 719 ff.) are all applicable to the normal-mode problem. In particular, we can conclude that the amplitude, $\xi_n(r)$, of the n-th normal mode has precisely n nodes; and that between each pair of nodes of $\xi_n(r)$ there is at least one node of each higher-order amplitude, $\xi_k(r)$, $k > n$.

There are two useful methods for calculating the amplitudes and frequencies of the normal radial modes of a stellar model. One is to solve the eigenvalue problem (4.8, 4.9) by trial-and error integrations; the other is to apply Rayleigh-Ritz techniques (*see e.g.*, MORSE and FESHBACH (1953), pp. 1117 ff.; also GOERTZEL and TRALLI (1960), pp. 215-224) to the variation principle (4.10). As a third alternative, if one only wishes to know how many of the normal radial modes of a given model are unstable, one can use the following method due to BARDEEN (1965): Integrate differential equation (4.8) with $\omega_n^{*2} = 0$ from the center of the star, where $\xi \sim r$, to the surface; and count the number, $\mathcal{N}^{(0)}$, of nodes in the resultant function $\xi^{(0)}(r)$. By virtue of the relationship between the nodes of successive eigenfunctions, the stellar model has either $\mathcal{N}^{(0)}$ or $\mathcal{N}^{(0)}+1$ unstable normal radial modes. If the surface of the stellar model is a singularity of eq. (4.8)—*e.g.* if Γ_1 is finite and ϱ^*/p^* diverges at the surface—then the number of unstable modes is precisely $\mathcal{N}^{(0)}$.

For a detailed discussion and comparison of these and other methods for studying normal radial modes see BARDEEN, THORNE, and MELTZER (1966).

Just as one can analyse the radial pulsation of an equilibrium configuration into normal modes

$$\xi(r, t) = \sum_n A_n \xi_n(r) \exp[i\omega_n^* t] , \tag{4.11}$$

so one can also analyse the pulsation energy into normal-mode components—at least so long as the configuration is stable. The total pulsation energy is equal to the kinetic energy $\mathcal{K}^*[\dot{\xi}]$ at a moment when $\xi(r, t) = 0$ (*i.e.* when $\mathcal{P} = 0$)

$$E_{\text{puls}} = \mathcal{K}^*[\dot{\xi}]|_{\xi=0} = 2\pi \sum_{k,n} A_k A_n \omega_k^* \omega_n^* \int_0^R W(r^2 e^{-\Phi} \xi_k)(r^2 e^{-\Phi} \xi_n)\, dr .$$

But according to the orthogonality theorem of Sturm-Liouville theory, the above integral vanishes unless $k = n$. Hence, the pulsation energy can be analysed into components

$$\left\{ \begin{aligned} E_{\text{puls}}^* &= \sum_n A_n^2 E_{\text{puls}}^{(n)*} , \\ E_{\text{puls}}^{(n)*} &\equiv 2\pi\omega_n^{*2} \int_0^R W(r^2 e^{-\Phi} \xi_n)^2\, dr . \end{aligned} \right. \tag{4.12}$$

4·2.2. Static approach to stability for zero-temperature stars (*). In certain cases of physical interest one can determine the precise number of

(*) The approach to stability described in this section is due to WHEELER (HTWW, p. 60), but the precise conditions under which it is valid are delineated for the first time here. See also BARDEEN, THORNE and MELTZER (1966); as well as MELTZER and THORNE (1966).

unstable normal radial modes for an equilibrium configuration without integrating the eigenvalue equation (4.8), and without using Chandrasekhar's variational principle (4.10). The « static analysis » which makes possible this counting of unstable modes is applicable in one form to zero-temperature stellar models, and in slightly different form to hot, isentropic models. Consider first the zero-temperature case.

The thermodynamic properties of matter at absolute-zero temperature are determined by a single equation of state (one degree of freedom)

$$p^* = p^*(\varrho^*, Z_1, \ldots, Z_N)\,. \tag{4.13}$$

In practice, in constructing zero-temperature stellar models one usually specifies the nuclear abundances $Z_1, \ldots, Z_N$ as functions of the density—*e.g.* by requiring that the matter be in its absolute lowest energy state — thereby putting the equation of state into the form

$$p^* = p^*(\varrho^*, Z_1[\varrho^*[, \ldots, Z_N]\varrho^*]) \equiv p^*(\varrho^*)\,. \tag{4.14}$$

The static approach to stability is applicable to those configurations with equations of state of this form for which no nuclear transformations occur as the density increases; *i.e.* for which

$$\mathrm{d}Z_1/\mathrm{d}\varrho^* = \mathrm{d}Z_2/\mathrm{d}\varrho^* = \ldots = \mathrm{d}Z_N/\mathrm{d}\varrho^* = 0 \qquad \text{at all } \varrho^*\,. \tag{4.15}$$

In the remainder of this Section we confine our attention to such configurations, while in the next Section and in Sect. 5·5.1 we generalize the static approach to other types of zero-temperature configurations.

As we shall see in Sect. 5·4.1, for matter obeying any given zero-temperature equation of state of the form (4.14) there is a one-parameter sequence of equilibrium configurations, which can be conveniently distinguished from each other by the central density, ϱ_c^*. The static approach to stability involves an analysis of the curve of mass, M^*, *vs.* radius, R, for this sequence of configurations. We adopt the convention that M^* be plotted upward and R be plotted to the right.

The key properties of the $M^*(R)$ curve for configurations in which (4.15) holds are these (see Fig. 2 for pictorialization in terms of a particular zero-temperature equation of state, that of SKYRME (1959), CAMERON (1959), and SAAKYAN (1963)):

a) One normal mode of radial oscillation changes stability at each peak or valley (« critical point ») in the $M^*(R)$ curve, and there are no changes of stability elsewhere. Proof: Configurations at which one radial mode changes stability are characterized by the fact that they possess a zero-frequency mode of radial

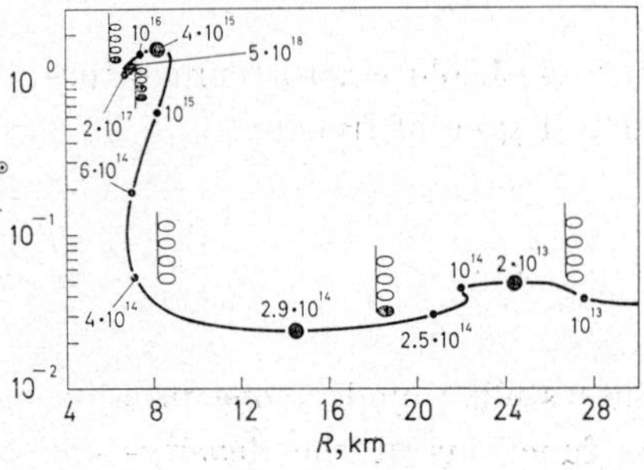

Fig. 2. – The $M^*(R)$ curve for the SKYRME (1959), CAMERON (1959), SAAKYAN (1963) equation of state for matter composed of pure neutrons. (For a specification of which version of the S-C-S equation of state is used here see MELTZER and THORNE (1966).) The curve is parametrized by central density, ϱ_c, in g/cm³. The critical points at which one normal radial mode changes stability are identified by large black dots. The normal radial modes are represented between each successive pair of critical points by a set of musical notes (ovals) with solid notes corresponding to unstable modes and open notes corresponding to stable modes. There are no critical points below $\varrho_c = 10^{13}$ g/cm³ (not shown in Figure); and we know from Newtonian theory that S-C-S configurations of $\varrho_c \sim 1$ g/cm³ are stable against all perturbations. Consequently, everywhere below $\varrho_c = 2\cdot10^{13}$ (first critical point) all normal radial modes are stable. At the first critical point the curve bends counterclockwise and one normal mode ($n = 0$) becomes unstable. At the second critical point ($\varrho_c = 2.9\cdot10^{14}$) the bend is clockwise, so the fundamental returns to stability. At the third critical point ($\varrho_c = 4\cdot10^{15}$) the bend is counterclockwise, so the fundamental mode becomes unstable again. At the fourth critical point ($\varrho_c = 2\cdot10^{17}$) the bend is counterclockwise so one more mode ($n = 1$) becomes unstable—and so it goes.

motion—*i.e.* they are characterized by the existence of other « near-by » equilibrium configurations into which they can transform themselves without the addition or removal of any baryons or of any mass-energy. Hence, configurations of changing stability are configurations which lie at extremal points in the curves $M^*(R)$ and $A(R)$. However, from expression (3.63) for the injection energy we see that an equilibrium configuration is extremal in $A(R)$ if and only if it is extremal in $M^*(R)$. Consequently, a necessary and sufficient condition for a configuration of changing stability is that $M^*(R)$ be extremal. QED.

b) At a critical point of the $M^*(R)$ curve for cold configurations the mode of changing stability is an even mode ($n = 0, 2, 4, \ldots$) if and only if the radius R decreases with increasing central density, $\mathrm{d}R/\mathrm{d}\varrho_c^* < 0$, in the neighborhood of the critical point; it is an odd mode ($n = 1, 3, 5, \ldots$) if and only if R increases, $\mathrm{d}R/\mathrm{d}\varrho_c^* > 0$. Proof: For a critical configuration the amplitude, $\xi_n(r)$, of the zero-frequency mode is identical to the motion, $\delta r(r)$, which carries the star from an equilibrium configuration on the low-density side of the critical point to one on the high-density side

$$\xi_n(r) \equiv \delta r(r) .$$

In such a motion across the critical point central density, ϱ_c, increases; *i.e.* the fluid moves inward near the center of the star. Hence, near $r = 0$ $\xi_n \equiv \delta r$ is negative. $\xi_n \equiv \delta r$ can be negative also at the surface of the star ($\mathrm{d}R/\mathrm{d}\varrho_c < 0$) if and only if ξ has an even number of nodes—*i.e.*, if and only if $n = 0, 2, 4, \ldots$—; and it can be positive at the surface ($\mathrm{d}R/\mathrm{d}\varrho_c > 0$) if and only if ξ_n has an odd number of nodes ($n = 1, 3, 5, \ldots$). QED.

c) *At a critical point of the $M^*(R)$ curve for cold configurations one mode becomes unstable with increasing ϱ_c if and only if the curve bends couterclockwise; and one mode becomes stable if and only if the bend is clockwise.* Proof: This criterion for the direction of stability change follows from criterion *b*) above, plus the knowledge that at very low central densities—*e.g.* for a sphere of cold matter the size of a basketball—cold configurations are stable against small radial perturbations. To convince oneself that criterion *c*) is, indeed, equivalent to *b*), one need only apply criterion *b*) to several hypothetical and as-pathological-as-desired $M^*(R)$ curves, and recognize that the results obtained are precisely those predicted by *c*). QED.

Properties *a*) and *b*), or *a*) and *c*) of the $M^*(R)$ curve enable one to calculate the precise number of unstable radial modes for each equilibrium configuration of any given zero-temperature equation of state for which nuclear abundances are independent of density (see, *e.g.* Fig. 2).

4.2.3. Generalizations of static approach to stability. The static approach to stability outlined in the last Section was derived under the rather restrictive assumption that the nuclear abundances which enter into the zero-temperature equation of state (4.14) are independent of density. This assumption was needed, for example, to allow the inference that at a critical point the zero-frequency amplitude, $\xi_n(r)$, is identical to the motion, $\delta r(r)$, which carries a star from an equilibrium configuration on the low-density side of the critical point to one on the high-density side.

The assumption that $\mathrm{d}Z_k/\mathrm{d}\varrho^* = 0$ is very severe; it is rarely satisfied in zero-temperature situations of physical interest. Consequently, in this Section we shall replace this assumption by others which are less restrictive.

We begin by noting that nuclear abundances never appear explicitly in the dynamical approach to stability (Sect. 4.2.1). For zero-temperature configurations the dynamical approach depends only on the equation of state $p^* = p^*(\varrho^*)$, upon the adiabatic index Γ_1, and upon the laws of general-relativistic mechanics. Consequently, the assumption $\mathrm{d}Z_k/\mathrm{d}\varrho^* = 0$ cannot affect stability directly; rather, it can affect stability only through the restriction

$$\Gamma_1 = (\varrho^* + p^*)\,p^{*-1}(\mathrm{d}p^*/\mathrm{d}\varrho^*)_{\text{as given by equation of state (4.14)}} \tag{4.16}$$

which it imposes on the relation between the adiabatic index and the equation of state. This reasoning allows us to conclude that *the static approach to stability* (properties *a*), *b*), and *c*) of the $M^*(R)$ curve as outlined in Sect. **4**.2.2) *is applicable to any family of zero-temperature configurations whose equation of state* (4.14) *and adiabatic index are related by* (4.16).

Assumption (4.16), like (4.15), is unnecessarily severe. The zero-temperature configurations of greatest current interest are configurations of matter catalyzed to the absolute endpoint of thermonuclear evolution—« cold, catalyzed matter ». (See Sect. **5**; also, HTWW.) Nuclear abundances in such configurations vary with density in such a manner as to keep the matter in its lowest-energy state; *i.e.* so as to minimize the total-mass energy per baryon, ϱ^*/n, subject to fixed baryon number density, n. For such configurations neither (4.13) nor (4.14) is valid; but, as we shall see in Sect. **5**.5.1, the static approach to stability is still applicable—albeit in slightly modified form

4.2.4. Static approach to stability for hot, isentropic configurations (*). A key point in the static analysis of the last Section is this, that the equilibrium configurations for any zero-temperature equation of state form a one-parameter family. By contrast, the equilibrium configurations for hot matter obeying a given fundamental equation

$$\varrho^* = \varrho^*(n, s^*, Z_1, \dots, Z_N) \tag{4.17}$$

form an infinite-parameter family. (We saw in Sect. **3**.4.3 that to fix uniquely an equilibrium configuration one must specify in addition to the fundamental eq. (4.17) the total number of baryons, the nuclear abundances as functions of radius, and the radial distribution of the entropy.)

In order to develop an $M^*(R)$ analysis of stability for hot stars one must select a suitable one-paramenter family of configurations out of this infinite-parameter set. There are several one-parameter families for which an $M^*(R)$ analysis can be developed; but one particular family stands out as of greatest physical interest (**). This is the one-parameter family of isentropic (*i.e.* marginally convective) configurations with fixed total number of baryons and fixed, radially-invariant nuclear abundances. Such a family of configurations can be parametrized by the radially-constant entropy per baryon, $s(r) \equiv s_0$; or, more conveniently, by the central density, ϱ_c. Physically speaking, successive configurations in such a family represent successive states of a single, quasi-statically contracting configuration which *a*) is in marginal convective equilibrium, and *b*) is too cool for thermonuclear reactions to take place. Stel-

(*) The results of this Section are due to BARDEEN (1965) see also BARDEEN, THORNE and MELTZER (1966).

(**) For a discussion of other usable one-parameter families and of some which are not usable, see BARDEEN (1965).

lar models of this type play an important role in certain theories of quasi-stellar radio sources (FOWLER (1964), (1966)).

Consider the one-parameter family of isentropic configurations for a given fundamental equation (4.17), a given total number, A, of baryons, and given nuclear abundances. For this family construct a curve of minus the binding energy,

$$(4.18)\qquad -E_B^* \equiv (\text{total mass-energy}) - (\text{rest mass}) \equiv M^* - M_0^* = M^* - \mu_B^* A\,,$$

vs. radius, R. This $-E_B^*(R)$ curve, like the $M^*(R)$ curve for zero-temperature configurations, plays a central role in the static analysis of stability. (We here use $-E_B^*[R]$ rather than $M^*[R]$ because the masses of the configurations in our sequence all differ only slightly from the constant rest mass M_0^*

$$M^*[R] = M_0^* + E_B^*[R] \approx M_0^* .)$$

The key properties of the $-E_B^*(R)$ curve which enter into the static analysis of stability are these (see Fig. 3 for pictorialization in terms of a hypothetical $-E_B^*[R]$ curve):

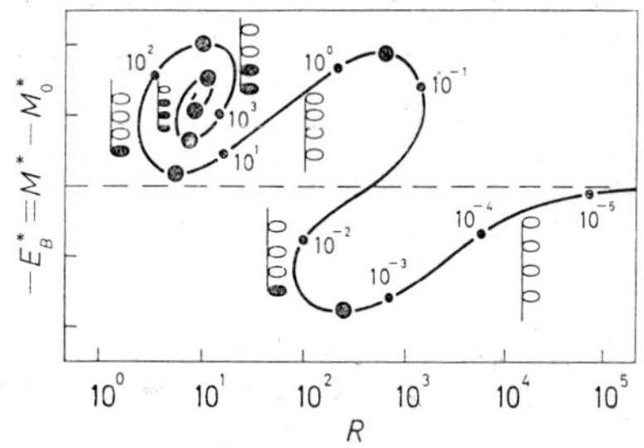

Fig. 3. – The $-E_B^*(R)$ curve for a hypothetical equation of state. The curve is parametrized by central density, ϱ_c. The critical points at which stability changes occur are indicated by large black dots. Between successive critical points each solid note represents one unstable normal radial mode and the open notes represent stable modes.

a) *One normal mode of radial oscillation changes stability at each peak or valley* (« *critical point* ») *in the* $-E_B^*(R)$ *curve, and there are no changes of stability elsewhere.*

Proof. The proof is similar to that of the analogous zero-temperature theorem. A point of changing stability on the $-E_B^*(R)$ curve corresponds to a configuration with a zero frequency mode of motion. But a configuration in our one-parameter family can have a zero-frequency mode if and only if there are other, slightly different configurations to which it can be transformed by a motion with these properties: 1) the motion is adiabatic; *i.e.* $\delta s^*(a) = 0$; 2) the motion is irreversible—in particular, nuclear abundances do not change; 3) the motion conserves the total number of baryons; and 4) the motion leaves the total mass-energy unchanged. If the initial configuration is in our isentropic, fixed-A, fixed-nuclear abundances family, then these properties of the zero-frequency motion guarantee that the final configuration is also in our family. Hence, the theorem is proved if we only can show that, of all infinitesimal motions along the $-E_B^*(R)$ curve, those which occur at a peak or valley

(« critical point ») are motions with the above four zero-frequency properties. Property 4), conservation of mass-energy, guarantees that the zero-frequency motions occur at critical points. But do all motions across critical points have the 4 properties? They clearly satisfy properties 2), 3), and 4). That they also satisfy property 1) can be seen as follows: The change in total-mass energy in moving across a critical point is the negative of the heat radiated

$$0 = \delta M^* = -\,\delta Q^* = -\int_0^A \delta q^*\, e^{\Phi}\, \mathrm{d}a = -\int_0^A T^* \delta s^*\, e^{\Phi}\, \mathrm{d}a\,. \tag{4.19}$$

Here δq^* is the heat radiated per baryon, e^{Φ} is the red-shift factor $(\Phi[\infty] = 0)$, and a is the number of baryons inside a given shell of matter. Because the initial and final configurations are both isentropic, δs^* is independent of radius and can be pulled out of the integral

$$0 = \delta s_0^* \int_0^A T^* e^{\Phi}\, \mathrm{d}a\,. \tag{4.20}$$

Equation (4.20) guarantees that $\delta s_0^* = 0$; hence, condition 1) is satisfied by motions across critical points. QED.

b) *At a critical point of the* $-E_{\mathrm{B}}^*(R)$ *curve the mode of changing stability is even* ($n = 0, 2, 4, \ldots$) *if and only if the radius*, R, *there decreases with increasing central density*, $\mathrm{d}R/\mathrm{d}\varrho_c^* < 0$; *it is odd* ($n = 1, 3, 5, \ldots$) *if and only if* R *increases*, $\mathrm{d}R/\mathrm{d}\varrho_c^* > 0$. The proof is identical to that for the zero-temperature case (Sect. 4.2.2).

c) *At a critical point of the* $-E_{\mathrm{B}}^*(R)$ *curve one mode becomes unstable with increasing* ϱ_c *if and only if the curve bends clockwise there*; *one mode becomes stable if and only if the bend is counterclockwise.* (That the correlation between stability and direction of bend is different here than in the zero-temperature case should not be disturbing; after all, the sequence of configurations considered here is very different in character from the zero-temperature sequence.) Proof of theorem: This criterion for the direction of stability change follows from criterion *b*), plus our knowledge that configurations of every low central density (very large radius; Newtonian theory applicable) are stable if they have $-E_{\mathrm{B}}^* < 0$ and unstable if $-E_{\mathrm{B}}^* > 0$. QED.

Properties *a*) and *b*), or *a*) and *c*) of the $-E_{\mathrm{B}}^*(R)$ curve enable one to calculate the precise number of unstable radial modes for each member of any sequence of isentropic equilibrium configurations which all have the same total number of baryons, A, and the same radially-invariant nuclear abundances. This method of diagnosing stability has been used quite extensively by FOWLER (1964, 1966) and by BARDEEN (1965).

4·3. *Stability properties of nonrotating configurations.* – Let us now turn our attention from the general theory of radial perturbations in relativistic stellar models to some of the more important results which have been obtained from that theory.

4·3.1. General relativity as a catalyzer of instabilities. A number of investigations of stellar stability have revealed that relativistic gravitational forces cause radial instabilities in stellar models which, according to Newtonian theory, would otherwise be stable. The most striking examples of general-relativistic instabilities come from the post-Newtonian approximation, where relativistic forces, which have a totally negligible effect upon the structure of a star, can make it unstable against small radial perturbations. FOWLER (1964, 1966) and CHANDRASEKHAR (1965*d*) have independently developed post-Newtonian criteria for the onset of general-relativistic instabilities. Chandrasekhar's analysis, which is based on the post-Newtonian limit of the variational principle (4.10), reveals this, that a post-Newtonian stellar model with adiabatic index, Γ_1, independent of radius is unstable if and only if its mass, M^*, and radius, R, satisfy

$$R < 2M^* K/(\Gamma_1 - 4/3). \tag{4.21}$$

Here K is a constant usually between 0.5 and 1.5, which depends only on the Newtonian structure of the star. Fowler's analysis, which is based not upon the dynamic approach to stability but on the static $-E_{\mathrm{B}}^*(R)$ approach, yields a similar result. This result plays an important role in Fowler's supermassive-star model for quasars (see lectures in this volume).

4·3.2. Manyfold instability of superdense stars. The $M^*(R)$ and $-E_{\mathrm{B}}^*(R)$ curves of Fig. 2 and 3 both spiral in toward a limiting point as central density mounts toward infinity. This spiraling is a signal that the configurations of higher and higher central density are more and more unstable.

DMITRIEV and HOLIN (1963), HARRISON (1965) and WHEELER (HTWW, Chapter 5) have shown independently that such high-density spiraling of the $M^*(R)$ curve, and the consequent onset of higher- and higher-order instabilities, are characteristic of zero-temperature configurations for a wide range of equations of state. More particularly, for any equation of state which approaches the form

$$p^* = (\gamma - 1)\varrho^* , \qquad \gamma = \text{const} , \tag{4.22}$$

at high density, the $M^*(R)$ curve approaches the high-density spiral

$$\begin{cases} M^* - M_\infty^* = C_M\, \varrho_c^{*-\alpha/2} \cos\left[\tfrac{1}{2}\beta \ln \varrho_c^* + \delta_M\right] , \\ R \;- R_\infty \;= C_R\, \varrho_c^{*-\alpha/2} \cos\left[\tfrac{1}{2}\beta \ln \varrho_c^* + \delta_R\right] , \end{cases} \tag{4.23}$$

where C_M, C_R, δ_M, δ_R, α, and β are constants, and

$$(4.24)\qquad \alpha = \frac{3}{2} - \frac{1}{\gamma}, \qquad \beta = \left[\frac{11}{\gamma} - \frac{9}{\gamma^2} - \frac{1}{4}\right]^{\frac{1}{2}}, \qquad \delta_M \neq \delta_R .$$

Similar formulae could be worked out for the $-E^*_{\rm B}(R)$ curves of hot, isentropic stellar models.

The static approach to stability, when applied to formulae (4.23) for the spiraling $M^*(R)$ curve, tells us that zero-temperature configurations of high central density ($\varrho_c \gtrsim 10^{19}$ g/cm³; cf. Sect. **5**) have

$$(4.25)\qquad \text{greatest integer less than } \{(\beta/2\pi)\ln(\varrho_c/\varrho_0)\}$$

unstable normal radial modes, where ϱ_0 is a constant. For realistic equations of state (Sect. **5**, Fig. 4)

$$(4.26)\qquad \varrho_0 \sim 10^{16}\ \text{g/cm}^3 .$$

Expression (4.25) for the number of unstable normal radial modes can also be derived by the dynamic approach to stability (see MELTZER and THORNE (1966) Sect. **3**-*d*).

4·4. *Stability of rotating stellar models.* – Thus far we have confined our attention to the stability of nonrotating stellar models. The only relativistic stability analyses performed to date on rotating stellar models are the post-Newtonian considerations of FOWLER (lectures in this volume), of ROXBURGH (1965), and of DURNEY and ROXBURGH (1965). The approaches used in these references are essentially generalizations of the post-Newtonian limit of the dynamic analysis of Section **4**·2.1.

4·5. *Summary.* – The principal conclusions from our discussion of stellar stability are these: The relativistic theory of radial perturbations of nonrotating equilibrium configurations is well understood. There are two approaches to radial stability—a dynamic approach, based on the equations of motion and energy properties of radial perturbations; and a static approach, based on mass-radius curves for certain sequences of equilibrium configurations. From each of these approaches one can obtain several different methods for studying the normal radial modes of a relativistic stellar model. The resultant methods were briefly described here and are catalogued and compared in detail by BARDEEN, THORNE, and MELTZER (1966). Applications of these methods reveal 1) that general relativity catalyzes radial instability in stellar models, and 2) that stellar models of very high central density have many unstable normal radial modes.

The relativistic theory of nonradial perturbations of nonrotating configurations has been developed only in the post-Newtonian approximation. In that approximation all nonradial dynamical instabilities are accompanied by convective instabilities and can be eliminated by efficient convection.

The only relativistic stability analysis of rotating configurations which has been performed to date is the post-Newtonian, « dynamic analysis » of FOWLER, ROXBURGH and DURNEY.

5. – White dwarfs, neutron stars, and hyperon stars.

We now have at our disposal all of the tools necessary to permit the detailed analysis of specific stellar models. There are two types of stellar configurations in which general relativity should play an important role: configurations near the endpoint of thermonuclear evolution (white dwarfs, neutron stars, hyperon stars); and supermassive configurations ($M \gtrsim 10^5 M_\odot$). This Section and the lecture by FINZI (1966) are concerned with the former type of configuration, while Sect. **6** and the lectures by FOWLER (1966) are concerned with the latter.

5'1. *Matter near the endpoint of thermonuclear evolution.* – In discussing configurations near the endpoint of thermonuclear evolution we begin with a brief description of the matter from which they are made. By « matter of baryon number density n, catalyzed to near the endpoint of thermonuclear evolution »—*catalyzed matter for short*—we mean matter at density n in which the nuclear abundances, $Z_1, \dots Z_N$, are such as to absolutely minimize the total mass-energy per baryon, ϱ^*/n. Such matter is in thermonuclear equilibrium; no rest mass-energy can be converted into thermal energy by any nuclear reaction. This does not mean, however, that no energy can be extracted from a sample of such matter. There may be thermal energy in the sample; hence the phrase « ... catalyzed to *near* the endpoint of thermonuclear evolution ». When a sample of catalyzed matter does not contain any thermal energy it is called *cold catalyzed matter*. For a careful and comprehensive discussion of the concept of cold catalyzed matter see HTWW, Chapter 9.

5'1.1. Thermodynamics of catalyzed matter. In situations of interest to us here the density of thermal energy, ε_T^*, of a sample of catalyzed matter is always very much less than the density of total mass-energy

$$\varepsilon_T^* \ll \varrho^* ; \tag{5.1}$$

and the thermal pressure is very much less than the pressure associated with the zero-point motion of the electrons and nuclei. Consequently, to a high degree of approximation the equations of state $p^* = p^*(n, T^*, Z_1, ..., Z_N)$ and $\varrho^* = \varrho^*(n, T^*, Z_1, ..., Z_N)$ are independent of temperature. They are also independent of $Z_1, ..., Z_N$ since the nuclear abundances are uniquely fixed once the baryon number density, n, is given.

$$(5.2)\qquad \begin{cases} p^* = p^*(n, T^*, Z_1, ... Z_N) = p^*(n, 0, Z_1[n], ..., Z_N[n]) \equiv p^*(n)\,, \\ \varrho^* = \varrho^*(n, T^*, Z_1, ... Z_N) = \varrho^*(n, 0, Z_1[n], ..., Z_N[n]) \equiv \varrho^*(n)\,. \end{cases}$$

The simplified equations of state (5.2) are related by the first law of thermodynamics as embodied in the equation

$$(5.3)\qquad \mathrm{d}\varrho^*/\mathrm{d}n = (\varrho^* + p^*)/n\,.$$

(This relation follows from eq. (2.12) with $\mathrm{d}s^* = 0$, plus the relation $\sum \bar{\mu}_k^* \mathrm{d}Z_k = 0$. The latter relation is valid for all changes $[\mathrm{d}Z_1, ..., \mathrm{d}Z_N]$, in chemical composition, which are compatible with the conservation laws of elementary particle physics, because we are dealing with matter at the endpoint of thermonuclear evolution in which no nuclear reactions can release energy.)

Relation (5.3) *together with a single equation of state*—$\varrho^*(n)$, $p^*(n)$ or $p^*(\varrho^*)$—*uniquely fixes any two of the quantities* (ϱ^*, p^*, n) *in terms of the third.* Throughout our work we shall (arbitrarily) use $p^* = p^*(\varrho^*)$ as our « primary » equation of state.

Although temperature, T^*, has no (significant) effect on the density of mass-energy or on the pressure of catalyzed matter, it is a very important determinant of the density of thermal energy

$$(5.4)\qquad \varepsilon_T^* = \varepsilon_T^*(\varrho^*, T^*) \to 0 \qquad \text{when } T^* \to 0\,.$$

In discussing stellar configurations of catalyzed matter we shall confine our attention to the thermodynamic parameters n, p^*, ϱ^*, T^*, and ε_T^*. If we wished we could also consider the entropy per baryon, s^*; the total internal energy, ε^*; the average baryonic rest mass, μ_B^*; the nuclear abundances, $Z_1, ..., Z_N$; the nuclear chemical potentials $\bar{\mu}_N^*, ..., \bar{\mu}_1^*$; and the *baryon chemical potential*, $\bar{\mu}^*$ which is defined by (cf. HTWW)

$$(5.5)\qquad \bar{\mu}^* \equiv \mathrm{d}\varrho^*/\mathrm{d}n = (\varrho^* + p^*)/n.$$

However, for clarity of presentation we shall exclude these supplementary parameters from discussion.

5·1.2. Equation of state of cold catalyzed matter. The equation of state of cold catalyzed matter, $p^* = p^*(\varrho^*)$,—which is also the equation of state of catalyzed matter (no temperature dependence)—has been calculated theoretically in various regions of density by a large number of workers including CHANDRASEKHAR (1935, 1939); OPPENHEIMER and SERBER (1938); OPPENHEIMER and VOLKOFF (1939); SCHATZMAN (1956); HARRISON, WAKANO and WHEELER (1958) see also HTWW, Chapter 10; CAMERON (1959); SALPETER (1960); AMBARTSUMYAN and SAAKYAN (1960); SAAKYAN (1963); SAAKYAN and VARTANYAN (1963*a*, *b*); SAAKYAN and CHUBARYAN (1963); TSURUTA (1964); TSURUTA and CAMERON (1965*b*, 1966*a*); GRATTON and SZAMOSI (1964); BARKER, BHATIA, and SZAMOSI (1966); BAHCALL and WOLF (1965*b*); and others.

The various calculated equations of state for cold catalyzed matter are in good qualitative agreement, but quantitatively there are some rather important differences, especially at densities $\varrho \gtrsim 10^{13}\,\text{g/cm}^3$. Crucial differences between the proposed equations of state are most clearly brought out not by curves of pressure *vs.* density, but by curves of the « adiabatic index »,

$$\gamma_{\text{eqn state}} \equiv (\varrho^* + p^*)\,p^{*-1}(\mathrm{d}p^*/\mathrm{d}\varrho^*)_{\text{as given by eqn. of state}}\,, \tag{5.6}$$

vs. density, ϱ^*. Such curves are shown in Fig. 4 for several of the more recent and plausible equations of state. (Ignore for the present the right half of Fig. 4.) The differences between the four curves of $\gamma_{\text{eqn state}}$ *vs.* ϱ^* are indicative of the present uncertainty in our knowledge of the equations of state of cold, catalyzed matter.

The equations of state of Fig. 4 can be understood by following the transformations which occur as an imaginary, small sample of cold catalyzed matter is compressed to higher and higher densities. At each stage in the compression all thermonuclear reactions in the sample must be catalyzed to their endpoints, and the resultant thermal energy must be removed.

At densities below $\varrho \sim 10^5\,\text{g/cm}^3$ only the H-W equation of state attempts to be accurate; no effort was taken to make the other three equations of state accurate here because such « low » densities are of little importance for superdense stellar configurations. In this low-density region our sample of cold, catalyzed matter is in the form of ^{56}Fe, the most tightly bound of all nuclei. At $\varrho = 7.86\,\text{g/cm}^3$ the pressure is zero, but the velocity of sound (cf. eq. (2.10))

$$v_s^* = p^*(\varrho^* + p^*)^{-1}\Gamma_1 = p^*(\varrho^* + p^*)^{-1}\gamma_{\text{eqn state}} \tag{5.7}$$

is finite. Consequently, $\gamma_{\text{eqn state}}$ is infinite. As the sample of matter is compressed from $7.86\,\text{g/cm}^3$ to $10^5\,\text{g/cm}^3$, the pressure is provided less and less by solid-state forces; more and more by the degenerate ^{56}Fe electrons. Consequently, $\gamma_{\text{eqn state}}$ decrease from ∞ toward $\frac{5}{3}$, the value for a *nonrelativistically* degenerate Fermi gas.

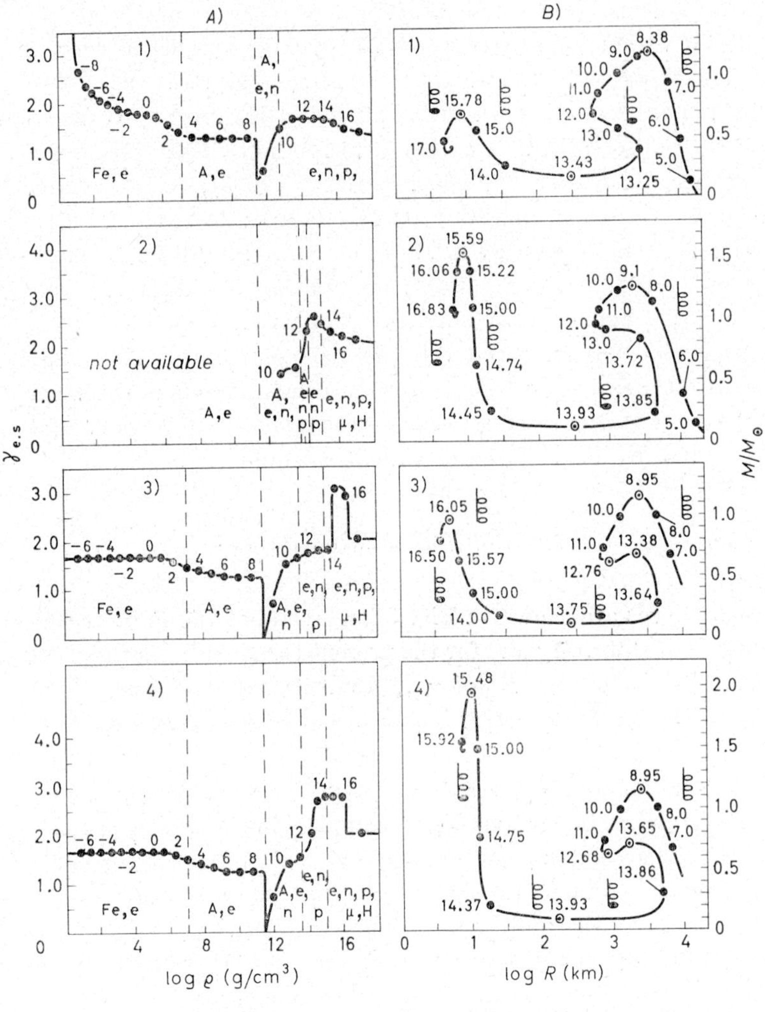

Fig. 4. – A) Several proposed equations of state for matter at or near the end-point of thermonuclear evolution, and B) the corresponding equilibrium configurations. The four equations of state shown are 1) H-W: Harrison - Wheeler, see HARRISON, WAKANO and WHEELER (1958), also Chapter 10 of HTWW; 2) S-V: Saakyan-Vartanyan, see SAAKYAN and VARTANYAN (1963a, b; 1964), also SAAKYAN and CHUBARYAN (1963); 3) V_β and 4) V_γ: Levinger-Simmons V_β, and V_γ see TSURUTA (1964), TSURUTA and CAMERON (1965a, 1966a). For each equation of state we plot the « adiabatic index » of eq. (5.6) against density of mass-energy, ϱ; and we parametrize each curve by p/c^2 measured in g/cm³. The nuclear constitution of the matter for each equation of state is indicated as follows: Fe, ^{56}Fe nuclei; A, nuclei more neutron rich than ^{56}Fe; e, electrons; n, free neutrons; p, free protons; μ, μ-mesons; H, hyperons. The Saakyan-Vartanyan equation of state is not available in the literature in tabular or analytic form for $\varrho < 3\cdot 10^{12}$ g/cm³. For discussion of equations of state see Sect. 5.1.2. The equilibrium configurations are represented by curves of total mass-energy, M^*, $vs.$ (co-ordinate) radius, R. These $M^*(R)$ curves are parametrized by central density, ϱ_c, measured in g/cm³. The musical notes beside the $M^*(R)$ curves indicate stability against small radial perturbations: Each solid note represents one unstable normal radial mode while the open notes represent stable modes. One normal mode changes stability at each peak or valley (circled dots) of the $M^*(R)$ curves. For a discussion of the equilibrium configurations see Sect. 5.4.1.

Above $\varrho = 10^5$ g/cm³ all four equations of state attempt to be accurate (*); and they are in good agreement up to $\sim 10^{13}$ g/cm³. Between 10^5 and 10^7 g/cm³ the pressure-providing electrons gradually become *relativistically* degenerate, and $\gamma_{\text{eqn state}}$ approaches $\frac{4}{3}$ in a manner first described by CHANDRASEKHAR (1935). Above $\varrho = 1.4 \cdot 10^7$ g/cm³ the rest mass of 62 $^{56}_{26}$Fe nuclei plus the rest mass of 44 electrons plus the rather large Fermi kinetic energy of 44 electrons exceeds the rest mass of 56 $^{62}_{28}$Ni nuclei. Consequently, as our sample of matter is compressed past $\varrho = 1.4 \cdot 10^7$ g/cm³ the nuclear reaction

$$62\,{}^{56}_{26}\text{Fe} + 44e^- \rightarrow 56\,{}^{62}_{28}\text{Ni} \tag{5.8}$$

must be catalysed to its endpoint. As the compression continues beyond this point, the rising electron Fermi energy induces new nuclear reactions similar to (5.8) but involving different nuclei. In these reactions more and more electrons are swallowed up to form new nuclei, which are more and more neutron rich. If electrons were not being swallowed up by nuclei, $\gamma_{\text{eqn state}}$ would hold steady at $\frac{4}{3}$ (relativistic Fermi gas) throughout the region $\varrho > 10^7$ g/cm³. However, the gradual removal of electrons causes pressure to increase more slowly with density than it would otherwise, and thereby keeps $\gamma_{\text{eqn state}}$ roughly constant, not at $\frac{4}{3}$, but at ~ 1.26. Such is the situation until the compression pushes our sample of matter up to $\varrho = 3 \cdot 10^{11}$ g/cm³. At this density the nuclei are so highly neutron rich ($^{122}_{39}$Y) that neutrons begin to drip off of them. When neutron drip is initiated at $\varrho = 3 \cdot 10^{11}$ g/cm³, most of the remaining electrons are suddenly swallowed up very rapidly with increasing density by the dripping nuclei. Consequently, as density increases through the region $\varrho \sim 3$ to $4 \cdot 10^{11}$ g/cm³, the degenerate electron pressure— and, hence, also the total pressure—remains almost constant; and $\gamma_{\text{eqn state}}$ plumets to ~ 0 and remains there. Above $\sim 4 \cdot 10^{11}$ g/cm³ the rising neutron degeneracy pressure becomes of the same order as the electron pressure, and then much larger. Consequently $\gamma_{\text{eqn state}}$ rises, reaching $\sim \frac{5}{3}$ (nonrelativistically degenerate neutron gas) at $\varrho \sim 10^{13}$ g/cm³.

In the density region above 10^{13} g/cm³ there are serious discrepancies among the equations of state of Fig. 4, and hence great uncertainties in our knowledge of the behaviour of cold catalyzed matter. Between 10^{13} and 10^{14} g/cm³ the few remaining nuclei all break up into their constituent nucleons—primarily neutrons—; and the sample of matter therefore becomes a mixture of degenerate neutron, proton, electron—and, at higher densities, muon and hyperon—gases interacting by nuclear and electromagnetic forces. Because nucleon-nucleon

(*) The S-V nuclear abundances in *this* density region are actually *not* those of cold, catalyzed matter; they are the slightly different abundances which one would expect of matter which has had only $\sim 10^{10}$ years to reach thermonuclear equilibrium. The effect upon the equation of state of this failure to be at the absolute endpoint of thermonuclear evolution is small.

interactions are only poorly understood, the equation of state of such a mixture is only poorly known. In the region $\varrho \gtrsim 10^{13}$ g/cm³ the four equations of state of Fig. 4 are based upon four different assumptions about the nature of nucleon-nucleon interactions:

The H-W assumption—which is probably incorrect—is that the effects of nucleon-nucleon interactions and of hyperon formation on the equation of state are negligible. Consequently, according to the H-W analysis, $\gamma_{\text{eqn state}}$ is $\frac{5}{3}$ (non-relativistically degenerate neutron gas) between $\varrho \approx 10^{13}$ and $\varrho \approx 10^{15}$ g/cm³; and it drops toward $\frac{4}{3}$ (relativistic degeneracy) above 10^{15} g/cm³.

The S-V equation of state assumes nucleon-nucleon interactions which are largely attractive below $\varrho \sim 3 \cdot 10^{13}$ g/cm³ but very repulsive above this density. Consequently, the S-V value of $\gamma_{\text{eqn state}}$ is less than $\frac{5}{3}$ at $\varrho < 3 \cdot 10^{13}$ g/cm³; but as the sample of matter is compressed beyond this density, $\gamma_{\text{eqn state}}$ shoots up to ~ 2.6 and then gradually falls back toward 2.0. At very high densities the S-V equation of state, $p^* = \varrho^*$ ($\gamma_{\text{eqn state}} = 2.0$) is the stiffest one compatible with the velocity of light (cf. eq. (5.7)) (*).

The V_β and V_γ equations of state, like S-V, involve nucleon-nucleon interactions which are at first mildly attractive, but then at higher densities, very repulsive. This explains the initially low ($<\frac{5}{3}$) values of $\gamma_{\text{eqn state}}$ in the region $\varrho > 10^{13}$ g/cm³, and the subsequent sudden rise of $\gamma_{\text{eqn state}}$ to about 3.0. For V_β the repulsive nuclear forces occur at much higher densities (smaller nucleon-nucleon separations) than for S-V or V_γ. The empirically-derived V_β and V_γ nuclear interaction potentials are based upon faulty assumptions at $\varrho > > 3 \cdot 10^{16}$ g/cm³ and therefore lead to a speed of sound exceeding the speed of light. In order to avoid this conflict with causality the calculated equations of state are cut off when p^* becomes equal to ϱ^*; and $p^* = \varrho^*$ ($\gamma_{\text{eqn state}} = 2.0$) is assumed from there on to the highest densities.

It should be emphasized that at densities $\varrho \gtrsim 10^{16}$ g/cm³ unsolved problems of-elementary-particle physics prevent us from having confidence in any proposed equation of state for cold catalyzed matter.

In his lectures in this volume SZAMOSI (1966) discusses in detail the formalism used to calculate equations of state in the region $\varrho \gtrsim 10^{13}$ g/cm³, the phenomenon of hyperon formation which occurs at $\varrho > 1.1 \cdot 10^{15}$ g/cm³, and the details of several equations of state, including V_β and V_γ.

5·1.3. Density of thermal energy. For catalyzed matter at densities above $\sim 10^5$ g/cm³, the thermal energy is concentrated partially in the

---

(*) Until recently it was generally believed that $p^* = \varrho^*/3$ ($\gamma_{\text{eqn state}} = \frac{4}{3}$) was the stiffest high-density equation of state compatible with the laws of physics. However, ZEL'DOVICH (1961) has shown that the equation of state $p^* = \varrho^*$ ($\gamma_{\text{eqn state}} = 2.0$; sound velocity = light velocity) is in principle attainable.

thermal tails of the Fermi energy distributions of the degenerate electron and baryon gases, and partially in the kinetic motion of the nondegenerate nuclei. From Fermi-Dirac theory one can show (cf. CHANDRASEKHAR (1939) p. 394) that the specific heat per particle, at constant volume, of a degenerate Fermi gas is

$$c_v = (\pi^2 k^2/\mu c^2)(\mu E_F/p_F^2)\,T\,. \tag{5.9}$$

Here k is Boltzman's constant, μ is the Fermion rest mass, p_F is the Fermi momentum at the top of the degenerate sea, and $E_F = (p_F c^2 + \mu^2 c^4)^{\frac{1}{2}}$ is the corresponding Fermi energy including rest mass. By integrating this specific heat per particle over temperature and summing over all of the Fermi gases present (electrons, neutrons, protons, muons, various hyperons), and by adding the thermal energy density of the nondegenerate nuclei, we obtain for the density of thermal energy as a function of total density of mass-energy and temperature (*)

$$\left\{\begin{aligned} &\varepsilon_T^*(\varrho^*, T^*) = \beta^*(\varrho^*)\,T^{*2} + \tfrac{3}{2} bnT^*\,,\\ &\beta^*(\varrho^*) = [\pi^2/2]\sum_j n_j(\varrho^*)\,E^*_{F-j}(\varrho^*)[p^*_{F-j}(\varrho^*)]^{-2}\,. \end{aligned}\right. \tag{5.10}$$

Here $n_j(\varrho^*)$ is the number density of fermions of type j, while p^*_{F-j} and E^*_{F-j} are the corresponding Fermi momentum and total Fermi energy, and bn is the number density of nondegenerate nuclei. Equation (5.10) is expressed in geometrized units.

Corresponding to any proposed equation of state $p^*(\varrho^*)$ for cold, catalyzed matter there is a well-determined *thermal function* $\beta^*(\varrho^*)$, which can be calculated from eq. (5.10)

As density decreases from $\sim 10^5\ \text{g/cm}^3$ toward 0, the orbital electrons of the iron nuclei gradually cease to form a degenerate Fermi gas, and eq. (5.10) gradually ceases to be correct. Since this low-density region is of physical interest only for descriptions of the very thin surface layers and atmospheres of superdense stars, and since the surface layers and atmospheres are actually not catalyzed to near the endpoint of thermonuclear evolution (see, *e.g.* TSURUTA and CAMERON (1966*b*)), we shall forgo any attempt to improve upon eq. (5.10) at low densities.

(*) GINZBURG and KIRZHNITS (1964) have suggested that the nucleon thermal excitation spectrum at high densities ($\varrho \gtrsim 10^{13}\ \text{g/cm}^3$) might resemble a gas of superconducting electrons, rather than being continuous. If such is the case, then expression (5.10) will not describe correctly the density of thermal energy.

5'2. *Equations of stellar structure.* – Having completed our description of the theory of matter near the endpoint of thermonuclear evolution, we now turn our attention to the equations which govern the structure of stellar configurations of such matter. The lack of influence of temperature upon the equation of state, $p^*(\varrho^*)$, of catalyzed matter results in a separation of the $16 + 3N$ coupled equations of stellar structure (3.11) into three more or less independent groups:

The first group—the *primary structure equations*—consists of three coupled equations for density of mass-energy, ϱ^*, pressure, p^*, and mass, m^*, as functions of co-ordinate radius, r

$$p^* = p^*(\varrho^*) , \tag{5.11a}$$

$$m^* = \int_0^r 4\pi r^2 \varrho^* \,\mathrm{d}r , \tag{5.11b}$$

$$\frac{\mathrm{d}p^*}{\mathrm{d}r} = -\frac{(\varrho^* + p^*)(m^* + 4\pi r^3 p^*)}{r(r - 2m^*)} . \tag{5.11c}$$

Equation (5.11*a*) is the equation of state of catalyzed matter; (5.11*b*) is the mass equation (3.11-2); and (5.11*c*) is the TOV equation of hydrostatic equilibrium (3.11-3). In studying configurations of catalyzed matter one usually chooses a particular value of the central density, $\varrho_c^* = \varrho^*(r = 0)$ and then numerically integrates eq. (5.11) outward from $r = 0$ to the point at which p^* reaches zero, which is the surface of the star. The values of r and m^* at the termination point are the stellar radius, R, and the total mass-energy, M^*.

If, in addition to ϱ^*, p^*, and M^*, one is also interested in the gravitational potential, Φ, of eq. (3.1), the number density of baryons, n, or the number of baryons, a, inside radius r, he can calculate them by integrating the following *secondary structure equations* along with the primary equations (5.11):

$$\mathrm{d}\Phi/\mathrm{d}r = -(\varrho^* + p^*)^{-1}(\mathrm{d}p^*/\mathrm{d}r) , \qquad \Phi(r = R) = \ln(1 - 2M^*/R)^{\frac{1}{2}} , \tag{5.12a}$$

$$\mathrm{d}n/\mathrm{d}\varrho^* = n/(\varrho^* + p^*) , \tag{5.12b}$$

$$a = \int_0^r 4\pi r^2 n(1 - 2m^*/r)^{-\frac{1}{2}} \mathrm{d}r . \tag{5.12c}$$

Equation (5.12*a*) is the source eq. (3.11-4) for Φ; and its boundary condition, which is derived from eq. (3.40), is chosen so as to make $\Phi(r = \infty) = 0$. Equation (5.12*b*) we have met previously as (5.3); and (5.12*c*) is the baryon number equation (3.11-1). Note that equations (5.12*a*, *b*) can be integrated in terms of the equations of state to give

$$(5.12a') \qquad \Phi(r) = \begin{cases} \ln(1-2M^*/R)^{\frac{1}{2}} - \int\limits_0^{p^*(r)} (\varrho^* + p^*)^{-1}\,\mathrm{d}p^*\,, & r<R\,, \\ \ln(1-2M^*/R)^{\frac{1}{2}}\,, & r>R\,, \end{cases}$$

$$(5.12b') \qquad n = \frac{\varrho^*+p^*}{\mu_{\mathrm{B}}^*(0)} \exp\left[-\int\limits_0^{p^*} \frac{\mathrm{d}p^*}{\varrho^*+p^*}\right] = \frac{(\varrho^*+p^*)\,e^{\Phi}}{\mu_{\mathrm{B}}^*(0)[1-2M^*/R]^{\frac{1}{2}}}\,.$$

Here $\mu_{\mathrm{B}}^*(0)$, the average baryonic rest mass at zero density, is $(1/56)\times$(the mass of an ^{56}Fe atom). Equation (5.12b'), when rearranged slightly, becomes a statement of the constancy of the injection energy for configurations of catalyzed matter (cf. eq. (3.62)) (*).

There is no mention whatsoever of temperature or of thermal energy in the primary or secondary structure equations (5.11), (5.12). If one is interested in the thermal properties of a configuration of catalyzed matter, he must integrate, in addition to eq. (5.11) and (5.12), the *thermal structure equations*:

a) Differential equations for thermal structure

$$(5.13a) \qquad \frac{\mathrm{d}(L_r^*\,e^{2\Phi})}{\mathrm{d}r} = -\frac{4\pi r^2\,e^{\Phi}}{(1-2m^*/r)^{\frac{1}{2}}}\left(\frac{\mathrm{d}\varepsilon_T^*}{\mathrm{d}t}\right),$$

$$(5.13b) \qquad \frac{\mathrm{d}(L_r^{(\nu)*}\,e^{2\Phi})}{\mathrm{d}r} = \frac{4\pi r^2\,e^{2\Phi}}{(1-2m^*/r)^{\frac{1}{2}}}\,n q_{(\nu)}^*\,,$$

$$(5.13c) \qquad \frac{\mathrm{d}(T^*\,e^{\Phi})}{\mathrm{d}r} = -\frac{3}{16\sigma^*}\,\frac{\varkappa^*\,\varrho^*}{T^{*3}}\,\frac{(L_r^*-L_r^{(\nu)*})\,e^{\Phi}}{4\pi r^2}\,(1-2m^*/r)^{-\frac{1}{2}} \approx$$

$$\approx 0 \text{ in regions where electrons or baryons are degenerate,}$$

$$\frac{1}{\varkappa^*} = \frac{1}{\varkappa_R^*} + \frac{3\varrho^*\,\lambda_c^*}{16\sigma^*\,T^{*3}}\,,$$

$$(5.13d) \qquad U_T^* = \int\limits_0^R \varepsilon_T^*\,e^{\Phi}\,4\pi r^2(1-2m^*/r)^{-\frac{1}{2}}\,\mathrm{d}r\,.$$

(*) Strictly speaking, the injection energy is not quite constant unless the thermal energy, ε_T^*, is distributed isentropically—which it is not in highly conducting superdense stars. However, deviations from constant injection energy will be of the order of $\varepsilon_T^*/\varrho^*$ which is extremely small.

b) *Gas characteristic relations*

(5.14*a*) $\varepsilon_T^* = \varepsilon_T^*(\varrho^*, T^*) = \beta^*(\varrho^*)\, T^{*2} + \frac{3}{2} bnT^*$,

(5.14*b*) $\lambda_c^* = \lambda_c^*(\varrho^*, T^*) \approx \infty$ in regions where electrons or baryons are degenerate,

(5.14*c*) $\varkappa_R^* = \varkappa_R^*(\varrho^*, T^*)$,

(5.14*d*) $q_{(\nu)}^* = q_{(\nu)}^*(\varrho^*, T^*)$.

All of the quantities appearing here are defined and discussed in Sect. **3** except the density of thermal energy, ε_T^*, which was discussed in Sections **5**·1.1 and **5**·1.3; and U_T^*, the *total thermal energy of the configuration.* U_T^* is defined as the total mass-energy which observers at $r = \infty$ can collect from the star's photon and neutrino radiation, as the star cools from its present state to zero temperature.

Equations (5.13*a*, *b*) are the equations of thermal equilibrium (3.11-5,6) with q^* and dn/dt set equal to zero (no thermonuclear energy release or change of density with temperature for catalyzed matter.) Equation (5.13*c*) is the equation of energy transport (3.11-7*a*) specialized to the case of no convection. Convection does not occur—except, perhaps, in the very thin, nondegenerate surface layer and atmosphere—because the high thermal conductivity of the degenerate electron and baryon gases maintains a temperature gradient well below the adiabatic limit. Expression (5.13*d*) for the total thermal energy is simply the integral, over the proper volume of the configuration, of the density of thermal energy red-shifted to account for the energy used up by photons and neutrinos as they climb out of the star's gravitational field. The gas characteristic relations (5.14) are expressions in terms of density and temperature for the thermal energy density, ε_T^*, the thermal conductivity, λ_c^*, the radiative absorption coefficient, $\varkappa_R^*$, and the rate, $q_{(\nu)}^*$, at which thermonuclear reactions convert thermal energy into outgoing neutrinos.

The thermal-structure equations (5.13), (5.14) are 8 coupled equations for the 8 quantities L_r^*, $L_r^{(\nu)*}$, T^*, U_T^*, ε_T^*, λ_c^*, $\varkappa_R^*$, and $q_{(\nu)}^*$. These equations must be subjected to the boundary conditions (cf. Sect. **3**·3)

(5.15) $$L_r^*(0) = 0\,, \qquad L_r^{(\nu)*}(0) = 0\,, \qquad T^*(R) = 0\,.$$

Note that in the equations of stellar structure (5.11)–(5.15) for configurations of catalyzed matter no mention is made of the parameters ε^*, s^*, q^*, $Z_1, \ldots, Z_N$, $\bar{\mu}_1^*, \ldots, \bar{\mu}_N^*$, $\alpha_1, \ldots, \alpha_N$, which enter into the more general structure equations (3.11). The parameters q^* and $\alpha_1, \ldots, \alpha_N$ are zero in catalyzed matter since no nuclear energy generation can occur there; the nuclear abundances $Z_1, \ldots, Z_N$ and chemical potentials $\bar{\mu}_1^*, \ldots, \bar{\mu}_N^*$, are not needed once the equation of state

$p^*(\varrho^*)$ and the thermal function $\beta^*(\varrho^*)$ have been calculated; the density of internal energy and the entropy per baryon, ε^* and s^*, are omitted because they play no important role in configurations of catalyzed matter.

5'3. *How to construct stellar models.* – To construct a model of a star near the endpoint of thermonuclear evolution and follow its subsequent thermal evolution one might proceed as follows: 1) Specify the central density, ϱ_c^*. 2) Integrate the primary and secondary structure equations (5.11) and (5.12) by the method described between those equations. 3) Take as the external gravitational field the Schwarzschild solution of Sect. 3'4.1. 4) Specify an initial temperature distribution, $T^*(r)$, satisfying $T^*(r=R)=0$. Solve the thermal equations (5.13) and (5.14) subject to boundary conditions (5.15) for the parameters L_r^*, $L_r^{(\nu)*}$, ε_T^*, $\mathrm{d}\varepsilon_T^*/\mathrm{d}t$, U_T^*, λ_c^*, $\varkappa_R^*$, $q_{(\nu)}^*$. This solution can be effected by a straighforward numerical integration from the center of the star to the surface. 6) Calculate a new value of the temperature at a later time, Δt, from

$$(5.16) \qquad T^*(r, \Delta t) = T^*(r, 0) + \{2\beta^*(\varrho^*[r])\, T^*(r, 0) + \tfrac{3}{2} b n(r)\}^{-1} \{\mathrm{d}\varepsilon^*(r, 0)/\mathrm{d}t\} \Delta t$$

(cf. eq. (5.14*a*)). 7) Repeat steps 5) and 6) until the stellar model has cooled to zero temperature.

In practice this computational method cannot yield very reliable results for the thermal evolution of a superdense star, since it assumes that the pressure, $p^*(\varrho^*)$, is independent of temperature in the nondegenerate surface layers as well as in the main body of the star. A more nearly correct treatment (see, *e.g.*, SCHATZMAN (1958), and TSURUTA and CAMERON (1966*b*) for Newtonian versions) would treat the thin surface layers by means of a temperature-dependent equation of state and would make use of the theory of stellar atmospheres.

5'4. *Structure and properties of configurations of catalyzed matter.* – We now have at our disposal all the tools necessary to an analysis and discussion of the structure and properties of configurations of catalyzed matter. In the next few Sections we shall examine the hydrostatic structure, the thermal structure, and the stability of such configurations.

5'4.1. Hydrostatic structure. Aside from thermal properties, which are considered in the next Section, *to each proposed equation of state for catalyzed matter there corresponds a one-parameter family of equilibrium configurations.* Once the central density has been specified, an integration of the primary and secondary structure equations uniquely fixes a configuration's mass, radius, and gravitational field, and its distributions of pressure, density, and baryons (*).

(*) The uniqueness of this determination depends upon the assumption that the equation of state, $p^*(\varrho^*)$, is monotonic. That this is necessarily so is shown by HTWW, p 102-104.

The main features of the one-parameter family of equilibrium configurations for a given equation of state are most clearly depicted by a curve of total mass-energy, M^*, *vs.* radius, R, parametrized by central density, ϱ_c^*. Such curves are shown in Fig. 4 for the H-W, S-V, V_β, and V_γ equations of state. The rather uniform shape of these four $M^*(R)$ curves can be understood as follows:

Consider the transformations undergone by an imaginary configuration of cold catalyzed matter, as baryons are added to it or taken away in just the right manner to keep it at the endpoint of thermonuclear evolution. The process of adding and removing baryons could be accomplished, for example, by the idealized routine described in Sect. **3**'5.7. Note that because of the constancy of the injection energy (*) it does not matter where in the equilibrium configuration the baryons are added; the addition of δA baryons is always accompanied by a mass increase of

$$\delta M^* = \mu_B^*(R)[1-2M^*/R]^{\frac{1}{2}}\delta A\,. \tag{5.17}$$

(Cf. eq. (3.63).) Here $\mu_B^*(R)$ is (1/56)×(mass of a ^{56}Fe atom).

At a central density of 7.86 g/cm³ the equilibrium configuration which we wish to follow is a ball of ^{56}Fe, the size of an apple. As more and more ^{56}Fe atoms are added to the ball, its central density, mass, and radius become larger and larger, until a configuration of $\varrho_c = 3\cdot 10^3$ g/cm³, $M = 0.011 M_\odot$, and $R = 1.8\cdot 10^4$ km is reached. (This configuration and all those of lower central density are too small to show up in Fig. 4.) At this point gravitational forces are becoming so strong that the addition of more ^{56}Fe nuclei causes the radius, R, to decrease rather than increase. This is roughly the beginning of the region of white dwarf stars (**).

As more ^{56}Fe nuclei are added to push the central density beyond $3\cdot 10^3$ g/cm³ and higher, the equilibrium configuration becomes more and more massive, its radius gets smaller and smaller, and internal gravitational forces become stronger and stronger. In the meantime, inside the configuration the orbital iron electrons become highly degenerate and begin to react with the ^{56}Fe nuclei

---

(*) See footnote (*) on p. 233.

(**) The white dwarfs which occur in nature are *not* catalyzed to near the endpoint of thermonuclear evolution because the reaction rates for the formation of neutron-rich nuclei at white dwarf temperatures and pressures are considerably slower than 10^{-10} per nucleus per year. However, the difference in nuclear composition between real white dwarfs and configurations of catalyzed matter has only a small effect on the equation of state. Consequently, realistic white dwarf models—as exemplified, *e.g.*, by the S-V configurations of Fig. 4 (cf. footnote (*) on p. 229)—are not too different from the configurations of catalyzed matter discussed here. For further discussion see, *e.g.*, SALPETER (1961), and HAMADA and SALPETER (1961).

to form neutron-rich nuclei (cf. Sect. 5'1.2). Eventually a critical point (first peak of $M^*[R]$ curve; $\varrho_c \approx 10^9$ g/cm^3; $M \approx 1.2\, M_\odot$, $R \approx 3000$ km; $A \approx \approx 1.4 \cdot 10^{57}$ baryons) is reached, at which point gravitational forces are so strong that the addition of one more baryon would force the configuration to collapse. This point is called the LHWW (Landau-Harrison-Wakano-Wheeler) *crushing point*; and the critical mass at this point is often called the *Chandrasekhar limit*.

Since the addition of one more baryon at the LHWW crushing point would induce gravitational collapse, one must now begin to *remove* baryons from the configuration in order to move it through equilibrium states of higher and higher central density. With the removal of baryons beyond the LHWW point the mass and radius decrease, the central density increases, and—according to the static approach to stability (Sect. 4'2.2 and 5'5.1)—the fundamental mode of radial pulsation of the configuration becomes unstable. The configuration remains unstable against small radial perturbations as more and more baryons are removed until the second critical point in the $M^*(R)$ curve is reached at $\varrho_c \sim 5 \cdot 10^{13}$ g/cm^3. (We ignore the two intermediate critical points for V_β and V_γ configurations, which signal the onset and removal of instability of the first harmonic of radial pulsation.) As baryons are removed and central density increases through the unstable region $10^9 \leqslant \varrho_c \leqslant 5 \cdot 10^{13}$, the cold catalyzed matter in the interior of the configuration is transformed from electrons plus neutron-rich nuclei into a mixture of degenerate neutron, proton, and electron gases. The peculiar behaviour of the equation of state as these nuclear transformations occur is largely responsible for the peculiar form of the $M^*(R)$ curve in this density region.

At the second critical point (minimum of $M^*(R)$ curve; « HWW*point* ») the removal of any additional baryons will force the configuration to explode or collapse. In order to move onward through equilibrium states of higher density one must now *add* baryons to the configuration; and this addition of baryons, according to the static analysis of stability, will make the fundamental mode of radial pulsation stable.

The stable equilibrium states through which the configuration now passes as baryons are added to it are called *neutrons stars* because the main constituents of the configuration are neutrons. (Because hyperons are also present in abundance for $\varrho_c > 10^{15}$ g/cm^3, the term hyperon stars is sometimes used as well.) The neutron stars extend from the HWW minimum of the $M^*(R)$ curve at $\varrho_c \approx 5 \cdot 10^{13}$ g/cm^3 the maximum at $\varrho_c \approx 5 \cdot 10^{15}$. This second maximum (third critical point) is called the « LOV *crushing point* » (LOV $\equiv$ LANDAU, OPPENHEIMER, VOLKOFF). Here, as at the LHWW crushing point, one must cease adding baryons and begin to remove them, in order to avoid collapse and to move the configuration along the $M^*(R)$ curve toward still higher central densities.

As baryons are removed to compress the configuration beyond the LOV crushing point, the fundamental mode of radial pulsation becomes unstable. The continued removal of baryons brings the configuration to a fourth critical point—a minimum in $M^*(R)$—beyond which baryons must be added, and at which the first harmonic of radial pulsation becomes unstable. There follow an infinite sequence of critical points as the $M^*(R)$ curve spirals inward toward a limiting state of infinite central density but finite mass and radius. At each critical point one more mode of radial pulsation becomes unstable (counterclockwise spiral). In the region $\varrho_c \gtrsim 10^{19}$ g/cm³ the spiraling $M^*(R)$ curve is described analytically by eqs. (4.22)-(4.24).

Because the above behavior is common to all four $M^*(R)$ curves of Fig. 4, we have confidence that this behavior correctly describes configurations of matter near the endpoint of thermonuclear evolution. (In connection with this, see MISNER and ZAPOLSKY (1964).) However, there are several important differences among the four curves, which reflect gaps in our understanding of configurations of catalyzed matter. These differences occur primarily in and above the neutron star region, where uncertainty about the nature of nucleon-nucleon interactions makes our knowledge of the equation of state unreliable. Roughly speaking, the lower the density at which repulsive nuclear forces become important and the stronger those forces are, the larger are the typical and maximum masses for neutron stars. Widely differing assumptions about repulsive nuclear forces lead to masses at the LOV crushing point which vary from $\sim 0.65 M_\odot$ to $\sim 2.0 M_\odot$. In Table III we present the mass, radius, and central density of the most massive, stable neutron star (LOV point) as predicted by a number of different equations of state. The maximum mass of a stable neutron star is an important determinant of the fates of the collapsed cores of supernovae (cf. FINZI (1966), WHEELER (1966)). The larger the maximum mass, the more frequently neutron stars will be formed in supernova explosions. The smaller the maximum mass, the more frequently the cores of supernovae will undergo catastrophic gravitational collapse to a general-relativistic singularity (see Sect. 7).

Each equation of state for cold catalyzed matter proposed thus far has yielded only two regions of stable equilibrium configurations—the white-dwarf region and the neutron-star region. However, it is conceivable (J. A. WHEELER, private communication) that elementary-particle processes not now understood might lead to a third region of stability at central densities $\varrho_c \gtrsim 10^{16}$ g/cm³. Although such a possibility is conceivable, it seems unlikely. At these very high densities the adiabatic index required for stability against radial perturbations probably exceeds 2.0, whereas causality (speed of sound less than speed of light) demands that Γ_1 and $\gamma_{\text{eqn state}}$ be $\leqslant 2.0$ at these densities.

For a much more extensive discussion of the hydrostatic properties of stars near the endpoint of thermonuclear evolution see HTWW.

TABLE III. – *Characteristics of the neutron star of maximum mass* (L-O-V *crushing point*) *as predicted by various equations of state* ([a]).

Equation of state and references ([b])	Central density, ϱ_c (g/cm^3)	Number baryons, $A/A_\odot$	Mass $M/M_\odot$	Radius R (km)
Ideal neutron gas (no hyperons or nuclear interactions): OPPENHEIMER and VOLKOFF (1939), INMAN (1965).	$3.9\cdot10^{15}$	0.738	0.712	9.27
Ideal neutron, proton, and electron gases (no hyperons or nuclear interactions). H-W: HARRISON, WAKANO, WHEELER (1958); HTWW.	$6.0\cdot10^{15}$	0.704	0.683	8.39
Ideal baryon gas (nucleons and hyperons but no nuclear interactions): AMBARTSUMYAN and SAAKYAN (1960, 1961).	$2.3\cdot10^{15}$	NA	0.634	11.0
Real nucleon gas (nuclear interactions but no hyperons):				
1) SKYRME (1959), CAMERON (1959), SAAKYAN (1963), INMAN (1965), TSURUTA (1964) ([c])				
cut-off at $p^* = \varrho^*/3$	$4.5\cdot10^{15}$	1.98	1.61	8.2
cut-off at $p^* = \varrho^*$	$4.8\cdot10^{15}$	2.08	1.70	7.7
2) SALPETER (1960)	NA	NA	NA	NA
3) AMBARTSUMYAN and SAAKYAN (1960, 1961)	$8\ \ \cdot10^{15}$	NA	1.05	6.5
4) GRATTON and SZAMOSI (1964), PACINI (1965) ([e])	$6\ \ \cdot10^{15}$	NA	0.85	8.1
5) INMAN (1965), case *c*.	$2.2\cdot10^{15}$	1.19	1.14	13.1
6) INMAN (1965), case *d*.	$2.0\cdot10^{15}$	1.71	1.60	13.0
Real baryon gas (nuclear interactions and hyperons):				
1) S-V: SAAKYAN and VARTANYAN (1963*a*, *b*; 1964)	$3.7\cdot10^{15}$	1.75	1.55	9.19
2) Levinger-Simmons V_β: TSURUTA (1964), TSURUTA and CAMERON (1966*a*) ([c])				
cut-off at $p^* = \varrho^*/3$	$1.1\cdot10^{16}$	1.15 ([d])	0.926	NA
cut-off at $p^* = \varrho$	$1.1\cdot10^{16}$	1.202 ([d])	0.973	5.103
3) Levinger-Simmons V_γ: TSURUTA (1964), TSURUTA and CAMERON (1966*a*) ([c])				
cut-off at $p^* = \varrho^*/3$	$2.9\cdot10^{15}$	2.28 ([d])	1.914	NA
cut-off at $p^* = \varrho^*$	$3.0\cdot10^{15}$	2.317 ([d])	1.953	9.8

([a]) For comparison, at the LHWW crushing point (maximum white-dwarf mass) $\varrho_c \approx 1\cdot10^9$ g/cm^3; $A/A_\odot \approx M/M_\odot \approx 1.2$; $R \approx 3000$ km. In the table «NA» means not available.

([b]) For discussions of equations of state see lectures by SZAMOSI (1966).

([c]) Equation of state arbitrarily set to $p^* = \varrho^*/3$ or $p^* = \varrho^*$ when that point is reached so as to avoid velocity of sound exceeding velocity of light.

([d]) This number is rest mass (cf. eq. (3.15)) in units of $M_\odot$, rather than $A/A_\odot$.

([e]) These numbers are for hard-core nucleon-nucleon repulsion at $r_c = 0.4\cdot10^{-13}$ cm.

5.4.2. Thermal structure. In discussing the thermal structure of configurations of catalyzed matter, we shall concentrate our attention on stable configurations—white dwarfs and neutron stars.

General relativity has only negligible effects upon the structure, both hydrostatic and thermal, of white dwarf stars. For this reason white dwarfs are normally studied within the framework of the Newtonian approximation. For Newtonian treatments of the thermal structure of white dwarfs see, *e.g.*, SCHATZMAN (1958), SCHWARZSCHILD (1958), and MESTEL (1965).

The thermal structure of neutron and hyperon stars was first investigated by CHIU (1964), by CHIU and SALPETER (1964), and by MORTON (1964) in connection with the possibility that X-ray emission from young neutron stars might be observable at the earth. More recent studies have been made by ELLIS (1965), by BAHCALL and WOLF (1965*a*, *c*), by FINZI (1965*a*), and by TSURUTA and CAMERON (1965*a*, 1966*b*). *For a review see the lecture of* FINZI (1966).

In all of these studies Newtonian theory was used for simplicity, since the accuracy desired was less than the 5 to 30% error which results from neglecting general relativity. However, in future calculations general-relativistic effects will probably be taken into account by means of the thermal-structure equations (5.13) (5.14), augmented by a more realistic analysis of the surface layers and atmosphere (cf. end of Sect. **5**.3), which are typically only a few meters thick.

5.5. *Stability and pulsations of configurations of catalyzed matter.* – We turn now from the equilibrium structure of stars near the endpoint of thermonuclear evolution to a discussion of their behavior under small radial perturbations, including: a «static» analysis of stability; numerical calculations of normal-mode frequencies and eigenfunctions; and the damping of pulsations. In this discussion of stability and pulsations we shall usually simplify matters by speaking in terms of *cold* catalyzed matter. This is allowable because the pulsation frequencies and eigenfunctions for configurations of catalyzed matter, like all other hydrostatic and hydrodynamic properties, are temperature-independent.

5.5.1. The static analysis of stability. The static, $M^*(R)$ approach to stability, as outlined in Sect. **4**.2.2 and **4**.2.3, is not applicable directly to configurations of cold, catalyzed matter because neither condition (4.15) nor (4.16) is satisfied by such configurations. In this Section we will modify slightly the $M^*(R)$ approach to stability to make it applicable to configurations of catalyzed matter. But before presenting the modified analysis, we must elucidate several key features of such configurations.

One key feature is this, that the adiabatic index Γ_1 for configurations of cold, catalyzed matter is not a unique function of density, ϱ^*. Rather, Γ_1 depends upon the frequency of the stellar pulsations, $|\omega|$, as well as upon ϱ^*. So long as $1/|\omega|$ is large compared to the relaxation times, t_{relax}, of the nuclear reactions required to keep the pulsating matter at the endpoint of thermonuclear evolution, the nuclear reactions proceed to completion as rapidly as the density changes. Hence,

$$(5.18a)\qquad \begin{cases} \Gamma_1(|\omega|, \varrho^*) = \gamma_{\text{eqn state}}(\varrho^*) \\ \qquad\equiv (\varrho^* + p^*)p^{*-1}(\mathrm{d}p^*/\mathrm{d}\varrho^*)_{\text{as given by eqn of state}} \quad \text{when} |\omega|^{-1} \gg t_{\text{relax}} . \end{cases}$$

On the other hand, when $1/|\omega|$ is small compared to t_{relax}, nuclear reactions occur hardly at all. Consequently,

$$(5.18b)\qquad \Gamma_1(|\omega|, \varrho^*) = \gamma_{\text{no reactions}}(\varrho^*) \equiv (\varrho^* + p^*)p^{*-1}(\partial p^*/\partial \varrho^*)_{\text{constant } Z_1, Z_2, \ldots Z_N} ,$$

when $|\omega|^{-1} \ll t_{\text{relax}}$.

In the intermediate case, where $1/|\omega|$ is of the same order as t_{relax}, Γ_1 is a complicated function of $|\omega|$, which might even be taken as complex—$\Gamma_1 = \Gamma_1^{(R)} + i\Gamma_1^{(I)}$—to account for pulsation damping by nuclear reactions. However, we shall temporarily ignore any imaginary part of Γ_1, leaving the discussion of pulsation damping to the end of this Section and to Sect. **5**˙5.3.

There is an important relationship between the values of Γ_1 for various frequencies: Consider a small sample of fluid at the endpoint of thermonuclear evolution. Let the volume of the sample be V_0 and its pressure be p_0. Compress the sample to volume $V_0 - \Delta V$, where $\Delta V \ll V_0$, at a rate of fractional volume change

$$\mathrm{d}(V/V_0)/\mathrm{d}t = -|\omega| .$$

According to the first law of thermodynamics the accompanying increase in total mass-energy of the sample is

$$(5.19)\qquad \Delta E^* = -\int_{V_0}^{V_0-\Delta V} p^* \mathrm{d}V = p_0^* \Delta V[1 + (\Gamma_1/2)(\Delta V/V_0) + \ldots],$$

where Γ_1 is the adiabatic index at density $\varrho_0^* = \varrho^*(p_0^*)$ and frequency $|\omega|$. The increase in mass-energy, ΔE^*, evidently depends by way of Γ_1 on the speed, $|\omega|$, with which the compression is performed. The slower the compression, the more nuclear reactions will proceed to completion; and, hence, the smaller will be ΔE^*. On the other hand, according to eq. (5.19), the smaller ΔE^* is, the smaller is Γ_1. These relations are possible only if $\Gamma_1(\varrho^*, |\omega|)$ is a non-decreasing function of $|\omega|$. Hence, Γ_1 must take on its minimum value at $|\omega| = 0$ and its maximum value at $|\omega| = \infty$.

$$(5.20)\qquad \gamma_{\text{eqn state}} \leqslant \Gamma_1(|\omega|, \varrho^*) \leqslant \gamma_{\text{no reactions}} .$$

Next consider a particular configuration at the endpoint of thermonuclear evolution. The squared angular frequency of its n-th normal mode, ω_n^2, can be calculated correctly from the *dynamical* approach to stability if and only if the correct adiabatic index, $\Gamma_1(|\omega|, \varrho^*)$, is used. If, instead, we were to use $\Gamma_1 = \gamma_{\text{eqn state}}$ or $\Gamma_1 = \gamma_{\text{no reactions}}$, we would obtain incorrect squared frequencies, ω_n^2 [eqn. state] or ω_n^2 [no reactions]. The inequality (5.20) between Γ_1, $\gamma_{\text{eqn state}}$, and $\gamma_{\text{no reactions}}$ imposes a similar inequality between the correct squared frequency, ω_n^2, and the incorrect ones:

$$\omega_n^2\,[\text{eqn state}] \leqslant \omega_n^2 \leqslant \omega_n^2\,[\text{no reactions}]\,. \tag{5.21}$$

Proof of inequality (5.21): Let $\omega_n^2[\gamma(\varrho^*)]$ be the squared frequency of the n-th normal mode of our particular configuration under the assumption that $\Gamma_1 = \gamma(\varrho^*)$. It is sufficient to show that, for any hypothetical adiabatic index $\gamma(\varrho^*)$ and some other *very slightly larger* index $\Gamma_1 = \gamma(\varrho^*) + \delta\gamma(\varrho^*)$, we necessarily have

$$\omega_n^2[\gamma + \delta\gamma] > \omega_n^2[\gamma]\,. \tag{5.22}$$

To prove this, we can apply standard, nondegenerate perturbation theory (*) to the eigenvalue eq. (4.8), thereby obtaining

$$\omega_n^{*2}[\gamma + \delta\delta\gamma] - \omega_n^{*2}[\gamma] = \tag{5.23}$$

$$= \frac{\int_0^R e^{3\Phi}(1 - 2m^*/r)^{-\frac{1}{2}} r^{-2} p^* \,\delta\gamma (r^2 e^{-\Phi} \xi_n)'^2 \,\mathrm{d}r}{\int_0^R W (r^2 e^{-\Phi} \xi_n)^2 \,\mathrm{d}r} + O[(\delta\gamma)^2]\,.$$

Here ξ_n is the eigenfunction corresponding to $\omega_n^2[\gamma]$. Because $\delta\gamma$ is very small and positive, the right-hand side of eq. (5.23) is positive. QED.

We now have the tools required for a proof that a modified form of the static approach to stability (Sect. **4**.2.2) is applicable to the (one-parameter) family of configurations at the endpoint of thermonuclear evolution. Our proof is based upon Fig. 5, where we show two portions of the dependence upon central density, ϱ_c, of the n-th squared frequency, ω_n^2. If the adiabatic index $\Gamma_1(|\omega|, \varrho^*)$ were equal to $\gamma_{\text{eqn state}}$ (eq. (5.18*a*)) at all frequencies, ω_n^2 would have the ϱ_c-dependence shown by the curve labeled ω_n^2[eqn. state]; and if Γ_1 were always equal

(*) For an account of perturbation theory see, *e.g.* MATHEWS and WALKER (1964), Chapter 10. An alternative proof of (5.22), in which no infinite series such as (5.23) arise, can be based on the Rayleigh-Ritz method for solving the variational equation (4.10). For an account of the Rayleigh-Ritz method see BARDEEN, THORNE and MELTZER (1966).

to $\gamma_{\text{no reactions}}$ (eq. (5.18b)), ω_n^2 would follow the curve ω_n^2[no reactions]. However, Γ_1 varies with frequency between the limits $\gamma_{\text{eqn state}}$ and $\gamma_{\text{no reactions}}$, so according to eq. (5.21) ω_n^2 moves about in the region between the limiting curves

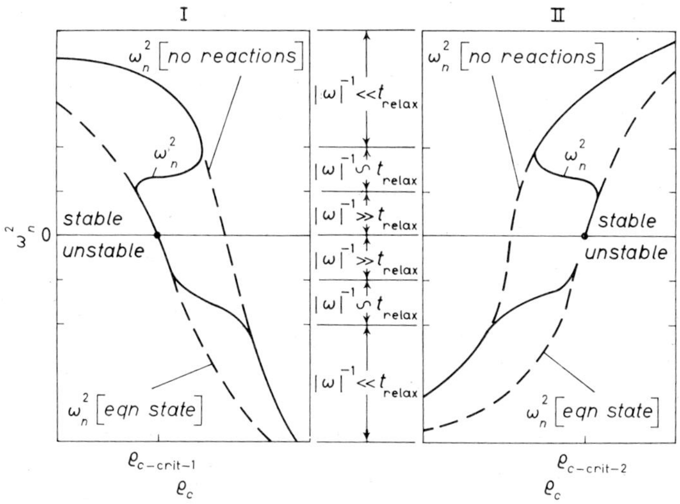

Fig. 5. – Stability behavior of the normal modes of radial pulsation of configurations of catalyzed matter near a critical point of the $M^*(R)$ curve. (Schematic.) The squared angular frequency, ω_n^2, of the mode of changing stability is shown as a function of central density, ϱ_c, in the neighborhoods of two typical critical points, $\varrho_{c\text{-crit-1}}$ and $\varrho_{c\text{-crit-2}}$. At $\varrho_{c\text{-crit-1}}$ the n-th normal becomes unstable with increasing central density. At $\varrho_{c\text{-crit-2}}$ it becomes stable. In the transition regions, $|\omega|^{-1} \sim t_{\text{relax}}$, pulsations are often damped extremely rapidly by nuclear reactions (*); and consequently, ω_n^2 is a complex function of ϱ_c, rather than real as idealized here.

ω_n^2(eqn. state) and ω_n^2[no reactions]. At low frequencies, where there is sufficient time for nuclear reactions to occur as the star pulsates, ω_n^2 coincides with ω_n^2[eqn. state]; at high frequencies it coincides with ω_n^2[no reactions]; and at intermediate frequencies it moves from one curve to the other.

At least this is the situation when pulsation damping has negligible effects upon the normal-mode eigenfunctions and frequencies. However, in the transition region, $|\omega_n|^{-1} \sim t_{\text{relax}}$,—and only there— the reactions which attempt to keep nuclear abundances at the endpoint of thermonuclear evolution can damp pulsations at a rate of the order of or larger than the pulsation frequency (*).

(*) The transition regions, $|\omega_n|^{-1} \sim t_{\text{relax}}$, of greatest physical interest occur near the LHWW point (maximum white-dwarf mass) and HWW point (minimum neutron-star mass), where the fundamental mode changes stability. (The LOV point is not of interest here because near that point ω_n^2 [no reactions] $= \omega_n^2$ [equation state].) Let $\omega_0 = \omega_0^{(R)} + i\omega_0^{(I)}$ in these transition regions, and for simplicity focus attention on the

Consequently, in the transition region ω_n is actually a complex function of ϱ_c, with an imaginary, damping part which may be large compared to the real part.

The static approach to stability, a generalization of which we wish to obtain, would be applicable if Γ_1 were equal to $\gamma_{\text{eqn state}}$ at all frequencies (cf. Sect. **4**˙2.3). Hence, the static approach predicts the stability behavior of the (incorrect) curve ω^2[eqn state]; it predicts that the n-th normal mode is stable for central densities $\varrho_c < \varrho_{c\text{-crit-1}}$ or $\varrho_c > \varrho_{c\text{-crit-2}}$ but unstable for $\varrho_c > \varrho_{c\text{-crit-1}}$ or $\varrho_c < \varrho_{c\text{-crit-2}}$ (cf. Fig. 5) The actual behaviour of the n-th normal mode is only slightly different from this prediction: For $\varrho_c < \varrho_{c\text{-crit-1}}$ or $\varrho_c > \varrho_{c\text{-crit-2}}$, the n-th mode is stable; but for $\varrho_c > \varrho_{c\text{-crit-1}}$ or $\varrho_c < \varrho_{c\text{-crit-2}}$, it is *both stable and unstable—i.e.* in these regions there are several normal radial modes of order n, corresponding to different adiabatic indices; and some of these modes are unstable, while others are stable.

These observations allow us to conclude that *the static approach to stability is applicable to the (one-parameter) family of configurations at the absolute end-point of thermonuclear evolution if it is restated in the following slightly modified form*: Construct a curve of total mass-energy, M^*, plotted upward *vs.* radius, R, plotted to right. This curve has the properties *a*), *b*), and *c*) of Sect. **4**˙2.2; and, in addition, it has the following property: *d*) *In the neighborhood of a peak or valley (critical point) of the $M^*(R)$ curve the squared frequency, ω_n^2, of the mode of changing stability, behaves as indicated in Fig* 5. *A configuration near the critical point, $\varrho_{c\text{-crit}}$, may have several normal modes of order n. If the configuration*

---

stable side of the critical point. One can show by the following analysis that *at the center of these transition regions $\omega_0^{(I)}$, the damping rate, is much larger than $\omega_0^{(R)}$, the pulsation frequency*. The proof proceeds by contradiction: *Assume* that $\omega_0^{(I)} < \omega_0^{(R)}$ when $\omega_0^{(R)} \approx (t_{\text{relax}})^{-1}$. At this frequency pulsations will drive all nuclear reactions nearly to completion each time the star is in a state of maximum compression or expansion. In driving the reactions to completion the star converts

$$\Delta E^* \approx (A/2)\left[(p^*/n)(\gamma_{\text{no reactions}} - \gamma_{\text{eqn state}})(3\xi/r)^2\right]_{\text{avg over star}} \sim (p_c^*/\varrho_c^*)\, M^* \left[(\gamma_{\text{no reactions}} - \gamma_{\text{eqn state}})(\xi/r)^2\right]_{\text{avg over star}}$$

of its pulsation energy to heat and outgoing neutrinos (cf. eq. (5.19)). But the total pulsation energy is (cf. eq. (4.12))

$$E^*_{\text{puls}} \sim M^* \omega_0^{*\,2} R^2 \left[(\xi/r)^2\right]_{\text{avg over star}} .$$

Consequently,

$$\omega_0^{(I)}/\omega_0^{(R)} \sim \Delta E^*/E^*_{\text{puls}} \sim (p_c^*/\varrho_c^*)(ct_{\text{relax}}/R)^2\,(\gamma_{\text{no reactions}} - \gamma_{\text{eqn state}})_{\text{avg}} .$$

For configurations near the LHWW and HWW points we have (cf. Fig. 4 and Sect. **5**˙5.2) $(\gamma_{\text{no reactions}} - \gamma_{\text{eqn state}}) \gtrsim 0.01$, $(ct_{\text{relax}}/R)^2 \gtrsim 10^{17}$, $(p_c^*/\varrho_c^*) \gtrsim 10^{-4}$. Hence, $\omega_0^{(I)}/\omega_0^{(R)} \gtrsim 10^{11}$. But this contradicts the assumption that $\omega_0^{(I)} < \omega_0^{(R)}$ QED.

is on the stable side of $\varrho_{c\text{-crit}}$, all of its modes of order n are stable; but if it is on the unstable side, at least one of its order-n modes is unstable.

In Sect. **5**˙4.1 we discussed the implications of this $M^*(R)$ stability analysis for configurations of catalyzed matter. Our main conclusion was that there are only two types of stable configurations: white dwarfs and neutron stars.

5˙5.2. Frequencies and eigenfunctions of normal radial modes. Although the « static » analysis has revealed to us the number of unstable normal radial modes of each configuration of cold catalyzed matter from $\varrho_c = 7.86\ \text{g/cm}^3$ to $\varrho_c = \infty$, it cannot tell us the frequencies or shapes of the normal modes, except at critical points of the $M^*(R)$ curve. To obtain such quantitative information between critical points one must use the « dynamic » approach to stability as described in Sect. **4**˙2.1.

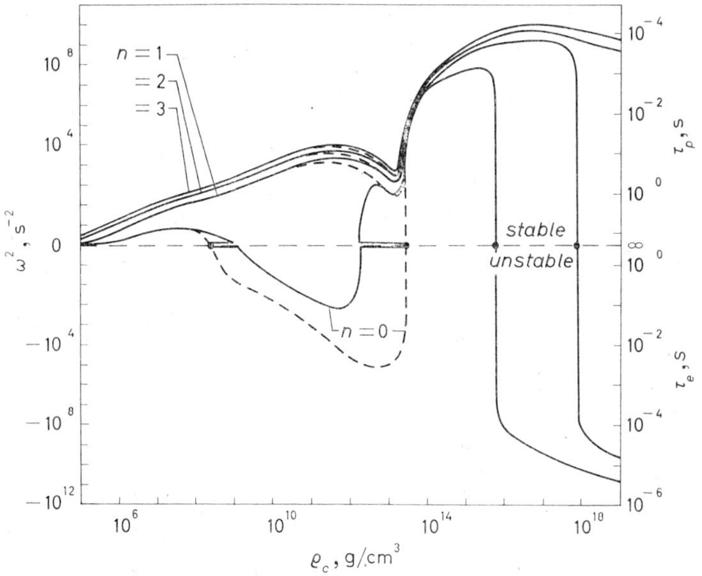

Fig. 6. – Squared angular frequencies as functions of central density for the lowest four normal radial modes of H-W-W configurations of catalyzed matter. (Based on MELTZER and THORNE (1966).) The right-hand vertical scale involves the pulsation period, $\tau_p = 2\pi/\omega$, for stable modes and the e-folding time, $\tau_e = 1/|\omega|$, for unstable modes. The solid curves represent the correct squared frequencies, while the thin dashed curves represent ω_n^2 [eqn. state] (cf. Sect. **5**˙5.1). The solid horizontal curves, which hug the $\omega^2 = 0$ axis between $2.5 \cdot 10^8$ and $1.3 \cdot 10^9\ \text{g/cm}^3$, represent the transition from ω_n^2 [no reactions] to ω_n^2 [eqn. state] and have amplitude-dependent periods and e-folding times $\geqslant 10^{10}$ years. The horizontal curves between $2.1 \cdot 10^{12}$ and $2.7 \cdot 10^{13}\ \text{g/cm}^3$ have amplitude-dependent periods and e-folding times $\geqslant 100$ days. In these transition regions pulsation-damping by nuclear reactions is very large (cf. footnote (*) on p. 243). At central densities below $10^8\ \text{g/cm}^3$ and above $10^{14}\ \text{g/cm}^3$, ω_n^2 [no reactions] is very nearly equal to ω_n^2 [eqn. state].

MELTZER and THORNE (1966) have recently calculated, by the dynamical approach, the squared frequencies and eigenfunctions of the lowest four radial modes of the H-W-W configurations of cold catalyzed matter (cf. top Section of Fig. 4). The results of those calculations are shown in Fig. 6. Because the typical pulsation periods and e-folding times are much shorter than the relaxation times for nuclear reactions ($|\omega|^{-1} \ll t_{relax}$), the squared frequencies are almost everywhere equal to ω_n^2[no reactions]. Only very near the $\omega^2 = 0$ axis —at $|\omega| \lesssim 10^{-10}$/y for the white-dwarf region; $|\omega| \lesssim 1/100$ days for the neutron-star region—does ω_n^2 make the transition from ω_n^2[no reactions] to ω_n^2[eqn. state]. As a consequence, the unstable white dwarfs of $2.5\cdot 10^8 < \varrho_c < 1.3\cdot 10^9$ are actually *metastable*—but « molasseslike » because of pulsation damping (*)—with e-folding times $\gtrsim 10^{10}$ years; and the neutron stars of $2.1\cdot 10^{12} < \varrho_c < 2.7\cdot 10^{13}$ are metastable but molasseslike, with e-folding times $\gtrsim 100$ days. The periods and e-folding times of the metastable configurations are amplitude-dependent as a result of the dependence of nuclear reaction rates upon pulsation amplitude (cf. MELTZER and THORNE (1966), Appendix A).

According to Fig. 6 the period of the fundamental mode of a white-dwarf star is typically ~ 10 s, while the fundamental period of a neutron star—in the absence of nucleon-nucleon forces—is $\sim 10^{-3}$ s. When nucleon-nucleon forces are included in the equation of state, the neutron-star fundamental period is reduced to $\sim 0.3\cdot 10^{-3}$ s (TSURUTA, WRIGHT, and CAMERON (1965); TSURUTA (1965); MELTZER and THORNE (1966)).

Figure 6 shows only the beginning of the high-density region, $\varrho_c \gtrsim 10^{19}$ g/cm³ in which more and more normal radial modes become unstable with increasing central density. Equation (4.25) for the number of unstable modes in this region, when adapted to the H-W equation of state, reads

$$(5.24)\quad \begin{cases} \text{number of unstable modes} = \\ \qquad = \text{greatest integer less than } \left\{\dfrac{47^{\frac{1}{2}}}{8\pi \log_{10} e} \log \varrho_c - 9.3\right\}, \\ \qquad = \text{greatest integer less than } \{0.63 \log \varrho_c - 9.3\}. \end{cases}$$

MELTZER and THORNE (1966) have calculated the eigenfunctions, $\xi_n(r)$, of the H-W-W normal radial modes corresponding to the frequencies of Fig. 6. In the white-dwarf region and in the upper neutron-star region ($\varrho_c \gtrsim 1\cdot 10^{15}$ g/cm³) the fundamental mode is very nearly homologous,

$$(5.25)\qquad \xi_0(r) \propto r,$$

(*) See fotnote (*) on p. 243.

and the harmonics are somewhat sinusoidal. However, for most unstable configurations and for neutron stars of central density $\varrho_c \leqslant 3\cdot 10^{14}$ g/cm³($M \leqslant 0.4 M_\odot$) the normal-mode eigenfunctions are far from homologous or sinusoidal.

5·5.3. Pulsation energy and the damping of normal radial modes. A numerical evaluation of eq. (4.12) by MELTZER and THORNE (1966) reveals that, in the absence of nucleon-nucleon interactions, a stable neutron star pulsating in its nearly homologous fundamental mode will have a pulsation energy of

$$E_{\text{puls}} \approx 1\cdot 10^{52}(\xi/r)^2 \text{ erg} . \tag{5.26}$$

Here (ξ/r) is the relative amplitude of pulsation. Nucleon-nucleon interactions, which increase the frequency of pulsation by a factor ~ 3, increase the pulsation energy by a factor $\sim 3^2 \approx 10$ (cf. eq. (4.12)). Hence, a more realistic estimate than (5.26) is

$$E_{\text{puls}} \approx 1\cdot 10^{53}(\xi/r)^2 \text{ erg} . \tag{5.27}$$

For comparison, the total mass-energy of the sun is $M_\odot c^2 = 1.8\cdot 10^{54}$ erg.

That the pulsation energy of a neutron star formed in a supernova explosion might be very large was originally reasoned from rough Newtonian considerations by HOYLE, NARLIKAR, and WHEELER (1964); by FINZI (1965*b*); and by CAMERON (1965*a*, *b*); and each of these physicists suggested astronomically observable consequences of such large pulsation energies. For a review, see the lecture by FINZI (1966); also WHEELER (1966).

Whether neutron-star pulsations are astrophysically important depends upon how rapidly and by what means they are damped. Among the mechanisms which may damp the pulsations are 1) the modified URCA reactions

$$\text{n}+\text{n}\rightarrow\text{n}+\text{p}+\text{e}+\bar{\nu}\,, \qquad \text{n}+\text{p}+\text{e}\rightarrow\text{n}+\text{n}+\nu\,, \tag{5.28}$$

which are driven by the rising and falling Fermi energies (FINZI (1965*b*, 1966); MELTZER and THORNE (1966); HANSEN (1966)); 2) reactions analogous to (5.28) involving μ^- and Σ^-; 3) shock waves generated in the stellar atmosphere by the pulsations (FINZI (1965*b*), CAMERON (1965*b*)); 4) hydromagnetic waves generated in the stellar magnetic field by pulsations (CAMERON (1965*a*, *b*)); 5) electromagnetic waves emitted by the vibrating magnetic field and the surrounding plasma (CAMERON (1965*b*)); 7) coupling of the normal radial modes to nonradial modes as a result of rapid stellar rotation, and the consequent damping by viscous forces and by gravitational radiation (ZEE and WHEELER (1966); WHEELER (1966)). The relative importance of these various mechanisms in stable neutron stars has yet to be determined for certain. However, the calculations of ZEE and WHEELER (1966) and of WHEELER (1966) suggest that, unless the neutron star can get rid of most of its angular momentum during the first few hours after formation, gravitational radiation will damp the normal radial modes to negligible amplitudes in a time of the order of a day.

5·5.4. Nonradial pulsations of neutron stars. Thus far we have considered only the radial pulsations of neutron stars. Since the catastrophic collapse of the stellar core, which, according to present theory (cf. COLGATE and WHITE (1964, 1966)), initiates a supernova explosion, will rarely if ever be completely symmetric, the resultant neutron star will pulsate nonradially as well as radially. However, according to calculations of ZEE and WHEELER (1966), gravitational radiation will damp out the nonradial modes in a fraction of a minute, leaving only radial pulsations behind.

5·6. *Summary.* – In Sect. **5** we have applied the tools developed in earlier Sections to the study of configurations of matter catalyzed to near the end-point of thermonuclear evolution. The equation of state of such matter, $p^*=p^*(\varrho^*)$, is independent of temperature under conditions of physical interest; and, as a consequence, the equations of stellar structure simplify considerably to the form (5.11)–(5.15). The hydrostatic structure of each solution to these equations is uniquely determined by a single parameter—*e.g.* the central density, ϱ_c; but the thermal structure evolves with time in a manner determined by the (arbitrary) initial temperature distribution.

The equation of state of cold, catalyzed matter and the corresponding equilibrium configurations are shown in Fig. 4. There are two types of stable configurations: white dwarfs, which are made of heavy nuclei plus a degenerate electron gas, and which have densities $\leqslant 10^9$ g/cm³; and neutron stars, which are made of a mixture of interacting neutron, proton, electron, and hyperon gases and have densities between 10^{13} and 10^{16} g/cm³. The maximum mass of a white-dwarf star is $\sim 1.2 M_\odot$, while that of a neutron star is not known for certain but lies between 0.7 and 2.0 $M_\odot$.

A modified form of the static approach to stability reveals that the normal modes of radial pulsation change stability in the strange manner of Fig. 5 at critical points of the $M^*(R)$ curve. The pulsation periods of white-dwarf stars are ~ 10 s, while those of neutron stars are $\sim 0.3\cdot 10^{-3}$ s. Neutron stars can store a sizable fraction of their rest mass in the form of radial pulsations; but nonradial pulsations are damped out in a fraction of a minute by gravitational radiation.

Observational aspects of neutron star theory are reviewed in the lecture of FINZI (1966) and in the article of WHEELER (1966); and the equation of cold catalyzed matter at high densities is the subject of Szamosi's (1966) lectures.

6. – Nondegenerate stellar models.

The analysis of equilibrium configurations of catalyzed matter (Sect. **5**) was considerably simplified over the general theory of stellar structure (Sect. **3**) by the fact that the equation of state, $p^* = p^*(\varrho^*, T^*)$, for catalyzed matter is independent of temperature. When we turn our attention to configurations of nondegenerate matter, the assumption that $p^*(\varrho^*, T^*)$ is independent of T^* is no longer tenable; and, consequently, the equations of thermal structure do not decouple from the equations of hydrostatic structure.

Does this mean that, in order to learn something of the structure of nondegenerate stars in general relativity, one must integrate the $16 + 3N$ structure equations (3.11) coupled together into one grand differential system with singularities of the equations at both the center and the surface of the star? No; fortunately, a method which dates back to the nineteenth century and is associated with such names as LANE, RITTER, and EMDEN enables one, *under certain restrictive circumstances*, to decouple the hydrostatic and thermal equations from one another even in highly nondegenerate configurations. This method effects such great simplifications, and the alternative of working with the full structure equations is so formidable, that all studies of specific nondegenerate, relativistic stellar models performed to date have utilized it.

Here in Sect. **6** we shall present the general relativistic form of the method for decoupling the thermal and hydrostatic equations; and we shall briefly describe the various relativistic stellar models which have been constructed by means of it.

6'1. *Method for decoupling thermal and hydrostatic equations.* – Consider an equilibrium configuration made of matter which obeys the two equations of state

$$p^* = p^*(n, T^*, Z_1, \dots, Z_N), \qquad \varrho^* = \varrho^*(n, T^*, Z_1, \dots, Z_N). \tag{6.1}$$

The full equations of stellar structure (3.11) will determine the hydrostatic and thermal structure of the configuration once the gas characteristic relations (3.11-10)–(3.11-16 + $3N$) and sufficient initial data (cf. Sect. **3'4**) have been specified. However, one sometimes knows *ab initio* that the particular energy transport-mechanism at work in the star will produce a temperature distribution, $T^*(r)$, which is related in some well-determined way to the distribution of baryons, $n(r)$

$$T^*(r) = T^*[n(r)]; \tag{6.2}$$

and one knows that the nuclear abundances, $Z_1, \dots, Z_N$, are related to the number density of baryons in some particular way

$$Z_k(r) = Z_k[n(r)] . \tag{6.2'}$$

When such relations are known to hold, one can combine them with the equations of state (6.1) to obtain relations between pressure and mass density and between pressure and number density

$$p^* = p^*(\varrho^*) , \qquad n = n(p^*) . \tag{6.3}$$

Since the effects of temperature upon the « hydrostatic » parameters (p^*, ϱ^*, n) are thereby eliminated, the equations of stellar structure now separate cleanly into hydrostatic equations and thermal equations.

The hydrostatic equations, which can be integrated without any further considerations of temperature or of energy transport, and which have no singularity at the surface of the star, are nearly the same as those used for configurations of catalyzed matter. They are

a) *Primary-structure equations*

(6.4*a*) $p^* = p^*(\varrho^*)$ (pressure-density relation (6.3)),

(6.4*b*, *c*) same as (5.11*b*, *c*).

b) *Secondary-structure equations*

(6.5*b*) $n = n(p^*)$ (relation (6.3)),

(6.5*a*, *c*) same as (5.12*a*, *c*).

Once the hydrostatic structure equations have been integrated, the temperature distribution, $T^*(r)$, is determined by eq. (6.2). The luminosity, $L^*(r)$, is then determined by the energy-transport equation (3.11-7) and by the equation of thermal equilibrium (3.11-5), which together must be compatible with the assumed temperature-density relation (6.2).

6·1.1. Configurations of perfect gas as an example. (Reference: TOOPER (1965).) For a perfect gas of constant average baryonic rest mass, μ_B^*, constant ratio of specific heats, Γ_4, and constant ratio, b, of number density of free particles to number density of baryons, the equations of state are

$$p^* = bnT^* , \qquad \varrho^* = \mu_B^* n + (\Gamma_4 - 1)^{-1} bnT^* . \tag{6.6}$$

In an equilibrium configuration of such a gas a mixture of convective and radiative transport will sometimes lead to the temperature-density relation

$$T^*/T_c^* = (n/n_c)^{1/N} , \tag{6.7}$$

where N is a constant, and where T_c^* and n_c are the central temperature and central density of baryons. For example, efficient convection would lead to the temperature distribution (6.7) with $N=(\Gamma_4-1)^{-1}$ (cf. eq. (3.37*b*), in which we here put $\Gamma_1=\Gamma_2=\Gamma_3=\Gamma_4$). By combining (6.7) with (6.6) we obtain the relations

$$p^* = p_c^*(n/n_c)^{1+1/N}\,. \tag{6.8a}$$

$$\varrho^* = \mu_B^*\, n_c(p^*/p_c^*)^{N/(1+N)} + (\Gamma_4-1)^{-1}p^*\,, \tag{6.8b}$$

which permit the equations of hydrostatic structure to decouple from the equations of thermal structure.

6·2. *Relativistic polytropes.* – In the Newtonian theory of stellar structure the *polytropic* pressure-density relation,

$$p/p_c = (\varrho/\varrho_c)^{1+1/N}\,, \tag{6.9}$$

is a good approximation to many realistic situations. The most reasonable relativistic generalization of this relation is eq. (6.8*a*). The alternative possibility

$$p^*/p_c^* = (\varrho^*/\varrho_c^*)^{1+1/N} \tag{6.10}$$

is unacceptable for two reasons: 1) at very high densities (6.10) leads to a velocity of sound exceeding the velocity of light; and 2) realistic physical situations rarely lead to relations of the form (6.10), except in the Newtonian realm.

In Newtonian theory the polytropic relation (6.9), together with the hydrostatic equations

$$m = \int_0^r 4\pi r^2 \varrho\,\mathrm{d}r\,, \qquad \mathrm{d}p/\mathrm{d}r = -\,G\varrho m/r^2\,, \tag{6.11}$$

is sufficient to permit the computation of the hydrostatic structure of a stellar model. However, in general relativity the polytropic relation (6.8*a*), together with the hydrostatic equations (6.4*b*, *c*) and (6.5*a*, *c*), are not sufficient to determine the hydrostatic structure. One also needs a relation between p^* and ϱ^*. We shall here adopt the convention that, when p^* and ϱ^* are related by an equation of the form (6.8*b*), and when $p^*(n)$ has the polytropic form (6.8*a*), then the resultant equilibrium configurations will be called *relativistic polytropic models*— or *relativistic polytropes* for short.

Relativistic polytropes arise not only as equilibrium configurations for a perfect gas; they also arise in other contexts—*e.g.* as approximations to neutron star configurations (GRATTON (1964*d*), TOOPER (1965)) and as approximations to certain massive stars in which radiation pressure is not negligible compared to gas pressure (IBEN (1963), BARDEEN (1965), GRATTON and GIANNONE (1965), TOOPER (1966)).

At first sight relativistic polytropic models appear to form a *five*-parameter family of equilibrium configurations; they depend upon the polytropic index, N, the adiabatic index, Γ_4, the ratio of central pressure to central rest-mass density,

$$\alpha^* = p_c^* / \mu_B^* n_c \,, \tag{6.12}$$

the central density of rest mass-energy, $\mu_B^* n_c$, and the baryonic rest mass, μ_B^*. In actuality only *three* of these five parameters —N, Γ_4, and α^*— enter into numerical integrations of polytropic models. The baryonic rest mass, μ_B^*, is easily removed from the equations of hydrostatic structure since it merely determines the constant ratio of the stellar rest mass to the total number of baryons, $M_0^*/A = \mu_B^*$, as well as the constant ratio of density of rest-mass energy to baryon number density, $\mu_B^* n/n = \mu_B^*$. The central density of rest mass-energy can also be removed from the structure equations, by choosing $(\mu_B^* n_c)^{-\frac{1}{2}}$ or some multiple of it as the unit of length in terms of which all other quantities are measured (*).

6·3. *Stellar models considered in the literature.* – Rather than present here the numerical solutions of the structure equation (6.4), (6.5) for relativistic polytropes and for other nondegenerate stellar models, we shall give a brief « guide » to some of the literature where such solutions can be found.

Relativistic polytropes have been studied by many physicists in several different contexts: BARDEEN (1965, 1966) has studied a number of particular polytropic models with various values of N, Γ_4, and α^* in connection with his interest in the relationship between binding energy and stability. TOOPER (1965) has presented a systematic treatment of isentropic polytropes—*i.e.* polytropes for which $\Gamma_4 = 1 + 1/N$. GRATTON (1964*a*, *b*, *c*, *d*; 1965), and GRATTON and GIANNONE (1965) have systematically studied polytropes with $\Gamma_4 = \frac{4}{3}$ in connection with the structures of neutron stars and of supermassive stars. TOOPER (1966)—see also FOWLER (1964, 1966) for the post-Newtonian approximation—has presented a complete account of polytropes of order $N = 3$ in connection with the theory of massive stars.

(*) As has been emphasized by BARDEEN (1965), the scale-invariance which permits one to eliminate $\mu_B^* n_c$ from the equations of hydrostatic structure is present whenever eqs. (6.3) can be put into the dimensionless form $p^*/\mu_B^* n_c = f(\varrho^*/\mu_B^* n_c)$ and $n/n_c = g(\varrho^*/\mu_B^* n_c)$. Here f and g are functions which may involve $\alpha^* = p_c^*/\mu_B^* n_c$ but must not involve p_c^*, ϱ_c^*, or n_c in any other way.

In addition to polytropes, several other nondegenerate, relativistic stellar models are treated in the literature: IBEN (1963) has studied massive hydrogen configurations with allowances in the equation of state for the effects of electron-positron pair formation. Iben's models are very nearly polytropes with $\Gamma_4 = \frac{4}{3}$. TOOPER (1964) has systematically treated the 3-parameter family of isentropic configurations for which

$$p^*/p_c^* = (\varrho^*/\varrho_c^*)^{1+1/N}\,, \qquad \mathrm{d}n/\mathrm{d}\varrho^* = n/(\varrho^* + p^*)\,. \tag{6.13}$$

A variation on these configurations of TOOPER, which is presented by GRATTON and GIANNONE (1965), avoids the difficulty of sound velocity exceeding light velocity at high densities. This variation is based upon the pressure-density relations

$$\left\{\begin{array}{ll} p^* = \left\{\begin{array}{l} K\varrho^{*1+1/N} \\ \varrho^*/3 \end{array}\right. & \begin{array}{l} \text{if } \varrho^* < (1/3K)^N\,, \\ \text{if } \varrho^* > (1/3K)^N\,, \end{array} \\ \mathrm{d}n/\mathrm{d}\varrho^* = n/(\varrho^* + p^*)\,. & \end{array}\right. \tag{6.14}$$

6·4. *Summary and commentary.* – The relativistic equations of stellar structure are greatly simplified by assuming that the mechanism of energy transport produces a temperature distribution related in some unique way to the distribution of baryons, $T^* = T^*(n)$. When such a relation is available, it can be used to eliminate temperature from the equations of state. The hydrostatic equations of stellar structure are then temperature-independent and can be integrated on a computer very easily.

This simplified method of studying stellar structure has been used in all investigations made until now of nondegenerate relativistic configurations. In Sect. **6**·2 and **6**·3 we presented a brief survey of the various models which have been studied to date.

Although this method of studying stellar structure may seem somewhat *ad hoc* and unphysical, it can often be used to obtain semiquantitative information about situations of interest. It was particularly useful during the pre-1940 period, when the foundations of the Newtonian theory of stellar structure were being laid; and it is performing a similarly valuable role today in the birth and infancy of the relatistic theory of stellar structure. However, we must emphasize that, one can rarely if ever place confidence in the quantitative details of (hopefully) realistic stellar models constructed by the above method, until after he has checked the details of those models by numerical integration of the full equations of stellar structure (3.11).

7. – Gravitational collapse to infinite density.

7·1. *Inevitability of collapse for massive stars. There is no equilibrium state at the endpoint of thermonuclear evolution for a star containing more than about twice the number of baryons in the sun* ($A > A_{max} \sim 2A_\odot$). This is one of the surprising—and disturbing— consequences of the discussion in Sect. **5** of configurations of catalyzed matter (cf. especially Fig. 4). Stated differently: A star with $A > A_{max} \sim 2A_\odot$ must eject all but A_{max} of its baryons—*e.g.*, through nova or supernova explosions — before settling down into its final resting state; otherwise there will be no final resting state for it to settle down into (*).

What is the fate of a star which fails to eject its excess baryons before nearing the endpoint of thermonuclear evolution? For example, after a very massive supernova explosion, what will become of the collapsed degenerate-neutron core, which contains more than A_{max} baryons? Such a supercritical mass cannot explode, since it is gravitationally bound and it has no more thermonuclear energy to release. Nor can it reach a static equilibrium state, since there exists no such state for so large a mass. There remains only one alternative; the supercritical mass must collapse, and collapse, and collapse, until it has reached infinite density and zero volume— or until the laws of classical general relativity break down and new, yet-to-be-discovered, quantum-gravitational forces halt the collapse.

The phenomenon of catastrophic gravitational collapse as described by classical general relativity will be the subject of this, the last major Section of these lectures. Throughout our discussion of collapse, except in the closing paragraphs, we shall ignore all quantum-gravitational effects.

7·2. *Hydrodynamic equations for a collapsing star.* – Because of the severe computational difficulties posed by nonspherical collapse, the hydrodynamic equations which govern relativistic collapse have been developed in explicit form only for situations with spherical symmetry. Within the framework of spherical symmetry PODURETS (1964*a*), MISNER and SHARP (1964*a*, *b*) BARDEEN (1964, 1965), and FIRMANI (1965) have all independently developed the equations for *adiabatic collapse* into forms suitable for numerical integration;

(*) The final resting state described here, being the lowest energy state for A_{max} baryons, is a nonrotating configuration. A *rotating* star, which has burned all its fuel and contains more than A_{max} baryons, can reach an equilibrium state, if its angular momentum is large enough, and if the magnetic field does not halt the rotation (HOYLE, NARLIKAR and WHEELER (1964)). However, the amount of rotation necessary to stabilize a star much larger than A_{max} is great enough that some, if not most of the supercritical stars in our universe are probably doomed to the catastrophic collapse which is described in the following pages.

MISNER (1965), and HERNANDEZ and MISNER (1966) have derived two alternative but equivalent forms for the equations of *collapse with escaping neutrinos*; MISNER and SHARP (1965, 1966) have derived the equations for *collapse with energy transport by photon diffusion, and with nuclear-energy generation*; and GINZBURG and OZERNOY (1964) have discussed *the behavior of a star's magnetic field during collapse.* In addition to this work on specifically spherical problems, the general-relativity theory of radiative transfer in more general dynamical situations has been developed by BARDEEN (1965) and by LINDQUIST (1966).

Thus far the exact equations of collapse, as analysed analytically in the above references and by numerical integrations elsewhere (PODURETS (1964*c*), BARDEEN (1965), FIRMANI (1965), and most extensively MAY and WHITE (1964), (1966)), have yielded little *new* insight into relativistic collapse. They have tended, instead, to confirm quantitatively the qualitative picture of collapse which was first brought to light by the pioneering work of OPPENHEIMER and SNYDER (1939). OPPENHEIMER and SNYDER discussed in detail the « free-fall » collapse of a spherical configuration in which gravitational forces completely overwhelm pressure forces. In the next few Sections we shall present a somewhat modernized version of the analysis of OPPENHEIMER and SNYDER, and we shall subsequently demonstrate that the qualitative features of this analysis cannot be modified by the presence of pressure forces inside the collapsing star.

7·3. *Free-fall collapse* (*).

7·3.1. Birkhoff's theorem. Before restricting our attention to the free-fall collapse of OPPENHEIMER and SNYDER, we must discuss an important feature of spherical collapse in general: *The geometry of space-time surrounding a collapsing, nonradiating, spherical configuration, like that around an equilibrium configuration* (Sect. **3**·4.1 and **3**·5.1), *is the Schwarzschild geometry*

$$ds^2 = (1 - 2M^*/r)\,dt^2 - (1 - 2M^*/r)^{-1}\,dr^2 - r^2(d\theta^2 + \sin^2\theta\,d\varphi^2)\,. \tag{7.1}$$

This result is called Birkhoff's theorem since it was first demonstrated by BIRKHOFF (1923) pp. 253-256. (For an alternative proof see TOLMAN (1934*a*), Sect. **99**.) Although Birkhoff's theorem is strictly valid only in the absence of radiation, it remains very nearly valid so long as the energy density in the radiation field is not strong enough to modify appreciably the geometry—*i.e.*, so long as the mass-energy radiated during the collapse is small compared to the star's total mass-energy (**).

(*) I am indebted to Prof. J. A. WHEELER for many enlightening discussions of the ideas in Sect. **7**.3.

(**) We shall delay until Sect. **7**·5.1 a discussion of stars which radiate a large fraction of their mass as they collapse.

Birkhoff's theorem is easily understood on physical grounds: Consider an equilibrium configuration which is unstable against gravitational collapse and which, like all equilibrium configurations (cf. Sect. 3'4.1), has the Schwarzschild geometry as its external gravitational field. Perturb this equilibrium configuration in a spherically-symmetry way so that it begins to collapse radially. The perturbation and subsequent collapse cannot affect the external gravitational field because, just as Maxwell's laws prohibit monopole electromagnetic waves, so Einsteins' laws prohibit monopole gravitational waves. There is no possible way for any gravitational influence of the radial collapse to propagate outward.

7'3.2. Free-fall collapse as depicted in Schwarzschild co-ordinates. One most readily and directly confronts the novel aspects of relativistic collapse by examining the time evolution of the radius, R, of a freely colapsing configuration. (R is defined by $4\pi R^2 =$ [surface area of collapsing star]; *i.e.*, R is the value of the Schwarzschild radial co-ordinate, r, at the surface.) Consider for definiteness a configuration with negligible internal pressure, which begins at Schwarzschild co-ordinate time $t = 0$ in a momentarily static state. Let the initial radius be R_i and the total mass be M^*. As the configuration collapses, its surface falls freely in the external Schwarzschild geometry. Consequently, the energy red-shift eq. (3.3) is applicable to any particle of matter on the surface of the star. When applied to such a particle, the red-shift equation yields the following relation between the velocity of collapse of the surface,

$$v_R^* = e^{-\Phi}(1-2M^*/R)^{-\frac{1}{2}}\mathrm{d}R/\mathrm{d}t = (1-2M^*/R)^{-1}\mathrm{d}R/\mathrm{d}t\,, \tag{7.2}$$

and the gravitation potential, $\Phi = \frac{1}{2}\ln(1-2M^*/R)$, at the surface:

$$(1-v_R^{*2})^{-\frac{1}{2}}e^{\Phi} = \text{const} = \exp[\Phi(r=R_i)]\,. \tag{7.3}$$

By rearranging this equation, one obtains a differential equation for the radius of the freely collapsing configuration as a function of (co-ordinate) time, t

$$\frac{\mathrm{d}R}{\mathrm{d}t} = -\left(\frac{2M^*}{R_i-2M^*}\right)^{\frac{1}{2}}\left(\frac{R_i}{R}-1\right)^{\frac{1}{2}}\left(1-\frac{2M^*}{R}\right). \tag{7.4}$$

The solution to this differential equation is most easily expressed in terms of a parameter η:

$$\left\{\begin{aligned} R &= (R_i/2)(1+\cos\eta)\,,\\ t &= 2M^*\ln\left[\frac{(R_i/2M^*-1)^{\frac{1}{2}}+\mathrm{tg}(\eta/2)}{(R_i/2M^*-1)^{\frac{1}{2}}-\mathrm{tg}(\eta/2)}\right]+\\ &\qquad +2M^*(R_i/2M^*-1)^{\frac{1}{2}}[\eta+(R_i/4M^*)(\eta+\sin\eta)]\,. \end{aligned}\right. \tag{7.5a}$$

The Schwarzschild co-ordinate time, t, to which R is here related, is *not* the proper time which would be measured by the clock of an experimental astrophysicist standing on the surface of the collapsing star. Rather, the astrophysicist's comoving clock would read

$$\tau^* = \int_0^t [(1 - 2M^*/R)\,\mathrm{d}t^2 - (1 - 2M^*/R)^{-1}\mathrm{d}R^2]^{\frac{1}{2}};$$

i.e., it would read

$$\tau^* = (\text{proper time on surface of star}) = (R_i^3/8M^*)^{\frac{1}{2}}(\eta + \sin\eta)\,. \tag{7.5b}$$

Equations (7.5) for the radius of a freely collapsing star as a function of time have a strange behavior: one might have expected the star to collapse to zero volume ($R \to 0$) after the elapse of a finite Schwarzschild coordinate time, t. However, as t becomes larger and larger, $\mathrm{d}R/\mathrm{d}t$ gets smaller and smaller; and in the limit $t \to \infty$ $[\mathrm{tg}(\eta/2) \to (R_i/2M^* - 1)^{\frac{1}{2}}]$, R decreases asymptotically to $2M^*$

$$R(t = \infty) = 2M^*\,. \tag{7.6}$$

Simultaneously, proper time as measured at the surface of the star approaches the *finite* value

$$\tau^*(t = \infty) = \left(\frac{R_i^3}{8M^*}\right)^{\frac{1}{2}} \cos^{-1}\left(\frac{4M^*}{R_i} - 1\right) + R_i\left(1 - \frac{2M^*}{R_i}\right)^{\frac{1}{2}}\,. \tag{7.7}$$

As proper time, τ^*, continues to increase beyond the value (7.7), the star continues to collapse (R decreases below $2M^*$), but the Schwarzschild co-ordinate time, t, now decreases rather than increases. Finally, after the elapse of a perfectly finite proper time,

$$\tau^*(R = 0) = \tau^*(\eta = \pi) = \pi(R_i^3/8M^*)^{\frac{1}{2}}\,, \tag{7.8}$$

the surface of the star has collapsed to a single point ($R = 0$). The corresponding final value of the co-ordinate time, t, is

$$t(R = 0) = 2\pi M^*(R_i/2M^* - 1)^{\frac{1}{2}}(1 + R_i/4M^*)\,. \tag{7.9}$$

This behavior of radius, R, as a function of co-ordinate time t, and proper time, τ^*, is exhibited graphically in the left half of Fig. 7 for a freely collapsing configuration of initial radius $R_i = 10M^*$. (Such an initial condition is representative of unstable, high-density configurations of catalyzed matter.)

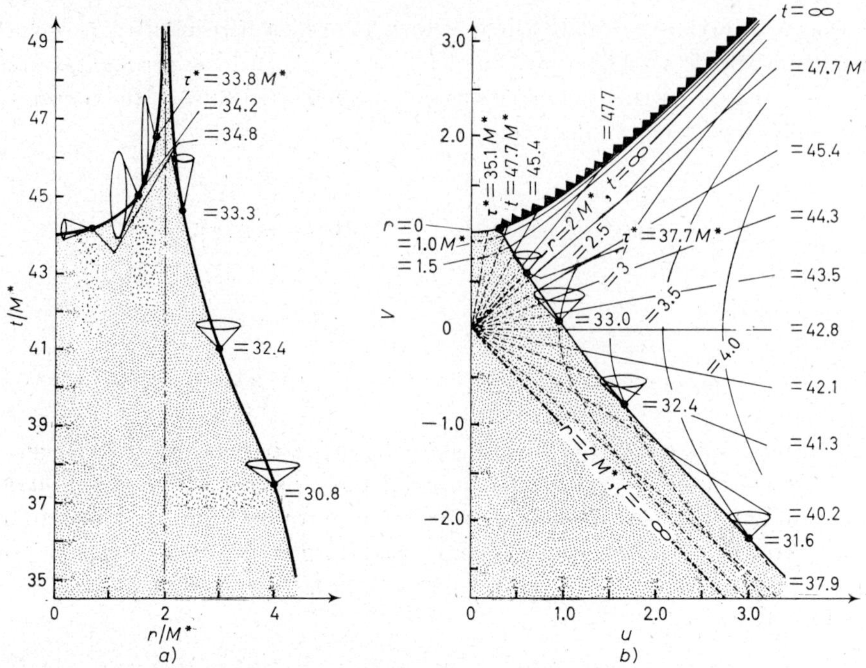

Fig. 7. – The free-fall collapse of a star of initial radius $R_i = 10M^*$ as depicted alternatively *a)* in Schwarzschild and *b)* in Kruskal co-ordinates. The region of space-time inside the collapsing star is stippled, while that outside is not. Only the geometry of the exterior region is that of Schwarzschild; for a discussion of the interior geometry see Sect. **7**˙3.6. The curve which separates the stippled and unstippled regions is the world line of the surface of the collapsing star. This world line is parametrized by proper time, τ^*, as measured by an observer who sits on the surface of the star; and light cones, as calculated from $ds^2 = 0$, are attached to it. Notice that, although the shapes of the light cones are not all the same relative to Schwarzschild co-ordinates, they are all the same relative to Kruskal co-ordinates. This is because light rays travel along 45 degree lines in the u-v plane ($dv = \pm du$), but they travel along curved paths in the r-t plane. The Kruskal space-time diagram shown here is related to the Schwarzschild diagram by eqs. (7.10) and (7.11*b*) *plus* a translation of Schwarschild time: $t \to t + 42.8\,M^*$. It is evident from these space-time diagrams that the free-fall collapse is characterized by a constantly diminishing radius, which drops from $R = R_i$ to $R = 0$ in a finite and short comoving proper time interval, $\Delta\tau^* = 35.1\,M^*$. The point $R = 0$ and the entire region $r = 0$ outside the star make up a physical « singularity » at which infinite tidal gravitational forces—according to classical, unquantized general relativity—can and do crush matter to infinite density.

7˙3.3. Free-fall collapse as depicted in Kruskal co-ordinates. The above description of the collapse of a freely falling star is quite pathological in the neighborhood of ($R = 2M^*$, $t = +\infty$). Is the strange form of the Schwarzschild space-time diagram (left half of Fig. 7) at this point, and for $R < 2M^*$, an indication of some strange new force which acts upon the star here? Is space really as badly twisted up near ($R = 2M^*$, $t = \infty$) as the left half of Fig. 7 would indicate? No. Physically speaking, there is nothing at all pathological about the geometry of space-time or the behavior of the star at ($R = 2M^*$, $t = \infty$). The pathology is all in the Schwarzschild co-ordinates (t, r, θ, φ) which we have used to describe the external gravitational field; and it is easily removed by transforming to a new, better-behaved co-ordinate system.

Several different co-ordinate systems have been used in the literature to describe in a reasonable manner the Schwarzschild space-time geometry which surrounds a collapsing star. The one most widely adopted in recent years is that of KRUSKAL (1960) (see also FULLER and WHEELER (1962)). Kruskal introduces new « time » and « radial » co-ordinates, v and u, which are related to the Schwarzschild t and r by

$$\text{(7.10)}\qquad \begin{cases} \left.\begin{aligned} u &= (r/2M^* - 1)^{\frac{1}{2}} \exp[r/4M^*] \cosh(t/4M^*) \\ v &= (r/2M^* - 1)^{\frac{1}{2}} \exp[r/4M^*] \sinh(t/4M^*) \end{aligned}\right\} & \text{for } r > 2M^* , \\ \left.\begin{aligned} u &= (1 - r/2M^*)^{\frac{1}{2}} \exp[r/4M^*] \sinh(t/4M^*) \\ v &= (1 - r/2M^*)^{\frac{1}{2}} \exp[r/4M^*] \cosh(t/4M^*) \end{aligned}\right\} & \text{for } r < 2M^* . \end{cases}$$

In terms of Kruskal co-ordinates the Schwarzschild geometry (7.1) is described by

$$\text{(7.11}a\text{)}\qquad ds^2 = f^2(dv^2 - du^2) - r^2(d\theta^2 + \sin^2\theta\, d\varphi^2) .$$

Here r is the Schwarzschild radial co-ordinate, which can be expressed in terms of $u^2 - v^2$ by

$$\text{(7.11}b\text{)}\qquad (r/2M^* - 1) \exp[r/2M^*] = u^2 - v^2 ;$$

and f^2 is defined in terms of r by

$$\text{(7.11}c\text{)}\qquad f^2 = (32M^{*3}/r) \exp[-r/2M^*] .$$

In the right half of Fig. 7 the free-fall collapse of a star with initial radius $R_i = 10M^*$ is shown relative to the Kruskal co-ordinate system. Note how reasonably the world line of the star's surface behaves in this Kruskal space-time diagram. The co-ordinate pathologies at $r = 2M^*$ have been removed entirely.

Several features of the Kruskal diagram for free-fall collapse should be emphasized: 1) In the Kruskal u-v plane curves of constant Schwarzschild radius, r, are the hyperbolae $v^2 - u^2 = \text{const}$; while curves of constant Schwarzschild time, t, are the radial lines $v/u = \text{const}$. 2) The pathological « point » ($r = 2M^*$, $t = \infty$) of the Schwarzschild diagram becomes the null ($ds^2 = 0$) line $u = v$ in the Kruskal diagram. 3) Light rays travel along 45 degree lines—$du = \pm dv$—in the Kruskal diagram. In this sense the Kruskal diagram is a close analogue of space-time diagrams of special relativity. 4) Although the Kruskal diagram is admirably suited to the description of the geometry of space-time near the surface of a collapsing star, it gives a somewhat pathological description of the region $r \gg M^*$ far from the star. In this far distant region, where space-time is very flat, one would like the u-v co-ordinate lines to form an inertial frame of reference (inertial in the sense of special relativity); but they do not. 5) Although it is possible for a man in a rocket ship to remain at a constant radius *outside* $r = 2M^*$ by pointing his rocket away from the star and firing his engines with an appropriate thrust, such a rocketeer cannot remain at a constant radius *inside* $r = 2M^*$. No matter how hard he fires his rockets, a rocketeer must always move along a timelike world line; but inside $r = 2M^*$ $(v > u)$ world lines of constant radius are spacelike. Hence, once a rocket ship follows the collapsing star in past $r = 2M^*$, it can never escape being pulled on in to $r = 0$. 6) This plight of the foolish rocketeer shows that, although the Schwarzschild geometry is static as seen by a certain family of observers (observers at fixed radius r) in the region $r > 2M^*$, there are no observers who see it as static in the region $r < 2M^*$.

Because of the key role played in the theory of collapse by the gravitational radius, $R_g = 2M^*$, of a star, it is of interest to examine the mean density of a collapsing star as it passes through its gravitational radius. Roughly speaking, the mean density at $R = R_g$ is

$$\bar{\varrho}^* \approx 3M^*/4\pi R_g^3 = 3/32\pi M^{*2} , \tag{7.12}$$

or, in conventional units,

$$\bar{\varrho} \approx 1.8 \cdot 10^{16} (M_\odot/M)^2 \text{ g/cm}^3 . \tag{7.12'}$$

Note that, although this density at the gravitational radius is above nuclear densities for a one-solar-mass star, it is only 1 g/cm for a supermassive star of $M = 10^8 M_\odot$.

7.3.4. Nature of the singularity at $r = 0$. The region $r = 0$ of the Schwarzschild geometry, into which the surface of a collapsing star contracts, is called a « general-relativistic singularity ». That this singularity is not merely a co-ordinate pathology as was the region $r = 2M^*$ in the Schwarzschild picture can be verified by examining the plight of an experimental astrophysicist who stands on the surface of a freely falling star as it collapses to $R = 0$.

As the collapse proceeds toward $R = 0$ the various parts of the astrophysicist's body experience different gravitational forces. His feet, which are on the surface of the star, are attracted toward the star's center by an infinitely mounting gravitational force; while his head, which is farther away, is accelerated downward by a somewhat smaller, though ever rising force. The difference between the two accelerations (« tidal force ») mounts higher and higher as the collapse proceeds, finally becoming infinite as R reaches zero. The astrophysicist's body, which cannot withstand such extreme forces, is stretched between head and foot to infinite length as R drops to zero.

But this is not all. Simultaneous with this head-to-foot stretching, the astrophysicist is pulled by the gravitational field into regions of space-time with ever-decreasing circumferential area, $4\pi r^2$. In order to accomplish this, tidal gravitational forces must compress the astrophysicist on all sides as they stretch him from head to foot. The circumferential compression is actually greater than the longitudinal stretching, so the astrophysicist, in the limit $R \to 0$, is crushed to zero volume and infinite length.

One can easily write down formulae to describe the stretching and compression of the astrophysicist after his body forces are overwhelmed by the gravitation forces. In this last stage of collapse each baryon in the astrophysicist's body falls freely toward $r = 0$ along a path which, in the Schwarzschild space-time diagram (left half of Fig. 7) has almost constant Schwarzschild time coordinate, t. The astrophysicist's feet touch the star's surface at one particular value of t—say $t = t_f$—while his head moves along the curve $t = t_h > t_f$. Consequently, the length of the astrophysicist's body increases according to the formula

$$(7.13a) \qquad l_{\text{Astroph}} = [-g_{tt}(R)]^{\frac{1}{2}}[t_h - t_f] = [2M^*/R]^{\frac{1}{2}}[t_h - t_f] \propto R^{-\frac{1}{2}} \propto (\tau_{\text{collapse}} - \tau)^{-\frac{1}{3}} .$$

Here $\tau = [-c^{-1}\int (g_{rr})^{\frac{1}{2}} \mathrm{d}r + \text{const}]$ is proper time as it would be measured by the astrophysicist if he were still alive. The gravitational field also constrains the baryons of the astrophysicist's body to fall along world lines of constant θ and φ during the final stages of collapse. Consequently, his cross-sectional area decreases according to the law

$$(7.13b) \qquad A_{\text{Astroph}} = [g_{\theta\theta}(R)\, g_{\varphi\varphi}(R)]^{\frac{1}{2}} \Delta\theta \Delta\varphi \propto R^2 \propto (\tau_{\text{collapse}} - \tau)^{\frac{4}{3}} .$$

By combining eq. (7.13a, b) we see that the volume of the astrophysicist's body decreases, during the last few moments of collaspe, according to the law

$$(7.13c) \qquad V_{\text{Astroph}} = l_{\text{Astroph}} A_{\text{Astroph}} \propto R^{\frac{3}{2}} \propto (\tau_{\text{collapse}} - \tau).$$

This crushing of matter to infinite density by infinitely large tidal gravitational forces can occur not only at the surface of the collapsing star; it can also occur at any other point along the $r = 0$ singularity of the external gravitational field. Hence, any foolish rocketeer who ventures below the radius $r = 2M^*$ of the external gravitational field is doomed to destruction.

In Sect. **7**·7 we shall discuss briefly the modifications which quantum-gravitational effects may impose on this classical picture of the crushing of matter to infinite density by tidal gravitational forces.

7·3.5. Free-fall collapse as seen by an external observer. Now that we have examined relativistic collapse as seen by an experimental astrophysicist on the surface of a collapsing star, let us next analyse it from the point of view of an astronomer who observes the collapse from a great distance. Suppose that the astrophysicist on the star sends a series of uniformly spaced signals to the astronomer to inform him of the progress of the collapse. These signals propagate along lightlike 45 degree lines in the Kruskal u-v space-time diagram of Fig. 8. The signals originate on the world line of the stellar surface and they are received by the distant astronomer when they intersect his hyperbolic world line, $r = \text{const} \gg M^*$. As the star collapses closer and closer to its gravitational radius, $R = 2M^*$, the signals, which are sent at regularly spaced intervals according to the astrophysicist's clock, are received by the astronomer at more and more widely spaced intervals. The astronomer does not receive a signal emitted just before the gravitational radius, $R = 2M^*$, is reached until after an infinite amount of time has elapsed; and he never receives signals emitted after the gravitational radius has been passed. Those signals, like the astrophysicist who sends them, get caught and destroyed in the singularity at $r = 0$.

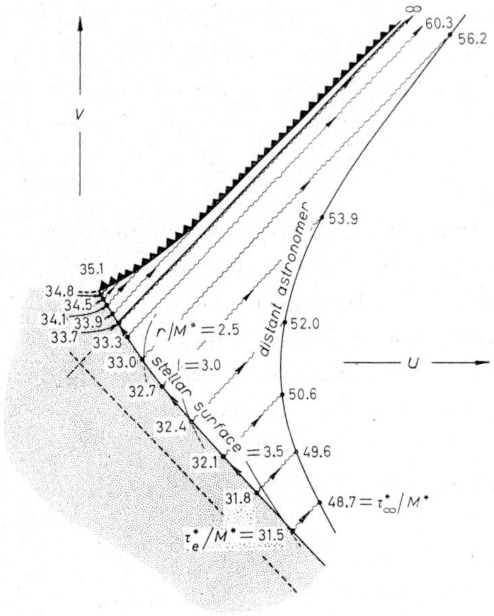

Fig. 8. – Kruskal diagram of the communication between a collapsing star of initial radius $R_i = 10\,M^*$ and a distant astronomer. As in Fig. 7, the interior of the star is stippled, but the exterior, Schwarzschild region is not. The wavy 45 degree lines represent the paths of radial light rays sent by an astrophysicist on the star's surface to the distant astronomer. The world lines of the stellar surface and of the astronomer are parametrized by the proper times at which the light rays are emitted and received. Light rays emitted after the star collapses through $R = 2\,M^*$ get caught in the singularity at $r = 0$.

Hence, to the distant astronomer, the collapsing star appears to slow down as it approaches its gravitational radius, light from the star becomes more and more red-shifted, and clocks on the star appear to run more and more slowly. It takes an infinite time for the star to reach its gravitational radius; and, as seen by the distant astronomer, the star never gets beyond there.

From the Kruskal diagram and eqs. (3.52) and (7.10), one can calculate the red-shift of radially travelling photons received from the center of the star's disk by the distant astronomer during the very late stages of collapse. One finds that the ratio of wavelength received to wavelength emitted is

$$\lambda_\infty/\lambda_e = \text{const}\times\exp[\tau^*_\infty/4M^*]\,, \tag{7.14}$$

where τ^*_∞ is proper time as measured by the very distant astronomer. Notice how short the e-folding time is

$$\tau_{e\text{-folding}} = 4GM/c^3 = 1.968\cdot 10^{-5}(M/M_\odot)\ \text{s}\,. \tag{7.15}$$

Formulae (7.14) and (7.15) are valid not only for a freely collapsing star, but also for a collapsing star of large internal pressure; and they are valid not only for radially travelling photons emitted from the surface of the star, but also—with a different multiplication constant—for neutrinos emitted from the star's center (*).

Neutrinos from the star's center all travel radially outward along paths which are not bent by the gravitational field. Consequently, the neutrino luminosity during the late stages of collapse decays according to the law

$$L^{(\nu)} = \text{const}\times\exp[-\tau^*_\infty/2M^*]\,. \tag{7.16}$$

One factor of $\exp[\tau^*_\infty/4M^*]$ comes from the red-shift of each neutrino, and the other comes from the increasing time interval between arrival of neutrinos. This formula was first derived by ZEL'DOVICH and PODURETS (1964).

The luminosity decay of light from the surface of the collapsing star is not so easily calculated. In addition to the red-shift and the increase in time between photons, which entered into eq. (7.16), one must consider :1) the bending of nonradial light rays in the star's gravitational field; 2) the aberration of light rays not emitted precisely radially; 3) the inability of a photon to escape from the star's gravitational field to infinity unless it is emitted from the star's surface within an angle

$$\theta_{\max} \propto (R/2M^* - 1) \tag{7.17}$$

of the vertical, as seen in the proper reference frame of a man standing on the star's surface; and 4) the fact that a photon emitted in a nonradial direction requires longer to reach the astronomer than one emitted radially. Effects 1)-3) tend to increase the rate of luminosity decay, while effect 4) tends to decrease

(*) For a more detailed discussion of most of the material in the remainder of this Section see the review by ZEL'DOVICH and NOVIKOV (1964).

the decay rate. PODURETS (1964*b*), who has examined all these effects, finds that 4) outweighs 1)–3) and thereby results in a decay of light from the star's surface of

$$L^{(\mathrm{ph})} = \mathrm{const} \times \exp\left[-\frac{4}{3\sqrt{3}}\frac{\tau^*_\infty}{2M^*}\right], \tag{7.18}$$

which is more gentle than the decay (7.16) of neutrinos from the star's center.

In any realistic collapse situation the decaying photon luminosity from the collapsing star would probably be masked by light from the lagging or exploding stellar atmosphere. However, predictions such as the above could be tested quite easily by a physicist in a space-ship near a collapsing star many thousands —or millions or billions— of years after the collapse was initiated. By this time the star would be a very black sink for photons and matter, observable only by virtue of its gravitational field. The physicist, having discovered such an invisible sink, could determine whether it was a collapsing star or a cold, dead neutron star by dropping a radio transmitter *radially* into the gravitational field. If the transmitter stopped functioning abruptly at a frequency red-shift of $\sim 10\%$, the physicist would know it had hit the surface of a neutron star. On the other hand, if the received intensity died out and was red-shifted exponentially with time, the object would be a collapsing star. During the late stages of fall the red-shift would be governed by eq. (7.14), while the intensity decay would obey

$$L^{(\mathrm{radio})} = \mathrm{const} \times \exp[-\tau^*_\infty/M^*], \tag{7.19}$$

(cf. ZEL'DOVICH and NOVIKOV (1964), eq. (15.11)). This intensity decay is steeper than $L^{(\nu)}$ of eq. (7.16) by virtue of the effects of 1) and 2) (cf. preceding Section) upon photons emitted very nearly, but not quite, radially. Such photon are received by the detection antenna because of its finite size.

7.3.6. Interior of a freely collapsing star. Thus far we have concentrated all of our attention on the surfaces of collapsing stars and on their external gravitational fields. We now turn to an examination of the interior regions. Rather than calculate from scratch the time evolution of the interior, we shall limit ourselves to a description of the results of such calculations for a particularly simple case: that of a freely collapsing star of initially uniform density. The collapse of such a configuration was originally analysed by OPPENHEIMER and SNYDER (1939), but the description presented below is due primarily to BECKEDORFF and MISNER (1962) and to BECKEDORFF (1962) (*). As the de-

(*) For descriptions of this homogeneous interior solution from different points of view, and of other *inhomogeneous* interiors, see TOLMAN (1934*b*), DATT (1938), KLEIN (1961), ZEL'DOVICH (1962, 1963*a*), HOYLE, FOWLER, BURBIDGE and BURBIDGE (1964), MCVITTIE (1964), CALLAN (1964), and HTWW, pp. 125-134.

scription which follows requires a prior familiarity with Friedmann's closed cosmological model, we shall begin with a brief review of it. For further details see, *e.g.* TOLMAN (1934*a*) parts III and IV, especially pp. 426-7; also LANDAU and LIFSCHITZ (1962), pp. 375-384.

The Friedmann universe has the space geometry of a 3-sphere. (A 3-sphere is the analogue in one higher dimension of the *surface* of an ordinary sphere.) In terms of hyperspherical co-ordinates (χ, θ, φ) and a time coordinate η, the Friedmann geometry is described by

$$ds^2 = a^2(\eta)[d\eta^2 - d\chi^2 - \sin^2\chi(d\theta^2 + \sin^2\theta\, d\varphi^2)] \,. \tag{7.20}$$

Einstein's field equations demand that the radius, a, of the Friedmann universe be the following function of time:

$$a = (a_0/2)(1 + \cos\eta) \,. \tag{7.21}$$

The density of mass-energy in the Friedmann universe is uniform and is related to the time-dependent radius by

$$\varrho^* = 3/(8\pi a^2) \,. \tag{7.22}$$

The material particles in the Friedmann universe always remain fixed with respect to the hyperspherical co-ordinates (χ, θ, φ), and the pressure always remains zero. Only the radius and density of the universe vary with time. Notice from eqs. (7.21) and (7.22) that the universe begins $(\eta = -\pi)$ in a singular state of zero radius, zero volume, and infinite density. As co-ordinate time, η, increases from $-\pi$ to 0, the universe expands to a maximum radius, $a = a_0$; and as η increases on past 0 to $+\pi$, it recontracts to a singular state of infinite density. Proper time as measured by a clock attached to the stationary matter is related to co-ordinate time by

$$\tau^* = \int a(\eta)\, d\eta = (a_0/2)(\eta + \sin\eta) \,. \tag{7.23}$$

Consequently, the total proper-time lapse from the creation of the universe to its destruction is $\tau^*(\pi) - \tau^*(-\pi) = \pi a_0$. The time evolution of the Friedmann universe could be illustrated by a series of embedding diagrams of the hypersurfaces of constant co-ordinate time, η. If one rotational degree of freedom —φ for example—were suppressed from the embedding diagrams, they would be simply a succession of ordinary spherical surfaces, which begin with radius $a = 0$, expand to $a = a_0$, and then contract back to $a = 0$.

To see the intimate relationship between a freely collapsing star of initially uniform density and the Friedmann universe, imagine the following surgical operation: 1) Take a Friedmann universe of radius $a = a_0$ at its moment of maximum expansion, $\eta = 0$; and slice off and discard the region $\chi_0 < \chi \leqslant \pi$, where χ_0 is some angle less than $\pi/2$. 2) Take a Schwarzschild geometry of mass $M^* = (a_0/2)\sin^3\chi_0$ at the moment $t = 0$; and slice off and discard the region $r < R_i = a_0 \sin\chi_0$. 3) Glue the retained pieces of Friedmann and Schwarzschild geometry together smoothly along their cut surfaces. The resultant object will be a momentarily static star of uniform density

$$\varrho_0^* = 3/(8\pi a_0^2)\,, \tag{7.24a}$$

of mass

$$M^* = (a_0/2)\sin^3\chi_0\,, \tag{7.24b}$$

and of radius

$$R_i = a_0 \sin\chi_0\,. \tag{7.24c}$$

An embedding diagram for this momentarily static, initial configuration is shown in Fig. 9 (curve *A-A′-A″* of history *A-B-C-D*, rotated about its vertical axis). The spherical cup, *A-A′*, of this embedding diagram is the interior of the star and comes from the truncated Friedmann universe. The parabolic funnel, *A′-A″*, which is capped by the spherical cup, is the external gravitational field and comes from the truncated Schwarzschild geometry.

Suppose that our patched-together star is released from its momentarily static state at $\eta = 0$ and allowed to collapse. How will its geometry and density distribution evolve with time? According to the calculations of OPPENHEIMER and SNYDER *the interior, truncated Friedmann universe and the exterior, truncated Schwarzschild geometry evolve just as though they had never been cut up and patched together.* In the interior region, the geometry as a function of η is described by eqs. (7.20) and (7.21), and the density remains uniform, increasing with time in accordance with eq. (7.22). The surface of the star, $\chi = \chi_0$, at which the join to the exterior Schwarzschild geometry is made, moves through the Schwarzschild space-time along the curve (7.5), which we have already discussed in great detail. Note that the time co-ordinate, η, which is used to describe the Friedmann interior (eqs. (7.20) and (7.21)) is identical to the parameter, η, used in describing the motion of the star's surface in the Schwarzschild geometry (eq. (7.5)).

In Fig. 9 we exhibit a space-time diagram for a freely collapsing star of $R_i/M^* = 2/\sin^2\chi_0 = 3$. This space-time diagram makes use of two co-ordinate patches: a Friedmann patch for the interior region, and a Kruskal patch for the exterior region. A photon, α, is emitted from the surface of the star and another, β, is emitted from the center just before collapse begins; and they both travel radially outward to $r = \infty$. A third photon, γ, is emitted radially from the center of the star at the last possible instant before it would be doomed to be caught in the singularity. Photon γ travels radially outward through the star and crosses its collapsing surface at the moment when $R = 2M^*$. γ then remains at $r = 2M^*$ forever, since it cannot move quite rapidly enough to escape

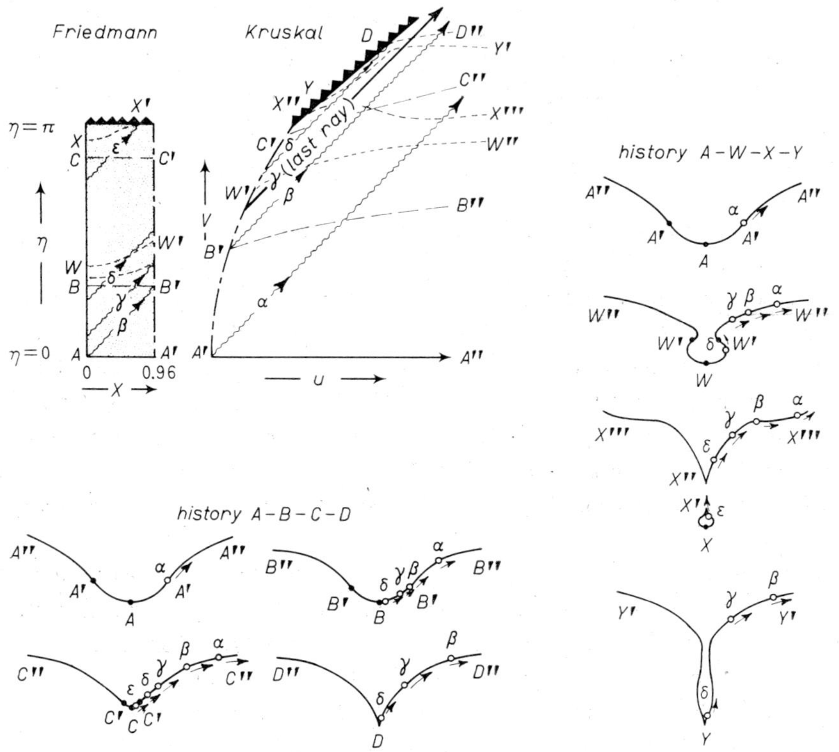

Fig. 9. – Space-time diagram and embedding diagrams for a freely collapsing star of uniform density with initial radius $R_i = 3M^*$. The space-time diagram consists of two co-ordinate patches: a Friedmann patch to cover the interior of the star and a Kruskal patch to cover the exterior. The join between the Friedmann and Kruskal patches, as regulated by eqs. (7.5) and (7.10), is indicated at several points by the letters A', B', W' and C'. The paths of several light rays, which are emitted from the center of surface of the star as it collapses, are shown as wavy 45 degree lines labeled with Greek letters. The $r = 0$ singularity into which the star collapses is indicated by saw teeth. Embedding diagrams are shown corresponding to 2 different ways of viewing the star's collapse—history A-B-C-D and history A-W-X-Y. These embedding diagrams are skeletonized in that they must be rotated about their vertical axes in order to become 2-dimensional surfaces analogous to Fig. 1. The several photons emitted from the center or surface of the star are indicated in the embedding diagrams by small circles. Notice that the hypersurfaces of which embedding diagrams are given intersect the singularity only tangentially. We do not consider *here* hypersurfaces which intersect the singularity at a finite angle in the u-v plane because such spacelike hypersurfaces cannot be embedded in a Euclidean space. Instead, a Minkowskian space (indefinite metric) must be used. For a discussion of embedding diagrams in Minkowskian spaces see THORNE (1965*a*).

from the star's gravitational field, nor quite slowly enough to be pulled into the singularity. A fourth photon, δ, and a fifth, ε, are emitted from the center of the star after the moment of no escape. Photon δ emerges from the star before being crushed, but it gets pulled into the singularity shortly thereafter. Photon ε, on the other hand, cannot even reach the star's surface before being crushed.

7'3.7. Embedding diagrams for free-fall collapse. Thus far we have described the geometry of space-time around and inside a collapsing star primarily in co-ordinate-dependent terms. Let us now use the technique of embedding diagrams to picture that geometry in a co-ordinate-independent manner.

We will need a sequence of embedding diagrams, each corresponding to the geometry of a spacelike hypersurface to the future of the preceding one, in order to describe the time development of the collapse geometry. But how are the hypersurfaces to be chosen? In Newtonian theory or special relativity, and also in the case of a general-relativistic equilibrium configuration (Sect. 3'5.1) one chooses hypersurfaces of constant time. But in dynamical regions of a curved space-time no naturally perferred time co-ordinate exists. This situation forces one to make a totally *arbitrary* choice of hypersurfaces for use in visualizing the time development of geometry, and to keep in mind how very arbitrary that choice was.

In Fig. 9 we use two very different choices of hypersurfaces to depict the time development of the geometry of a particular freely collpasing star. In both of these representative histories the initial configuration, A-A'-A'', is the one which we constructed by patching together momentarily static Friedmann and Schwarzschild geometries. History A-B-C-D depicts the time development of this initial 3-geometry as sampled by a succession of hypersurfaces which have constant Friedmann time, η, in the interior region. As depicted in this history, the interior region remains always a spherical cup of half angle χ_0, but it contracts from radius $R = a_0 \sin\chi_0$ to $R = 0$ as time increases. The matter in the star is all crushed to infinite density simultaneously when R reaches zero, and the external Schwarzschild «funnel» develops a cusplike singularity at that point. As time increases further, this cusp pulls the region $r < 2M^*$ of the funnel into $r = 0$ at such a fast rate that the outward-traveling photon δ is gobbled up and crushed.

The collapse geometry as sampled by hypersurfaces A-W-X-Y looks quite different from that revealed by A-B-C-D. As time passes, a neck develops in the geometry just outside the surface of the star. This neck becomes tighter and tighter and then pinches off, leaving the star completely isolated from the rest of the universe, and leaving a deadly cusplike singularity in the exterior geometry where the star used to be. The isolated star, in its own little closed universe, continues to contract until it is crushed to infinite density; while the external geometry begins to develop another neck, and the cusp quickly gobbles up photon δ.

The extreme difference between histories A-B-C-D and A-W-X-Y serves as a warning that only a small part of the dynamics of collapse can be captured by embedding diagrams or by an examination of representative 3-geometries. The dynamics is four dimensional; but embedding diagrams only sample two- or at best three-dimensional projections of it.

7·4. *Spherical collapse with internal pressure forces.* – So far as the external gravitational field is concerned, the only difference between a freely collapsing star and a collapsing, spherically-symmetric star with internal pressure is this, that the surfaces of the two stars move along different world lines in the exterior Schwarzschild geometry. Because the exterior geometry is the same in both cases, *the qualitative aspects of free-fall collapse as described in Sects.* **7**·3.1 *through* **7**·3.5 (and also the quantitative equations (7.1), (7.6), and (7.10)–(7.19)) *can be carried over directly to the case of nonnegligible internal pressure.* For example, the vast difference between what is seen and experienced by a man on the surface of the collapsing star and what is seen by a distant observer is preserved.

An important and fascinating question to ask is this: Can large internal pressures in any way prevent a collapsing star from being crushed to infinite density by infinite tidal gravitational forces? From the Kruskal diagram of Fig. 8 it is evident that, once a star has passed inside its gravitational radius ($R < 2M^*$), no internal pressures, regardless of how large they may be, can prevent the star's surface from being crushed in a singularity. The surface must move along a timelike world line, and all such world lines inside $r = 2M^*$ hit $r = 0$. BARDEEN (private communication) has shown that, for spherical collapse, inside the gravitational radius pressure forces are not only powerless to prevent *the star's surface* from being crushed; they also cannot prevent *any part of the interior* from being crushed. The *entire* star is doomed once it has passed the gravitational radius.

The interior dynamics of spherically collapsing stars with pressure are not so well understood as the exterior dynamics. However, major advances in our understanding of the interior dynamics are now being made by means of numerical computations and analytic analyses (for references see Sect. **7**·2); and in these computations and analyses no surprising new features have been encountered which did not occur in the simple, uniform-density, free-fall collapse of Sect. **7**·3.6 and **7**·3.7.

7·5. *Collapse in totally realistic situations.* Until recently it was often argued (see, *e.g.*, LIFSCHITZ and KHALATNIKOV (1963)) that the general-relativistic singularity at $r = 0$ was a feature peculiar to spherically symmetric collapse, so that small deviations from spherical symmetry could prevent a singularity from arising and could thus save a collapsing star from being crushed to infinite density. Recent analyses have revealed, however, that those arguments were incorrect: General-relativistic singularities are an essential and (almost) unavoidable aspect of gravitational collapse once the collapse has proceeded past the gravitational radius, $R = 2M^*$, or past the analogue of $R = 2M^*$ for non-spherical bodies. Let us review the analyses which lead to this conclusion, and make the conclusion more precise.

7.5.1. Trapped surfaces and the evolution of singularities. I spherically-symmetric collapse the external, Schwarzschild gravitational field is divided into two regions of very different character by the « event horizon » $r = 2M^*$. The region inside $r = 2M^*$ can be distinguished from the exterior region by either of two properties. The first, a *global property*, is this, that after the surface of a collapsing star has passed into the region $r < 2M^*$, the star's surface cannot escape being crushed in a singularity of infinite tidal gravitational forces. The second distinguishing property of $r < 2M^*$ is a *local* (or *quasi-local*) *property*: A bundle of radial light rays inside $r = 2M^*$ is convergent (the light rays move closer together as they propagate) whether it is an « outgoing » bundle or an « ingoing » bundle (cf. Fig. 8). Is the global property of the evolution of a singularity related in any intimate way to the local property of convergent outgoing and ingoing light rays? By posing this question and answering it affirmatively, PENROSE (1965) has made one of the greatest contributions in the history of general relativity.

PENROSE begins by generalizing the property of convergent outgoing and ingoing light rays to asymmetric regions of space-time. His generalization is motivated by a close examination of the 2-dimensional, spherical surfaces

$$(r = \text{const} < 2M^*,\ t = \text{const}) \equiv (u = \text{const},\ v = \text{const} > u) \tag{7.25}$$

in the Schwarzschild geometry. When related to these 2-surfaces the property of convergent light rays states: *Light rays emitted from one of these 2-surfaces in the perpendicular, outward direction converge toward each other as they propagate; and inward light rays perpendicular to the 2-surface also converge.* PENROSE calls any closed 2-surface, spherically symmetric or not, which has this property a *trapped surface*; and he suggests that asymmetric regions of space-time which contain trapped surfaces are analogous to the region $r < 2M^*$ of the Schwarzschild geometry.

The analogue between regions of space-time containing trapped surfaces and the Schwarzschild region $r < 2M^*$ is made explicit by the following theorem, which is Penrose's most important result (we state the theorem in more physical, but less precise language than that of Penrose): *Consider a star undergoing completely realistic gravitational collapse* (*i.e.*, asymmetric collapse with rotation, radiation, magnetic fields, shock waves, etc.) *in a universe which has the following properties*:

1) *The universe is open*; *i.e.*, on some initial spacelike hypersurface it has infinite area (*).

2) *Along every timelike world line in the universe the future direction is uniquely distinguished from the past.*

3) *At each point of spacetime the density of mass-energy as measured by an arbitrary observer in his own proper reference frame is nonnegative.*

4) *General relativity is the correct theory of gravitation.*

If a trapped surface evolves during stellar collapse in such a universe, then either or both of the following must occur subsequently:

a) *A general relativistic singularity evolves.* This singularity need not be characterized by an infinite density of mass-energy, but it must be a region beyond which either photons or matter—and probably both—cannot continue to exist (**)

or

b) another universe suddenly attaches itself to the star's universe. (Equivalently, but in more mathematical terms, the star's universe does not possess an initial Cauchy hypersurface) (***).

This theorem establishing the intimate connection between trapped surfaces and singularities is extremely powerful. Only two modifications would be needed to enable us with confidence to infer that singularities *necessarily* follow the evolution of a trapped surface in our own universe: the elimination of condition 1) and the elimination of possibility *b*) as an alternative to *a*). PENROSE (private communication) believes that it may, indeed, be possible to eliminate 1) by a reformulation of the proof of the theorem; but he is not optimistic about eliminating *b*) as an alternative to *a*).

(*) This assumption was not stated explicitly in Penrose's (1965) paper, but he points out in a private communication that it is necessary to his proof.

(**) For examples of particularly strange types of singularities see SHEPLEY (1964; 1965*a*, *b*), as well as the description by TAUB and MISNER (1966) of the join between the Taub universe and the NUT universe. For discussions of the ways in which magnetic fields in collapsing bodies affect the structure of the singularities, see KHALATNIKOV (1965) and THORNE (1964).

(***) For examples in which *both b*) and *a*) follow the evolution of a trapped surface see the extension by GRAVES and BRILL (1960) of the Reisner-Nordstrom solution, and the extension by BOYER and LINDQUIST (1966) and by CARTER (1966) of the Kerr solution.

7·5.2. Small deviations from spherical symmetry. According to the analysis of Penrose, the evolution of a trapped surface during gravitational collapse is a key indicator that something strange will subsequently happen to the geometry of spacetime—that either a singularity will halt the collapse, or that another universe will attach itself to ours, or both. Hence, at this point in the discussion we should ask whether trapped surfaces are a typical feature of stellar collapse, or whether they are peculiar to the case of spherical symmetry.

That trapped surfaces are somewhat typical has been shown recently by DOROSHKEVICH, ZEL'DOVICH, and NOVIKOV (1965) by means of an analysis of small perturbations of a collapsing star from spherical symmetry. Their argument, in rough outline, is as follows: In the idealized case of spherical symmetry a collapsing star feels no special or peculiar forces as it passes through its gravitational radius $R = 2M^*$. Consequently, there should be no peculiar forces available at $R = 2M^*$ to magnify enormously small initial deviations from spherical symmetry; the deviations, if sufficiently small initially, will remain small until after $R = 2M^*$ is passed. But small perturbations in the neighborhood of $R = 2M^*$ cannot prevent the evolution of a trapped surface (for proof see DOROSHKEVICH *et al.*). Hence, *a collapsing star, which is initially nearly spherical and has only a little angular momentum, generates trapped surfaces during the late stages of collapse.*

DORESHKEVICH *et al.* not only prove that trapped surfaces evolve during slightly aspherical collapse; they also discuss the evolution of nonspherical and rotational perturbations during the collapse. Most interesting of all is their discovery that, as the star approaches its gravitational radius, all multipole perturbations in the gravitational field seen by an *external* observer die away to zero; whereas rotational perturbations remain finite.

7·6. *Gravitational collapse to a singularity in other contexts.* – According to general-relativity theory, gravitational collapse to a singularity is not a phenomenon confined to massive and supermassive stars. Rather, it is a phenomenon which easily can occur in any large aggregate of matter—in galactic nuclei, in quasi-stellar sources, in the universe as a whole, etc. For example, collapse to a singularity—or the time-reversed explosion from one— is a feature common to almost all relativistic cosmological models (see, *e.g.*, SHEPLEY (1964, 1965*a*, *b*), HAWKING and ELLIS (1965), HAWKING (1965, 1966), GEROCH (1966)). That there is an intimate relationship between the collapse of a cosmological model and the collapse of a star is hinted at by the analysis of Sect. 7·3.6. (See also HTWW, pp. 137-141.)

Gravitational collapse to a singularity can occur, in principle, in small agglomerations of matter as well as in large ones. However, when the mass of a configuration is less than $M_{\text{LOV}} \sim 1.5 M_{\odot}$, the collapse must be initiated not by classical processes, but by the quantum-mechanical tunneling of a potential barrier. For a discussion of this phenomenon and of the fantastically slow rates associated with it, see HTWW.

Collapse to a singularity can occur even in the absence of matter if space-time is sufficiently curved intrinsically, or if it contains enough gravitational radiation. For a discussion see WHEELER (1964*b*).

7'7. *The issue of the final state* (*). – The crushing of matter to infinite density by infinite tidal gravitational forces is a phenomenon with which one cannot live comfortably. From a purely philosophical standpoint it is difficult to believe that physical singularities are a fundamental and unavoidable feature of our universe. On the contrary, when faced with a theory which predicts the evolution of a singular state, one is inclined to discard or modify that theory rather than accept the suggestion that the singularity actually occurs in nature. Such was the case with Rutherford's theory of the atom, which was needed to explain α-scattering experiments, but which predicted the evolution of a physical singularity—the spiraling of orbital electrons into the atomic nucleus as a result of radiation reaction. It was to avoid this singularity and thereby explain atomic spectra that BOHR suggested quantizing the energy states available to orbital electrons. Just as quantization of classical mechanics prevented physical singularities from evolving in Rutherford's atom, so quantization of general-relativity theory may prevent physical singularities from evolving in gravitational collapse.

That quantum-gravitational effects must play an important role in the very late stages of collapse is evident on two grounds: 1) When densities in excess of 10^{49} g/cm³ are reached, the radii of curvature of space-time become smaller than the Compton wave lengths of elementary particles (cf. Sect. **2'1**); and, consequently, the intrinsic properties of elementary particles are modified by tidal gravitational effects. 2) The gravitational field, like all fields, must undergo quantum fluctuations; and the characteristic size of gravitational fluctuations is the Planck length

$$L^* = (\hbar G/c^3)^{\frac{1}{2}} = 1.616\cdot 10^{-33}\ \text{cm} \tag{7.26}$$

(see WHEELER (1962) pp. 76-77). Surely such fluctuations in the geometry of space-time will have a profound effect upon the dynamics of collapse when the collapse has proceeded so far that the radii of curvature of space-time are of the order of L^*! Note that this stage of collapse occurs at a density of

$$\begin{cases} \varrho^{*-\frac{1}{2}} \sim (\text{radii of curvature}) \sim L^*\,, \\ \varrho \quad\ \sim 10^{93}\ \text{g/cm}^3\,. \end{cases} \tag{7.27}$$

(*) The ideas in the first three and the last two paragraphs of this section are due primarily to J. A. WHEELER; see WHEELER (1964*b*) and HTWW, pp. 138-147.

In what manner will quantum gravitational effects modify the classical picture of collapse to a singularity? This question cannot be answered with confidence until the foundations of the quantum theory of gravitation are well understood. However, it seems probable, in analogy with familiar quantum-mechanical scattering problems, that *the quantum theory of catastrophic collapse will be characterized, not by a singular final state as is the classical theory, but by a probability amplitude for this, that, or another physically reasonable outcome.*

Already in the development of the quantum theory of gravitation, highly idealized calculations by DEWITT (1966) and his students indicate that this probability-amplitude picture of collapse is reasonable: DEWITT *et. al.* have partially solved, in two different ways, the problem of quantizing the gravitational field of the Friedmann universe, and both of their partial solutions suggest that the probability amplitude for the contracting universe to « bounce » in this, that, or another manner, rather than be crushed to infinite density, is very high—perhaps unity. However, because the quantum effects which cause the bounce do not become important until a density of the order of 10^{93} g/cm^3 is reached, little or no information could be transmitted from the collapsing phase of the universe, through the quantum bounce, and into the re-expanding phase.

From these results of DEWITT *et. al.* it seems reasonable—though far from necessary!—to expect that the transformation of catastrophic collapse into catastrophic explosion may be a general feature of the quantum theory of gravitation. If so, does this mean that an external observer, who watches a star collapse toward its gravitational radius and then waits sufficiently long, will see the star suddenly explode back out? No! There is a large region of space-time separating the event horizon, $r = 2M^*$, of the Schwarzschild geometry from the quantum region

$$r \lesssim r_{\text{quantum}} \sim 10^{-20} (M/M_{\odot})^{\frac{1}{3}} \text{ cm} . \tag{7.28}$$

(Note: $r \lesssim r_{\text{quantum}}$ is the region where the radii of curvature of space-time, $(r^3/M^*)^{\frac{1}{2}}$, are of the order of or small compared to the Planck length, $L^* = 1.616 \cdot 10^{-33}$ cm.) In the region $r_{\text{quantum}} \ll r < 2M^*$ stellar dynamics are governed by the familiar laws of classical general relativity. However (cf. Fig. 8), a star cannot explode outward from the quantum region, through this classical region of trapped surfaces, and into the outside universe, except by reversing its direction of motion in time; and a time-reversed, exploding star would appear to an external observer to be a collapsing antistar (whatever that is). Consequently, it is difficult to understand how a quantum-mechanical reversal of collapse in the region $r \lesssim r_{\text{quantum}}$ could cause a star to explode (in the conventional sense of the word « explode ») back out, through the event horizon $r = 2M^*$ which swallowed it in the collapsing phase. More reasonable is the suggestino that quantum effects cause a collapsing star to bounce and then re-explode, not back to where it came from, but into another region of the universe (multiply-connected space-time geometry; difficulties with causality), or into some other universe (*). However, the peculiar and ill-understood nature of quantized space-time may well invalidate any description such as this of the outcome of collapse.

The above considerations are indicative of the deep problems of principle posed by the phenomenon of gravitational collapse. Some of the other issues raised by this confrontation between classical gravitation theory and the fundamental principles of quantum theory are discussed by Wheeler (1964*b*, 1965) and by HTWW (especially pp. 138-147). These quantum-gravitational issues include: the breakdown of the classical concepts of space and time; the question of whether the law of baryon conservation has any meaning within the context of collapse; the phenomenon of dynamical changes in the topology of space-time; and the relationship between elementary-particle physics and the quantum theory of gravitation.

In the words of Wheeler (1964*b*), p. 501. « There have been few occasions in the history of physics when one could surmise more surely than he does now, in the case of gravitational collapse, that he confronts a new phenomenon, with a mysterious nature of its own, waiting to be unraveled. »

(*) For further discussions along this line see Novikov (1964).

BIBLIOGRAPHY

Akeley, E. S., 1931, *Phil. Mag.*, **11**, 330.

Ambartsumyan, V. A. and G. S. Saakyan, 1960, *Astr. Žur.*, **37**, 193; English translation in *Soviet Astronomy, A. J.*, **4**, 187.

Ambartsumyan, V. A. and G. S. Saakyan, 1961, *Astr. Žur.*, **38**, 785; English translation in *Soviet Astronomy, A. J.*, **5**, 601.

Bahcall, J. N., 1964, *Ap. J.*, **139**, 318.

Bahcall, J. N. and R. A. Wolf, 1965*a*, *Phys. Rev. Letters*, **14**, 343.

Bahcall, J. N. and R. A. Wolf, 1965*b*, *Phys. Rev.*, **140**, B 1445.

Bahcall, J. N. and R. A. Wolf, 1965*c*, *Phys. Rev.*, **140**, B 1452.

Bardeen, J. M., 1964, paper presented at the *Second Texas Symposium on Relativistic Astrophysics*, Austin, Texas, December, 1964; proceedings to be published by University of Texas Press.

Bardeen, J. M., 1965, unpublished *Ph. D. Thesis*, Caltech, available from University Microfilms, Inc. (Ann. Arbor, Michigan).

Bardeen, J. M., K. S. Thorne and D. W. Meltzer, 1966, *Ap. J.*, **145**, 505.

Barker, B. M., M. S. Bhatia and G. Szamosi, 1966, submitted for publication.

BECKEDORFF, D. L., 1962, *Terminal Configurations of Stellar Evolution*, unpublished *A. B. Senior Thesis*, Princeton University.
BECKEDORFF, D. L. and C. W. MISNER, 1962, unpublished.
BIRKHOFF, G. D., 1923, *Relativity and Modern Physics* (Cambridge, Mass.).
BONDI, H., 1964, *Proc. Roy. Soc. London*, A **282**, 303.
BONDI, H., 1965, chapters in *Lectures on General Relativity*, vol. **1** of proceedings of 1964 Brandeis Summer Institute in Theoretical Physics (Englewood Cliffs, N. J.).
BOYER, R. H., 1965*a*, *Proc. Camb. Phil. Soc.*, **61**, 527.
BOYER, R. H., 1965*b*, *Proc. Camb. Phil. Soc.*, **61**, 531.
BOYER, R. H. and R. W. LINDQUIST, 1966, *Journ. Math. Phys.*, in press.
BUCHDAHL, H. A., 1959, *Phys. Rev.*, **116**, 1027.
BURBIDGE, G. R., 1963, chapter in *Star Evolution, Proceedings S.I.F.* vol. XXVIII, p. 95.
BURBIDGE, G. R., E. M. BURBIDGE, and A. R. SANDAGE, 1963, *Rev. Mod. Phys.*, **35**, 947.
CALLAN, C. G., jr., 1964, unpublished *Ph. D. Thesis*, Princeton University, available from University Microfilms, Inc. (Ann Arbor, Michigan).
CALLEN, H. B., 1960, *Thermodynamics* (New York).
CAMERON, A. G. W., 1959, *Ap. J.*, **130**, 884.
CAMERON, A. G. W., 1965*a*, *Nature*, **205**, 787.
CAMERON, A. G. W., 1965*b*, *Nature*, **206**, 1342.
CARTER, B., 1966, *Phys. Rev.*, **141**, 1242.
CHANDRASEKHAR, S., 1935, *M. N.*, **95**, 207.
CHANDRASEKHAR, S., 1939, *Introduction to the Study of Stellar Structure* (Chicago).
CHANDRASEKHAR, S., 1961, *Hydrodynamic and Hydromagnetic Stability* (Oxford).
CHANDRASEKHAR, S., 1964*a*, *Ap. J.*, **138**, 185.
CHANDRASEKHAR, S., 1964*b*, *Phys. Rev. Letters*, **12**, 114, 437.
CHANDRASEKHAR, S., 1964*c*, *Ap. J.*, **140**, 417.
CHANDRASEKHAR, S., 1965*a*, *Phys. Rev. Letters*, **14**, 241.
CHANDRASEKHAR, S., 1965*b*, *Ap. J.*, **142**, 1488.
CHANDRASEKHAR, S., 1965*c*, *Ap. J.*, **142**, 1513.
CHANDRASEKHAR, S., 1965*d*, *Ap. J.*, **142**, 1519.
CHANDRASEKHAR, S. and N. R. LEBOVITZ, 1964, *Ap. J.*, **140**, 1517.
CHIU, H. Y., 1964, *Annals of Physics*, **26**, 364.
CHIU, H. Y. and E. E. SALPETER, 1964, *Phys. Rev. Letters.*, **12**, 412.
CLARK, G. L., 1947, *Proc. Cambridge Phil. Soc.*, **43**, 164.
CLARK, G. L., 1948, *Phil. Mag.*, **39**, 747.
CLARK, G. L., 1950, *Proc. Roy. Soc. London*, A **201**, 510.
COCKE, W. J., 1965, *Ann. Inst. Henri Poincaré*, **2**, 283.
COLGATE, S. A. and R. H. WHITE, 1964, *The Hydrodynamic Behavior of Supernova Explosions*, University of California Lawrence Radiation Laboratory Report UCRL-7777.
COLGATE, S. A. and R. H. WHITE, 1966, *Ap. J.*, **143**, 626.
COX, A. N., 1965, chapter 3 of *Stellar Structure*, L. H. ALLER and D. B. MCLAUGHLIN, ed., (Chicago).
CURTIS, A. R., 1950, *Proc. Roy. Soc. London*, A **200**, 248.
DARWIN, C., 1959, *Proc. Roy. Soc. London*, A **249**, 180.
DATT, B., 1938, *Zs. f. Phys.*, **108**, 314.
DEWITT, B., 1966, submitted for publication.
DICKE, R. H., 1964, *Experimental Relativity* (New York).

DICKE, R. H., P. J. E. PEEBLES, P. G. ROLL and D. T. WILKINSON, 1965, *Ap. J.*, **142**, 414.

DMITRIEV, N. A. and S. A. HOLIN, 1963, chapter in *Voprosi Kosmogonii*, **9** (Moscow).

DOROSHKEVICH, A. G., YA. B. ZEL'DOVICH and I. D. NOVIKOV, 1965, *Žurn. Ėksp. Teor. Fiz.*, **49**, 170; English translation in *Soviet Physics-JETP*, **22**, 122 (1966).

DURNEY, B. and I. ROXBURGH, 1965, *Nature*, **208**, 1304.

EINSTEIN, A., 1956, *The Meaning of Relativity* (Princeton, N. J.).

ELLIS, D. G., 1965, *Phys. Rev.*, **139**, B 754.

FAIRBANK, H. W. and C. W. F. EVERITT, 1966, work in progress.

FINZI, A., 1965*a*, *Phys. Rev.*, **147**, B 472.

FINZI, A., 1965*b*: *Phys. Rev. Letters*, **15**, 599.

FINZI, A., 1966, this volume p. 302.

FIRMANI, C., 1965, unpublished *Ph. D. Thesis*, University of Rome.

FOWLER, W. A., 1964, *Rev. Mod. Phys.*, **36**, 545, 1104.

FOWLER, W. A., 1966, this volume p. 313.

FULLER, R. W. and J. A. WHEELER, 1962, *Phys. Rev.*, **128**, 919.

GEROCH, R., 1966, *Phys. Rev. Letters*, **17**, 445.

GINZBURG, V. L. and D. A. KIRZHNITS, 1964, *Žurn. Ėksp. Teor. Fiz.*, **47**, 2006; English translation in *Soviet Physics-JETP*, **20**, 1346 (1965).

GINZBURG, V. L. and L. OZERNOY, 1964, *Žurn. Ėksp. Teor. Fiz.*, **47**, 1030; English translation in *Soviet Physics-JETP*, **20**, 689 (1965).

GOERTZEL, G. and N. TRALLI, 1960, *Some Mathematical Methods of Physics* (New York).

GRATTON, L., 1964*a*, chapter in *Padova Symposium on Cosmology* (Florence).

GRATTON, L., 1964*b*, *Rend. Acc. Lincei*, **37**, 222.

GRATTON, L., 1964*c*, *Rend. Acc. Lincei*, **37**, 354.

GRATTON, L., 1964*d*, paper presented at the *Second Texas Symposium on Relativistic Astrophysics*, Austin, Texas, December 1964, proceedings to be published by University of Texas Press.

GRATTON, L., 1965, *Rend. Acc. Lincei*, **38**, 25.

GRATTON, L. and P. GIANNONE, 1965, *Mem. Soc. Astr. Ital.*, **36**, 445.

GRATTON, L. and G. SZAMOSI, 1964, *Nuovo Cimento*, **33**, 1056.

GRAVES, J. C. and D. R. BRILL, 1960, *Phys. Rev.*, **120**, 1507.

GREENSTEIN, J. L., 1960, *Stellar Atmospheres* (Chicago).

HAMADA, T. and E. E. SALPETER, 1961, *Ap. J.*, **134**, 683.

HÄMEEN-ANTTILA, K. A. and E. ANTTILA, 1966, *Annales Academiae Scientiarum Fennicae*, A. VI, 191.

HANSEN, C. J., 1966, *Nature*, **211**, 1069.

HARRISON, B. K., 1965, *Phys. Rev.*, **137**, B 1644.

HARRISON, B. K., K. S. THORNE, M. WAKANO and J. A. WHEELER, 1965, *Gravitation Theory and Gravitational Collapse* (Chicago). Cited in text as HTWW.

HARRISON, B. K., M. WAKANO and J. A. WHEELER, 1958, chapter in Onzième Conseil de Physique Solvay, *La structure et l'évolution de l'univers* (Brussels).

HARTLE, J. B., 1966, *Bull. Am. Phys. Soc.*, **11**, 340.

HARTLE, J. B. and D. H. SHARP, 1965, *Phys. Rev. Letters*, **15**, 909.

HARTLE, J. B. and D. H. SHARP, 1966, *Ap. J.*, in press.

HAWKING, S. W., 1965, *Phys. Rev. Letters*, **15**, 689.

HAWKING, S. W., 1966, *Phys. Rev. Letters*, **17**, 444.

HAWKING, S. W. and G. F. R. ELLIS, 1965, *Physics Letters*, **17**, 246.

HERNANDEZ, W. C. and C. W. MISNER, 1966, *Ap. J.*, **143**, 452.

HILL, H. and C. ZANONI, 1966, work in progress.

HOYLE, F., W. A. FOWLER, E. M. BURBIDGE and G. R. BURBIDGE, 1964, *Ap. J.*, **139**, 909.

HOYLE, F., J. V. NARLIKAR and J. A. WHEELER, 1964, *Nature*, **203**, 914.

IBEN, I., 1963, *Ap. J.*, **138**, 1090.

INMAN, C. I., 1965, *Ap. J.*, **141**, 187.

KERR, R. P., 1963, *Phys. Rev. Letters*, **11**, 522.

KERR, R. P., 1965, chapter in *Quasi-Stellar Source and Gravitational Collapse,* I. ROBINSEN, A. SCHILD and E. SCHUCKING, eds. (Chicago).

KHALATNIKOV, E. M., 1965, *Žur, Èksp. Teor. Fiz.*, **48**, 261; English translation in *Soviet Physics-JETP*, **21**, 172 (1965).

KIPPENHAHN, R., 1963, *Proc. S.I.F.* Course XXVIII p. 330.

KLEIN, O., 1961, in *Werner Heisenberg und die Physik unserer Zeit* (Braunschweig).

KRUSKAL, M. D., 1960, *Phys. Rev.*, **119**, 1743.

LANDAU, L. D. and E. M. LIFSCHITZ, 1962, *The Classical Theory of Fields* (Reading, Mass.), second edition.

LEBOVITZ, N. R., 1965*a*, *Ap. J.*, **142**, 229.

LEBOVITZ, N. R., 1965*b*, *Ap. J.*, **142**, 1257.

LEDOUX, P. and TH. WALRAVEN, 1958, *Handbuch der Physik,* **51**, 458, S. FLÜGGE, ed. (Berlin).

LIFSCHITZ, E. M. and I. M. KHALATNIKOV, 1963, *Usp. Fiz. Nauk,* **80**, 391; English translation in *Soviet Physics-Uspekhi,* **6**, 495 (1963).

LINDQUIST, R. W., 1966, *Annals of Physics,* **37**, 487.

MCVITTIE, G. C., 1964, *Ap. J.*, **140**, 401.

MATHEWS, J. and R. L. WALKER, 1964, *Mathematical Methods of Physics* (New York).

MAY, M. M. and R. H. WHITE, 1964, paper presented at *Second Texas Symposium on Relativistic Astrophysics*, Austin, Texas, December 1964; proceedings to be published by University of Texas Press.

MAY, M. M. and R. H. WHITE, 1966, *Phys. Rev.*, **141**, 1232.

MELTZER, D. W. and K. S. THORNE, 1966, *Ap. J.*, **145**, 514.

MESTEL, L., 1965, chapter 5 of *Stellar Structure,* L. H. ALLER and D. B. MCLAUGHLIN, ed. (Chicago).

MISNER, C. W., 1965, *Phys. Rev.*, **137**, B 1360.

MISNER, C. W. and D. H. SHARP, 1964*a*, *Phys. Rev.*, **136**, B 571.

MISNER, C. W. and D. H. SHARP, 1964*b*, paper presented at *Second Texas Symposium on Relativistic Astrophysics*, Austin, Texas, December 1964; proceedings to be published by University of Texas Press.

MISNER, C. W. and D. H. SHARP, 1965, *Physics Letters,* **15**, 279.

MISNER, C. W. and D. H. SHARP, 1966, paper in preparation.

MISNER, C. W. and H. S. ZAPOLSKY, 1964, *Phys. Rev. Letters,* **12**, 635.

MORSE, P. M. and H. FESHBACH, 1953, *Methods of Theoretical Physics,* 2 volumes (New York).

MORTON, D. C., 1964, *Ap. J.*, **140**, 460.

NOVIKOV, I. D., 1964, *Astr. Žur.*, **41**, 1075; English translation in *Soviet Astronomy-AJ*, **8**, 857.

OPPENHEIMER, J. R. and R. SERBER, 1938, *Phys. Rev.*, **54**, 530.

OPPENHEIMER, J. R. and H. SNYDER, 1939, *Phys. Rev.*, **56**, 455.

OPPENHEIMER, J. R. and G. VOLKOFF, 1939, *Phys. Rev.*, **55**, 374.

PACINI, F., 1965, *Mem. Soc. Astron. Ital.*, **36**, 323.

PAPAPETROU, A., 1953, *Ann. der Physik,* **12**, 309.

PAPAPETROU, A., 1966, *Ann. Inst. Henri Poincaré,* in press.

PENROSE, R., 1965, *Phys. Rev. Letters*, **14**, 57.

PODURETS, M. A., 1964*a*, *Astr. Žur.*, **41**, 28; English translation in *Soviet Astronomy-AJ*, **8**, 19.

PODURETS, M. A., 1964*b*, *Astr. Žur.*, **41**, 1090; English translation in *Soviet Astronomy-A.J.*, **8**, 868.

PODURETS, M. A., 1964*c*, *Doklady Acad. Nauk USSR*, **154**, 300; English translation in *Soviet Physics-Doklady*, **9**, 9 (1964).

POUND, R. V. and J. L. SNIDER, 1964, *Phys. Rev. Letters*, **13**, 539.

REEVES, H., 1965, chapter 2 of *Stellar Structure*, L. H. ALLER and D. B. MCLAUGHLIN, eds. (Chicago).

ROBINSON, I., A. SCHILD and E. SCHUCKING, 1965, *Quasistellar Sources and Gravitational Collapse* (Chicago).

ROSS, D. K. and L. I. SCHIFF, 1966, *Phys. Rev.*, **141**, 1215.

ROXBURGH, I. W., 1965, *Nature*, **207**, 363.

SAAKYAN, G. S., 1963, *Astr. Žur.*, **40**, 82; English translation in *Soviet Astronomy-A.J.*, **7**, 60 (1963).

SAAKYAN, G. S. and E. V. CHUBARYAN, 1963, *Soobshch. Byurakan. Obs.*, **34**, 99.

SAAKYAN, G. S. and YU. L. VARTANYAN, 1963*a*, *Soobshch. Byrakan Obs.*, **33**, 55.

SAAKYAN, G. S. and YU. L. VARTANYAN, 1963*b*, *Nuovo Cimento*, **30**, 82.

SAAKYAN, G. S. and YU. L. VARTANYAN, 1964, *Astr. Žur.*, **41**, 193; English translation in *Soviet Astronomy-A.J.*, **8**, 147 (1964).

SALPETER, E. E., 1960, *Ann. of Phys.*, **11**, 393.

SALPETER, E. E. 1961, *Ap. J.*, **134**, 669.

SCHATZMAN, E., 1956, *Astr. Žur.*, **33**, 800.

SCHATZMAN, E., 1958, *White Dwarfs* (New York).

SCHIFF, L. I., 1960, *Proc. Nat. Acad. Sci. USA*, **46**, 871.

SCHIFF, L. I., 1966, lectures in *Proceedings of the American Mathematical Society* 1955 *Summer Seminar on Relativity and Astrophysics*, to be published.

SCHWARZSCHILD, K., 1916, *Berl. Ber.*, p. 189.

SCHWARZSCHILD, M., 1958, *Structure and Evolution of the Stars* (Princeton, N. J.).

SCIAMA, D., 1966, this volume, p. 418.

SHAPIRO, I. I., 1964, *Phys. Rev. Letters*, **13**, 789.

SHAPIRO, I. I., 1966*a*, *Phys. Rev.*, **141**, 1219.

SHAPIRO, I. I., 1966*b*, *Phys. Rev.*, **145**, 1005.

SHEPLEY, L. C., 1964, paper presented at the *Second Texas Symposium on Relativistic Astrophysics*, Austin, Texas, December 1964; proceedings to be published by University of Texas Press.

SHEPLEY, L. C., 1965*a*, unpublished *Ph. D. Thesis*, Princeton University, available from University Microfilms, Inc. (Ann Arbor, Michigan).

SHEPLEY, L. C., 1965*b*, *Proc. Nat. Acad. Sci. U.S.A.*, **52**, 1403.

SKYRME, T. H. R., 1959, *Nuclear Physics*, **9**, 665.

SYNGE, J. L., 1960, *Relativity: The General Theory* (Amsterdam).

SZAMOSI, G., 1966, this volume p. 281.

TAUB, A. H., 1948, *Phys. Rev.*, **74**, 328.

TAUB, A. H. and C. W. MISNER, 1966, paper in preparation.

THORNE, K. S., 1964, paper presented at *Second Texas Symposium on Relativistic Astrophysics*, Austin, Texas, December 1964; proceedings to be published by University of Texas Press.

THORNE, K. S., 1965*a*, chapter 7 of *Quasi-Stellar Sources and Gravitational Collapse*, I. ROBINSON, A. SCHILD and E. SCHUCKING, eds. (Chicago).

THORNE, K. S., 1965*b*, unpublished *Ph. D. Thesis*, Princeton University, available from University Microfilms, Inc. (Ann Arbor, Michigan).
THORNE, K. S., 1965*c*, *Science*, **150**, 1671.
THORNE, K. S., 1966, *Ap. J.*, **144**, 201.
THORNE, K. S. and J. A. WHEELER, 1965, *Bull. Am. Phys. Soc.*, **10**, 15.
TOLMAN, R. C., 1934*a*, *Relativity, Thermodynamics and Cosmology* (Oxford).
TOLMAN, R. C., 1934*b*, *Proc. Nat. Acad. Sci. U.S.A.*, **20**, 169.
TOLMAN, R. C., 1939, *Phys. Rev.*, **56**, 364.
TOOPER, R. F., 1964, *Ap. J.*, **140**, 434.
TOOPER, R. F., 1965, *Ap. J.*, **142**, 1541.
TOOPER, R. F., 1966, *Ap. J.*, **143**, 465.
TSURUTA, S., 1964, unpublished *Ph. D. Thesis*, Columbia University.
TSURUTA, S., 1965, *Nature*, **207**, 364.
TSURUTA, S. and A. G. W. CAMERON, 1965*a*, *Nature*, **207**, 364.
TSURUTA, S. and A. G. W. CAMERON, 1965*b*, *Canadian J. Phys.*, **43**, 2056.
TSURUTA, S. and A. G. W. CAMERON, 1966*a*, *Canadian J. Phys.*, **44**, 1895.
TSURUTA, S. and A. G. W. CAMERON, 1966*b*, *Canadian J. Phys.*, **44**, 1863.
TSURUTA, S., J. P. WRIGHT and A. G. W. CAMERON, 1965, *Nature*, **206**, 1137.
WEBER, J., 1964, section in *Relativity, Groups and Topology*, C. DEWITT and B. DEWITT, eds. (New York).
WHEELER, J. A., 1962, *Geometrodynamics* (New York).
WHEELER, J. A., 1964*a*, chapter 10 of *Gravitation and Relativity*, H. Y. CHIU and W. F. HOFFMANN, eds. (New York).
WHEELER, J. A., 1964*b*, chapter in *Relativity, Groups and Topology*, C. DEWITT and B. DEWITT, eds. (New York).
WHEELER, J. A., 1965, lecture presented at Deutsche Akademie der Wissenschaften zu Berlin, November 1965; to be published.
WHEELER, J. A., 1966, article in *Annual Reviews of Astronomy and Astrophysics*, vol. **4**, L. GOLDBERG, ed. (Palo Alto, Cal.).
WRIGHT, J. P., 1964, *Phys. Rev.*, **136**, B 288.
WRIGHT, J. P., 1965, *Nature*, **208**, 65.
ZEE, A. and J. A. WHEELER, 1966, paper in preparation.
ZEL'DOVICH, YA. B., 1961, *Žurn, Ėksp. Teor. Fiz.*, **41**, 1609; English translation in *Soviet Physics-JETP*, **14**, 1143 (1962).
ZEL'DOVICH, YA. B., 1962, *Žur. Ėksp. Teor. Fiz.*, **43**, 1037; English translation in *Soviet Physics-JETP*, **16**, 732 (1963).
ZEL'DOVICH, YA. B. 1963*a*, *Usp. Fiz. Nauk*, **80**, 357; English translation in *Soviet Physics-Uspekhi*, **6**, 475.
ZEL'DOVICH, YA. B., 1963*b*, *Voprosi Kosmogonii*, **9**, 157, proceedings of the *Theoretical Seminar on Major Problems of Astrophysics*, Tarta, 7-13 July 1962 (Akademii Nauk SSSR, Moscow).
ZEL'DOVICH, YA. B. and I. D. NOVIKOV, 1964, *Usp. Fiz. Nauk*, **84**, 377; English translation in *Soviet Physics-Uspekhi*, **7**, 763 (1965).
ZEL'DOVICH, YA. B. and I. D. NOVIKOV, 1965, *Usp. Fiz. Nauk*, **86**, 447; English translation in *Soviet Physics-Uspekhi*, **8**, 522 (1966).
ZEL'DOVICH, YA. B. and M. A. PODURETS, 1964, *Doklady Acad. Nauk SSSR*, **156**, 57; English translation in *Soviet Physics-Doklady*, **9**, 373.

Properties of Cold Dense Matter.

G. SZAMOSI

University of Windsor - Windsor
IV Sezione del Centro di Astrofisica del CNR - Roma

Introduction.

It has been suggested by several authors that very dense matter (nuclear density and above) might play important roles in astrophysics and in cosmology.

It was AMBARTSUMYAN who first suggested that the initial stage of the evolution of stars, galaxies or clusters of galaxies might be very dense matter. According to him (AMBARTSUMYAN 1958, 1960) the chief process of the evolution is not, as it has usually been assumed by the majority of astronomers, the formation of stars and galaxies from less dense interstellar gas to more dense compacts but the common formation of both kinds of matter from dense « protostellar » bodies to states of lower density. His theory would not exclude the possibility of condensation of interstellar gas but it claims that the main process is the evolution from dense into less dense states. These ideas of Ambartsumyan might be considered as a continuation and extension of his former work on the star associations (AMBARTSUMYAN 1953). Just as in the case of star associations we have groups of stars (among them young ones) whose motions seem to originate from one point, AMBARTSUMYAN points out that in the case of galaxies there are many examples which show that galaxies and spiral arms are formed from matter originally contained in the nuclei of galaxies. If so then these nuclei must have small spatial dimensions and very-high density (see also NOVICOV 1964, NE'EMAN 1965).

This hypothesis has led AMBARTSUMYAN and his co-workers to work out a simple theory of the chemical composition of cold dense matter. This analysis in a somewhat more up-to-date form will be the subject of the first part of this lecture.

Much earlier it had been suggested by BAADE and ZWICKY (BAADE and ZWICKY 1934) that the energy release of a supernova might result from the formation of a star having a density above that of a white dwarf. (The theoretical possibility of a star with very dense core was considered even earlier by LANDAU (1932).) Current ideas about the theory of supernovae lead to the assumption that the imploding core of a supernova would end up as an object, the density of which is considerably higher than that of a white dwarf. Such an object would be composed mainly of neutrons and is called a neutron star (sometimes called an hyperon star). In recent years several attempts have been made to discover neutron stars in their cooling period with the help of X-ray spectroscopy. No conclusive results have emerged as yet from these experiments. In fact even the order of magnitude of the cooling period seems to be so sensitive about the assumption of the nature of the interactions between hadrons that there is no general agreement about this point either. We are not concerned here with the theory of observability as it is to be discussed in Finzi's seminar separately. In the second part of this lecture we shall rather review some of the attempts which have been made to establish an equation of state for cold dense matter. The equation of state enables one to discuss the question of the gravitational collapse and stability both in Newtonian and Einsteinian gravitation and it is also relevant to the cooling problem of neutron stars. The problem of gravitational collapse and stability is not discussed here either as this is the topic of Thorne's lectures.

1. – Properties of very dense matter.

1·1. – The first detailed analysis of very dense matter was given in a paper by AMBARTSUMYAN and SAAKYAN in 1960 (AMBARTSUMYAN and SAAKYAN, 1960). (The fact that hyperons would be components of dense matter was independently suggested by CAMERON in 1959.) We shall now follow and extend their analysis and discuss the simple model of noninteracting particles (BARKER *et al.* 1966).

We shall not be concerned with the question of how this type of matter came into existence. We assume that at least we can imagine its existence and would analyse first its chemical composition under the following assumptions:

1) The superdense system is in its ground state ($T = 0$).

2) The conservation of baryon number holds rigorously.

3) Macroscopic charge neutrality.

The first condition enables us to determine the composition of our system with the help of a variational principle, taking into account conditions 2) and 3) as auxiliary conditions. It is important to realize that our reasoning here is pure thermodynamics and our results do not depend in any way on reaction cross-sections, interaction constants and the likes.

We specify first that besides electrons, protons and neutrons we shall have muons, pions and we shall take into account all the elementary particles the existence of which is established and whose spin values are reasonably well known. We use the most recent tables available for us (ROSENFELD *et al.* UCRL-8030 Part I, March 1965). Our notations conform with those given in the Seminar of Prof. DALLAPORTA. We shall have neither neutrinos (ν_e) nor antineutrinos ($\bar{\nu}_e$) or neutrettos (ν_μ, $\bar{\nu}_\mu$) as components of dense matter as we assume that they escape from the system. Their chemical potential is, therefore, put equal to zero. We shall not have the antiparticles of the above-mentioned particles nor shall we have π^+, π^0 or kaons or mesonic resonances of any kind. Nothing would prevent the decay or annihilation of these particles.

The situations would, of course, be the reverse as far as the electric charge and baryonic number is concerned if the «initial conditions» would specify the matter as composed of antiprotons and positrons. In no case would we have π^0-mesons or kaons or mesonic resonances of any kind as stable components because these particles decay to bosons and in an independent-particle picture nothing would prevent their decay.

Let us now write down the variational principle mentioned above and discuss it a little. The total energy of our system is clearly

$$E = \sum{}^{(F)} a_k \int_0^{x_{0k}} x^2 \sqrt{1 + x^2}\, dx + \sum{}^{(B)} n_j m_j x^2 , \tag{1}$$

where $\sum^{(F)}$ means a sum over all possible fermion states, $\sum^{(B)}$ over all boson states, $x_{0k} = p_k/m_k c$ where $p_k \sim n_k^{\frac{1}{3}}$ is inversely proportional to the average distance between the particles in question and x_0 basically means the ratio of the Compton wave length of the particle to the average distance. The factor a_k is a numerical factor times the spin weight of the particles in question.

The conservation of the baryon number gives a restriction on the density

$$\varphi_1 = \sum{}^{(y)} x_{0k}^3 - c_1 = 0 , \tag{2}$$

where the sum is now over all the baryons and finally the macroscopic charge neutrality yields

$$\varphi_2 = \sum{}^{(F)} b_k (x_{0k}^{(+)3} - x_{0k}^{(-)3}) + \sum{}^{(B)} (n_j^{(+)} - n_j^{(-)}) - c_2 = 0 , \tag{3}$$

where b_k is the isotopic-spin weight (which describes the charge states the same way ordinary-spin weight describes the spin states). Our only equation (variational principle) to solve is

$$\delta(E + \lambda_1 \varphi_1 + \lambda_2 \varphi_2) = 0 \, , \tag{4}$$

where the variation is with respect to the densities (x-s and n-s respectively). λ_1 and λ_2 are the Lagrangian multipliers to conditions 2) and 3). The actual working out of the problem is the simplest approach to obtain the composition of dense matter. We completely forget about strong interactions as well as about gravitation. In fact we completely forget about all interactions and consider the problem as a free-particle one. The decay processes are taken into account phenomenologically and no distinction is being made between so-called « elementary » particles and « resonances ».

The results of carrying out the calculations are the following. The number of neutrons begin to overwhelm that of the protons at the density $7 \cdot 10^{30}$, *i.e.* much below nuclear density. If we compress matter further the ratio of n_n/n_p increases but in a wide range of densities no change would appear in the actual composition of matter. Only if we go over nuclear density and reach the value $5 \cdot 10^{38}$ for the neutron density (the corresponding electron density is about $5 \cdot 10^{36}$) shall we have the appearance of muons as stable components of matter. The equations yielding this particular value are

$$m_p(1 + x_{0p}^2)^{\frac{1}{2}} = m_n(1 + x_{0n}^2)^{\frac{1}{2}} - m_e x_{0e} \quad \text{(ultrarelativistic electrons)} \, ,$$

$$m_e x_{0e} = m_\mu (1 + x_{0\mu}^2)^{\frac{1}{2}} \, ,$$

$$x_{0e}^3 + x_{0\mu}^3 = x_{0p}^3 \, ,$$

the last equation being again the condition for charge neutrality.

Increase further the density and we find the hyperons and the baryonic resonances as stable components of matter. We shall not detail the calculations here but quote only the results. These are given in Table I. The notations of the various particles are the same as in Dallaporta's seminar. The results of the first three columns are identical to those of AMBARTSUMYAN and SAAKYAN. From there on the results are different partly because in the original work of AMBARTSUMYAN and SAAKYAN the charge of the $\mathcal{N}_{3,3}$ particle (they called it p*) is taken as single while in fact it has isotopic spin $\frac{3}{2}$. This also explains the temporary disappearance of the muons in this calculation. Furthermore, while in the quoted work of AMBARTSUMYAN and SAAKYAN only twelve particles and resonances were taken into account (see also SAAKYAN and VARTANIAN, 1964), the present calculation considers 44, in fact all which were known in March 1965, with sufficient accuracy to include their data into the table. Hence we have included the $\Xi_{1,3}^{**}$ particle which is listed as $\Xi_{1,2}$ in the Table given by DALLAPORTA. Otherwise the

TABLE I.

Threshold densities		Symbol for stable particles	Threshold densities		Symbol for stable particles
neutron / (fermi)^3	baryon / (fermi)^3		neutron / (fermi)^3	baryon / (fermi)^3	
0.0	$7.37 \cdot 10^{-9}$	n	10.5	123.1	Ω^-
0.46	0.465	μ^-	11.5	146.5	$Y^{**0}_{1,3}$
0.61	0.62	Σ^-	12.5	171.6	$\mathcal{N}^0_{1,5}$
0.94	1.21	$\mathcal{N}^-_{3,3}$	13.0	184.8	$Y^-_{1,5}$
0.96	1.26	μ^0	13.5	198.7	$Y^{**+}_{1,3}$
1.40	2.55	muons disappear	14.0	213.0	$\mathcal{N}^+_{1,5}$
1.75	3.76	Σ^0	15.0	243.3	$\Sigma^{**-}_{1,3}$ $Y^0_{1,5}$
2.3	6.00	$\mathcal{N}^0_{3,3}$	16.5	292.8	$Y^+_{0,5}$
2.5	6.95	Ξ^-	17.0	310.4	$\Xi^{**0}_{1,3}$ $Y^+_{1,5}$
2.6	7.47	Σ^+	19.0	386.0	$\mathcal{N}^-_{3,7}$
3.1	10.5	$\mathcal{N}^+_{3,3}$	21.0	468.0	$\mathcal{N}^0_{3,7}$
3.5	13.4	Ξ^0	24.0	604.6	$\mathcal{N}^+_{3,7}$
3.8	15.9	$Y^{*-}_{1,3}$ $\mathcal{N}^{++}_{3,3}$	26.0	702.0	$\mathcal{N}^{++}_{3,7}$
4.7	24.9	$Y^{*0}_{1,3}$	35.0	1189	$\mathcal{N}^0_{1,9}$
5.1	29.6	$Y^{*0}_{0,1}$	38.0	1365	$\mathcal{N}^+_{1,9}$
5.7	37.2	$Y^{*+}_{1,3}$	41.0	1549	$\mathcal{N}^-_{3,11}$
6.6	49.8	$\Xi^{*-}_{1,3}$	45.0	1808	$\mathcal{N}^0_{3,11}$
7.5	63.9	$\mathcal{N}^0_{1,3}$ $Y^{*0}_{0,3}$	51.0	2223	$\mathcal{N}^+_{3,11}$
7.8	69.0	$\Xi^{*0}_{1,3}$	57.0	2665	$\mathcal{N}^{++}_{3,11}$
8.9	89.4	$\mathcal{N}^+_{1,3}$	72.0	3854	muons reappear
9.7	105.6	$Y^{**-}_{1,3}$	98.0	6070	π^-

notations are the same as in that Table and we refer to them for such data as masses, hypercharge, etc.

The following general formula holds

$$n_k = n_j \left[1 - \left(\frac{a_k}{n_j}\right)^{\frac{2}{3}}\right]^{\frac{3}{2}}$$

where $j = \mathrm{n}$ if k refers to a neutral particle, $j = \mathrm{p}$ if k refers to a positively charged particle, $j = \Sigma^-$ if k refers to a negatively charged particle, $j = \mathcal{N}_{3,3}$ if k refers to doubly charged particle.

The sequence is not that of increasing mass and the reason for this is that besides the energy relations, the charge neutrality also needs to be maintained. The last phase in our development appears around $6 \cdot 10^{42}$. At this density the pion state is favourable to a muon state and π^- mesons begin to appear In the original calculations of Ambartsumyan the appearance of pions occurred at a hundred times smaller baryon density.

If we assume that superdense matter in its asymptotic form is a primeval (pre-stellar) form of matter in our universe, it is interesting to speculate on the following question. Given the asymptotic condition of superdense matter, is the form of the matter that evolvs from it unique? In other words if the « initial conditions » were somewhat different (we cannot suggest any reason for this change but it seems to be interesting to speculate on this possibility) what other forms of matter could possibly evolve? As a simple example we may consider one such possible model of matter, namely matter evolving from the asymptotic superdense state subject to the usual conditions of electric charge conservation and baryon conservation as well as i) strict conservation of total hypercharge per baryon and ii) separate conservation of number of electrons and number of muons. The constrains i) and ii) then prevent any weak reactions among the various constituents.

We note that under the above conditions besides pions, kaons can be expected to be stable components of this hypothetical matter however, the heavier mesons cannot because these are known to decay via the strong or electromagnetic interactions which conserve hypercharge. Since the electron (muon) number is conserved, the number of electrons (muons) would remain constant given by the initial conditions.

For actually calculating the composition of superdense matter under these conditions, we can readily adopt the eqs. (1), (2) and (3) to include the kaons and omit the electron and muon terms. The conservation of hypercharge can be expressed by a condition similar to the one which expresses the conservation of ordinary charge. The total hypercharge per baryon (y) is, however, an arbitrary quantity; at least we cannot give its value at present and consequently we cannot obtain a definite answer as to the composition of superdense matter under the given conditions. Unlike the electric charge, there seems to be no a priori reason to fix the hypercharge density of a macroscopic sample of matter to be zero or indeed any other number. There seem to be, however, two values of y which may be considered as especially interesting. The first one is the asymptotic value found with the observed spectrum of elementary particles as known to us at present, $y = 0.49$. With this value we can expect pions and/or kaons to be stable components of matter at lower densities. This is because the kaons could maintain the conservation of hypercharge with lower energy than the baryons. The lepton densities would not change and their values remain constant throughout. It should also be noted that p, n, Λ^0, $\Sigma^\pm$, Ξ^{0-} and Ω^- would be stable even at the lowest densities because all the known decay reactions of these particles will be forbidden by either i) or ii). The second choice for y comes about if we adopt the unitary symmetry theory of elementary particles and hence take the total charge as well as the total hypercharge of the basic set of baryons zero. In this case we shall have neither pions nor kaons as stable components of matter at high densities, as the baryons themselves can maintain the electric charge as well as the hypercharge neutrality. So we may note that as far as their behaviour in a superdense ensemble is concerned pions and kaons play very similar roles in conserving the charge and hypercharge respectively.

1·2. – We neglect all interactions between the particles. The electromagnetic interaction between charged particles can easily be taken into account, in principle, by a relativistic Thomas-Fermi method which, so it seems, is well developed and could probably be applied without much difficulty. Its effect on the behaviour of the object is probably very small due to the over-all charge neutrality.

More intriguing is the possible effect of the strong interactions. We neglected them, so to speak, in two different levels. The first one which need not pose, in principle, a very difficult problem is the neglect of nuclear forces. I say its inclusion is not, in principle, very difficult if we are below and around nuclear density. In fact we considered just this problem in Sect. **2**.

We neglect the strong interactions in another level which poses a more intricate problem. This is the following. We have heard from Prof. Dallaporta's Seminar that we cannot really make a distinction between «strong interaction» and «strongly interacting» particles. In fact as far as we can understand it today strongly interacting particles are the manifestations of the strong interaction and hence to say that we neglect the strong interaction means that we neglect the basis of the very existence of those particles and also all intrinsic connections between them.

To be more specific let us consider, only as an example, the simplest and earliest composite model of strongly interacting particles *i.e.* the Fermi-Yang model where the nucleon and the antinucleon were the primary particles and the pion is assumed to be composed of them

$$\pi = \bar{\mathcal{N}}\mathcal{N}$$

(here $\bar{\mathcal{N}}$ means the antiparticle to $\mathcal{N}$).

We have shown in the free-particle approximation that pions would appear as stable components of matter when the threshold energy of the muons would be favourable to it. We did not take, however, into account the correlation between the free nucleons and the bound nucleons in the pion. The same problem may be present in any composite model. An estimate of this correlation effect can be given. The underlying problem is, of course, that: under what circumstances can one consider a pair of fermions as bosons, *i.e.* no correlations between the boson and the rest of the fermions.

Call $a_k^\dagger$ an operator which creates a fermion with a momentum k. The a_k's obey the usual commutation relations for fermion operators

$$[a_k, a_{k'}]_+ = [a_k^\dagger, a_{k'}^\dagger]_+ = 0 , \qquad [a_k^\dagger, a_{k'}]_+ = \delta_{kk'} .$$

Then the operator

$$P^\dagger = \sum c(k)\, a_k^\dagger a_{-k}^\dagger ,$$

where $\sum c(k)^2 = 1$, would create a fermion pair with zero center-of-mass momentum. Now to gain some insight into the nature of the pair of fermions (composite particle) created by $P^\dagger$ we calculate the commutation relations for them. A straightforward calculation yields

$$[P^\dagger, P^\dagger] = [P, P] = 0 ,$$
$$[P^\dagger, P] = \sum_k c(k)^2 (1 - a_{-k}^\dagger a_{-k} - a_k^\dagger a_k) = 1 - \sum_k c(k)^2 (n_k + n_{-k}) ,$$

where $n_k = a_k^\dagger a_k$: We see now that, in general, a pair of fermions represent neither a boson nor a fermion. The deviation from the boson behaviour is represented by the sum on the right-hand side of the commutator and its role depends on the actual form of the momentum distribution function as well as on the state vector on which the commutation relation would act. We consider two cases. If the state vector is the absolute vacuum $|0\rangle$ then, independent of the form of $c(k)$, $[P^\dagger, P] = 1$ and the pair behaves like a boson. If the state vector is that of a Fermi gas at zero temperature $|\varphi\rangle = \left(\prod_{i=1}^{N} a_i^\dagger\right)|0\rangle$ then we obtain

$$[P^\dagger, P]|\varphi\rangle = \left(1 - 2 \sum_{k \le k_F} c(k)^2\right)|\varphi\rangle ,$$

where k_F is the Fermi momentum of the gas. If now $c(k)$ is such that $c(k) \sim 0$ if $k < k_F$, then again we obtain a bosonlike behaviour. If, however, $c(k)$ does not have this property then the behaviour is not bosonlike at all and we expect then correlation between the free and composite particles. To give a crude example for this consideration take the π^-. In the Fermi-Yang (as well as in the Sakata) model $\pi^- = \bar{p}n$. The mass of the pion is about seven per cent of the mass of the $\bar{p}+n$ system. Hence the mass defect is about ~ 1700 MeV. The kinetic energy inside the potential well is certainly larger than that but no model would give an idea as of its magnitude. If we put say 2000 MeV as for the kinetic energy of the components this would correspond to a density of a neutron gas $3\cdot 10^{40}$ particles/cm³. The simple model of AMBARTSUMYAN gives the same order of magnitude for the threshold density for the appearance of the stable pions. Clearly in this case there might be a very strong correlation between the pions and nucleons and the result of a free-particle treatment might be illusory. To take into account ordinary nuclear forces would not help in this respect. A different assumption about the data of the structure of the pion might give different results but it is clear that the structure and compositions of elementary particles could have a strong effect on the actual picture of the chemical composition of dense matter.

2. – Equation of state at very high densities.

2'1. – In the second part of this lecture I shall first consider ZEL'DOVICH's argument about the relativistic limits of the equation of state of macroscopic matter, then proceed and give a brief review of some of the equations of state of dense neutron matter which have been proposed in the literature.

Consider the pressure of an ensemble of particles. The energy momentum tensor is

$$T = \left\langle n_0\, m \frac{\mathrm{d}x_\mu}{\mathrm{d}s}\frac{\mathrm{d}x_\nu}{\mathrm{d}s}\right\rangle_{\mathrm{av}} = n\left\langle m \frac{\mathrm{d}x_\mu}{\mathrm{d}t}\frac{\mathrm{d}x_\nu}{\mathrm{d}s}\right\rangle_{\mathrm{av}}, \tag{5}$$

where n_0 is the rest density of the particles, n is the observable density, $\mathrm{d}s$ is the proper time element, t is the co-ordinate time and μ and ν go from 1 to 4 $(x_\mu = ict)$.

The pressure is now defined as (momentum transfer)

$$p = \tfrac{1}{3} T_{kk} \qquad \text{(sum over } k = 1, 2, 3 \tag{6}$$

and the energy density is simply

$$\varrho = - T_{44} . \tag{7}$$

For an ensemble of free particles $T_{\nu\nu} \leqslant 0$, in fact, we find

$$3p - \varrho = - m_0 c^2 \sqrt{1-\beta^2} \leqslant 0 \tag{8}$$

and the equality holds only if $m_0 = 0$, *i.e.* in case of a photon or neutrino gas. Then the equation of state is

$$p = \tfrac{1}{3}\varrho\,, \tag{9}$$

which was considered as the maximum value for the pressure at given energy density in a relativistic ensemble. From (5) we have for the speed of sound

$$c_s = \frac{1}{\sqrt{3}}\,c\,.$$

In 1962 Zel'dovich (ZEL'DOVICH, 1962) constructed as an example a physical system which gave for $c_s = c$ or the equation of state

$$p = \varrho\,. \tag{10}$$

He considered an ensemble of particles at rest interacting via a finite-range vector field (Proca field). The energy momentum tensor of the field is

$$T_{\mu\nu} = \delta_{\mu\nu}\left(-\frac{1}{8\pi}F^2_{\lambda\varrho} - \frac{2}{8\pi}A^2_\varrho\right) + \frac{2}{4\pi}A_\mu A_\nu + \frac{1}{4\pi}F_{\mu\varrho}F_{\nu\varrho} \tag{11}$$

where A_μ is the field vector $F_{\nu\mu} = \partial_\nu A_\mu - \partial_\mu A_\nu$ and $\varkappa^{-1}$ is the range of the field. As we consider macroscopic systems and interactions of the range of the order of the nuclear forces we neglect $\partial/\partial x$, $\partial/\partial y$, $\partial/\partial z$ with respect to $\varkappa^{-1}$ and consider the static case ($\partial/\partial t = 0$). Then we obtain from (7), (2) and (3) the eq. (6).

Similar results can be obtained if one considers a system interacting via an attractive scalar field (MARX and NEMETH, 1964). The relativistic hard core model of GRATTON and SZAMOSI (GRATTON, 1964) also yields this limit in the ultrarelativistic approximation.

In case of a repulsive field the condition $c_s \leqslant c$ is valid only if we do not use too singular potentials. For static potentials more singular than $1/r$ we have $c_s > c$ and hence the assumption would be incompatible with the special theory of relativity.

2'2. – Of the equations of state appeared in the literature I shall consider very briefly those proposed by AMBARTSUMYAN and SAAKYAN (1960), CAMERON (1959), SALPETER (1960), GRATTON and SZAMOSI (1964) and TSURUTA (1964).

The approach of AMARTSUMYAN and SAAKYAN is the following. Write the total energy of dense matter in the following form

(12) $E =$ the total kinetic energy of the fermions present $+ n_\pi m_\pi c^2 + nU(n)$.

Here n_π is the pion density, $U(n)$ is the potential energy per particle due to nuclear forces. To obtain $U(n)$ we consider the nuclear model which was presented by GOMES, WALECKA and WEISSKOPF (1958). Similar starting point was considered in a more recent and more detailed calculation by BAHCALL and WOLF. (BAHCALL and WOLF, 1965.)

From this model (often called independent pair model) we know the value of the potential energy at and around equilibrium nuclear density. We assume that the potential is the same for all particles and extrapolate its value at different densities from the potential energy-density diagrams taken from the paper of WEISSKOPF *et al.* (The effect of the repulsive core is considered as part of the potential here, and is also tabulated in the GOMES, WALECKA and WEISSKOPF paper.) It is assumed that the diagrams are reliable in the density region $10^{37} \leqslant n \leqslant 10^{39}$.

The potential energy per particle decreases with increasing density, reaches a minimum (40 MeV) at $n = 4 \cdot 10^{38}$ and then again increases rapidly with increasing density, the increase beginning at $n = 5 \cdot 10^{38}$ which is only slightly lower than the Ambartsumyan free particle threshold density for the appearance of Σ^- particles.

This approach breaks down at a density corresponding to the average separation 0.4 fermi as there the hard core effects may play a fundamental role.

In this equation of state, the effect of the hard core is considered by a cut-off. The assumptions that all the baryons can be treated on equal footing at all densities and the neglect of the effect of the nuclear interaction on the chemical potential are not very realistic and they are likely to inhibit the validity of this particular equation of state, over a wide density region (BAHCALL and WOLF, 1965). AMBARTSUMYAN and SAAKYAN in a subsequent paper integrated the Einstein hydrostatic equilibrium equations using the equation of state described above. Their results are given in Thorne's lectures.

Cameron's investigations about the nature and the equation of state of dense matter, in fact, preceded the papers of AMBARTSUMYAN and SAAKYAN. Cameron's assumption about nuclear interaction is different from that of AMBARTSUMYAN and SAAKYAN. To describe the equation of state of dense matter he choses a semiempirical representation of the nuclear energy as function of the density. This approach is due to SKYRME and has been applied succesfully in nuclear physics.

It is based on the assumption of a simple three-body effective potential for nuclear interaction and represents quite well many of the observed properties of nuclei. Cameron used the nonrelativistic form of the energy expression for the kinetic energy. According to this approach the energy density in a neutron gas is represented by the following expression:

$$\varrho = 7.98\cdot 10^{9} n^{5/3} + 9.79\cdot 10^{-6} n^{8/3} - 1.381\cdot 10^{5} n^{2}\,, \tag{13}$$

from here the expression for the pressure becomes

$$P = 5.32\cdot 10^{9} n^{5/3} + 1.63\cdot 10^{-5} n^{8/3} - 1.381\cdot 10^{5} n^{2}\ (^{*})\,. \tag{14}$$

The energy expression given by formula (9) is found graphically in Fig. 1. The hard-core region in Cameron's treatment is also excluded by a cut-off.

It should be noted that in his 1959 calculation CAMERON extended the validity of the nonrelativistic kinetic-energy expression and the integration of the equations of hydrostatic equilibrium gave a too large critical mass (see Thorne's notes about the original and corrected values of the critical mass).

Salpeter's approach to determine the equation of state of neutron matter is an empirical one. Consider first a low-density neutron gas. A very realistic expression for the energy is given then by SALPETER which is (we use a somewhat different notation)

$$E = E_{\text{kin}}\left\{1 - \frac{20}{g\pi}\, k_{\text{F}} \left\langle\frac{\delta(k)}{k}\right\rangle_{\text{av}}\right\}, \tag{15}$$

where E_{kin} is just the kinetic energy of a free Fermi gas, k_{F} is the wave number of the Fermi top, $\delta(k)$ is the $1S$ phase shift for low-energy neutron-neutron scat-

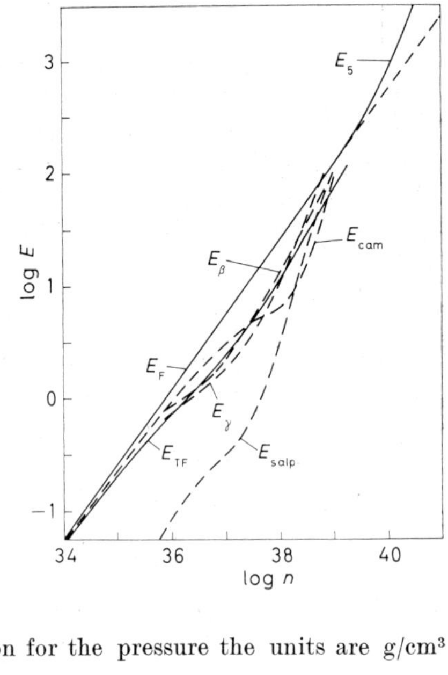

Fig. 1. – Energy of a neutron gas. Abscissae are the logarithm of number density in cm^{-3}, ordinates are the logarithm of the average energy per particle minus the proper energy in MeV. The curves are labelled as follows: E_{F} corresponds to the free particle (nonrelativistic); E_{TF} corresponds to the Thomas-Fermi model eq. (20); E_{Cam} and E_{Salp} to Cameron's and Salpeter's equations; E_5 to eq. (23) with $\alpha = 0.5$; E_β and E_γ to Tsurata's theory equations (24) and (25) of page 20, respectively).

(*) In eq. (13) and in the following equation for the pressure the units are g/cm^3 and dyn/cm^2 respectively.

tering. $\langle\,\rangle_{av}$ means averaging on the relative moments of neutron pairs. $\delta(k)$ can now be taken from experiment without making detailed assumptions about nuclear interaction. For low-energy scattering (very low densities) $\delta(k)$ can be taken from the zero-energy effective-range formula and then $\delta(k) \approx a_s k$ (where a_s is the zero-energy singlet scattering length) and $\delta(k)/k \approx a_s = \text{const.}$ From an analysis of the average of the phase shift SALPETER concludes that for r_0 $\left(= \left((3/4\pi)(1/n)\right)^{\frac{1}{3}}\right)$ having values between 5 and 10 fermi $\delta(k)$ can be taken such that the total energy

$$E \approx 0.1\, E_{\text{kin}}$$

and there would be no bound states for a low-density gas. The equation of state of Salpeter is given graphically again in Fig. 1. It is to be noted that for the low-density region a different analysis gives a somewhat different equation of state also based on the experimental $1S$ phase shift. (For details see below the considerations of GRATTON *et al.*)

At densities comparable to nuclear density SALPETER uses the Bethe-Fermi semi-emprical binding-energy expression, thus again the results might be considered as quite independent of theories. An analysis of the adoption of the constants of the semi-emprical formula to all neutron matter leads to the following expression of the energy in the nuclear density region:

$$\varrho = \frac{1}{r_0^2}\,(0.157 + 0.710\, r_0^{-1} + 0.321\, r_0^{-2} + 0.697\, r_0^{-3} - 1.368\, r_0^{-1,21})\, 29.0 \;\; (\text{in MeV})$$

if we assume that the coefficient of the symmetry term in the semi-empirical formula is 29 MeV (SALPETER also discusses other possibilities).

Turning to higher densities the effect of the hard core is taken into account in a rather static manner. Assume a hard repulsive core of the radius of 0.45 fermi. There is then an upper limit to the density at which density spheres of radius 0.225 fermi around each baryon form a closely packed lattice. At a density corresponding $r_0 = 0.25$ fermi, the matter thus becomes incompressible and the pressure infinite. At somewhat lower density the average density per particle is mainly the zero-point energy which arises from the requirement that the wave functions vanish when two spheres touch. The energy depends very little on the quantum statistics nor on the larger-range nuclear potential. We estimate the energy per particle by an approximate form of the « cell » method. We consider all spheres except one fixed with their centers at the lattice points of a regular lattice and allow the one sphere to move in the cell formed by the fixed spheres. The nearest point of contact with one of the fixed spheres is about $1.8\, r_0 - 0.45$ fermi away from the equilibrium position of the moving sphere and we simply replace the « cell » by a sphere of this radius. The total zero-point momentum is then $k = \hbar\pi \cdot$ $\cdot(1.8 r_0 - 0.45$ fermi) on our model and the kinetic energy per particle is $c(\sqrt{k^2 + M^2c^2} - Mc)$. The error according to Salpeter could be a factor of two or three. This kinetic energy equals the rest energy at $r_0 = 0.6$ fermi at nucleon rest mass.

The pressure can now be calculated which (with the hard-core radius 0.45 fermi) becomes infinite at $r_0 = 0.25$ fermi.

The fact that the pressure increases without limit does not seem to be consistent with the special theory of relativity. Another approach for the hard-core problem, which is free from this difficulty, is presented below.

The approach by GRATTON and SZAMOSI (1964) consists of employing two different models.

The first one is nonrelativistic; it is considered to be valid up to nuclear densities ($n_n \sim 2$ or $3 \cdot 10^{38}$ particles per cm^3). In this region we have calculated the energy as a function of the density with the help of a Thomas-Fermi model.

This is a suitably modified version of the nuclear model developed by GOMBAS (1957). In this model the interaction is supposed to be a purely attractive Yukawa potential with a Majorana exchange. The only adjusted parameter is the interaction strength, which we have adopted as a phenomenological constant throughout the above stated density region.

Gombas' model gives a remarkably good description of over-all nuclear properties like binding energy and average density. This may give the comfortable feeling that the superfluous amount of Majorana exchange (the total interaction instead than one half of it, as it follows from medium-energy scattering experiments) is about to take care of the neglected hard-core interaction, at least in the description of average properties for a many-body nuclear system.

The weakest points of the theory are the failure to predict the actual density distribution in nuclei, and also the fact that the adjusted interaction is about 1.4 times too large than one should expect from low-energy (^1S) experimental interaction data. In our problem it is possible that this defect might lead to a somewhat too large correction for nuclear interaction in the low-density region (see below). Apart from this, however, the simple and easily manageable theory seems to give a reasonable description of the physical system in question.

The second model is a relativistic one. It refers to densities higher than the nuclear density. One expects that in this region (approximately $10^{38} \leqslant$ $\leqslant n \leqslant 10^{40}$) not only the above-mentioned model but also all of the existing models for nuclear matter would fail to describe the physical situation. There are three effects which would dominate the physical picture in this region, none of which is taken into consideration in the theories of nuclear matter:

a) the kinetic energy of the neutron gas becomes relativistic;

b) the effect of the hard core becomes overwhelming in the interaction;

c) the creation of hyperons.

We have not considered here the third effect and have treated only the first two. The model is a simple semi-classical one. We neglect all interactions and consider only the relativistic energy of a hard-core nucleon gas. Since we are in a high-energy region, the effect of the hard core is considered as an excluded volume effect in a relativistic way.

Let us detail the calculations.

a) *Nonrelativistic treatment.* – We treat the neutron gas in a density range of about $(10^{31} \div 10^{38})$ particles per cm^3. The lower limit of the density guarantees the chemical stability against η-decay (free-particle limit) while the upper limit is about the density of nuclear matter. As explained above, we have used here a treatment where the energy of the system consists of the zero-point Fermi energy plus interaction energy in the Hartree-Fock approximation. The elementary interaction is supposed to be a two-body interaction. More precisely, we assumed a purely attractive potential of the Yukawa type with a Majorana exchange, $-\gamma \exp[-x]/x \cdot P_r$, where γ is the coupling constant and P_r is the Majorana operator. $x = \mu r$ where r is the distance and $\mu^{-1} = 1.3 \cdot 10^{-13}$ cm is the range of the forces in this theory. The adjusted value of γ is given by GOMBAS as $\mu\gamma = 70.4$ MeV.

Of course, we considered only neutron-neutron interactions. The total energy was given by GOMBAS; in a somewhat condensed notation it reads

$$E = E_k(1 - a\varphi(y)) \tag{16}$$

where

$$E_k = \frac{3}{5}\frac{\hbar^2}{2m_n}k_F^2 \tag{17}$$

with the Fermi wave number

$$k_F = 3.058\, n^{\frac{1}{3}}\,, \tag{18}$$

n is the number density, $a = (\frac{5}{3}2\pi)(\mu g^2/m_n c^2)$, $g^2 = \frac{4}{3}(m_n/m_\pi)^2\gamma$; m_n is the mass of the neutron, m_π is that of the pion, $y = k_F/\mu$ and the function $\varphi(y)$ is defined as follows

$$\varphi(y) = y^{-5}\left\{6y^4 - y^2 + \left(\frac{1}{4} + 3y^2\right)\ln(1 + 4y^2) - \frac{8}{y^2}\,\mathrm{tg}^{-1}\,2y\right\}. \tag{19}$$

Consider first the low-density region. At very low densities the neutron gas can be considered as a free Fermi gas. Then the average energy is given by eq. (15). As the density increases one has to correct (15) by taking into account the interaction. At densities where the average distance between particles is still much larger than the range of the forces

$$r_{\mathrm{av}} = (9\pi/4)^{\frac{1}{3}} k_{\mathrm{F}}^{-1} \gg \mu^{-1} ,$$

one can expand φ in powers of y; retaining only the lower terms, eq. (19) becomes

$$E = E_k \left\{ 1 - \frac{8a}{3} y \left[1 - \frac{6}{5} y^2 + \frac{72}{35} y^4 \right] \right\} . \tag{20}$$

This expression is plotted in Fig. 1 in the low-density region ($n < 10^{36}$ cm^{-3}). At higher densities we used the exact expression of eq. (19). The most puzzling feature of the low-density region is the great difference between eq. (20) and the result given by SALPETER.

The difference is not due the method of evaluation. SALPETER uses a very realistic treatment by evaluating the energy shift directly from the low-energy scattering data. It is done by using the eq. (15).

The average is to be taken over the relative moments of neutron pairs. The phase shift may be directly expressed by the coupling constant with the help of a formula given by CZIFFRA, MCGREGOR, MORAVCSIK and STAPP and by GRASHIN (CZIFFRA *et al.* 1960; GRASHIN 1959).

The result of the averaging can be given in finite terms. Here, however, we consider again only the low-density limit of the energy, obtaining

$$E = E_k \left\{ 1 - \frac{32a}{9} y \left[1 - \frac{3}{5} y^2 + \frac{24}{35} y^4 \right] \right\} . \tag{21}$$

One notices the similarity between eqs. (20) and (21).

As to the actual value of the energy shift, one uses the coupling constants of the Thomas-Fermi theory or, possibly, not too consequently the phase-shift values from experiment. In both cases the deviations from eq. (13) are not significant. The second approach even increases a bit the deviation between our calculation and Salpeter's. This deviation may be explained by noting that SALPETER considers δ a constant independent of k and averages over $1/k$ only. In the density region considered here, however, we will have to consider encounters with relative energies from about 10 keV to 5 MeV. In this whole region the phase-shift varies with k and its variation cannot be neglected, since the averaging gives to δ a weight proportional to $1/k$ and, therefore, the values by δ corresponding to low k have a very large weight.

Hence the energy shift is given by eq. (19) or with a tolerable approximation by eqs. (10)-(21).

Once E is known, the pressure is given by

$$P = n^2 \frac{dE}{dn} = \frac{1}{9\pi^2} k_F^4 \frac{dE}{dk_F},$$

or, from eq. (19),

$$(22) \qquad P = P_F \left\{ 1 - \frac{3a}{8} \frac{1}{y} \frac{d}{dy} [y^2 \varphi(y)] \right\},$$

where P_F is the pressure of an ordinary Fermi gas at absolute zero temperature:

$$P_F = \frac{2}{15\pi^2} \frac{\hbar^2}{2m_n} k_F^5 .$$

Figure 2 compares the pressure computed with the help of the present model with that obtained by CAMERON.

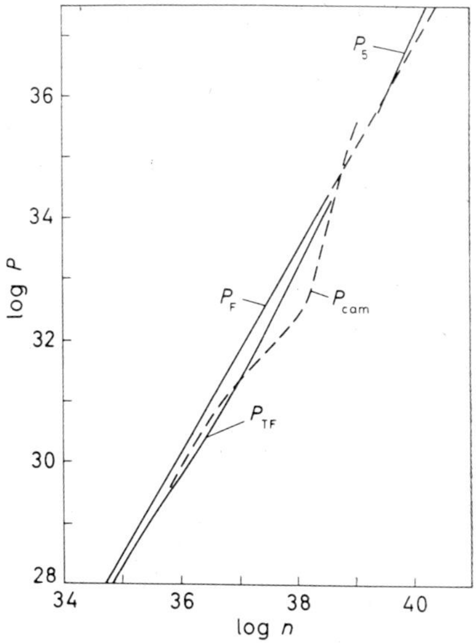

Fig. 2. – Pressure of a neutron gas. Abscissae are the logarithm of number density in cm^{-3}, ordinates are the logarithm of pressure in bar. The curves are labelled as follows: P_F corresponds to the free particles; P_{TF} corresponds to the Thomas-Fermi model eq. (22); P_{Cam} to Cameron's model; P_5 tot he equations of page 299 with $\alpha = 0.5$.

b) Relativistic treatment. – At high densities, *i.e.* in the region where $n > 10^{39}$, we adopt a different approach. As it is pointed out above, theories of ordinary nuclear matter do not seem to apply to this region. This is valid, of course, also for the Thomas-Fermi model described in the previous Section.

Our basic assumption in treating this density region is that the hard core effects and particularly the increase of kinetic energy due to the hard core dominate over all other interactions. We also consider the kinetic energy relativistically in this region. Since the well-known low-energy quantum-mechanical approach to the hard-core problems does not seem to apply in this region, we adopt a semi-classical treatment.

At very high-energy the de Broglie wavelength becomes smaller than the hard core radius; hence we feel justified in assuming that the main effect is due to the excluded volume and in neglecting all quantum-mechanical effects, except, of course, Pauli's principle. In this sense the method is semi-classical just as the original Thomas-Fermi method is.

The relativistic treatment yields the following result (*). The equation

(*) In the following discussion it is tacitly assumed that the zero-energy distribution function for hard cores is the same type of step function as it is in the case of point

relating the number density $n = N/V$ to x is, easily seen to be

$$n = \frac{8\pi}{3}\left(\frac{m_n c^2}{h}\right)^3 \frac{x^3}{1 + \alpha h(x)},$$

where

$$x = P_F/m_n c\,, \qquad \alpha = \frac{8\pi}{3}\left(\frac{mc}{h}\right)^3 v_0\,, \qquad h(x) = \frac{3}{2}\left(x\sqrt{1+x^2} - \sin h^{-1}x\right)$$

α is twice the ratio of v_0 to the volume of a sphere with radius equal to the Compton wavelength of the particles. α is the hard core parameter of the model.

The average energy per particle and the pressure are easily obtained by remembering that

$$E = m_n c^2 \langle 1 + P^2/m^2c^2\rangle_{av}$$

and

$$P = n^2 \frac{dE}{dn}.$$

From here we obtain

$$(23)\qquad \begin{cases} E = m_n c^2 g(x)/x^3\,, \\ P = \dfrac{\pi}{3} m_n c^2 \left(\dfrac{m_n c}{h}\right)^3 \dfrac{f(x)}{1 + \alpha e(x)}\ (^*)\,, \end{cases}$$

---

particles. This assumption is, in fact, not valid. If we calculate the distribution function which minimizes the energy we find (BARKER *et al.*, 1966 II) that above a certain density it is, in general, a step function such that all the states up to a certain critical momentum (which depends on the size of the hard core) are unoccupied and all the states from the critical momentum to the Fermi momentum are occupied. This surprising result can be readily understood on physical grounds in the following way. The volume of a given particle decreases as its momentum increases due to the Lorentz contraction. Thus the particles with higher momentum contribute less to the co-volume than the particles with lower momentum. Smaller co-volume means, more particles can be accomodated in a given momentum range. Therefore in effect we have two competing processes: pushing the particles of lower momentum to higher momentum states obviously means these particles have higher energy, but at the same time this decreases the co-volume, making it possible for more particles to be put in a given momentum range. Above the critical density the fact that one can put more particles in a given momentum range overcompensates for the increase in energy due to the fact that the particles have higher momenta, thus leading to an over-all lowering in energy per particle. For a detailed proof see the quoted paper. It should however be added that as far as the actual values of the physical quantities are concerned the treatment given in the text is fairly accurate. Both set of equations give the same expressions in the low-density as well as for the high-density limits. Also at the intermediate values the numerical difference is small.

(*) Equations (23) and (24) are different from those given in the paper of GRATTON and SZAMOSI (1964) as in the original the pressure had not been calculated correctly. We are thankful to Dr. BARKER for pointing out this error.

where g and f are the well-known functions for a relativistic Fermi gas

$$g(x) = \tfrac{3}{8}(x + 2x^3)\sqrt{1 + x^2} - \sinh^{-1} x \,,$$
$$f(x) = (2x^3 - 3x)\sqrt{1 + x^3} + 3 \sinh^{-1} x \,,$$

and

$$e(x) = h(x) - \frac{x^3}{1 + x^2} \, (^*) \,.$$

For $\alpha = 0$ or for small α, the above equations reduce to the standard equations for a relativistic gas at zero temperature. But for finite α and very large x some interesting properties of the model are to be noted. It is easily seen that, when $x \to \infty$,

$$e(x) = \tfrac{1}{2}x^2 \,, \qquad h(x) = \tfrac{3}{2}x^2 \,, \qquad g(x) = \tfrac{3}{4}x^4 \,, \qquad f(x) = 2x^4 \,.$$

Hence, when $x \to \infty$,

$$n = \frac{2}{3v_0} \,, \qquad E = \frac{3}{4}\, m_n c^2 x = \frac{9}{8}\, m_c c^2 v_0 n \,,$$
$$P = nE \,.$$

The properties of the gas are, thus, determined only by the constants $m_n c^2$ (the rest energy of the particles) and v_0 (their rest volume), as they ought to be. When $x \to \infty$, the number density goes to infinity. This means that, notwithstanding the hard core, it is possible to squeeze an infinitely large number of particles into a finite volume; this is due to the fact that the average volume of the particles reduces to a point, because of the Lorentz contraction, since the particles will move faster and faster as the density increases. Of course, the energy needed to do that increases with n^2. The pressure formula is that expected for an extreme relativistic gas with a repulsive hard core as it was given by ZEL'DOVITCH in a field-theoretical context.

It may also be noted that the mass density is, obviously, $\varrho = nE/c^2$, so that the equation of state in which one is interested, for instance, when discussing a neutron star, becomes at very high densities

$$P = \varrho c^2 \,.$$

At smaller densities it is given in parametric form by

$$\varrho = \frac{8\pi}{3}\, m_n \left(\frac{m_n c^2}{h}\right)^3 \frac{g(x)}{1 + \alpha h(x)} \,,$$
$$P = \frac{\pi}{3}\, m_n c^2 \left(\frac{mc}{h}\right)^3 \frac{f(x)}{1 + \alpha h(x)} \,.$$

For $\alpha = 0$ or small α, it reduces to the well-known equation of state for a relativistic gas of free particles.

A more recent attempt to construct an equation of state in the density range $4\cdot10^{38} < n < 2.8\cdot10^{40}$ is due to TSURUTA (*Thesis*, Columbia University, 1964) (*). The basic assumption is that the nuclear potential is the type introduced by LEVINGER and SIMMONS (1961). It is characterized by the following assumptions. The neutron-neutron potential is well behaved and velocity-dependent. It has been estimated by LEVINGER and SIMMONS that ordinary perturbation theory is applicable for these potentials, in fact in the above-mentioned density region the second approximation of the perturbation theory is already negligible. Two types of potentials are used in the calculation of TSURUTA which are called V_β and V_γ and are defined as follows:

$$V_\beta = - V_0 J_1(r) - \frac{\hbar^2 \lambda}{mc}\,\delta(r-c) + \frac{\lambda}{m}\,\nabla J_2(z)\,, \tag{24}$$

where

$$V_0 J_1(r)\begin{cases} = 51\ \text{MeV} & (r<b),\\ = -\ \text{OPEP} & (r>b), \end{cases} \qquad J_2(r) = \begin{cases} 1 & r<c\\ \frac{1}{2} & r=c\\ 0 & r>c \end{cases}$$

and OPEP is short for one-pion exchange potential and equals

$$\text{OPEP} = -\,10.83\exp[-\,0.708r]/0.708r\ \text{MeV}$$

while $b = 1.6$ fermi, $c = 0.5$ fermi, $\lambda = -\,1.64$.

$$V_\gamma = - V_0 J_1(r) - \frac{h^2}{m}\left(\nabla^2 \omega(r) + \omega(r)\,\nabla^2\right), \tag{25}$$

where

$$V_0 J_1(\boldsymbol{r}) = [1+2\omega(r)]\left\{112\exp[-\,1.4r)] - \frac{\hbar^2}{m}\,\frac{(\omega^1(r))^2}{[1+2\omega(r)]^2}\right\}$$

and

$$\omega(r) = 5\exp[-\,3.6r]\,.$$

V_β has four adjustable parameters (V_0, b, c, λ) and gives a satisfactory fit to the ^1S and ^1D phase shift from 20 MeV to 340 MeV experiments. (The OPEP used in V_β does not contain any adjustable parameter.) V_γ describes the low-

(*) Thanks are due to Dr. A. G. W. CAMERON for sending me the manuscript of the quoted thesis.

energy experiments well and gives a good fit to the ^1S phase shifts and ^1D phase shifts. It turns out that the rather complicated form of this potential gives a simple form for an effective potential that can be used in a transformed Schrödinger equation.

These potentials also prevent the collapse of the nuclear matter. Tensor and spin orbit forces are not included. The actual calculation is somewhat lengthy to reproduce here. We refer to the quoted sources, and remark here only that relativistic energy is used in calculating the pressure. The results of the calculations of the energy density are given in Fig. 1. The results of the hydrostatic equilibrium calculations are also given in Thorne's paper.

* * *

The author is very much indebted to Profs. L. GRATTON, A. FINZI and G. MARX for many illuminating discussions on the subject.

BIBLIOGRAPHY

AMBARTSUMYAN, V. A., 1953, *Dokl. Akad. Nauk Arm.*, **16**, 73.
AMBARTSUMYAN, V. A., 1958, *Proc. Solvay Congress.*
AMBARTSUMYAN V. A. and G. S. SAAKYAN, 1960, *Astr. Journ. USSR*, **37**, 193; 1960, *Sov. Astro.*, **4**, 187.
BAADE, W. and F. ZWICKY, 1934, *Proc. Nat. Acad. of Sc.*, **20**, 259.
BAHCALL, J. N. and R. A. WOLF, 1965, *Phys. Rev. Letters*, **14**, 343.
BARKER, B. M., M. S. BHATIA and G. SZAMOSI, 1966, *Nuovo Cimento*, **44**, 109.
BARKER, B. M., M. S. BHATIA and G. SZAMOSI II: (to appear).
CAMERON, A. G. W., 1959, *Ap. Journal*, **130**, 884.
CZIFFRA, P., M. H. MCGREGOR, M. J. MORAVCSIK and H. P. STAPP, 1959, *Phys. Rev.*, **114**, 880.
GOMBAS, P., 1957, *Fortschr. d. Phys.*, **5**, 159.
GOMES, L. C., J. D. WALECKA and V. F. WEISSKOPF, 1958, *Ann. of Phys.*, **3**, 241.
GRASHIN, A. F., 1959, *Žurn. Ėxp. Theor. Fiz.*, **36**, 1717.
GRATTON, L. and G. SZAMOSI, 1964, *Nuovo Cimento*, **33**, 1056.
LANDAU, L. D., 1932, *Phys. Z. Sowjetunion*, **1**, 285.
MARX, G. and J. NEMETH, 1964, *Acta Phys. Hung.*, **18**, 77.
NE'EMAN, Y., 1965, *Ap. Journal*, **141**, 1303.
NOVICOV, I. D., *Astr. Žurn.*, **41**, 1075 (1964).
SAAKYAN, G. S. and A. A. VARTANIAN, 1963, *Nuovo Cimento*, **30**, 82.
SALPETER, E. E., 1960, *Ann. of Phys.*, **11**, 393.
TSURUTA, S. (Thesis, Columbia University, 1964).
ZEL'DOVICH, YA. B., 1962, *JETP*, **14**, 1143.

Present Status of the Neutron-Star Hypothesis.

A. FINZI (*)

IV Centro d'Astrofisica del CNR - Frascati, Roma

1. – The creation of neutron stars in supernova explosions.

I shall deal, in this lecture, with the question of the observability of neutron stars and, more generally, with the recent attempts to confirm the old hypothesis of the formation of neutron stars in supernova outbursts. I shall deal almost exclusively with neutron stars formed in type I supernovae. In the case of type I supernovae, the mass of the pre-supernovae can be given with confidence, and must be about one solar mass. The neutron stars created in the explosion will then be relatively light, so that we do not have to worry about the problem of the critical mass (TSURUTA and CAMERON, 1965). Besides, the effects of general relativity for these stars should be of the order of 10% only, so that we can use the more convenient Newtonian theory. Finally, the density of the core should not exceed 10^{15} g cm^{-3}, so that the independent-particle model should provide reliable results for the degenerate gas of the core.

Because of these reasons, we may hope that it will be easier to build a convincing theory of type I supernovae than of other objects considered in relativistic astrophysics, and this could justify the amount of work put in their study, although in the general economy of the universe, type I supernovae are probably less important than Q.S.S., Q.S.G., radio galaxies and Seyfert galaxies.

Type I supernovae are observed in elliptical as well as in spiral galaxies. The age of stars in elliptical galaxies should be of the order of 10^{10} years; therefore, the mass of the stars should not greatly exceed the solar mass. On the other hand, a star of mass below the Chandrasekhar limit, 1 to 1.2 $M_\odot$, is not likely to undergo gravitational collapse. We conclude that the mass of the pre-supernovae should be about one solar mass.

If a star of one solar mass collapses until a density of the order of nuclear

---

(*) Presently at California Institute of Technology, Pasadena, California.

density is reached, the gravitational energy set free is of the order of 10^{53} erg. The huge energy set free in the collapse suggested already in 1932 to BAADE and ZWICKY (1934) the idea of the creation of neutron stars in supernova outbursts. A possible mechanism by which a fraction of the gravitational energy could be transformed to the exploding shell has recently been indicated by COLGATE: In the final stage of the process, the supernova collapses with a velocity approaching that of free fall, since the gravitational energy set free in the collapse is immediately lost by the star in the form of neutrinos. As the density increases, the star becomes opaque to the neutrinos; at that moment the emission in the outer layers may become smaller than the absorption of neutrinos emitted from the inner core, which is denser and hotter. As a consequence, in the external layers the implosion will be stopped, and these layers will be hurled into space, while the central core will condense into a neutron star. A few percent of the neutrinos emitted from the core need to be absorbed by the external layers in order to account for the energy released by type I supernovae. The idea that absorption of neutrinos may play an essential part in the process, is not in contradiction with the fact that neutrinos escape almost freely from a neutron star; in fact, during the collapse the nuclear gases are only partially degenerate.

Theoretically neutron stars have been studied by LANDAU (1932), by OPPENHEIMER and VOLKOFF (1939), and more recently by CAMERON (1959), by HAMADA and SALPETER (1961) and by AMBARTSUMIAN and co-workers (1960, 1961). At least for stars of not too large a mass, these studies are so convincing, that I almost dare to say that the interior of a neutron star is one of the best known regions of the Universe.

The majority of astrophysicists, on the other hand, became interested in neutron stars only after the discovery of nonsolar X-rays by GIACCONI, GURSKY, PAOLINI and ROSSI (1962, 1963). Soon after the announcement of their observations, the idea that the observed flux represents the thermal emission of neutron stars created in recent galactic supernovae was advanced independently by various authors (MORTON, 1964; FINZI, 1964; CHIU and SALPETER, 1964). More recently, BOWYER, BYRAM, CHUBB and FRIEDMAN (1964*a*) discovered an intense X-ray source in the direction of the Crab Nebula. At that moment, most people became convinced that the neutron-star hypothesis had finally been confirmed.

2. – The thermal radiation of neutron stars.

The intensity of the source in the Crab Nebula is about $1.5 \cdot 10^{-8}$ erg cm^{-2} s^{-1}; taking into account the distance of the Nebula, the emission power of the source must be about $3 \cdot 10^{36}$ erg s^{-1}. The obvious task was therefore to calculate the electromagnetic emission to be expected from a neutron star 910 years old, in order to see if this was in agreement with the above figure of $3 \cdot 10^{36}$ erg s^{-1}.

The thermal conductivity of the core is very high, so that the core must be practically isothermal. Taking into account the thermal conductivity of the external layers, it should be possible to calculate the electromagnetic emission of the surface from the temperature of the core.

In order to calculate the temperature of the core one must assume that the star was very hot at the time it was created, and consider which mechanisms have contributed to its cooling. It is found in this way that the emission of electromagnetic radiation from the surface and of plasma neutrinos from the external layers, can be neglected in comparison with the emission of neutrinos from the core caused by beta-interactions (FINZI, 1965*a*).

The emission of neutrinos from the core has been calculated by BAHCALL and WOLF (1965) and by myself (FINZI, 1965*a*), and I will refer mainly to my calculations for the obvious reason that I know them better.

In this calculation it was assumed that the mass of the neutron star was $1.2 \cdot 10^{33}$ g, or about $0.6\, M_\odot$. The density of the core was assumed to have a constant value $\varrho = 6 \cdot 10^{11}$ g cm^{-3}. Further, the different particles of the core were described as free Fermi particles. At the density of $6 \cdot 10^{14}$ g cm^{-3} only neutrinos, protons and electrons should be present. The Fermi level E_n of the degenerate neutron gas should be about 93 MeV; the Fermi levels E_e and E_p of the electrons and protons at chemical equilibrium can be deduced from the condition that $E_p + E_e = E_n + E_0$ ($E_0 = 0.78$ MeV is the decay energy of the neutron) and that the Fermi momenta of the electrons and protons must be equal, since the particle densities of electrons and protons are necessarily the same. One finds in this way $E_e = 89.5$ MeV and $E_p = 4.3$ MeV. The Fermi momenta will be $P_n = 435$ MeV/c, $P_e = P_p = 90$ MeV/c. The number of proton-electron pairs per total number of particles will then be $(P_e/P_n)^3 = 0.009$.

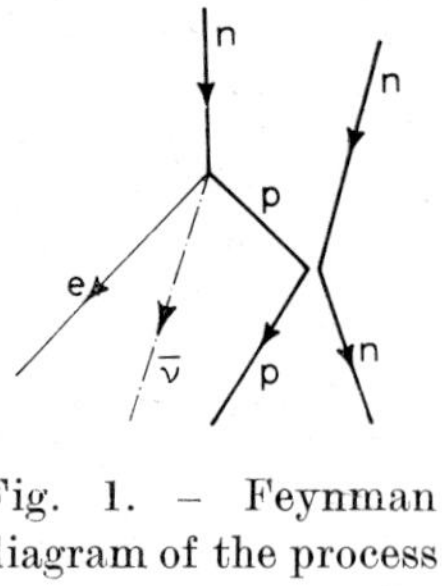

Fig. 1. – Feynman diagram of the process $n + n \to n + e + p + \bar{\nu}$.

The reactions contributing mostly to the cooling are then found to be

$$n + n \to n + p + e + \bar{\nu} \qquad (1)$$

and the inverse reaction

$$p + e + n \to n + n + \nu\,, \qquad (2)$$

We point out that these reactions are going on even at chemical equilibrium when the temperature is different from zero.

In reaction (1) a neutron of energy close to the Fermi energy decays into an electron, a proton, and an antineutrino (Fig. 1). However, when a free neutron of 93 MeV decays, a proton of about the same energy and an electron of a few hundred keV at most, are created. In the present case, states of energy much below 89.5 MeV are not allowed to the electron; therefore, only an electron of approximately that energy, together with an antineutrino and a virtual proton of a few MeV, can be created in the decay. The virtual proton carries a momentum comparable to that of the neutron which has decayed; it is converted into a real particle by elastic scattering with a second neutron of energy close to the Fermi energy. In the scattering, very little energy is exchanged; the second neutron simply modifies its direction of motion.

Conversely, in reaction (2), a proton of energy close to the proton Fermi energy scatters elastically with a neutron of energy close to the neutron Fermi energy (Fig. 2). The proton is scattered into a virtual proton with momentum in the range of 435 MeV/c; after the collision with an electron near the top of the electron sea, the two particles are transformed into a neutron of about 93 MeV and a neutrino. Our calculations give for the energy lost by the star through reactions (1) and (2)

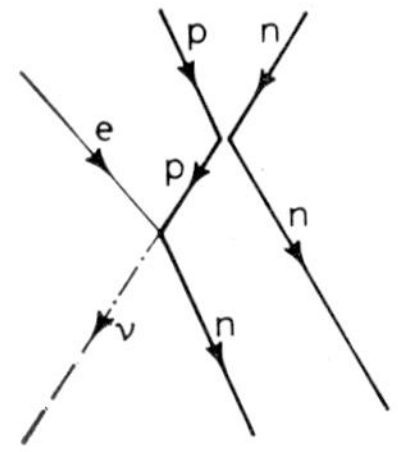

Fig. 2. – Feynman diagram of the process $p+e+n \to n+n+\nu$.

$$L_{\text{Ur}} = 8.83 \cdot 10^{37} \, (T_c/10^9)^8 \text{ erg s}^{-1} ,$$

where T_c is the temperature of the core. The thermal capacity of a degenerate neutron gas of density $6 \cdot 10^{14}$ g cm^{-3} is about $3.5 \cdot 10^{-4}\, T$ erg g^{-1} deg^{-1}; that of the star is therefore $4.2 \cdot 10^{29}\, T_c$ erg deg^{-1}. If only cooling by reactions (1) and (2) is taken into account, the core temperature is given by that solution of the differential equation

$$\text{(3)} \qquad \frac{\mathrm{d}T}{\mathrm{d}t} = -\frac{L_{\text{Ur}}}{4.2 \cdot 10^{29} T} = -0.21 \left(\frac{T}{10^9}\right) ,$$

which is infinite at $t = 0$. The solution is $T = 3.04 \cdot 10^{10} \cdot t^{-\frac{1}{6}}$. The age of the neutron star in the Crab Nebula is $t = 910$ years $= 2.87 \cdot 10^{10}$ s; the solution of eq. (3) gives for the core temperature of that star the value $T_c = 5.51 \cdot 10^8$ °K.

From the core temperature, the emission power of the star could be deduced if the thermal conductivity of the external layers were known. The main temperature gradient should be in the two external layers, the nondegenerate layer and the layer where only nuclei and degenerate electrons are present (Finzi, 1965*a*). There do not seem to be, as yet, reliable expressions of the thermal conductivity of these layers, and for this reason we must be content with a rough estimate of the emission power of the star; our calculations lead us to expect an emission power about one order of magnitude smaller tha that of the X-ray source discovered recently in the Crab Nebula (BOWYER, BYRAM, CHUBB and FRIEDMAN, 1964*a*). This means, of course, that the source cannot be interpreted as the thermal radiation of the star.

Approximately at the time when these calculations were completed, about one year ago, FRIEDMAN and co-workers observed the source during a lunar occultation (BOWYER, BYRAM, CHUBB and FRIEDMAN, 1964*b*), and found that its angular size was not very much smaller than that of the optical object in the Crab Nebula. The conclusion to be drawn was therefore that neither the neutron-star hypothesis had been confirmed so far, nor the Friedman experiment had disproved it in any way, since the neutron star could not be expected to be as bright as the observed X-ray source.

One may add that a test of the neutron-star hypothesis by X-ray observation will probably become possible in the next few years; in fact, a starlike object having an emission power one-tenth of that of the source in the Crab Nebula will become detectable either by a more refined experiment during lunar occultation, or by means of the X-ray telescope developed by GIACCONI.

This statement is subject, however, to two provisos:

1) GINZBURG and KIRZHNITZ (1965) have suggested that the nucleons in a neutron star may form a superfluid at temperatures less than or of the order of 10^{10} °K. The superfluid gaps that would then appear in the neutron and proton energy spectra could significantly reduce the rates of reactions (1) and (2). It is not yet possible to calculate the energy gaps with any precision because they depend strongly on the complicated nucleon-nucleon interactions in neutron-star matter. However, preliminary calculations by RUDERMAN and by WOLF, which are based on the Bardeen-Cooper-Schrieffer theory of superconductivity, indicate that the neutron energy gap is zero at densities greater than about $2 \cdot 10^{14}$ g cm^{-3}, although it may be large at lower densities. The protons, on the other hand, are expected to form a superfluid for most of the densities of interest, but the gap in the proton spectrum should never be greater than about 0.5 MeV. As a consequence of proton superconductivity, the rates of reactions (1) and (2) could perhaps be reduced by one or even two orders of magnitude.

On the other hand, the thermal capacity of the star is determined mainly by the properties of the neutron gas; since the neutron gas should notbe superfluid in the region of density larger than $2 \cdot 10^{14}$ g cm^{-3}, the thermal capacity of the star should not be greatly reduced by the effects of superfluidity. In conclusion, the core temperature and the luminosity of a neutron star should be increased when the effects of superfluidity are taken into account; the above statement that the neutron star in the Crab Nebula should be observable should not have to be modified.

2) As mentioned above BAHCALL and WOLF have calculated the neutrino emission from the core. Their method of calculation is very different from mine, and they have attempted to modify slightly the independent-particle picture to take account of strong interactions. Their numerical result for the energy loss by reactions (1) and (2) is, however, in reasonably good agreement with mine, a very encouraging fact, since it shows that the emission rate is rather insensitive to the model of strong interactions, about which little is known with certainty.

The most singular prediction made by BAHCALL and WOLF with their model for strong interactions is, however, that π^- should already be present at a density of $6\cdot 10^{14}$ g cm^{-3}. If π^- are present, antineutrinos will be produced also by the reaction

$$n+\pi^- \to n+e+\bar{\nu}\,, \tag{4}$$

in which a π^- decays into an electron and an antineutrino. The reasons why a neutron must take part in the reaction is that in the decay of a free π^- the rest energy is divided almost equally between the electron and the $\bar{\nu}$. In the present case, only states of energy close to electron Fermi energy E_e are allowed to the electrons, therefore almost all the rest energy of the pion must go to the electron.

The energy loss by reaction (4) would be so large, that the neutron star should become invisible very soon after the outburst.

3. – The light curves of type I supernovae and the vibrational energy of the neutron stars.

I shall deal now with an attempt to obtain an alternative confirmation of the neutron-star hypothesis, based on the possibility the hypothesis seems to offer to interpret the exponential light curves of type I supernovae.

A type I supernova reaches a maximum absolute photographic magnitude of about -19 a few weeks after the explosion, and declines by approximately two magnitudes during the following month. After that, during a period of perhaps two years, the luminosity declines exponentially; assuming that the mechanism responsible for the exponential decay starts to operate soon after the explosion, and neglecting the bolometric correction, the total energy released exponentially would be about $2\cdot 10^{49}$ erg. In order to account for a moderate bolometric correction, we shall take, in the following, the energy released exponentially to be $4\cdot 10^{49}$ erg.

It was generally assumed that this energy was released in the decay of some radioactive element; this assumption was based on the belief that the half-value time $t_{\frac{1}{2}}$ for the luminosity was about 54 days for all type I supernovae. It must be said, however, that BURBIDGE, BURBIDGE, FOWLER and HOYLE (1957), who had advanced this hupothesis, had themselves pointed out a serious difficulty: The largest fraction of the fission energy should go into the kinetic energy of the fragments, and would not be easily converted into visible light. Therefore, the exponential decay of the radioactive energy could still not give an exponential decay for the luminosity.

Besides, recent investigations have confirmed the exponential character of the light curves, but have indicated at the same time that the half-value time is not always the same, randing from 34 to 68 days (BERTAUD, 1964). Since it is impossible to assume that in each supernova a different radioactive element is providing the main source of energy, we should probably look for another explanation of the phenomenon. On the other hand, once radioactive energy is ruled out, it is very difficult to imagine a different process taking place in a rarefied gas and causing an exponential energy release.

The present suggestion is that the energy released exponentially originates in the neutron star. There seem to be only two ways in which $4 \cdot 10^{49}$ erg can be stored in a neutron star: in the form of thermal energy, or in the form of vibrational energy. Soon after its creation in a supernova outburst, the neutron star is likely to be hot and its modes of vibration are likely to be excited. However, thermal energy is easily ruled out: An energy of $4 \cdot 10^{49}$ erg corresponds to an internal temperature of around $1.4 \cdot 10^{10}$ °K; at this temperature the thermal-energy content (which is proportional to T_c^2, since the thermal capacity is proportional to T_c) must decrease with time t approximately like $t^{-\frac{1}{3}}$, since T_c was found to decrease like $T^{-\frac{1}{6}}$. Moreover, thermal energy should be released mainly in the form of neutrinos.

We assume, therefore, that the energy of the observed radiation is released in the dissipation of the vibrational energy of the star. Neglecting the effects of general relativity, one can establish the relation

$$W = \tfrac{1}{2}(\Gamma - \tfrac{4}{3})\,\Omega[\xi_{\mathrm{av}}]^2 \,,$$

where $\Omega \approx 10^{53}$ erg is the potential energy of the star and $\xi = \delta r/r$ is the ratio of the radial displacement δr of a point during an expansion, to the distance r of the point from the center of the star. Γ is the adiabatic exponent defined by $\delta P/P = \Gamma \delta\varrho/\varrho$; in the core of the star the radiation pressure is negligible in comparison with the gas pressure, while the degenerate gas is almost completely nonrelativistic; therefore Γ is only slightly less than $\frac{5}{3}$ (LANDAU and LIFSHITZ, 1958), if nuclear forces are not taken into account. In conclusion, the value of ξ_{av} leading to $W = 4 \cdot 10^{49}$ erg should be about 0.05.

Taking for definiteness the half-value $t_{\frac{1}{2}}$ for the luminosity to be $5 \cdot 10^6$ s, the dissipation of vibrational energy needed to ensure the exponential light curve is, on the other hand,

$$\frac{\ln 2}{t_{\frac{1}{2}}} W = \frac{\ln 2}{t_{\frac{1}{2}}} \frac{1}{2} (\Gamma - 4/3)\, \Omega [\xi_{av}]^2 = 2.3 \cdot 10^{45} [\xi_{av}]^2 \text{ erg s}^{-1} .$$

It is encouraging to recognize that an energy $W = 4 \cdot 10^{49}$ erg is approximately the maximum energy which can be stored for a sufficiently long time in the star in the form of vibrations. To show this, we point out that the equilibrium concentration of neutrons, protons and electrons in the degenerate gas of the neutron star is a function of the density. In a pulsating star the density varies periodically; therefore the concentration is most of the time different from the equilibrium concentration. For densities slightly higher than nuclear density, like those in the core of the star, the equilibrium concentration of electrons and protons increases with increasing density. Therefore, when the gas is compressed, reaction (1) will transform some neutrons into protons and electrons, plus antineutrinos which will escape. Conversely, when the gas is expanded, reaction (2) will transform some protons and electrons into neutrons, plus neutrinos which will escape. These two reactions will proceed at the expense of the vibrational energy of the star.

We have calculated (FINZI, 1965*b*) the dissipation of vibrational energy caused by these reactions, describing again the core of the star as a Fermi gas of noninteracting particles of density $\varrho = 6 \cdot 10^{14}$ g cm^{-3}. The method of calculation is similar to the one used for the calculation of the loss of heat by reaction (1) and (2) and the dissipation of vibrational energy by the star turns out to be $\sim 10^{52} [\xi_{av}]^8$ erg s^{-1}.

As a consequence of the high exponential, this dissipation is very large in comparison with the energy lost in the exponential decay, $2.3 \cdot 10^{45} [\xi_{av}]^2$ erg s^{-1}, until ξ_{av} is reduced to $(2.3 \cdot 10^{45}/10^{52})^{\frac{1}{6}} = 0.078$; after that it becomes quite negligible. This means that during the first few days after the outburst the reaction just described will reduce the vibrational energy to the value $\frac{1}{2}(\Gamma - 4/3)\, \Omega\, 0.078^2 = 1.01 \cdot 10^{49}$ erg (*). Subsequently, the mechanism responsible for the exponential decay will dominate.

(*) K. THORNE has drawn my attention to an error in my evaluation of the maximum vibrational energy that can be released exponentially. The value of $1.01 \cdot 10^{49}$ erg ought to be divided by a factor of $3^{8/3}$.

This decrease would however be approximately compensated by a comparable increase when nuclear interaction is taken into account. Taking nuclear interaction into account modifies the estimate for the vibrational energy available in two ways. First, the ratio between the equilibrium concentration of neutrons and protons would in general have a weaker dependence on density, so that for a given ξ_{av} neutrino emission would be smaller. Secondly, for a given ξ_{av}, the vibrational energy would be larger when repulsive nuclear forces are introduced into the equation of state.

The main unsolved problem is to find out how the vibrational energy is transferred to the surface, where it will be radiated away. It is easily recognized that the vibrational energy cannot be dissipated in the interior and then transferred to the surface by thermal conduction. In fact, during the early stages, the energy radiated per unit area of the surface, $L_{bol}/4\pi R^2$, should be of the order of 10^{29} erg s^{-1} cm^{-2}. On the other hand, even assuming a central temperature T_c of the order of 10^{10} °K, the temperature gradient should be only of the order of $T_c/R \approx 10^4$ deg cm^{-1}; the thermal conductivity needed to ensure the transfer of the energy radiated should be then $\approx 10^{25}$ erg s^{-1} deg^{-1} cm. We have stated above that the thermal conductivity of the core is very high; it is not that high, however. An estimate based on the approximate relation: thermal conductivity = thermal capacity per unit volume × velocity of the particles × mean free path, suggests a conductivity in the range of 10^{22} to 10^{23} erg s^{-1} deg^{-1} cm. The simplest way to ensure the energy transfer would probably be by means of a shock wave accompanying each vibration; when the shock wave reaches the atmosphere, its energy is dissipated.

Many spectroscopic observations on variable stars, especially on Cepheids of type II, have in fact been interpreted in terms of shock waves going through the atmospheric layers (LEDOUX and WALRAVEN, 1958; ROSSELAND, 1949); it seems doubtful, however, that the shock waves are produced by the same mechanism in the case of the *Cepheids* and in that of the neutron stars. In this latter case, the exponential decay could formally be accounted for by assuming an imperfect reflection at the surface of the star, and by visualizing the vibration in the form of a wave moving from the center to the surface and back. The ratio of the period of vibration of the neutron star (which is less than 10^{-3} s) to the half-value time $t_{\frac{1}{2}}$ of the luminosity, is about 10^{-10}; therefore the observed exponential decay would be ensured by assuming that the coefficient of reflection at the suface differs from unity by about 10^{-10}.

For simplicity we shall assume that the energy released exponentially is emitted from the surface of the neutron star in the form of black-body radiation. In reality, things are certainly not as simple as that since the star will necessarily have an extended and unstable atmosphere. Let us then consider, for instance, the situation about 100 days after the explosion and let us assume that by that time the absolute photographic magnitude is reduced to —16, corresponding to an emission $L_{bol} = 7.2 \cdot 10^{41}$ erg s^{-1}. The energy radiated per unit area of the surface of the neutron star, $L_{bol}/4\pi R^2$, will be $1.42 \cdot 10^{29}$ erg s^{-1} cm^{-2}, the effective temperature $2.24 \cdot 10^8$ °K and the mean energy of the thermal photons about 90 keV. This means that the neutron star will radiate in the region of hard X-rays.

In the expanding envelope of the supernova these hard X-rays will be absorbed mainly by K-electrons of ions of the iron group. The energetic photoelectrons produced in this way will in general lose part of their energy in the form of bremsstrahlung before they are captured again by ions. The softer X-rays produced by bremsstrahlung or by recombination will ionize or excite other ions. The absorption of radiation and the re-emission of softer radiation will go on until photons are produced without enough energy to excite ions; these photons will escape from the envelope. The first excited level of most ions lies only a few eV above the fundamental level; therefore the photons which escape should have energies of a few eV. In conclusion, the observed radiation should be produced by bremsstrahlung and by recombination and de-excitation. In the blue part of the spectrum some absorption lines should be present.

The most important characteristic of the rarefied gas of the envelope shouɼd be its extreme degree of ionization. This ionization may be described by the statement that a K-orbit of an ion of the iron group has a probability of the order of 0.1 of not being filled. The exceptionally high degree of ionization in the envelope is probably the main reason for the peculiar character of the spectrum of type I supernovae (MINKOWSKI, 1939), where not a single line has been identified so far.

A fraction of the primary photons emitted by the neutron star may be able to escape from the envelope. This fraction depends very strongly on the abundance of the elements of the iron group and on the distribution of velocities in the expanding envelope and is therefore impossible to calculate at present. Assuming, for instance, that 10% of the primary photons do escape, the flux of X rays from a type I supernova, 30 million light years away and 50 to 100 days after the outburst, should be of the order of 10^{-11} erg s^{-1} cm^{-2}. On the other hand, there is about one type I supernova per year in a sphere of radius of 30 million light years. The primary photons should be detectable by counters carried by balloons.

BIBLIOGRAPHY

AMBARTSUMIAN, V. A. and G. S. SAAKYAN, 1960, *Soviet Astron. A. J.*, **4**, 187.

AMBARTSUMIAN, V. A. and G. S. SAAKYAN, 1962, *Soviet Astron. A. J.*, **5**, 601.

BAADE, W. and F. ZWICKY, 1934, *Proc. Nat. Acad. Sciences*, XX, 259.

BAHCALL, J. N. and R. A. WOLF, 1965, *Phys. Rev. Letters*, **14**, 343.

BERTAUD, C., 1964, *Ann. d'Astrophys.*, **27**, 548.

BOWYER, S., E. T. BYRAM, T. A. CHUBB, and H. FRIEDMAN, 1964*a*, *Nature*, **201**, 1307.

BOWYER, S., E. T. BYRAM, T. A. CHUBB, and H. FRIEDMAN, 1964*b*, *Science*, **146**, 912.

BURBIDGE, E. M., G. R. BURBIDGE, W. A. FOWLER, and F. HOYLE, 1957, *Rev. Mod. Phys.*, **29**, 547.

CAMERON, A. G. W., 1959, *Astrophys. J.*, **130**, 884.

CHIU, H. Y. and E. E. SALPETER, 1964, *Phys. Rev. Letters*, **12**, 413.

FINZI, A., 1964, *Astrophys. J.*, **139**, 1398.
FINZI, A., 1965*a*, *Phys. Rev.*, **137**, B 472.
FINZI, A., 1965*b*, *Phys. Rev. Letters*, **15**, 599.
GIACCONI, R., H. GURSKY, F. R. PAOLINI, and B. B. ROSSI, 1962, *Phys. Rev. Letters*, **9**, 439.
GIACCONI, R., H. GURSKY, F. R. PAOLINI, and B. B. ROSSI, 1963, *Phys. Rev. Letters*, **11**, 530.
GINZBURG, V. L. and D. A. KIRZHNITZ, 1965, *Soviet Physics JETP*, **20**, 1346.
HAMADA, T. and E. E. SALPETER, 1961, *Astrophys. J.*, **134**, 683.
LANDAU, L., 1932, *Physik. Zeits. Soviet Union*, **1**, 285.
LANDAU, L. D. and E. M. LIFSHITZ, 1958, *Statistical Physics*, Pergamon Press, p. 158.
LEDOUX, P. and T. WALRAVEN, 1958, *Variable Stars, Handbuch der Phys.* LI (Berlin) p. 353.
MINKOWSKI, R., 1939, *Astrophys. J.*, **89**, 156.
MORTON, D. C., 1964, *Nature*, **201**, 1308.
OPPENHEIMER, J. R. and G. M. VOLKOFF, 1939, *Phys. Rev.*, **55**, 374.
ROSSELAND, S., 1949, *The Pulsational Theory of Variable Stars* (Oxford).
TSURUTA, S. and A. W. G. CAMERON, 1965, *Nature*, **207**, 364.

Supermassive Stars, Quasars, and Extragalactic Radio Sources (*).

W. A. FOWLER
California Institute of Technology - Pasadena

1. – Introduction.

In this (Sects. **1** to **7**) and the following lecture (Sects. **8** to **16**) our concern will be the revolution which has occurred in astronomy during the past two decades. Radio astronomers throughout the world—in Australia, England, the Netherlands, the Soviet Union, Italy and the United States—have been the real heroes of the revolution. They have not only detected radio waves from extragalactic sources but have succeeded in pin-pointing the location of these sources on the celestial sphere.

In these lectures the first purpose will be to discuss the observational work which makes possible the identification of radio sources with optical objects observable through large telescopes. The second purpose will be to consider various suggestions which have been made concerning the source of the prodigious energies involved in the radio objects. Background references are HOYLE, FOWLER, BURBIDGE and BURBIDGE (1964) and FOWLER (1964; 1965*a*, *b*; 1966).

The fundamental problem is this—what physical phenomenon is the source of the energy? Ordinary stars shine on nuclear energy. Are the nuclear resources in supermassive stars sufficient to meet the observed energy requirements in radio objects or must we turn to other mechanisms—annihilation, multi-supernovae, stellar collisions, gravitational collapse, or new and unknown phenomena—to explain radio « stars » and « galaxies ». In case nuclear reac-

(*) This lecture is a revised and updated version of papers originally presented before the American Philosophical Society, Philadelphia, April 1964, and the Belfer Science Forum, Yeshiva University, November 1964.

tions in supermassive stars are effective, then we must ask whether these stars are stable or unstable during nuclear burning. After the exhaustion of nuclear fuel, what happens? In addition, the mechanisms of transfer of energy from the raw form in which it is produced to the exotic forms exhibited in the radio sources must be studied.

2. – The optical identification of radio sources.

The development in many places throughout the world of radio telescopes capable of determining positions to better than ten seconds in angle have led to a significant breakthrough in the *observation* and *identification* of radio sources. As one example, radio astronomers at the California Institute of Technology have constructed at the Owens Valley Radio Observatory in Bishop, California, an interferometer consisting of two 90-foot dishes which can be separated by distances up to 1000 meters, yielding a limiting angular resolution near 10^{-4}.

The precise determination of the position of a radio object makes possible an accurate comparison with the position of optical objects visible through large conventional telescopes which have very high angular resolution because of the short wave length of visible light. The ultimate objective is to make an «identification» of the radio source with an optical object. Radio astronomers at the California Institute of Technology have the unique advantage of being able to co-operate with staff members of the Mount Wilson and Palomar Observatories in using the 200-inch Hale Telescope on Mount Palomar for making position comparisons and identifications.

Early identifications, made before great precision had been reached in the radio observations, indicated that in some cases radio sources seemed to be associated with pairs of galaxies in close proximity and perhaps even in collision. This led naturally to the assumption that the energy freed in such a collision might be the source of the radio energy. It is now believed that collision energy is inadequate in this regard but more important the great majority of the more precise identifications for radio sources outside of our galaxy, the Milky Way, are with single, isolated galaxies and not with pairs of galaxies.

Until recently there has been no way to determine directly the distance to the radio objects of interest although red-shift measurements have been made on the 21 cm atomic-hydrogen line from nearby objects and are being rapidly extended to more distant objects. On the other hand the distance to the galaxy can be calculated if optical red-shift measurements have been made and if the red shift is assumed to be proportional to distance in accordance with Hubble's Law.

3. – The energy requirements of the radio sources.

Identification with an optically red-shifted galaxy thus makes it possible to determine the absolute luminosity of radio sources from the measured apparent luminosity, that is, the radio flux at the earth in erg cm^{-2} s^{-1} can be translated into the total rate of energy emission in erg s^{-1} at the source with the additional assumption of isotropic emission. (The possibility that the radio waves are directed at the earth is rightly given scant attention.) The results are staggering. More than 50 radio sources have been listed by MATTHEWS, MORGAN and SCHMIDT (1964) with luminosities exceeding 10^{38} erg s^{-1} and ranging up to $2\cdot10^{45}$ erg s^{-1}, the values for 3C 295 (the 295th object in the third Cambridge University catalogue of radio sources). The optical luminosity of the sun is $4\cdot10^{33}$ erg s^{-1} and that from the galaxy is approximately 10^{44} erg s^{-1}. Thus 3C 295 has a radio luminosity almost 10^{12} times that of the optical emission from the sun and more than ten times that from the galaxy.

The total amounts of energy required to sustain these luminosities can be calculated in several ways. It is reasonable to assume that the minimum age to be assigned to the sources is that given by dividing the observed dimensions by the velocity of light. Actually the linear growth of the sources might well have taken place at considerably smaller velocities. Even so the ages fall in the range 10^5 to 10^6 years or 10^{13} seconds in order of magnitude and thus the cumulative emissions are at least as high as $2\cdot10^{58}$ erg.

Another method of determining the total energy involved in the radio sources is based on the assumption that the radio emission is synchrotron radiation from high-energy electrons spiraling in a magnetic field extending throughout the object. This process is thought to be the most efficient for the generation of radio waves and accounts qualitatively at least for the polarization observed in many of the sources. The synchrotron theory implies that energy is *stored* in the radio objects in the form of magnetic field energy and relativistic electron energy. The magnetic field energy is proportional to the mean square of the field intensity (B) and to the volume. The total energy of the electrons is proportional to the rate at which they emit energy, the radio luminosity, divided by the three-halves power of the field intensity and the square root of the characteristic radio frequency emitted. Thus for a given observed volume, luminosity and radio emission spectrum the total energy is equal to a term proportional to B^2 plus one proportional to $B^{-\frac{3}{2}}$. The field intensity is, of course, unknown but even so the total energy exhibits a minimum as a function of B and this minimum can be readily determined. The values for the minimum stored energy even exceed those of the minimum cumulative energies. In the case of the *Hercules* A source the minimum stored energy, if the only high-energy particles are electrons, is approximately 10^{60} erg. The theory does not explicitly indicate the method by which the electrons are accelerated to high energy but it is reasonable to assume, as is the case in the cosmic radiation, that the nuclear component (mostly protons) of the neutral medium or plasma must have considerably greater total energy content than do the electrons. Upon taking this factor into account the stored energy in *Hercules* A, for example, is almost 10^{61} erg. Because of their greater mass the protons do not take part in the synchrotron emission.

In coming to a realistic estimate of the energy requirements in radio objects there remains the knotty problem concerning the efficiency with which the energy generated has been converted into relativistic particles and magnetic fields. Acceleration mechanisms employed in terrestrial laboratories are notoriously inefficient but this may well be due to the very small scale, astrophysically speaking, within which such mechanisms must operate. However, it is estimated that even in solar flares not more than a few per cent of the energy released is in the form of relativistic particles, the main energy release occurring in mass motion and electromagnetic radiation.

On the above basis, the figure $2\cdot10^{62}$ erg is frequently quoted as a representative value of the energy requirement in the large radio sources and for the purposes of argument this figure will be accepted as the *maximum* value in what follows. Suggestions have been made which modify the simple synchrotron model in such a way as to reduce the energy requirements. The magnetic field can be imagined to have a «clumpy» structure such that the effective emitting volume where the field is highest, is much smaller than the over-all volume observed. The magnetic field energy is proportional to the emitting volume not the over-all volume. The emission may come from groups of electrons radiating coherently and thus much more efficiently. Detailed studies of modifications along these lines will be necessary before the energy problem can be considered to be solved.

It will be noted that there is considerable disparity in the two estimates which it is possible to make for the energy *requirements* in the extended radio sources. On the one hand the *cumulative emissions* range up to $2\cdot10^{58}$ erg while the *stored energies* on the synchrotron model have been estimated to be as high as $2\cdot10^{62}$ erg.

4. – Supermassive stars (*).

The immensity of $2\cdot10^{62}$ erg, can best be appreciated by a comparison with the equivalent rest-mass energy of a single star, for example, the sun. The

(*) The designation *supermassive* applies throughout these lectures to stars with mass $M > 10^3 M_\odot$. The prefix *super* will frequently be omitted but the stars under discussion in this paper are not to be confused with stars with M between $30M_\odot$ and $100M_\odot$ which are frequently called massive stars.

mass of the sun is $2 \cdot 10^{33}$ g and the square of the velocity of light is $(3 \cdot 10^{10})^2 \sim 10^{21}$ erg per gram. Thus Einstein's relation between energy and mass

$$E = Mc^2 \tag{1}$$

becomes numerically

$$E \approx 2 \cdot 10^{54} (M/M_\odot) \text{ erg} \tag{2}$$

where $M/M_\odot$ is the stellar mass expressed in units of the solar mass. We see then that the energy stored on the synchrotron theory in particles and magnetic fields in the invisible radio objects requires the original production of energy of the order of that obtained by the complete annihilation of the mass of one-hundred millions suns, $10^8\, M_\odot$. The problem can be taken in a quite literal sense on the grounds that the conversion of mass is the fundamental mechanism for the production of energy. On this basis the problem reduces to how, when and where did the conversion take place.

Before proceeding it is advisable to write Einstein's relation in a form more directly applicable to the problem under consideration as follows

$$\Delta E = (M_0 - M)c^2 = 2 \cdot 10^{54}(M_0 - M)/M_\odot \text{ erg}, \tag{3}$$

where ΔE is the energy made available from a system of particles with total rest mass M_0 when by some mechanism the mass, measured through gravitational or inertial effects by an external observer, has been reduced to M. The quantity ΔE is the energy store available for transformation at varying efficiencies into the various observable forms—γ-ray, X-ray, optical, radio, neutrino and high-energy particle emission.

In principle it is possible for M to decrease to zero but not to negative values and so the maximum available energy is indeed $M_0 c^2$. One mechanism by which this can occur is through the annihilation of equal amounts of matter and antimatter. This mechanism has been discussed by TELLER (1965). The main problem has to do with the assembly of matter and antimatter in sufficient quantities on a time scale no greater than that associated with the assumed explosive origin of these objects. Although annihilation will not be discussed further in this paper, it may prove to be the ultimate solution to the problem.

The success of the idea of nuclear energy generation in stars led quite naturally to the extension of this idea to the radio sources. HOYLE and FOWLER (1963*a*) investigated the possibility that a mass of the order of $10^8\, M_\odot$ has condensed into a simple star in which the energy generation takes place. On this point of view, using the standard theory of stellar structure in Newtonian hydrostatic equilibrium, one immediately obtains optical luminosities of the order of 10^{46} erg s^{-1} and lifetimes for nuclear energy generation of the order of 10^6 to 10^7 years so that the over-all energy release is approximately 10^{60} ergs. (See Sect. **8** for additional details.)

There is, of course, a basic limitation inherent in thermonuclear energy generation. The conversion of hydrogen into helium involves the transformation of only 0.7 per cent of the rest mass into energy and further nuclear burning leading to the most tightly bound nuclear species near iron brings this figure only to slight less than one per cent. Thus $M_0 - M$ in eq. (3) is at most equal to $0.01\, M_0$ and the complete nuclear conversion of 10^8 solar masses of hydrogen into iron-group elements leads to the release of $2 \cdot 10^{60}$ erg. In general

$$\Delta E_{\text{nucl}} < 2 \cdot 10^{52}\, M_0/M_\odot \text{ erg}\,. \tag{4}$$

Equation (4) is expressed in terms of an upper limit for the following reason. In the observed stars with masses ranging approximately from 1 to 100 $M_\odot$ the conversion never seems to reach completion before steady mass loss or supernova explosion terminates the life of the star. Thus it is clear that the nuclear generation of $2 \cdot 10^{62}$ erg, the maximum value discussed above, involves at least $10^{10}\, M_\odot$. This figure corresponds to the entire mass of a medium size galaxy! On the other hand, the nuclear generation of $2 \cdot 10^{58}$ erg, the minimum value discussed above, involves the order of $10^6\, M_\odot$. This figure corresponds to the mass of the larger globular clusters of stars in the halo of the galaxy and in other galaxies. If globular clusters are involved in the energy production, it need not necessarily take place at the center of the galaxy.

In the massive galaxies associated with the strong radio sources there seemed to be no observational evidence for the abnormal heavy-element concentration which would presumably follow from the nuclear conversion of $10^{10}\, M_\odot$. If the larger energy requirements are accepted, it can be argued that nuclear energy might prove inadequate and so HOYLE and FOWLER (1963*b*) turned to another possibility, gravitational energy. On classical Newtonian theory the gravitational binding energy of a system of rest mass M_0 with maximum radius R is approximately given by

$$\Omega = \frac{3}{5-n}\,\frac{GM_0^2}{R} \approx \frac{2GM_0^2}{R}\,, \tag{5}$$

where n is the polytropic index which has been arbitrarily chosen equal to 3.5 in the final approximation given. If no energy is stored in the system which remains as « cold » gas or « dust » then Ω becomes ΔE, the energy freed by the system on condensing from the dispersed state in which the gravitational interaction can be neglected. If eq. (5) is written

$$\Delta E_{\text{grav}} = \Omega \approx \left(\frac{2GM_0}{Rc^2}\right) M_0 c^2 \tag{6}$$

it will be seen that the dimensionless quantity $2GM_0/Rc^2$ is just the fraction of the rest-mass energy made available. Classical Newtonian theory places no limitation on $2GM_0/Rc^2$ but the theory of general relativity limits it to unity at the Schwarzschild limit. Thus

$$\Delta E_{\text{grav}} < M_0 c^2 \leqslant 2 \cdot 10^{54}\, M_0/M_\odot \text{ erg} \tag{7}$$

in agreement with the statement made previously that M could not become negative.

In what way can use be made of the release of gravitational energy? We assume that in some way this energy is removed from the collapsing core and is either absorbed in the outer envelope or is completely lost by the star. In either case the hydrostatic balance in the envelope is destroyed and the envelope material is ejected with high velocity. The energy loss from the core may occur through photon or neutrino emission. Another possibility exists if the massive star is in rotation. After the exhaustion of nuclear energy the star will contract with the contraction of the core being much more rapid than that of the envelope. It is reasonable to suppose that the angular momentum of the core will be conserved once it has contracted away from the envelope and that eventually the core will become unstable to fission into two bodies rotating about each other as in a binary star. Such a system loses rotational energy by radiating gravitational waves.

All emission mechanisms suffer from the limiting effect of the gravitational red shift. In order for gravitational energy to be released from the core it is necessary that the core contract or that $(GM_0/Rc^2)_{\text{core}}$ increase. But the red shift in radiation is just proportional to this dimensionless quantity in first order. Radiation arrives at a distant observer with less energy than that calculated by a local observer where the radiation is emitted. This is true for all forms of energy transfer, by particles as well as radiation. Thus the rate of any form of energy loss by the core is greatly reduced as $(GM_0/Rc^2)_{\text{core}}$ increases and, as a result, the energy loss is not *complete* as implied in eq. (6) where it was assumed that no internal energy of motion or radiation remained in the star during contraction. As a matter of fact even the most optimistic calculations have not revealed mechanisms whereby a contracting massive star can transfer more than a few per cent of the gravitational energy of its core to the outer envelope. The gravitational release of energy may be somewhat more efficient than nuclear release but not by a large factor. Thus the release of $2 \cdot 10^{62}$ erg must, on just about any grounds, involve a mass of the order of $10^{10}\, M_\odot$. The large elliptical galaxies associated with radio sources have total mass estimated at $10^{12}\, M_\odot$. Thus if $2 \cdot 10^{62}$ erg is indeed the correct value for the energy requirement in radio galaxies, then of the order of one per cent of the mass of the galaxy has been involved in the generation of this energy.

5. – Quasars.

It has been noted previously that HOYLE and FOWLER (1963*a*) had obtained *optical* luminosities of the order of 10^{46} erg s^{-1} for a massive star of $10^8 M_\odot$ in hydrostatic equilibrium and in fact it was found that the luminosity is just proportional to the mass for $M > 10^3 M_\odot$. These large optical luminosities did not seem to have any immediate connection with the extended radio sources since the problem concerning the transformation of the optically emitted energy into high-energy electrons and magnetic fields remained unsolved.

However, at the same time that these calculations were being made, an observational discovery of great significance was made in Pasadena by SCHMIDT (1963) and was quickly confirmed by OKE (1963) and by GREENSTEIN and MATTHEWS (1963). It had been known for some time that certain of the radio sources were located in coincidence with starlike objects which apparently had diameters too small to be resolved by optical telescopes and which showed on photographic plates as diffraction images characteristic of the telescope. These objects were called « radio stars ».

The Pasadena group pioneered in the use of the 200-inch Hale Telescope on Mount Palomar to investigate the spectroscopy of these « radio stars ». For several years their investigations of four of these objects led nowhere; they were unable to understand the peculiar emission lines of the spectra which the telescope revealed. There the matter rested until SCHMIDT began studying the spectrum of a fifth object catalogued by Cambridge University radio astronomers as 3C 273. This time the Gordian knot was cut. Several of the emission lines from 3C 273 formed a simple harmonic pattern, with separation and intensity decreasing toward the ultra-violet. The lines obviously belonged to a series of the type expected from hydrogen or any other atom that had been stripped of all electrons but one. SCHMIDT soon concluded that no atom gave the observed wave lengths. If he assumed, however, that the spectrum lines had been shifted toward the red by 16 per cent, the observed wave lengths agreed with those of hydrogen. Shortly thereafter OKE found the H_α line in exactly the position predicted by the red-shift hypothesis and GREENSTEIN and MATTHEWS found an even greater red shift of 37 per cent in 3C 48 when they properly identified the lines observed as corresponding to well-known lines from the elements oxygen, neon and magnesium.

GREENSTEIN and SCHMIDT (1964) soon showed that the red shifts could not be gravitational red shifts associated with large masses confined to regions of very small radius. The masses involved are found to be quite large but the radii of the emitting regions are so great that the gravitational red shift is negligible. They suggested that their « quasi-stellar » objects or « quasars » are extragalactic and that the red shifts arise from the general cosmological expan sion of the universe. With this interpretation they were then able to determine the luminosity distance for the objects and to convert the observed apparent luminosities into absolute luminosities. The calculations indicated that the quasars have optical luminosities of the order of 10^{46} erg s^{-1} or more than one-hundred times the optical luminosity of our Galaxy. The quasars may or may not be located in galaxies, but if they are, they outshine the surrounding galaxy so that it is lost in the diffraction pattern of the quasars' image.

The optical luminosities of the quasars are very high, $\sim 10^{46}$ erg s^{-1}, but there is no convincing evidence that these objects have lifetimes in excess of 10^5 to 10^6 years. Thus the cumulative optical emission is the order of 10^{59} erg which is well within the nuclear resources of a star with $M = 10^8 M_\odot$. Only seven per cent of the hydrogen of such a massive star need be converted into helium to release this amount of energy. Because of the small volume the stored energies required are small.

It is now well established that the quasars exhibit variability in optical luminosity (SMITH and HOFFLEIT 1963; MATTHEWS and SANDAGE 1963; SANDAGE 1964; SHAROV and EFREMOV 1963; GEYER 1964). In addition to luminous flashes with durations of the order of days or weeks there is some evidence for cyclic variations with periods of the order of ten years. It is generally agreed that the occurrence of the cyclic variations is crucial to the question whether the primary radiation object is a single coherent massive star $\left((10^3 \div 10^{10})\, M_\odot\right)$ as originally proposed by HOYLE and FOWLER (1963*a* 1963*b*) or a system of smaller stars $\left((1 \div 10^2)\, M_\odot\right)$ as discussed by numerous authors (BURBIDGE 1961; HOYLE and FOWLER 1965; GOLD AXFORD and RAY 1965; WOLTJER 1964; ULAM and WALDEN 1964; FIELD 1964). It is difficult on the basis of collisions or supernova outbursts in a system of many stellar objects to explain variations which exhibit a fairly regular periodicity. Thus, without prejudice to the problem of the reality of the cyclic variations since only additional and more precise observations will settle this matter, the possibility is investigated in what follows that such variations can arise from nonlinear relaxation oscillations in a single massive star. The star is taken to have no rotation and to be spherically symmetric with all physical parameters depending only on the radial variable. Rotation or other mechanisms which destroy the spherical symmetry change the behavior of the star markedly and will be mentioned briefly at the end of the lecture and will be discussed in detail in Sects. **8** to **16**.

It has also been suggested that the quasars are local. TERRELL (1964, 1965) has proposed the hypothesis that the quasars were ejected at relativistic velocities in an explosive event at the center of the *Galaxy* some 10^6 to 10^7 years ago. HOYLE and BURBIDGE (1965, 1966) have suggested that a likely candidate to give rise to the quasars in our vicinity is NGC 5128 which is a powerful radio source in which at least two outbursts appeared to have occurred. In this case some objects with blue shifts may be expected.

On the local hypothesis the characteristic distances for the quasars are 1 to 10 megaparsec rather than 10^3 to 10^4 megaparsec as on the cosmological hypothesis. TERRELL (1965) suggests that the quasar masses are $\sim 10^4 M_\odot$ rather than the value 10^8 to $10^{10} M_\odot$ required if the observed red shifts are cosmological. *Thus on either the local or the cosmological hypothesis, supermassive stars, as defined in this lecture, are required.* Furthermore the original local outburst involved masses of the same order of magnitude as those attributed to the quasars themselves on the cosmological hypothesis. Consequently, in the remainder of the following Sections reference to the quasars will be made on the basis that they are cosmological objects but this is not a necessary condition for the arguments put forward.

6. – Relaxation oscillations in nonrotating supermassive stars.

The rapid generation of nuclear energy during the general-relativistic collapse of a massive star is considered to be the triggering agent for the relaxation oscillations. From the standpoint of the model discussed in HOYLE and FOWLER (1965) it is necessary to assume that the early fragmentation in the original gas cloud resulted in the formation of stars small enough ($< 10 M_\odot$) that significant nuclear evolution (consumption of hydrogen) did not occur in the time scale ($\sim 3 \cdot 10^6$ years) in which stellar collisions reduced the system of stars once again to a single gaseous object. Thus the starting point is a massive star, say $M \sim 10^6 M_\odot$, with a characteristic dimension of 10^{17} cm, central temperature of the order of 10^5 °K, with pressure support due almost entirely to radiation and a structure closely approximating that of a polytrope of index $n = 3$ (FOWLER and HOYLE, 1963, 1964). The composition is the same as that of the original gas cloud, for example, $X = 0.75$, $Y = 0.22$ and $Z = 0.03$. After some exhaustion of hydrogen a representative composition for purposes of computation will be taken to be $X = 0.50$, $Y = 0.47$, $Z = 0.03$ with Z primarily made up of CNO-nuclei.

General-relativistic considerations lead to dynamic instability in nonrotating massive stars when the radius falls below a certain critical value (IBEN 1963; FOWLER 1964; CHANDRASEKHAR 1964*a*, *b*, 1965*a*; MCVITTIE 1964; GRATTON 1964; ZEL'DOVICH 1964). In what follows we make use of the post-Newtonian approximation in the notation of FOWLER (1964). The significant results are illustrated in Fig. 1 where the energy content of the star exclusive of the rest mass energy of the constituent particles is presented as a function of the radius and central temperature. The heavy solid curve represents the equilibrium binding energy in solar rest-mass energy equivalent units given by the post-Newtonian approximation. The decrease to a minimum at a certain outer radius and central temperature followed by a rise into the unbound

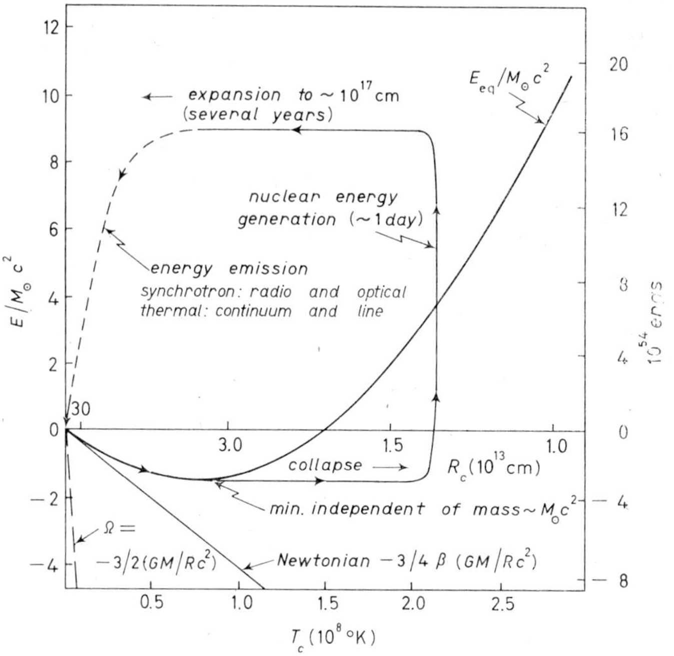

Fig. 1. – The internal energy of a nonrotating massive star ($2.5\times10^5 M_\odot$, $L=4\times10^{46}$ erg/s(3 C–273), $L\tau=1.6\times10^{55}$ erg, $\tau=13y$) in excess of the rest-mass energy is shown as a function of radius and central temperature. The heavy curve shows the energy required for hydrostatic equilibrium when general-relativistic considerations are taken into account. This curve deviates quadratically from the linear Newtonian term and reaches a minimum with absolute value the order of $M_\odot c^2$ at $R\sim4\times10^{13}$ cm, $T_c\sim0.7\times10^8$ °K. This minimum is reached before nuclear energy generation begins in the interior. A general relativistic collapse occurs which is stopped and reversed by hydrogen burning through the CNO bi-cycle in a time of approximately one day near $R\sim10^{13}$ cm, $T_c\sim2\times10^8$ °K. A radial shock wave is initiated and the resulting expansion extends to a radius of approximately 10^{17} cm in a time scale of the order of several years. Damping of the expansion occurs through radio and optical synchrotron emission and by nonequilibrium continuum and line emission. The over-all process can best be described as a relaxation oscillation. The case illustrated employs the luminosity and period observed for the quasar in 3C-273B which is assumed to be at the cosmological distance corresponding to its red shift.

region is in marked contrast to the linear decrease exhibited by theNewtonian term, $-3\beta GM/4Rc^2$. To the left of the minimum in the « classical » range an adiabatic perturbation toward smaller radii leads to more energy than that required for equilibrium and thus to more pressure than that necessary for hydrostatic equilibrium. Thus the contraction is opposed as will clearly also be the case for a perturbing expansion and thus the system is inherently stable. The same argument used to the right of the minimum (FOWLER 1964) indicates that a contraction leads to less pressure than that needed for hydrostatic equilibrium while an expansion leads to more so that the system is dynamically unstable to *adiabatic* perturbations.

The equilibrium energy in the post-Newtonian approximation can be written for $n=3$ as

$$\frac{E_{eq}}{Mc^2} = -\frac{3}{8}\beta\left(\frac{2GM}{Rc^2}\right) + \frac{3}{16}\left(\frac{3}{\pi}\right)^{\frac{1}{2}} R_3 \left(\frac{2GM}{Rc^2}\right)^2 + \dots, \tag{8}$$

where $R_3 = 6.897$ is one of the constants of integration for the polytropic equation for $n=3$. From Eddington's quartic equation the ratio of gas pressure to total pressure is given for small values by FOWLER and HOYLE (1964) as

$$\beta \approx 6(\Gamma_1 - 4/3) \approx \frac{4.28}{\mu}\left(\frac{M_\odot}{M}\right)^{\frac{1}{2}} \ll 1, \tag{9}$$

where μ is the mean molecular weight and $\Gamma_1 = \mathrm{d}\ln p/\mathrm{d}\ln\varrho$, with p, the pressure and ϱ, the density. For $M = 10^4$ to $10^8\, M_\odot$, $\beta \sim 10^{-1}$ to 10^{-3}. In massive stars the main pressure support is that due to radiation, β is small, the Newtonian term in (8) is small and the post-Newtonian term becomes significant for small values of $R_g/R = 2GM/Rc^2$ of the order of β. The limiting gravitational radius or Schwarzschild radius is designated by

$$R_g = 2GM/c^2 = 3\cdot 10^5\,(M/M_\odot)\ \text{cm}\,. \tag{10}$$

The critical radius can be determined by setting the derivative of (8) equal to zero in which case

$$\frac{R_{cr}}{R_g} = \left(\frac{3}{\pi}\right)^{\frac{1}{2}}\frac{R_3}{\beta} = \frac{6.74}{\beta} \sim \left(\frac{M}{M_\odot}\right)^{\frac{1}{2}} \sim 10^2 \text{ to } 10^4\,. \tag{11a}$$

Numerically it is found that

$$R_{cr} = 3.4\cdot 10^5\,(M/M_\odot)^{\frac{3}{2}}\ \text{cm} \sim 10 \text{ to } 10^7 \text{ light seconds}\,. \tag{11b}$$

At this point and in what follows it will be assumed that the gross internal structure of the stars is insensitive in first order to static or dynamic changes in E/Mc^2 of the order of β. Thus the equations relating central temperature and density with the radius for a polytrope with $n=3$ can be freely employed. In fact the second-order term in eq. (8) is correctly derived by using first-order terms where required. The critical central temperature and density are thus

$$T_{cr} = \frac{\Re c^2}{2\mu a^{\frac{1}{4}} G^{\frac{3}{4}} M} = \frac{1.25\cdot 10^{13}}{\mu}\left(\frac{M_\odot}{M}\right)\ {}^\circ\text{K} \sim \sim 10^9 \text{ to } 10^5\ {}^\circ\text{K for } M \sim 10^4 \text{ to } 10^8\, M_\odot\,, \tag{12}$$

$$\varrho_{cr} = \frac{2.54\cdot 10^{17}}{\mu^3}\left(\frac{M_\odot}{M}\right)^{\frac{7}{2}}\ \text{g cm}^{-3} \sim \sim 10^4 \text{ to } 10^{-10}\ \text{g cm}^{-3} \text{ for } M \sim 10^5 \text{ to } 10^8\, M_\odot. \tag{13}$$

Moreover it is possible to show (FOWLER 1964*a*) that eq. (8) can be expanded in increasing powers of T with only the linear and quadratic terms retained in the post-Newtonian approximation.

The minimum equilibrium energy at R_{cr}, T_{cr}, ϱ_{cr} turns out to be independent of the stellar mass and is given by

$$E_{eq}^{min} = -\frac{3M_3 \mathfrak{R}^2 c^2}{4\mu^2 R_3 a^{\frac{1}{2}} G^{\frac{3}{2}}}, \tag{14}$$

where $M_3 = 2.018$ is the second constant of integration for the polytropic equations for $n = 3$. Equation (14) can be rewritten by introducing $\mathfrak{R}^4/a = (15/\pi^2)(\hbar^3 c^3/M_u^4)$ and after evaluation of numerical factors becomes

$$E_{eq}^{min} = -\frac{0.27}{\mu^2}\left(\frac{\hbar c}{GM_u^2}\right)^{\frac{3}{2}} M_u c^2 \sim -10^{57}\cdot 10^{-24} c^2 \sim 10^{33} c^2 , \tag{15}$$

where M_u is the atomic mass unit. It is well known that the dimensionless gravitational interaction constant $GM_u^2/\hbar c$ is very small, of order 10^{-38}. The corresponding fine-structure constant in electromagnetism is $e^2/\hbar c = 1/137$. As indicated in eq. (15) this leads to

$$E_{eq}^{min} \sim - M_\odot c^2 \sim - 2\cdot 10^{54}\ \text{erg} , \tag{16}$$

which indicates that the maximum binding energy of a nonrotating massive star is the order of one solar mass-energy equivalent. More precisely

$$E_{eq}^{min} = -\frac{0.51}{\mu^2} M_\odot c^2 = -\frac{0.91\cdot 10^{54}}{\mu^2}\ \text{erg}. \tag{17}$$

In a first appraisal of the problem it is interesting to consider eq. (16) in relation to the luminosity of the quasars which is of order $L \sim 10^{46}$ erg s^{-1} (GREENSTEIN and SCHMIDT 1964, and OKE 1965). The Helmholtz-Kelvin contraction time, E_{eq}^{min}/L, with this luminosity is thus of the order of several years. This will also be the cycle time if energy of the order of the binding energy is supplied by nuclear burning during an oscillation or pulsation. It is indeed just this general idea which is now explored in somewhat greater detail.

The stellar masses which will prove to be of greatest interest fall in the range $10^5 M_\odot$ to $10^6 M_\odot$. For this mass range eq. (12) indicates that $T_c \sim 10^8$ to 10^7 °K. The rate of energy generation by the CNO bi-cycle at these temperatures and the corresponding low densities is considerably less than that required to maintain a luminosity of the order of 10^{46} erg s^{-1}. Thus when the star reaches the minimum energy in Fig. 1, collapse will commence and will continue until temperatures are reached at which nuclear energy generation becomes adequate for stability. Collapse will in fact be halted when, over the appropriate time interval, the nuclear energy generation matches that required to supply $E_{eq} - E_{eq}^{min}$. Collapse will be reversed to expansion in approximately the same time interval so that the nuclear processes overshoot and deliver in each pulse or cycle the following amount of energy

$$\mathscr{E}_{cyc} = 2(E_{eq} - E_{eq}^{min}) = 2|E_{eq}^{min}|(x_n - 1)^2 = \frac{1.82 \cdot 10^{54}}{\mu^2}(x_n - 1)^2 \text{ erg}, \tag{18}$$

where $x_n = T_n/T_c$ and T_n is the temperature at which the nuclear burning takes place while T_{cr} is the critical temperature for the minimum in E_{eq}. The factor of 2 also follows directly from the conservation of momentum during the stopping and reversal of the collapse. The quadratic dependence on the temperature term in x_n follows directly from the fact that in eq. (8) for E_{eq} only linear and quadratic terms in $R^{-1} \propto T$ are retained. In $E_{eq} - E_{eq}^{min}$ only the quadratic term remains. To determine T_n requires knowledge of the time scale for collapse and of the rate of energy generation in the CNO bi-cycle at elevated temperatures.

The time scale for nuclear burning during general-relativistic collapse can be calculated with sufficient accuracy using the post-Newtonian approximation for the acceleration which can be written (see Sect. **10**) as follows:

$$\left\{\begin{aligned} \ddot{r}(1 + \ldots) &= -\frac{\mathrm{d}p}{\mathrm{d}r}\frac{(1 + v^2/c^2 - 2GM_r/rc^2)}{(\varrho + p/c^2)} - \frac{GM_r}{r^2}\left(1 + \frac{4\pi p r^3}{M_r c^2}\right) \quad \text{(all } r\text{)}, \\ &\approx \frac{1}{\varrho_0}\frac{\mathrm{d}p}{\mathrm{d}r}\left(1 - \frac{u}{\varrho_0 c^2} - \frac{p}{\varrho_0 c^2} + \ldots\right) - \\ &\quad - \frac{4}{3}\pi G \varrho_0 r\left(1 + \frac{u}{\varrho_0 c^2} + \frac{3p}{\varrho_0 c^2} + \ldots\right) \quad \text{(post-Newtonian, center)}, \\ &\approx \frac{1}{\varrho_0}\frac{\mathrm{d}p}{\mathrm{d}r} - \frac{4}{3}\pi G \varrho_0 r \quad \text{(Newtonian, center)}. \end{aligned}\right. \tag{19}$$

In eq. (19), r is the Lagrangian radial co-ordinate, p is the pressure, u is the internal energy density, ϱ_0 is the mass-density, ϱ is the mass-energy density in mass units and M_r is the mass-energy interior to r. Relativistic terms have not been explicitly indicated on the left-hand side of eq. (19). The first term on the right-hand side is relativistically exact, the second term is the post-Newtonian approximation at the center of the star, while the third term is the customary Newtonian approximation at the center. In this Newtonian approximation at hydrostatic equilibrium, $\ddot{r} = 0$. Thus to first order $\ddot{r}$ is just the difference of the first post-Newtonian terms on the right-hand side and the post-Newtonian terms on the left-hand side are not needed and have not been explicitly presented. It will be noted that the difference in the post-Newtonian terms is proportional to $(2u+4p)/\varrho_0 c^2 \sim 10p/\varrho_0 c^2$ for $u \sim 3p$ as is the case in massive stars where radiation pressure dominates.

Standard methods of integration applied to eq. (19) with $\ddot{r}=\dot{r}=0$ at the initial critical conditions lead, for small $(p/\varrho_0 c^2)_{cr} \approx (aT^4/3\varrho_0 c^2)_{cr}$, to

$$\frac{\dot{T}}{T} \approx -\frac{\dot{r}}{r} \approx \left(\frac{40\pi aG}{9c^2}\right)^{\frac{1}{2}} T_{\rm cr}^2 x(x^2-2x\ln x-1)\,, \tag{20}$$

$$\approx \left(\frac{40\pi aG}{27c^2}\right)^{\frac{1}{2}} T_{\rm cr}^2 x(x-1)^{\frac{3}{2}} \qquad \text{for } 1<x<2\,, \tag{21}$$

$$\sim \left(\frac{aG}{c^2}\right)^{\frac{1}{2}} T_{\rm cr}^2 x^2(x-1)^{\frac{1}{2}} \qquad \text{for } 2<x<10\,, \tag{22}$$

where $x=T/T_{cr}$. Solving for the e-folding time in T or r one finds numerically for eq. (22), which is the case of primary interest, that

$$\tau_{\rm gc} \equiv T/\dot{T} = \frac{{\rm d}t}{{\rm d}\ln T} \sim \frac{1.3\cdot 10^5}{T_8^2(x-1)^{\frac{1}{2}}}\ {\rm s}\,. \tag{23}$$

Thus the e-folding time in temperature or radius for general relativistic gravitational collapse (gc) at hydrogen burning temperatures, $(T_n)_8 \sim 2$, in massive stars for which $(T_{\rm cr})_8 \sim 1$ is somewhat less than one day. This is considerably greater than the classical free-fall (ff) time which is

$$\tau_{\rm ff} = (8\pi G\varrho/3)^{-\frac{1}{2}} = 1340\,\varrho^{-\frac{1}{2}}\ {\rm s} \sim 10^3\ {\rm s}\,.$$

However it is the shortness of $\tau_{\rm gc}$ relative to the over-all period of order 10 years which illustrates the extreme nonlinearity of the oscillations under consideration.

In the discussion in HOYLE and FOWLER (1965) of the behavior of CNO-burning of hydrogen in massive stars it was noted that the proton capture reaction by nuclei such as ^{13}N proceed at a rate comparable to the beta-decay of ^{13}N and that alpha-particle reactions lead to some transmutation of the CNO nuclei into heavier nuclei. However these are not serious effects in the cases of primary interest in this paper and it is sufficiently accurate to make the assumption that all CNO nuclei actively participate and remain as catalysts, mostly as ^{14}N ($\sim 0.9Z$), and that the rate of energy generation is primarily determined by the ^{14}N(p, γ) reaction for which HEBBARD and BAILEY (1963) give the empirical parameters, $S_0 = 2.75 \pm 0.50$ keV$\cdot$barn and $\langle {\rm d}S/{\rm d}E\rangle \approx 0$. This leads to a slight modification of the results of CAUGHLAN and FOWLER (1962). When expressed as a power law in temperature near $T_8 \sim 2$ the nuclear energy generation rate for the HCNO-burning is

$$\varepsilon \approx 3.7\cdot 10^{12}\,\varrho XZT_8{}^8\ \ {\rm erg\,g^{-1}\,s^{-1}} \approx 5.6\cdot 10^{10}\,\varrho T_8{}^8\,,\quad X=0.50\,,\quad Z=0.03\,. \tag{24}$$

In a massive star with polytropic index $n=3$, FOWLER and HOYLE (1964) express the density in their eq. (B.120) as

$$\varrho \approx 130 \left(\frac{M_\odot}{M}\right)^{\frac{1}{2}} T_8^{\,3} \text{ g cm}^{-3}\,, \tag{25}$$

so that

$$\varepsilon \approx 7.3\cdot 10^{12} \left(\frac{M_\odot}{M}\right)^{\frac{1}{2}} T_8^{11} \text{ erg g}^{-1}\text{ s}^{-1}\,. \tag{26}$$

FOWLER and HOYLE (1964) also give the energy generation averaged over the star and using their equation (C.84) one finds

$$\bar{\varepsilon} \approx 4.4\cdot 10^{11} \left(\frac{M_\odot}{M}\right)^{\frac{1}{2}} T_8^{11} \text{ erg g}^{-1}\text{ s}^{-1}\,. \tag{27}$$

This is still a quantity effectively representative of the central region of the stellar interior. As noted above, eq. (27) must not be used when the burning becomes rapid enough that beta-decay processes limit the rate of energy generation. The limit comes when the time for the conversion of four protons into helium is just the sum of the mean lifetimes for proton capture by ^{14}O (100 s) and ^{15}O (180 s) and is given by

$$\bar{\varepsilon} \sim \left(\frac{4}{14.5}\cdot\frac{6.0\cdot 10^{18}}{280}\right) Z \sim 5.9\cdot 10^{15} Z \text{ erg g s}^{-1} \sim 1.8\cdot 10^{14}\,, \qquad Z = 0.03\,. \tag{28}$$

The limiting temperature given by combining eqs. (27) and (28) is

$$T_8 < 1.7 \left(\frac{M}{M_\odot}\right)^{1/22} <\sim 3 \text{ for } M = 10^5 \text{ to } 10^6\, M_\odot\,. \tag{29}$$

The simplest procedure is now to equate $\bar{\varepsilon}$ multiplied by the stellar mass and by the effective time for nuclear burning to $\mathscr{E}_{\text{cyc}}$ given by eq. (18). The effective time can be estimated as follows. The quantity $\bar{\varepsilon}\tau_{\text{gc}}$ varies approximately as T^9. The e-folding time for T^9 is $\frac{1}{9}$ that for T. However the velocity is reduced from its initial value to zero and is then reversed by the energy generation so that the effective time for nuclear burning during each cycle is $(4/9)\,\tau_{\text{gc}}$. Thus

$$\mathscr{E}_{\text{cyc}} = \tfrac{4}{9}\,\bar{\varepsilon}\tau_{\text{gc}}\, M\,. \tag{30}$$

Equations (12), (18), (23), (27) and (30) can be combined to yield

$$\frac{M}{M_\odot} \approx 1.0\cdot 10^5 \,\frac{(x_n)^{18/17}}{(x_n-1)^{5/17}} \sim 10^5\,(x_n)^{13/17}\,, \tag{31}$$

where $x_n = T_n/T_{cr}$ as before. T_{cr} is the critical temperature at which collapse begins and T_n is now the temperature at which the hydrogen burning generates $\mathscr{E}_{cyc}$ in the available time determined by the reversal of the collapse. Equations (18) and (31) then yield (for $x_n \sim 3$ as found below)

$$\mathscr{E}_{cyc} \sim 10^{41} \left(\frac{M}{M_\odot}\right)^{34/13} \text{erg} . \tag{32}$$

In this equation $\mu = 0.73$ has been used corresponding to $X = 0.50$, $Y = 0.47$, $Z = 0.03$.

We have now arrived at the nuclear energy generated in the pulse which triggers each relaxation oscillation or cycle. This must be equal to the total luminosity L for all forms of radiation multiplied by the cycle period τ_{cyc} so that

$$L\tau_{cyc} \sim 10^{41} \left(\frac{M}{M_\odot}\right)^{34/13} \text{erg} \tag{33}$$

or

$$\frac{M}{M_\odot} \sim 2\cdot 10^{-16} (L\tau_{cyc})^{13/34} . \tag{34}$$

In the case of the quasar 3C 273 the observations indicate $L \sim 4\cdot 10^{46}$ erg s^{-1} (OKE 1965) and $\tau_{cyc} \sim 13\, y \sim 4\cdot 10^8$ s (SMITH and HOFFLEIT 1963) so that $L\tau_{cyc} \sim 1.6\cdot 10^{55}$ erg and

$$\frac{M}{M_\odot} \sim 2.5\cdot 10^5 .$$

Corresponding to this value for $M/M_\odot$ it is found from eq. (12) that $(T_{cr})_8 \sim 0.7$ and from eq. (31) that $x_n \sim 3$ so that $(T_n)_8 \sim 2$. These values are illustrated in Fig. 1. At $(T_{cr})_8 \sim 0.7$ the stellar radius is $\sim 4\cdot 10^{13}$ cm while at $(T_n)_8 \sim 2$ the radius is $\sim 1.3\cdot 10^{13}$ cm. The Schwarzschild limiting radius is $\sim 8\cdot 10^{10}$ cm.

It will be noted in eq. (32) that $\mathscr{E}_{cyc}$ varies as a fairly high power, ~ 2.6, of the stellar mass. Thus $\mathscr{E}_{cyc}$ rapidly approaches the total nuclear energy content of the star. At this point the nuclear energy would suffice for only one pulse of energy generation. These considerations lead to the conclusion that relaxation oscillations without serious overshooting due to excessive energy generation can only take place in *nonrotating* stars with mass not exceeding $\sim 10^6\, M_\odot$. It may prove significant that this is the order of magnitude of the mass of the larger globular clusters.

The above discussion has treated the relaxation oscillations almost solely in terms of energy considerations. Damping and stabilizing mechanisms will be discussed in the sequel but an important point in this connection should be noted at this time. The time spent during the oscillation with $R < R_{cr}$ when the star is dynamically unstable is very short compared to the over-all period being of the order of one day. Thus practically the entire oscillation occurs with $R > R_{cr}$ during which the star is dynamically stable as in the classical, nonrelativistic case. The maximum radius reached during the oscillation will be the order of the ratio of 10 years to 1 day multiplied by R_{cr} or approximately 10^{17} cm. The classical period for linear oscillations is not strictly applicable to the very large amplitude oscillations under discussion. This period is given by $\Pi \sim (\beta \bar{\varrho} G)^{-\frac{1}{2}}$ and is of the order of 10 years for the mean density in a star with $M \sim 2.5 \cdot 10^5 M_\odot$ (3C-273) at an intermediate stage between the minimum ($R_n \sim 10^{13}$ cm) and maximum ($R_{max} \sim 10^{17}$ cm) excursions of the relaxation oscillations.

Equation (34) yields the mass of a nonrotating central stellar object having properties consistent with the product of the luminosity and period of a variable quasar such as 3C-273 if the period is that for relaxation oscillations in the star maintained by energy generation through HCNO-burning. The actual period will be determined by other considerations to be discussed later. At this point we turn our attention to the cumulative emissions from 3C-273.

The mass given by eq. (35) can only satisfy the cumulative energy requirement for 3C-273 if the lifetime is relatively short. The nuclear energy resources for $M = 2 \cdot 10^5 M_\odot$ are at most $4 \cdot 10^{57}$ erg from eq. (4). For a luminosity equal to $4 \cdot 10^{46}$ erg s^{-1} this yields a lifetime of 10^{11} s or 3000 years. The number of relaxation oscillations is approximately 250. GREENSTEIN and SCHMIDT (1964) discuss a model for the quasar in 3C-273 with lifetime equal to 10^3 years. They emphasize that on this basis the quasar is considerably younger than the associated objects in 3C-273, namely the radio halo surrounding the quasar and the optical jet. The quasar has then to be taken as a later event unassociated with the origin of the older, large scale components of 3C-273.

In the next Section we will present in detail the modifications to the discussion presented here which are necessary if the value obtained for the mass from an equation such as (34) is to be substantially increased. Suffice it to note that the introduction of rotation or turbulent kinetic energy leads to a substantial increase in the mass in which the nuclear burning can take place without excessive overshooting during the relaxation oscillations. This Section will be concluded with a brief enumeration of considerations connected with the energizing and damping of relaxation oscillations in such a way that stable pulsations are possible. We lean havily on the quasar models discussed by GREENSTEIN and SCHMIDT (1964) and by OKE (1965) in this enumeration. These considerations are illustrated schematically in Fig. 2.

1) LEDOUX (1941) has shown that the relative radial displacement at the center of a pulsating massive star in which $\Gamma_1 \sim \frac{4}{3}$ can be comparable in magnitude to that throughout the star and particularly at the surface. This means that nuclear energy generation at the center is extremely effective in triggering pulsations in the massive stars under discussion in this paper.

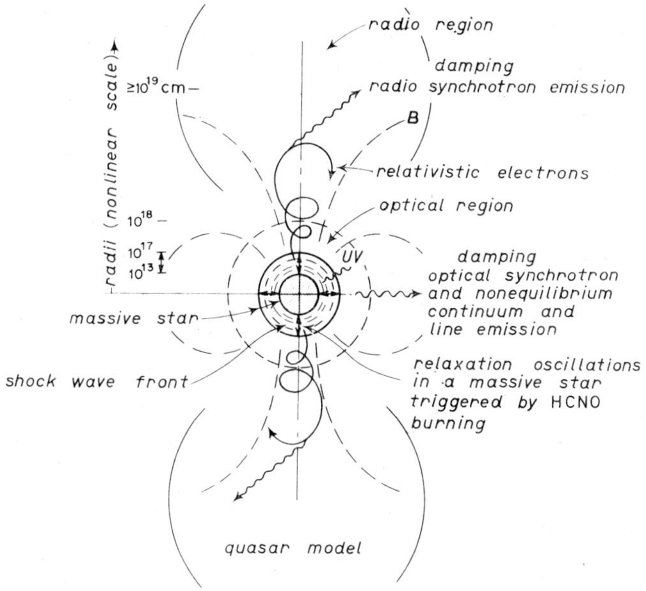

Fig. 2. – Schematic model for a quasar. Large-amplitude relaxation oscillations between radii of 10^{13} and 10^{17} cm are energized in a massive star by HCNO burning at a temperature near $2 \cdot 10^8$ °K. Shock waves transmit the energy to the tenuous outer envelope from which relativistic particles are ejected into the region surrounding the star. An associated dipole magnetic field channels the relativistic particles into two large-scale regions ($\geqslant 10^{19}$ cm) in which radio synchrotron emission occurs. Optical synchrotron radiation is emitted from the region immediately surrounding the star ($\sim 10^{18}$ cm). Non-equilibrium continuum and line emission are also stimulated in this region by ultra-violet radiation from the star. It is this region which is visible and not the star itself. If the quasars are local all dimensions should be reduced by a factor ~ 100.

2) LEDOUX (1941) and SCHWARZSCHILD and HÄRM (1959) have emphasized that the problem of stability in massive stars depends critically on the mechanism of heat leakage in the envelope which serves to damp the oscillations energized in the core. They show that *pulsational instability* is to be expected for stellar masses above a critical value of the order of $\sim 10^2 M_\odot$, *if the only processes of heat transfer and loss are ordinary convection and radiation.* This can be understood on the basis that the radiative luminosity is proportional to $R^2 T^4$ which in turn is proportional to R^{-2} so that at the large radii occurring during the expansion, $L_{rad} \propto R^{-2}$ is ineffective as a damping mechanism.

3) What is required are damping mechanisms which are effective at large radii and low surface densities. It is therefore suggested that the extraordinary modes of energy emission evidenced by the quasars, namely, radio synchrotron emission, optical synchrotron emission as well as nonequilibrium continuum and line emission serve as the damping agents in stabilizing the pulsations. It is the over-all rate of these emissions relative to the nuclear energy generation per pulse which determines the period of the oscillations. As discussed previously these emissions take place predominantly while $R > R_{cr}$ during which the star is dynamically stable.

4) As noted in the discussion of relaxation oscillations the nuclear energy generation takes place in the period of the order of a day which is very short compared to the observed over-all periods of approximately 10 years. This nuclear pulse will lead to the propagation of a radial shock wave outward from the center of the star. From the work of Ôno, Sakashita and Ohyama (1961), Ohyama (1963) and Colgate and White (1964) it is known that such a shock wave will reach relativistic velocities in the tenous outer envelope of the star and will there generate relativistic particles which are then ejected into the region surrounding the star. This high-energy process becomes an especially effective damping agent during the latter stages of expansion when surface densities are low. It is generally believed that shock-wave acceleration results in the production of relativistic particles with total energies comparable to that for nonrelativistic particles. This seems to be required by the quasar observations.

5) The ejection of relativistic particles leads to the formation of the region with dimensions of the order of 10^{18} cm in which an optical synchrotron continuum can be generated in the presence of an associated magnetic field. This region is in fact relatively transparent to high-energy particles which can leak out to form a much more extended region with dimensions of the order of 10^{19} cm or even greater in which radio synchrotron emission takes place. The reader is referred to Greenstein and Schmidt (1964) for detailed description of the regions under discussion. If the quasars are local these dimensions must be reduced by a factor ~ 100.

6) If the over-all magnetic field has dipole structure then the ejection of the relativistic particles will tend to occur parallel to the dipole axis and to result in the formation of a two-component radio source as is frequently observed. For the field strengths required by synchrotron theory, the Larmor radii of the relativistic particles are quite small compared to the dimensions of the radio sources. On this picture the line of centers of the radio components would lie along the axis of rotation even for an inclined magnetic dipole. For the line of centers to be perpendicular to the axis of rotation it is necessary to

consider other possibilities such as the fission mechanism discussed by HOYLE and FOWLER (1965) and FOWLER (1964).

7) From the original work of HOYLE and FOWLER (1963*a*) on supermassive stars the *surface* temperature is estimated to be the order of 10^5 °K during the hydrogen burning stage in the *interior*. Intense ultra-violet emission at this temperature will amply suffice to excite nonequilibrium continuum and line emission from the 10^{18} cm region in which optical synchrotron radiation is also generated. At the same time the high opacity presented to the ultraviolet radiations would make observation of the embedded supermassive star impossible.

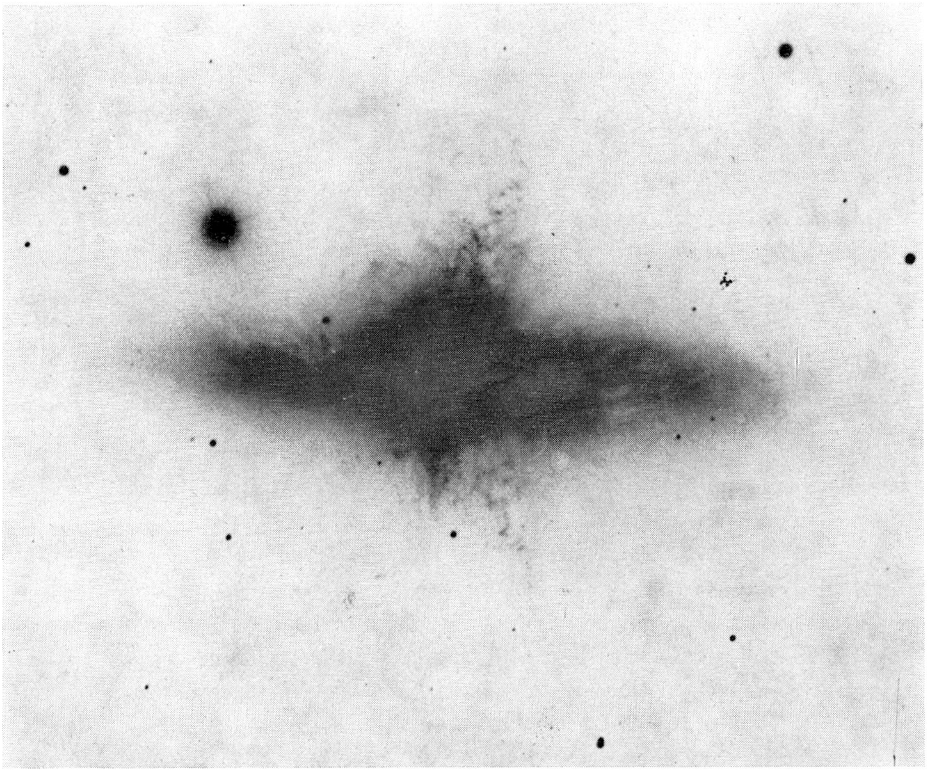

Fig. 3. – Photograph of the galaxy M82 taken with the 200-inch Hale telescope on Mt. Palomar in H_α light. Note the complex filamentary structure expanding from the center of the galaxy. LYNDS and SANDAGE (1963) point out that the total mass of the expanding material could be as great as $5.6 \cdot 10^6 M_\odot$. This exceeds the mass which can be stabilized during hydrogen burning by ordinary pressure forces because of general relativistic effects. It is suggested that the explosion is the result of the general relativistic instability discussed in the text.

8) Upon the exhaustion of nuclear energy resources, gravitational collapse occurs in a nonrotating massive star. For a rotating star collapse can also occur if mechanisms for the transfer of angular momentum are effective. In the case of collapse, gravitational energy becomes available and the evolution of a quasar into an extended radio source may become possible as discussed by FOWLER (1964).

9) LYNDS and SANDAGE (1963) have shown that the peculiar optical and radio galaxy M82, shown in Fig. 3, exhibits a complex filamentary system which contains a mass of expanding material which may be as large as $5.6 \cdot 10^6 M_\odot$ moving with kinetic energy equal to $2.4 \cdot 10^{55}$ erg. The expansion velocities are determined to be proportional to the distance from the galactic center and the data suggest that the primary explosive event took place $1.5 \cdot 10^6$ years ago. On the basis of the ideas presented in this lecture it seems reasonable to suggest that M82 was the site of the formation of a supermassive star with $M > 10^6 M_\odot$ which was not stabilized by rotation or internal turbulent energy. Thus effective damping of nuclear energy generation failed to occur. The burning of $\sim 3 \cdot 10^{-4}$ of the original hydrogen sufficed to supply the observed expansion energy. The burning *in toto* of $\sim 10^{-3}$ of the original hydrogen sufficed to supply all the observed energies, kinetic, magnetic, luminous and that stored in ionization and high-energy electrons.

7. – Summary to this point.

The work described in this lecture constitutes a return to the early point of view of HOYLE and FOWLER (1963*a*, *b*) that supermassive stars can meet the energy requirements in radio sources, specifically in the quasars. General relativity leads to dynamic instability in nonrotating massive stars but the result is relaxation oscillations energized by hydrogen-burning rather than catastrophic collapse at least for masses not exceeding $10^6 M_\odot$. It is noted that the introduction of rotation or turbulent kinetic energy raises this limit by several orders of magnitude and that Sects. **8** to **10** will treat this matter. It is emphasized that the exotic forms of energy emission observed in the quasars can serve to damp the relaxation oscillations in such a way that stable pulsations result. It is thus suggested that quasars consist of pulsating supermassive stars, energized by nuclear reactions, with radio and optical emissions from extended surrounding regions which the star excites with ultraviolet radiation and relativistic particles. With the exhaustion of nuclear energy, gravitational energy may become available and the evolution of a quasar into an extended radio source becomes possible. It is suggested that exploding galaxies such as M82 developed a supermassive star with $M > 10^6 M_\odot$ which was not stabilized by rotation or internal turbulent energy so that effective damping of nuclear burning failed to occur.

8. – Rotation and stability of Supermassive stars (*).

In Sects. **1** to **7** an attempt was made to understand the source of the energy requirements in quasars and extragalactic radio sources in terms of nuclear and gravitational energy release in supermassive stars. It was found that the conversion of hydrogen into helium could take place in stars with mass up to $10^6 M_\odot$ during stable regimes of reasonable duration characterized by non-linear relaxation oscillations with periods similar to those observed. It was emphasized that the damping of these oscillations required mechanisms for energy transfer and emission other than radiation and convection. It was suggested that the necessary requirements were met by transfer through relativistic shock waves, by the development of magnetic fields, by the acceleration of electrons to high energies, and by the production of radio and optical synchrotron emission.

Because the onset of general-relativistic instability occurs in stars with $M > 10^6 M_\odot$ at temperatures far below those necessary for nuclear burning, damping cannot be effective once the nuclear processes are triggered. In this Section it will be shown that the general-relativistic instability is removed by rotation in stars with mass at least as high as $10^8 M_\odot$ and perhaps as high as $10^9 M_\odot$. Other stabilizing mechanisms are briefly mentioned.

HOYLE and FOWLER (1963*a*) showed that the radiative luminosity of a *stable* supermassive star ($M > 10^3 M_\odot$) is proportional to the mass according to the approximate relation

$$L \approx 2 \cdot 10^{38} (M/M_\odot) \text{ erg s}^{-1} , \tag{37}$$

where M is the mass of the star and $M_\odot$ is the mass of the sun. On the assumption that one-half of the hydrogen in the star is processed to helium the available energy is

$$Q \approx \tfrac{1}{2} \cdot 7 \cdot 10^{-3} Mc^2 \approx 6 \cdot 10^{51} (M/M_\odot) \text{ erg} , \tag{38}$$

so that the lifetime for the main-sequence stage of a supermassive star is

$$\tau \approx Q/L \approx 3 \cdot 10^{13} \text{ s} \approx 10^6 \text{ y} \tag{39}$$

independent of mass. It was also found that hydrogen burning through the CNO bi-cycle takes place at a central temperature near $8 \cdot 10^7$ °K and that the effective surface temperature during hydrogen burning is approximately $7 \cdot 10^4$ °K

(*) This Section is a revised and updated version of a paper originally presented before the National Academy of Sciences (USA), Washington, April 1965, and published in the *Astrophysical Journal*, **144**, 180 (1966).

indicating strong emission in the ultra-violet. A major unsolved problem concerned the mechanism by which the optical energy output is transformed into the high-energy particles and magnetic field necessary to produce the radio emission on the basis of current synchrotron theory.

The discovery (SCHMIDT 1963; OKE 1963; GREENSTEIN and MATTHEWS 1963) and subsequent investigation (GEENSTEIN and SCHMIDT 1964; OKE 1965) of the quasi-stellar radio sources or quasars shows that starlike objects associated with certain radio sources do indeed have very large luminosities in the optical range. The observed luminosities are claimed to be of the order of 10^{46} erg s^{-1} which is that expected from eq. (1) for $M \sim 10^8 M_\odot$. Lifetimes (GREENSTEIN and SCHMIDT 1964) of the quasars fall in the range 10^3 to 10^6 years on various models. Thus it is tempting to associate the source of energy in the quasars with nuclear burning in massive stars. Subsequent gravitational energy release and possible connections with the *extended* radio sources are left aside for the time being. In fact, the association with quasars and radio galaxies is not the only motivation for this lecture. The stability of massive stars is a problem of interest and significance *per se*.

Support for the massive star model is given by the observed variability (SMITH and HOFFLEIT 1963; MATTHEWS and SANDAGE 1963; SHAROV and EFREMOV 1963; SANDAGE 1964; GEYER 1964) of the optical radiation from the quasars. In addition to luminous flashes with durations of the order of days or weeks, there is evidence for cyclic variations with periods of the order of ten years. There is now good evidence for short-period radio variations (DENT 1965; MALTBY and MOFFET 1965) but it is not yet possible to decide whether or not these are cyclic. It is generally agreed that the occurrence of the cyclic variations is crucial to the question whether the primary radiating object is a single coherent massive star (HOYLE and FOWLER 1963*a*, *b*) or a system of smaller stars as discussed by numerous authors (BURBIDGE 1961; WOLTJER 1964; ULAM and WALDEN 1964; FIELD 1964; HOYLE and FOWLER 1965; GOLD, AXFORD and RAY 1965). It is difficult on the basis of random collisions or supernova outbursts in a system of many stellar objects to explain variations which exhibit a regular periodicity. Furthermore, if the quasar dimensions are small enough, as would now seem to be the case, then collisions become very frequent and lead in a short time to a continuous medium which condenses into a single star.

Thus, without prejudice to the problem of the reality of the cyclic variations since only additional and more precise observations will settle this matter, the possibility is discussed that such variations can arise from pulsations in a single massive star. In the major conclusion of Sect. 3 it is shown that the general-relativistic instability which occurs in nonrotating stars is removed during nuclear burning by a relatively small amount of rotation especially if differential rotation is taken into account.

An elegant treatment of the stability of supermassive stars using the exact equations of general relativity has been given by CHANDRASEKHAR (1964*a*, *b*; 1965*a*) and applications to polytropic gas spheres have been made by TOOPER (1964) and GRATTON (1964). An analysis of the binding energy has been given by IBEN (1963) and a general discussion of the binding energy and the various modes of oscillation has been given by BARDEEN (1965). In the interest of simplicity and some gain in physical insight the following discussion will be restricted to the post-Newtonian approximation (FOWLER 1964) to the relativistic equations.

This restriction can be justified on the grounds that only the Newtonian and post-Newtonian terms in the Schwarzschild line element have been verified in the three so-called crucial tests of general relativity. There is even some question concerning the correspondence between observation and theory in the advance of the perihelion of *Mercury* which constitutes a test of the coefficient of the post-Newtonian term in the line element.

In determining the post-Newtonian terms a further approximation is made in that these terms are evaluated using the equilibrium configurations given by the Newtonian approximation. It must be emphasized that this cannot be justified without recourse to the detailed analysis of the exact formal solutions and the post-Newtonian approximation as given by CHANDRASEKHAR. Only by such a detailed analysis can the conditions be determined under which this procedure gives a fair approximation to the correct results.

Even though it has important effects, rotation can be taken to be small and need only be treated in the Newtonian approximation and only for the case where distortion from spherical symmetry can be neglected. The two starting points will be 1) the equation for the binding energy of a star in hydrostatic equilibriums and 2) the radial equation for dynamic equilibrium throughout the star. The object is to derive useful relations for the binding energy and for the frequency of the fundamental mode of radial oscillation and to exhibit the connection between these two quantities. Because of the order of approximation to which the derivations are restricted, the results are applicable only to supermassive stars ($M > 10^3 M_\odot$) in which the ratio β of gas pressure to gas plus radiation pressure is small ($\beta < 0.1$) and can be approximated by eq. (A.21) in the Appendix.

9. – Binding energy of a supermassive star in hydrostatic equilibrium.

Neglecting rotation for the time being and assuming the star to be spherically symmetric it is possible to define three masses in exact general-relativistic terms. The total mass which determines the star's over-all gravitational and internal properties is given by

$$M = \int \mathrm{d}M_r = \int \varrho \, \mathrm{d}V = 4\pi \int \varrho r^2 \, \mathrm{d}r \,. \tag{40a}$$

An observer at a distance from the star large compared to its radius would observe the Newtonian gravitational attraction exerted by the star on a test mass to be proportional to M. In eq. (40*a*), $\mathrm{d}V$ is the Schwarzschild *co-ordinate* volume, $\varrho = \varrho_0 + u/c^2$ is the total mass-energy density in mass units per unit *co-ordinate* volume, ϱ_0 is the rest mass density of nuclei and ionization electrons and u is the internal energy density of gas and radiation, and includes the rest mass-energy of particles created in the medium at elevated temperatures such as electron-positron pairs (see the Appendix for further discussion). The radial variable in Schwarzschild co-ordinates, r, has the property that it automatically includes internal gravitational energy when an equation with the simplicity of (40*a*) is used to sum over the ϱ measured by a local observer at r. The integration is taken from zero to R, the *co-ordinate* radius of the star, which is not equal to the *proper* radius of the star. M_r is the total mass-energy in mass units internal to r.

The rest mass is found by integrating ϱ_0 over *proper* volume elements according to the equation

$$M_0 = \int \varrho_0 \left(1 - \frac{2GM_r}{rc^2}\right)^{-\frac{1}{2}} \mathrm{d}V \,, \tag{40b}$$

where G is the gravitational constant and the square-root term converts *co-ordinate* volume to *proper* volume. M_0 can be determined by dispersing the constituent material at any time to infinity at zero temperature. Because of atomic and nuclear processes ϱ_0 and thus M_0 at one time may not be the same as at another time. When hydrogen is converted into helium the rest mass per nucleon changes. Unlike the creation and annihilation of pairs such nuclear changes may be irreversible during contraction and re-expansion. In the circumstances under discussion the number of nucleons remains invariant and it is only necessary to exercise care at a given time in stipulating the nuclear characteristics of the stellar material, *i.e.*, the « composition » throughout the star.

The proper mass of the star exclusive of gravitational energy is given by

$$M_p = \int \varrho \left(1 - \frac{2GM_r}{rc^2}\right)^{-\frac{1}{2}} \mathrm{d}V \,, \tag{40c}$$

where again the conversion to a *proper* volume element has been made. Using these three masses two binding energies can be defined. The gravitational binding energy, Ω, of the star which is taken to be positive and thus opposite in sign to the negative gravitational energy is given by

$$(41)\qquad \Omega = (M_p - M)c^2 = \int \varrho c^2 \left[\left(1 - \frac{2GM_r}{rc^2}\right)^{-\frac{1}{2}} - 1\right] dV \to$$

$$\to \int \frac{GM_r}{r} \varrho \, dV \qquad \text{(Newtonian approximation)}.$$

The binding energy, E_b, of the star is equal but opposite in sign to the total energy, E, exclusive of the rest mass energy and is given by

$$(42)\qquad -E_b = E = (M - M_0)c^2 .$$

In eq. (42) nuclear binding has been excluded from E_b or E in the sense that it is included in M_0. This choice is arbitrary but is found to be the most convenient when treating the conversion of nuclear energy into internal energy. Thus E can increase when M_0 decreases as is the case when hydrogen is converted into helium. At the same time E can decrease as M decreases as is the case when energy is radiated away by the star.

Since M_r is related to ϱ and not to ϱ_0 it is convenient to retain ϱ and u expressing E so that

$$(43)\qquad E = \int u \left(1 - \frac{2GM_r}{rc^2}\right)^{-\frac{1}{2}} dV + \int \varrho c^2 \left[1 - \left(1 - \frac{2GM_r}{rc^2}\right)^{-\frac{1}{2}}\right] dV ,$$

$$(44)\qquad = H - \Omega .$$

The first term in eq. (43) is the proper internal energy of the star, which we designate by H in eq. (44). The second term in eq. (43) is the mass-energy of the star minus the proper mass-energy. If the sign is reversed this is just the gravitational binding energy (taken positive), which we designated by Ω in eq. (41).

It is now appropriate to expand H and Ω, to retain only the Newtonian (subscript 0) and post-Newtonian (subscript 1) terms and to introduce the Newtonian term for the rotational energy which we designate by Ψ_0. The result is

$$(45)\qquad E \approx H_0 - \Omega_0 + \Psi_0 + H_1 - \Omega_1 ,$$

$$(46)\qquad \approx \int u \, dV - \int \frac{GM_r}{r} \varrho \, dV + \frac{1}{2} \int r^2 \omega^2 \sin^2\theta \, \varrho \, dV +$$

$$+ \int \frac{GM_r}{rc^2} u \, dV - \frac{3}{2} \int \frac{G^2 M_r^2}{r^2 c^2} \varrho \, dV .$$

The definition of the various terms in eq. (45) will be obvious from the order of the terms in (46). In eq. (46) ω is the angular velocity and θ is the polar angle measured from the axis of rotation. It will develop that $H_0 - \Omega_0$ is proportional to β and is thus small and comparable to $H_1 - \Omega_1$. We discuss only cases where Ψ_0 is comparable within a factor of ten to these two differences in the internal and gravitational energy terms.

10. – Equation of dynamic equilibrium.

Again neglecting rotation for the moment, the exact general-relativistic equation for dynamic equilibrium in the spherically symmetric case has been written by MISNER and SHARP (1964) and others as

$$y^2 \ddot{r} + y\dot{r}^2 \frac{\mathrm{d}y}{\mathrm{d}r} = -\frac{1}{\varrho}\frac{\mathrm{d}p}{\mathrm{d}r}\left(\frac{1 + y^2\dot{r}^2/c^2 - 2GM_r/rc^2}{1 + p/\varrho c^2}\right) - \frac{GM_r}{r^2} - \frac{4\pi Gpr}{c^2}, \tag{47}$$

where

$$y = \frac{\varrho + p/c^2}{\varrho_0} = 1 + \frac{u}{\varrho_0 c^2} + \frac{p}{\varrho_0 c^2}. \tag{48}$$

It will be noted that the left-hand side of eq. (47) can be written in the more compact form $y\,\mathrm{d}(y\dot{r})/\mathrm{d}t$.

We now proceed to write eq. (47) in the post-Newtonian approximation and to apply it to small perturbations (δ) about hydrostatic equilibrium. Conditions at equilibrium will be designated by the subscript eq. It will be clear that the two terms containing $\dot{r}^2$ can be neglected since $\dot{r} = \dot{r}_{eq} = 0$ at hydrostatic equilibrium and $\delta\dot{r}^2 = 2\dot{r}_{eq}\,\delta\dot{r}_{eq} = 0$ to first order. This leaves $y^2\ddot{r}$ on the left-hand side of eq. (47) where the Newtonian term in y is unity and the post-Newtonian terms are much smaller than unity in all applications made in what follows. After the manipulations on eq. (47) which follow, it will develop that the Newtonian term on the right-hand side is small and comparable to the post-Newtonian term. Thus it is unnecessary to retain second-order terms in the factor y^2 and in eq. (47) we replace y^2 in $y^2\ddot{r}$ by unity.

Since the left-and side of eq. (47) has now been reduced to the classical Newtonian acceleration, $\ddot{r}$, with no ambiguities in space-time measurements, it will be clear that small rotational effects can be introduced in the approximation of the Newtonian centrifugal acceleration, $r\omega^2 \sin^2\theta$. Thus the post-Newtonian equivalent of (47) for small rotation in supermassive stars is

$$\ddot{r} \approx r\omega^2 \sin^2\theta - \frac{1}{\varrho}\frac{\mathrm{d}p}{\mathrm{d}r}\left(1 - \frac{p}{\varrho c^2} - \frac{2GM_r}{rc^2} + \dots\right) - \frac{GM_r}{r^2} - \frac{4\pi Gpr}{c^2}. \tag{49}$$

Since $\mathrm{d}p/\mathrm{d}r = -\varrho G M_r/r^2$ in Newtonian, hydrostatic equilibrium with no rotation, eq. (49) can be written, to the order of the approximations being made in this discussion, as

$$\ddot{r} \approx r\omega^2 \sin^2\theta - \frac{1}{\varrho}\frac{\mathrm{d}p}{\mathrm{d}r} - \frac{GM_r}{r^2}\left(1 + \frac{p}{\varrho c^2} + \frac{2GM_r}{rc^2} + \dots\right) - \frac{4\pi G p r}{c^2}. \tag{50}$$

Multiply eq. (50) by $r\varrho\,\mathrm{d}V$ and integrate over the entire star. The result is

$$\int r\ddot{r}\varrho\,\mathrm{d}V \approx -\int 4\pi r^3\,\mathrm{d}p - \int \frac{GM_r}{r}\varrho\,\mathrm{d}V + \int r^2\omega^2\sin^2\theta\,\varrho\,\mathrm{d}V - \\ - \int \frac{GM_r}{rc^2} p\,\mathrm{d}V - 2\int \frac{G^2 M_r^2}{r^2 c^2}\varrho\,\mathrm{d}V - 4\pi\int \frac{Gpr^2}{c^2}\varrho\,\mathrm{d}V. \tag{51}$$

The first and last terms on the right-hand side can be integrated by parts from $r = 0$ where $M_r = 0$ to $r = R$ where $p = 0$ to yield

$$\int r\ddot{r}\varrho\,\mathrm{d}V \approx 3\int p\,\mathrm{d}V - \Omega_0 + 2\Psi_0 + \int \frac{GM_r}{rc^2} p\,\mathrm{d}V - 3\int \frac{G^2 M_r^2}{r^2 c^2}\varrho\,\mathrm{d}V. \tag{52}$$

From the discussion in the appendix $p = (\Gamma_4 - 1)u \approx 1/3(1 + \beta/2)u$ so that $p \approx 1/3u$ when β is small and it is natural to define a mean value of Γ_4 such that

$$\int p\,\mathrm{d}V = (\bar{\Gamma}_4 - 1)\int u\,\mathrm{d}BV.$$

To the approximation of interest we can use this same $\bar{\Gamma}_4$ in the fourth term on the right-hand side of eq. (52). The result is the virial equation

$$\int r\ddot{r}\varrho\,\mathrm{d}V \approx 3(\bar{\Gamma}_4 - 1)H_0 - \Omega_0 + 2\Psi_0 + (\bar{\Gamma}_4 - 1)H_1 - 2\Omega_1. \tag{53}$$

Under conditions of hydrostatic equilibrium, $\ddot{r} = 0$ everywhere and a simple virial relation is obtained between H_0, Ω_0, etc. For numerical calculations of the binding energy it is most convenient to eliminate H_0 in substituting into eq. (45) and the result is

$$E_{\mathrm{eq}} \approx -\frac{3\bar{\Gamma}_4 - 4}{3(\bar{\Gamma}_4 - 1)}\Omega_0 - \frac{5 - 3\bar{\Gamma}_4}{3(\bar{\Gamma}_4 - 1)}\Psi_0 + \frac{2}{3}H_1 + \frac{5 - 3\bar{\Gamma}_4}{3(\bar{\Gamma}_4 - 1)}\Omega_1. \tag{54}$$

Equation (A.20) then yields

$$E_{\mathrm{eq}} \approx -\frac{\bar{\beta}}{2}\Omega_0 - (1 - \bar{\beta})\Psi_0 + \frac{2}{3}H_1 + (1 - \bar{\beta})\Omega_1. \tag{55}$$

For small $\bar{\beta}$ in massive stars

$$E_{eq} \approx -\frac{\bar{\beta}}{2}\,\Omega_0 - \Psi_0 + \frac{2}{3}\,H_1 + \Omega_1\,, \tag{56}$$

where, in recapitulation,

$$\Omega_0 = \int \frac{GM_4}{r}\,\varrho\,\mathrm{d}V = 4\pi G \int \varrho r M_r\,\mathrm{d}r\,, \tag{57}$$

$$\Psi_0 = \tfrac{1}{2}\int r^2\omega^2 \sin^2\theta\,\varrho\,\mathrm{d}V = \pi \int \varrho r^4 \omega^2 \sin^3\theta\,\mathrm{d}r\,\mathrm{d}\theta\,, \tag{58}$$

$$H_1 = \int \frac{GM_r}{rc^2}\,u\,\mathrm{d}V = \frac{4\pi G}{c^2}\int u r M_r\,\mathrm{d}r \approx \frac{12\pi G}{c^2}\,p r M_r\,\mathrm{d}r, \tag{59}$$

$$\Omega_1 = \frac{3}{2}\int \frac{G^2 M_r^2}{r^2 c^2}\,\varrho\,\mathrm{d}V = \frac{6\pi G^2}{c^2}\int \varrho\, M_r^2\,\mathrm{d}r\,. \tag{60}$$

In the last approximation in eq. (59) we have used $p = (\Gamma_4 - 1)u \approx u/3$ for massive stars. In eq. (56) it will be noted that all terms are *small* when this equation is applied to *slowly rotating, massive stars.* This circumstance arises from the fact that $H_0 - \Omega_0$ in eq. (45) becomes proportional to $\bar{\beta}$ through eq. (53) and (A.19).

11. – Adiabatic radial pulsation.

In order to determine the angular frequency, σ_R, of the fundamental mode or radial oscillation eq. (53) is applied to a perturbation of the form

$$\frac{\delta r}{r} = \frac{\delta R}{R}\exp[-i\sigma_R t]\,. \tag{61}$$

The result is

$$-\sigma_R^2 I\,\frac{\delta R}{R} \approx 3(\bar{\Gamma}_1 - 1)\,\delta H_0 - \delta\Omega_0 + 2\,\delta\Psi_0 + (\bar{\Gamma}_1 - 1)\,\delta H_1 - 2\,\delta\Omega_1\,, \tag{62}$$

where

$$I = \int r^2\,\varrho\,\mathrm{d}V \tag{63}$$

is the moment of inertia of the star about the origin of co-ordinates. I is equal to $\frac{3}{2}$ the usual moment of inertia about the axis of rotation if the distortion from spherical symmetry is ignored. In deriving eq. (62) use has been made of eq. (A.31) in the Appendix. Again we overlook the fact that the average Γ_1 in the coefficient of δH_1 is not quite the same as that in the coefficient of δH_0. If the oscillation is adiabatic the energy equation becomes

$$\delta E = \delta H_0 - \delta\Omega_0 + \delta\Psi_0 + \delta H_1 - \delta\Omega_1 = 0\,. \tag{64}$$

If eq. (64) is employed to eliminate δH_0 in eq. (62) the result is

$$-\sigma_R^2 I \frac{\delta R}{R} = (3\bar{\Gamma}_1 - 4)\,\delta\Omega_0 + (5 - 3\bar{\Gamma}_1)\,\delta\Psi_0 - 2(\bar{\Gamma}_1 - 1)\,\delta H_1 - (5 - 3\bar{\Gamma}_1)\,\delta\Omega_1. \tag{65}$$

12. – Applications to polytropic models.

Within the approximations which have been carefully specified, eqs. (54) and (65) are quite general. Further elucidation requires that Ω_0, etc., be specified as functions of the stellar radius R and mass M and that $\delta\Omega_0$, etc. be related to δR through these quantities. This can only be done for specific stellar models. For our purposes polytropic models specified by the index n in the relation $pV^{1+1/n} = \text{const}$ or $p = \text{const}\,\varrho_0^{1+1/n}$ are of sufficient diversity and accuracy.

Considerable simplification arises from the fact that our interest is concentrated on *slowly rotating, massive stars* in which the Newtonian terms in eq. (54) and (65) are small and of the same order of magnitude as the post-Newtonian terms. This means that the integrals for Ω_0, Ψ_0, H_1 and Ω_1 can be evaluated using the run of the variables throughout the star given by the solution of the classical Lane-Emden polytropic equations without rotation. In particular it is not necessary to distinguish between ϱ_0 and ϱ nor between M_0 and M in keeping with the general presumption that $M_0 - M$ is small compared to either one of them. Only one new physical concept must be introduced—namely that for an *isolated* star, angular momentum must be conserved through all stages of contraction or of oscillation.

The Newtonian gravitational binding energy in units of Mc^2 can be expressed in terms of the convenient dimensionless parameter $2GM/Rc^2$ as

$$\frac{\Omega_0}{Mc^2} = \frac{3}{2(5-n)}\left(\frac{2GM}{Rc^2}\right), \tag{66}$$

so

$$\frac{\delta\Omega_0}{\Omega_0} = -\frac{\delta R}{R}\,. \tag{67}$$

Rotational terms in Ω_0 result in terms of order $\beta\omega^2$ in E or σ_R^2 and can be neglected when both β and ω^2 are small. The Newtonian rotational energy is given in terms of the *conserved* angular momentum, Φ, by

(68) $$\frac{\Psi_0}{Mc^2} = \frac{\Phi^2}{2(ckMR)^2}$$

where for *uniform* rotation $k = (2I/3MR^2)^{\frac{1}{2}}$ is the radius of gyration in units of R and $\Phi = k^2 MR^2 \omega = \text{const}$. Differential rotation will be discussed in what follows. Once established under the conservation of angular momentum for all mass elements in a star, differential rotation requires $\Psi_0 \propto R^{-2}$ just as for uniform rotation so that in any case

(69) $$\frac{\delta\Psi_0}{\Psi_0} = -2\frac{\delta R}{R}.$$

It has been shown (FOWLER 1964) that the integrals for H_1 and Ω_1 in units of Mc^2 involve the dimensionless parameter $(2GM/Rc^2)$ to the second power as might be expected on general grounds. Numerical coefficients can be derived analytically for some polytropes and can be evaluated numerically for others. For the quantities of greatest interest, the result can be expressed as

(70) $$\frac{H_1}{Mc^2} = \zeta'_n \left(\frac{2GM}{Rc^2}\right)^2,$$

(71) $$\frac{\Omega_1}{Mc^2} = \zeta''_n \left(\frac{2GM}{Rc^2}\right)^2,$$

and

(72) $$\frac{2}{3}\frac{H_1}{Mc^2} + \frac{\Omega_1}{Mc^2} = \zeta_n \left(\frac{2GM}{Rc^2}\right)^2,$$

where, for example, $\zeta'_0 = 0.064$, $\zeta''_0 = 0.161$, $\zeta_0 = 0.204$, $\zeta'_1 = 0.116$, $\zeta''_1 = 0.241$, $\zeta_1 = 0.318$, $\zeta'_2 = 0.219$, $\zeta''_2 = 0.417$, $\zeta_2 = 0.563$, $\zeta'_3 = 0.513$, $\zeta''_3 = 0.923$, $\zeta_3 = 1.265$, $\zeta'_4 = 2.12$, $\zeta''_4 = 3.66$ and $\zeta_4 = 5.07$. BARDEEN and ANAND (1966) have shown that $\zeta_n \approx 5.07/(5-n)^2$.

In any case

(73) $$\frac{\delta H_1}{H_1} = \frac{\delta\Omega_1}{\Omega_1} = -2\frac{\delta R}{R}.$$

Thus eq. (65) becomes

(74) $$\sigma_R^2 I \approx (3\Gamma_1 - 4)\,\Omega_0 + 2(5 - 3\Gamma_1)\,\Psi_0 - 4(\Gamma_1 - 1)H_1 - 2(5 - 3\Gamma_1)\,\Omega_1.$$

The Newtonian terms in this equation are identical to those given by CHAN-

DRASEKHAR and LEBOVITZ (1962) in their eq. (111). For $\bar{\Gamma}_1 \approx 4/3 + \bar{\beta}/6$ and $\bar{\beta}$ small as in supermassive stars

$$\sigma_R^2 I \approx \frac{\bar{\beta}}{2}\,\Omega_0 + 2\Psi_0 - \frac{4}{3}\,H_1 - 2\,\Omega_1\,. \tag{75}$$

In those cases where $\bar{\Gamma}_1$ and $\bar{\Gamma}_4$ can be taken to be equal, as for example when $\bar{\beta}$ is small and $\bar{\Gamma}_1 \approx \bar{\Gamma}_4 \approx 4/3 + \bar{\beta}/6$, then it will be clear from eqs. (54), (66), (68), (70). (71) and (74) that

$$\sigma_R^2 \approx 3(\bar{\Gamma}_1 - 1)\,\frac{R}{I}\,\frac{\mathrm{d}E_{\text{eq}}}{\mathrm{d}R}\,, \qquad \bar{\Gamma}_1 \approx \bar{\Gamma}_4\,, \tag{76}$$

$$\approx \frac{R}{I}\,\frac{\mathrm{d}E_{\text{eq}}}{\mathrm{d}R}\,, \qquad \beta \ll 1\,. \tag{77}$$

This important relation has been previously (FOWLER 1964) used in the case of nonrotating massive stars and will be discussed further in what follows. A circumstance under which eqs. (76) and (77) do not hold will be noted near the conclusion of this paper.

In order to make the analysis which follows as transparent as possible it will prove expedient to specify a particular polytropic index. For massive stars it is well known that the case $n = 3$, for which $\beta = \text{constant}$, yields a fairly accurate representation for the internal structure. For $n = 3$, eqs. (56) and (75) become

$$\frac{E_{\text{eq}}}{Mc^2} \approx -\frac{3}{8}\,\beta\left(\frac{2GM}{Rc^2}\right) + 1.265\left(\frac{2GM}{Rc^2}\right)^2 - \frac{1}{2}\left(\frac{\Phi}{ckMR}\right)^2, \qquad n = 3\,, \tag{78}$$

$$\sigma_R^2 \approx \frac{Mc^2}{I}\left[\frac{3}{8}\,\beta\left(\frac{2GM}{Rc^2}\right) - 2.53\left(\frac{2GM}{Rc^2}\right)^2 + \left(\frac{\Phi}{ckMR}\right)^2\right]. \qquad n = 3\,. \tag{79}$$

These equations display the Newtonian gravitational term in $1/R$, the Newtonian rotational term in $1/R^2$ and the general-relativistic post-Newtonian term in $1/R^2$. The dependence on powers of $1/R$ can be replaced by dependence on powers of the central temperature, T_c, by use of the relation (FOWLER 1964)

$$T_c = \frac{5.83\cdot 10^{18}}{R}\left(\frac{M}{M_\odot}\right)^{\frac{1}{2}}, \qquad n = 3\,. \tag{80}$$

13. – Rotational stability *vs.* general relativistic instability.

The fundamental mode of radial oscillation becomes dynamically unstable when $\sigma_R^2 < 0$ or σ_R becomes imaginary in eq. (61). In the case of no rotation,

$\Phi = 0$, it has been noted (CHANDRASEKHAR 1964*a*, *b*; FOWLER 1964) that instability sets in for contraction below a critical radius given for $\sigma_R^2 \leqslant 0$ in eq. (79) by

$$R_{cr} = \frac{6.74}{\beta} R_g = 3.4 \cdot 10^5 \left(\frac{M}{M_\odot}\right)^{\frac{3}{2}} \text{cm}\,, \qquad \Phi = 0,\ n = 3\,, \tag{81}$$

where $R_g = 2GM/c^2$ is the limiting gravitational radius or Schwarzschild coordinate radius and β has been evaluated using $\mu = 0.73$ for a representative mixture of 50 per cent hydrogen, 47 per cent helium and 3 per cent heavy elements by mass. From eqs. (80) and (81) the critical central temperature, above which instability sets in, is

$$T_{cr} = 1.7 \cdot 10^{13} (M_\odot/M)\ {}^\circ\text{K}\,, \qquad \Phi = 0,\ n = 3\,. \tag{82}$$

At the critical radius and central temperature, E_{eq} reaches a minimum value and the binding energy reaches a minimum value as indicated by eq. (77). This is illustrated in Fig. 4 for $M = 10^6\, M_\odot$ where $E_{eq}/M_\odot c^2$, σ_R and the period $\Pi = 2\pi/\sigma_R$ are shown as functions of R and T_c. In the calculations $I = 0.113\, MR^2$ for a polytrope of index $n = 3$ has been used. The situation can be understood physically in the following way. To the left of the minimum in E_{eq} in the Newtonian range an adiabatic perturbation (constant E) toward smaller radii leads to more energy than that required for equilibrium and thus, for any physically reasonable equation of state, to more pressure than that necessary for hydrostatic equilibrium. Thus the contraction is opposed. An adiabatic perturbation toward larger radii leads to less energy and less pressure than that required for hydrostatic equilibrium and thus expansion is opposed. The same argument used to the right of the minimum indicates that a contraction leads to less pressure than that needed for hydrostatic equilibrium while an expansions leads to more so that the system is dynamically unstable to adiabatic perturbations. It will be noted that the minimum E_{eq} given by $-9\bar{\beta}^2 Mc^2/64\zeta_n(5-n)^2$ has magnitude $0.028\bar{\beta}^2 Mc^2 \sim M_\odot c^2$, which is independent of the mass M, and that the mini-

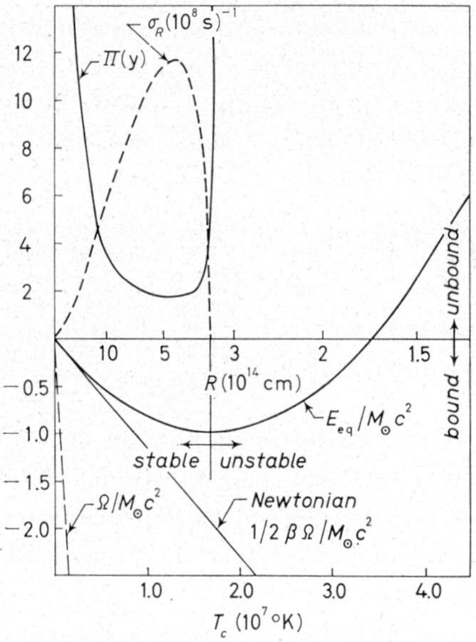

Fig. 4. – The binding energy and the frequency and period of the fundamental mode of radial oscillation in a nonrotating star with mass equal to $10^6\, M_\odot$.

mum period during stable contraction is of order of one year. In general the minimum period is given by

$$\Pi_{\min} = 1.7\cdot 10^{-12}\,(M/M_\odot)^2\ \text{y}\,, \qquad \Phi = 0,\ n = 3\,. \tag{83}$$

The critical temperature is only $1.7\cdot 10^7$ °K for $M = 10^6\,M_\odot$ and this is considerably below the temperature of $8\cdot 10^7$ °K which, it has been previously noted (HOYLE and FOWLER 1963*a*), is necessary for hydrogen burning through the CNO bi-cycle. This means that there is no source of the energy required for hydrostatic equilibrium above $1.7\cdot 10^7$ °K or for contraction below $3.5\cdot 10^{14}$ cm so that the instability results in gravitational collapse until the onset of nuclear burning. The resulting relaxation oscillations for $M \leqslant 10^6\,M_\odot$ have been discussed in the previous Sections. For $M \geqslant 10^6\,M_\odot$, the onset of hydrogen burning is not sufficient to prevent continued gravitational collapse in a nonrotating star. This has placed a serious limitation on the energy available in that model which depicts quasars as nonrotating massive stars undergoing relaxation oscillations since hydrogen burning in a star with $M = 10^6\,M_\odot$ yields only $\sim 10^{58}$ erg and the required energies are in some cases of the order of 10^4 times this figure.

In eq. (79) the general-relativistic term which leads to instability varies as R^{-2} and is negative. For constant angular momentum, Φ, the rotational term also varies as R^{-2} but is positive. *Thus for large enough Φ, the general-relativistic instability discussed above is removed by rotation.* In physical terms the rotation prevents the gravitational collapse which would otherwise result from the general-relativistic instability. Relative to the magnitude of the angular momentum common to astronomical systems the required Φ is quite small. For the rotational and general relativistic terms in eq. (79) to cancel, the critical angular momentum for stability is given by

$$\Phi_{cr} = (2k^2\zeta_n)^{\frac{1}{2}}\,\frac{2GM^2}{c}\,, \tag{84}$$

where we have generalized to any n. Since the angular momentum is conserved it is simplest to calculate Φ_{cr} at the stage where the stellar mass is dispersed uniformly as a gaseous cloud. In this case $n = 0$, $k^2 = \frac{2}{5}$ and $\zeta_0 = 0.204$ so that

$$\frac{\Phi_{cr}}{M} = 3.6\cdot 10^{15}\left(\frac{M}{M_\odot}\right)\ \text{cm}^2\ \text{s}^{-1}\,. \tag{85}$$

Even for $M = 10^8\,M_\odot$ this angular momentum per unit mass is very small compared to the typical value, 10^{30} cm² s^{-1}, which applies to the rotation of the solar system in the *galaxy*.

The rotational effects are illustrated for a star with mass $M = 10^8 M_\odot$ in Fig. 5 and 6. Figure 5 exhibits the dependence of $E_{eq}/M_\odot c^2$ on R and T, while Fig. 6 shows the dependence of the period Π on these same quantities. The curves have been calculated for $f = 0$, 0.99, 1 and 2 where f is the ratio of the rotational energy to the « general-relativistic » energy represented by the post-Newtonian terms in eqs. (56) and (72). For a given angular momentum f remains constant during homologous contraction. The calculations have been made for polytropic index $n = 3$.

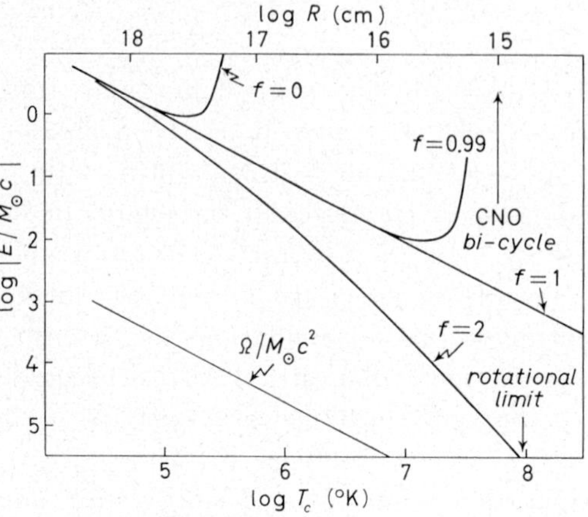

Fig. 5. – The binding energy of a rotating star with mass equal to $10^8 M_\odot$. $f = E(\text{rot})/E(\text{gen.rel.})$.

It will be noted that dynamic stability at the temperature required for hydrogen-burning through the CNO bi-cycle sets a lower limit on f equal to unity. For reasons to be discussed in the next Section large values of f are irrelevant since angular-momentum loss occurs if the original angular momentum is very large. The period of the fundamental radial oscillations at hydrogen burning varies rapidly with f being of the order of 1 year for $f = 1$ and 10 days for $f = 2$. It is extremely doubtful, however, that small-amplitude linear oscillations characterized by exactly these periods will occur. From the work of LEDOUX (1941) and of SCHWARZSCHILD and HÄRM (1959) it is more probable that large amplitude, nonlinear pulsations will be set up at the onset of nuclear burning followed by a longer period of expansion to large radius and then recontraction during which the energy is transmitted to the surface of the star and radiated away. Relaxation oscilla-

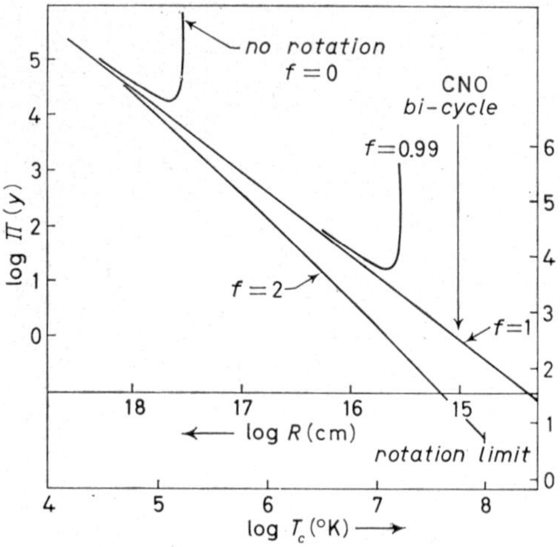

Fig. 6. – The period of the fundamental mode of radial oscillation of a rotating star with mass equal to $10^8 M_\odot$. $f = E(\text{rot})/E(\text{gen.rel.})$.

tions of this nature in supermassive stars have been previously discussed and the possible connections with the periodicity and exotic forms of energy emission in quasi-stellar objects have been pointed out. Only one point need be added to that discussion: variations in the magnetic field which accompany the oscillations will accelerate electrons to relativistic energies through the betatron mechanism.

Here we emphasize that rotation extends the mass range in which stable relaxation oscillations triggered by hydrogen-burning can occur up to masses of the order of $10^8 M_\odot$ or somewhat more. This extends the available nuclear energy in such objects to at least 10^{60} erg. These limits were $10^6 M_\odot$ and 10^{58} erg without rotation. With rotation as the stabilizing agent, a star of mass $10^8 M_\odot$ can serve as the energy source in a quasar with total luminosity equal to $2 \cdot 10^{46}$ erg s^{-1} for a period as long as 10^6 years as noted in Sect. **8**.

For the record we note the period in supermassive stars with $f=1$, $n=3$, $k^2=0.075$, $\mu=0.73$:

$$\Pi = \left(\frac{8\pi^2 k^2 R^3}{\beta G M}\right)^{\frac{1}{2}} = \left(\frac{6\pi k^2}{\beta G \bar{\varrho}}\right)^{\frac{1}{2}}, \tag{86}$$

$$= 2.8 \cdot 10^{-21} R^{\frac{3}{2}} \left(\frac{M_\odot}{M}\right)^{\frac{1}{4}} \text{y}, \qquad n=3, \tag{87}$$

$$= 3.9 \cdot 10^7 T_c^{-\frac{3}{2}} \left(\frac{M}{M_\odot}\right)^{\frac{1}{4}} \text{y}, \qquad n=3. \tag{88}$$

This is just the Newtonian period without rotation for small β.

In eq. (86), $\bar{\varrho}$ is the mean density of the stellar matter. Note that for $f=1$ the rotational energy just cancels the post-Newtonian general-relativistic energy in eq. (79). Equations (86) to (88) are derived from the Newtonian term in eq. (79). Figure 6 illustrates the rapid decrease in Π as f is increased.

In concluding this Section it can be pointed out that any physical phenomenon which leads to a positive term proportional to $1/R^2$ in the binding energy eq. (78) will, if large enough, remove the general relativistic instability in supermassive stars. Thus turbulent kinetic energy associated with convection or internal magnetic disturbances scales as $1/R^2$ and will be effective in this regard. This has been discussed by BARDEEN and ANAND (1966).

14. – The limit of rotational stability.

Even through the rotation required to remove the general-relativistic instability is quite clearly available under typical astronomical circumstances as discussed in the previous Section, the question arises whether the required angular momentum will lead to equatorial instability before sufficient contraction and high enough central temperature for hydrogen burning is reached.

It is first necessary to prescribe somewhat more precisely the central temperature required for hydrogen-burning through the CNO bi-cycle. Equation (27) gave the average energy generation per gram per second, $\bar{\varepsilon}$, throughout the star and, when multiplied by the mass, this yields the nuclear energy generation rate as

$$(89) \qquad M\bar{\varepsilon} \approx 8.8 \cdot 10^{-44} \left(\frac{M}{M_\odot}\right)^{\frac{1}{2}} T_c^{11} \text{ erg s}^{-1} \,.$$

When $M\bar{\varepsilon}$ from eq. (89) is equated to L from eq. (37) it is found that the central temperature, T_{cn}, required for *nuclear* energy generation through the CNO bi-cycle is

$$(90) \qquad T_{cn} \approx 2.5 \cdot 10^7 \left(\frac{M}{M_\odot}\right)^{1/22} \,^\circ\text{K} \qquad \text{[CNO bi-cycle]}\,,$$

so that $T_{cn} \approx 6 \cdot 10^7$ °K for $M = 10^8 M_\odot$. This is lower than the estimate, $T_{cn} \sim 8 \cdot 10^7$ °K, found originally by HOYLE and FOWLER (1963*a*) but is somewhat more precise. It will be noted that the critical central temperature, eq. (82), for general relativistic instability is *less* than that required for hydrogen-burning, eq. (90), for all masses $M \gtrsim 4 \cdot 10^5 M_\odot$. This emphasizes the limitation on nonrotating models for supermassive stars.

With the required temperature in hand it is now necessary to ascertain the limiting central temperature at which rotation, governed by the conservation of angular momentum, leads to the equatorial instability characterized by loss of mass at the equator. It is probably true that a star survives this instability and that nuclear energy generation at the center is not terminated by the loss of mass at the surface but none the less this limitation is well worth investigating in some detail. The analysis which has been made to the present point in this paper has been limited to spherical symmetry in the post-Newtonian approximation. Thus the conclusions to follow require that the angular momenta considered be smaller than the critical angular momentum at which distortion from spherical symmetry is large.

The problem is best discussed in terms of angular velocity rather than angular momentum since the critical limiting angular velocity is given quite simply by equating centrifugal force to gravitational force. In terms of angular velocity the rotational energy can be written as

$$(91) \qquad \Psi_0 = \tfrac{1}{2} K^2 M R^2 \omega_R^2 \,.$$

Equation (91) has been written to include the case of differential rotation; $\omega_R = \omega(R)$ is the angular velocity at the equatorial radius and K is a constant which can be determined when $\omega = \omega(r)$ is specified as a function of the radius. For uniform rotation $\omega = \omega_R$ and $K = k$, the radius of gyration in units of R.

When differential rotation is considered the rotational instability may first occur at an arbitrary radius in the equatorial plane. It will be sufficient for our purposes to consider instability at the periphery and at the center. In the first case the critical angular velocity for instability is given by

$$\omega_{\mathrm{CR}}^2 = \frac{GM}{R^3} = \frac{4}{3}\pi G\bar{\varrho}\,, \qquad \text{at } r = R\,, \tag{92}$$

where $\bar{\varrho}$ is the mean density of the stellar material. In the second case the critical angular velocity is given by

$$\omega_{\mathrm{cr}}^2 = \left(\frac{GM_r}{r^6}\right)_c = \frac{4}{3}\pi G\varrho_c\,, \qquad \text{at } r = 0\,, \tag{93}$$

where ϱ_c is the central density. Note that

$$\frac{\omega_{\mathrm{cr}}}{\omega_{\mathrm{CR}}} = (\varrho_c/\bar{\varrho})^{\frac{1}{2}} = 7.37\,, \qquad n = 3\,, \tag{94}$$

Equations (91) through (94) can be manipulated to yield

$$\frac{\Psi_0}{Mc^2} = \frac{1}{4}K^2\alpha^2\left(\frac{2GM}{Rc^2}\right) \propto \frac{1}{R}\,, \tag{95}$$

where

$$\alpha = \omega_R/\omega_{\mathrm{CR}}\,, \tag{96}$$

which is convenient when the instability first occurs at the periphery, or

$$\alpha = \left(\frac{\varrho_c}{\bar{\varrho}}\right)^{\frac{1}{2}}\left(\frac{\omega_R}{\omega_c}\right)\left(\frac{\omega_c}{\omega_{\mathrm{cr}}}\right), \tag{97}$$

which is convenient when the instability first occurs. at the center. The angular velocity at the center is designated by $\omega_c = \omega(0)$. For uniform rotation $\omega_c = \omega_R$. In this case instability first occurs at the periphery and eq. (96) should be used although (97) is formally correct.

For a given type of differential rotation ω_R/ω_c is a fixed constant. It will be assumed in what follows that equatorial instability sets in for $\omega_R/\omega_{\mathrm{CR}} = 1$ or $\omega_c/\omega_{\mathrm{cr}} = 1$ and that angular momentum transfer to a small amount of mass lost by the star keeps the appropriate ratio constant thereafter. When this is the case Ψ_0/Mc^2 is proportional to R^{-1} and not to R^{-2} as was the case before the onset of equatorial instability.

It should be noted that eq. (95) should not be taken to imply that the factor 2 does not appear on the right-hand side of eq. (69). Equation (95) applies to the relatively slow changes between equilibrium states. During the faster changes which occur during small radial oscillations it would seem reasonable to assume that angular momentum is conserved. Then eqs. (69) and (75) can be employed as written with Ψ_0 evaluated from (95) with α given by eq. (96) or (97). Under the circumstances it will be clear that eq. (77) no longer holds and that dynamical instability ($\sigma_R^2 = 0$) no longer sets in at the minimum in the equilibrium energy curve.

In order to illustrate these points in the simplest possible manner, consider only stars for which $K^2\alpha^2 \gg \bar{\beta}$ so that $\bar{\beta}\Omega_0/2$ can be neglected in comparison with Ψ_0 in eq. (56) and with $2\Psi_0$ in eq. (75). Then from eq. (56), (72) and (95) one has

$$-\frac{E_b}{Mc^2} = \frac{E_{eq}}{Mc^2} \approx -\frac{1}{4}K^2\alpha^2\left(\frac{2GM}{Rc^2}\right) + \zeta_n\left(\frac{2GM}{Rc^2}\right)^2. \tag{98}$$

When this is differentiated with respect to R with all coefficients held constant the maximum binding energy $E_b^{max} = |E_{eq}^{min}|$ is found to be

$$\frac{E_b^{max}}{Mc^2} \approx \frac{K^4\alpha^4}{64\zeta_n} \tag{99}$$

and occurs at the radius

$$R(E_b^{max}) \approx \frac{8\zeta_n}{K^2\alpha^2}\left(\frac{2GM}{c^2}\right) \approx \frac{3.0\cdot 10^6}{K^2\alpha^2}\left(\frac{M}{M_\odot}\right)\ \text{cm}, \qquad n = 3, \tag{100}$$

and at the central temperature

$$T_c(E_b^{max}) \approx 1.95\cdot 10^{12} K^2\alpha^2\left(\frac{M_\odot}{M}\right)^{\frac{1}{2}}\ {}^\circ\text{K}, \qquad n = 3. \tag{101}$$

It will be noted that E_b^{max} is independent of the original angular momentum Φ possessed by the star before the onset of angular momentum transfer. It can be shown that this is only true if the original angular momentum was large enough that the original rotational energy was equal to or greater than twice the post-Newtonian relativistic term. If this is looked at from another point of view it becomes clear that angular momentum transfer or loss will automatically reduce an originally large angular momentum to the point where the rotational energy is given by eq. (95) and the maximum binding energy by eq. (99). The consequences in terms of gravitational and nuclear energy release will be emphasized in what follows. A mechanism for the loss of large amounts of angular momentum has been discussed in the case of the sun by HOYLE (1960).

It need only be argued that such a mechanism can be effective for supermassive stars as well as has clearly been the case for the sun and other stars.

When $\bar{\beta}\Omega_0/2$ is neglected in eq. (75), it becomes

$$(102) \qquad \sigma_R^2 \approx \frac{Mc^2}{I}\left[\frac{1}{2}K^2\alpha^2\left(\frac{2GM}{Rc^2}\right) - 2\zeta_n\left(\frac{2GM}{Rc^2}\right)^2\right] \approx \frac{2E_b}{I} \approx \approx \frac{1}{3}\left(\frac{c^3}{2GMk}\right)^2\left[K^2\alpha^2\left(\frac{2GM}{Rc^2}\right)^3 - 4\zeta_n\left(\frac{2GM}{Rc^2}\right)^4\right].$$

Thus instability sets in with $\sigma_R^2 = 0$ at one-half the radius given by eq. (100) and at twice the temperature given by eq. (101). Thus the critical radius for instability is

$$(103) \qquad R_{cr} = R(\sigma_R^2 = 0) \approx \frac{1.5\cdot 10^6}{K^2\alpha^2}\left(\frac{M}{M_\odot}\right)\ \text{cm}, \qquad n = 3,$$

and the critical central temperature is

$$(104) \qquad T_{cr} = T_c(\sigma_R^2 = 0) \approx 3.9\cdot 10^{12} K^2\alpha^2\left(\frac{M_\odot}{M}\right)^{\frac{1}{2}}\ {}^\circ\text{K}, \qquad n = 3.$$

These equations are to be compared respectively with eqs. (11) and (12). It will be apparent from eqs. (56), (75) and (98) that the binding energy is zero where $\sigma_R^2 = 0$. The maximum value for σ_R or the minimum period occurs when binding energy is a maximum. When $\bar{\beta}\Omega_0/2$ is not neglected, $\sigma_R^2 = 0$ occurs between E_{eq}^{min} and $E_{eq} = 0$.

For uniform rotation $K^2 = k^2 = 0.075$ for a polytrope of index 3 and thus $T_c(E_b^{max})$ is only $1.5\cdot 10^7$ °K and T_{cr} is only $3\cdot 10^7$ °K for a star with $M = 10^8 M_\odot$ even when the maximum $\alpha = \omega_R/\omega_{CR} = 1$ is used in eq. (103). This is not sufficient for hydrogen burning since $6\cdot 10^7$ °K is required by eq. (90). The limiting mass which can be stabilized by uniform rotation during hydrogen burning is approximately $10^7 M_\odot$.

Differential rotation with an increase in angular velocity toward the center of the star results in a marked increase in K^2 and thus in T_{max}. Two models with differential rotation have been considered. In the first model the massive star is assumed to contract from a cloud with polytropic index $n = 0$ to a structure with index n in such a way that each *spherical* shell retains its angular momentum. This model is not self-consistent in that the Newtonian equation for hydrostatic equilibrium cannot be satisfied by a polytropic relation between p and ϱ when the centrifugal forces are not neglected. The second model is that of STOECKLY (1965) in which the star contracts in such a way that the angular momentum is conserved in each *cylindrical* shell (but not each ring) parallel to the axis of rotation. In this model the polytropic relation may be employed when centrifugal forces are included in the equation for hydrostatic equilibrium. The results for the two models are fortunately very similar as will be noted in the following tabulation:

n	0	1	2	3	4
K^2 (spherical model)	0.400	0.629	1.14	2.61	10.8
K^2 (cylindrical model)	0.400	0.624	1.10	2.47	9.8

In the spherical contraction model the angular velocity throughout the star relative to that at the periphery is given by

$$\frac{\omega_r}{\omega_R} = \left(\frac{M_r}{M}\right)^{\frac{2}{3}} \left(\frac{R}{r}\right)^2 = (\bar{\varrho}_r/\bar{\varrho})^{\frac{2}{3}} , \tag{105}$$

where $\bar{\varrho}_r$ is the mean density internal to r and $\bar{\varrho}$, as before, is the mean density for the entire star. The maximum angular velocity occurs at the center and is given by

$$\frac{\omega_c}{\omega_R} = (\varrho_c/\bar{\varrho})^{\frac{2}{3}} = (54.18)^{\frac{2}{3}} = 14.3 , \qquad n = 3 , \tag{106}$$

where ϱ_c is the central density. Equation (106) has been evaluated for a polytrope, in this case $n=3$, in spite of the lack of self-consistency noted above. For the case of cylindrical contraction, for which the polytropic model can be employed without difficulty, the numerical value in eq. (106) becomes 10.9 instead of 14.3.

It will now be clear from eqs. (94) and (106) that rotational instability when centrifugal forces match gravitational forces occurs first at the center rather than at the periphery in these cases of differential rotation. Thus eq. (97) is to be employed at this point rather than eq. (96) in determining the consequences of differential rotation.

The critical temperature given by eq. (104) occurs at zero binding energy and requires that a large supply of energy become available after the maximum binding energy or the minimum total energy is reached at one-half the critical temperature. Thus it would appear that nuclear-energy generation must at least start at $T_c(E_b^{\max})$ and so this temperature will now be computed. For the contraction with angular momentum conservation in each cylindrical shell up to the point of rotational instability in a polytrope of index $n=3$ it is found that $K^2=2.47$ and $\alpha^2=0.456(\omega_c/\omega_{cr})^2$. Thus

$$T_c(E_b^{\max}) \approx 2.20\cdot 10^{12} \left(\frac{\omega_c}{\omega_{cr}}\right)^2 \left(\frac{M_\odot}{M}\right)^{\frac{1}{2}} . \tag{107}$$

If this temperature is equated to T_{cn} from eq. (90), the solution will yield the maximum mass in which nuclear energy generation is triggered before the maximum binding energy is reached. The result is

$$\frac{M}{M_\odot} \leqslant 10^9 \left(\frac{\omega_c}{\omega_{cr}}\right)^{11/3}. \tag{108}$$

Equation (108) indicates that the limiting mass is quite sensitive to the choice of ω_c/ω_{cr}, *i.e.*, to the value of the angular velocity ω_c at which centrifugal forces may tend to disrupt the star rather than lead to stable angular momentum transfer and small mass loss. If $\omega_c = \omega_{cr}$ then $M \leqslant 10^9 M_\odot$ but a more conservative choice would seem to be $M \leqslant 10^8 M_\odot$. In Fig. 5 and 6 which are drawn for $M = 10^8 M_\odot$ the rotational limit indicated is for $(\omega_c/\omega_{cr})^2 = \frac{1}{2}$. This limit has not been reached at $6 \cdot 10^7$ °K at which hydrogen burning takes place.

It is of interest to calculate the maximum binding energy, eq. (99), for the example discussed above with $K^2 = 2.47$, $\alpha^2 = 0.456(\omega_c/\omega_{cr})^2$ and $\zeta_3 = 1.265$. The calculation yields

$$\frac{E_b^{max}}{Mc^2} \approx 0.016 \left(\frac{\omega_c}{\omega_{cr}}\right)^4. \tag{109}$$

Again the result is quite sensitive to the choice of ω_c/ω_{cr} but for the maximum reasonable choice of unity it is seen that E_b^{max} can be 1.6 per cent of Mc^2 which is about 5 times that from the burning of one-half the hydrogen of the star. Since this energy must be lost during contraction it is another source for the observed energy emissions in quasars. It will be noted this arises fundamentally because the coefficient of Ψ_0 in eq. (55) is $1 - \bar{\beta}$ and $\bar{\beta}$ is small in supermassive stars. In ordinary stars $\bar{\beta} = 1$ and the term in Ψ_0 in eq. (55) vanishes; the binding energy is $\frac{1}{2}\Omega_0$ with or without rotation since rotational energy and internal kinetic energy enter into the virial theorem in the same manner.

15. – Dynamic and rotational periods.

The dynamic period of the fundamental mode of radial oscillation has been given in eqs. (86) through (88) for the case in which rotation is just large enough to cancel the post-Newtonian term in eq. (79). If rotation is limited only by equatorial instability the rotational term is larger than the term in β in eq. (79) and is also larger than the post-Newtonian term in eq. (102) during the early stages of contraction. Hydrogen-burning occurs during this early stage except for $M \geqslant 10^9 M_\odot$. Thus a useful approximation for the dynamical period with large rotation is

$$\Pi \approx \left(\frac{6\pi^2 k^2 R^3}{K^2 \alpha^2 G M}\right)^{\frac{1}{2}}, \tag{110}$$

$$\approx 5.5\cdot 10^{-21} R^{\frac{3}{2}} \left(\frac{M_\odot}{M}\right)^{\frac{1}{2}} \text{y}, \qquad n = 3, \tag{111}$$

$$\approx 7.7\cdot 10^{7}\, T_c^{-\frac{3}{2}} \left(\frac{M}{M_\odot}\right)^{\frac{1}{4}} \text{y}, \qquad n = 3. \tag{112}$$

In deriving (110), $I = \frac{2}{3} k^2 MR^2$ has been used. The numerical values are for $n=3$, $k^2=0.075$, $\zeta_3=1.268$, $K^2=2.47$, $\alpha^2=0.456$. When the temperature required for hydrogen burning, eq. (90), is substituted into (112) the result is

$$\left|\begin{aligned} \Pi(T_{cn}) &\approx 6.1\cdot 10^{-4} \left(\frac{M}{M_\odot}\right)^{2/11} \text{y}, \\ &\approx 0.22 \left(\frac{M}{M_\odot}\right)^{2/11} \text{day}, \end{aligned}\right. \qquad n = 3, \tag{113a}$$

so that the periods during nuclear energy generation range from ~ 1 to 6 days for $M = 10^3$ to $10^8 M_\odot$ for large rotation.

However if rotation just balances the general-relativistic term during hydrogen burning it is necessary to use (88) and (90) to obtain

$$\left|\begin{aligned} \Pi(T_{cn}) &\approx 3.1\cdot 10^{-4} \left(\frac{M}{M_\odot}\right)^{19/44} \text{y}, \\ &\approx 0.11 \left(\frac{M}{M_\odot}\right)^{19/44} \text{day}. \end{aligned}\right. \qquad n = 3, \tag{113b}$$

The periods given by this expression extend up to one year for $M = 10^8 M_\odot$. *Thus, depending on the amount of rotation, supermassive stars should have dynamical periods for small oscillations in the range from one day to one year. Nonlinear effects can increase the upper limit to tens of years.*

A minimum is eventually reached in the period as the post-Newtonian general-relativistic term becomes important. This minimum period is given by

$$\Pi_{\min} \approx \frac{256\pi k \zeta_n^{\frac{3}{2}}}{3K^4\alpha^4} \left(\frac{2GM}{c}\right), \tag{114}$$

$$\approx 2.6\cdot 10^{-11} \left(\frac{M}{M_\odot}\right) \text{y}, \qquad n = 3, \tag{115}$$

$$\approx 1.0\cdot 10^{-8} \left(\frac{M}{M_\odot}\right) \text{day}, \qquad n = 3. \tag{116}$$

The minimum period is very short being the order of only one day even for $M = 10^8\, M_\odot$. The periods given in (110) through (116) are quite sensitive to the choice for ω_c/ω_{cr} in α and could be an order of magnitude greater for a more conservative choice that the $\omega_c/\omega_{cr} = 1$ used here.

If eqs. (92) and (96) are employed it can be shown that in the early stage of contraction the rotational period at the periphery is given by

$$P_R = \frac{2\pi}{\omega_R} \approx \left(\frac{4\pi^2 R^3}{\alpha^2 G M}\right)^{\frac{1}{2}}, \tag{117}$$

$$\approx \left(\frac{2K^2}{3k^2}\right) \Pi = 4.7\Pi, \qquad n = 3. \tag{118}$$

The central rotational period is an order of magnitude shorter. As contraction proceeds Π approaches a minimum while P_R does not. At the minimum in Π it is found that

$$P_R(\Pi_{\min}) \approx \left(\frac{K^2}{6k^2}\right)^{\frac{1}{2}} \Pi_{\min} = 2.3\Pi_{\min}. \tag{119}$$

The peripheral velocity is given by

$$v_R = \omega_R R \approx \left(\frac{\alpha^2 G M}{R}\right)^{\frac{1}{2}} \tag{120}$$

so that

$$\frac{v_R}{c} \approx 10^{-7} \left(\frac{M}{M_\odot}\right)^{\frac{1}{4}} T_c^{\frac{1}{2}}, \qquad n = 3. \tag{121}$$

For $T_c = 10^8$ °K and $M = 10^8\, M_\odot$ the peripheral velocity is 10 % of the velocity of light. If it is assumed that the rotational angular velocity continues to decrease beyond the stellar surface according to (105), $\omega_r \sim r^{-2}$, $v_r \sim r^{-1}$, then the rotational velocity of the emission region (Fig. 2) is only 10^{-3} to 10^{-4} of the velocity of light.

16. – Conclusion.

The results presented in Sects. **8** to **15** constitute an extension of the previous material in Sects. **1** to **7** on relaxation oscillations in supermassive stars. It has been shown that a relatively small amount of rotation is sufficient to remove the general-relativistic instability which arises in such stars when rotation is absent. The post-Newtonian equations for the binding energy and for the frequency of the fundamental mode of radial oscillations have been derived and close connection between these two quantities has been exhibited. The equatorial instability associated with contraction under rotation has been investigated and the results used to estimate the limiting mass in which hydrogen burning can be effective as a source of energy during relaxation oscillations. For differential rotation this limit is found to be at least $10^8\,M_\odot$ and perhaps as high as $10^9\,M_\odot$ whereas, without rotation, the limit arising from general-relativistic considerations is $10^6\,M_\odot$. For uniform rotation the limit is $10^7\,M_\odot$.

The masses of supermassive stars which can be observed as quasars thus cover a range of at least a factor of 100. By eq. (37) the luminosities thus vary by this same factor. This means that the red-shift magnitude diagram for quasars should exhibit a band approximately five magnitudes in width. The objects on the left edge of this band are of greater luminosity and greater mass than those on the right edge and thus by eqs. (113*a*, *b*) should have longer periods than those to the right.

APPENDIX

In this Appendix the relations used in the main text between the internal energy density u, and pressure p, both in erg cm^{-3}, are discussed and the use of various expressions for the « effective ratio of specific heats » is clarified. It is sufficiently general for our purposes to consider the medium to be approximately nondegenerate and to be made up of nuclei, ionization electrons, electron-positron pairs and radiation as treated in detail by FOWLER and HOYLE (1964). Then from eqs. (B.62) and (B.43) of this reference one has

$$u = xnkT + 2n_+ m_e c^2 + aT^4\,, \tag{A.1}$$

$$p = qnkT + \tfrac{1}{3}aT^4\,, \tag{A.2}$$

where $n = n_0 + n_N + 2n_+$ is the number density of all particles—ionization electrons, nuclei and electron-positron pairs—, x is the mean kinetic energy per particle in units of kT and q is a factor, close to unity in value, which incorporates the deviations from Boyle's law in the gas. The internal energy density includes everything except the rest mass-energy density, $\varrho_0 c^2$, of the nuclei and the associated ionization electrons.

The number density of paired electrons and positrons is

$$2n_+ \approx (n_0^2 + 4n_1^2)^{\frac{1}{2}} - n_0\,, \tag{A.3}$$

where

$$n_0 = Zn_N = \frac{\varrho_0 Z}{M_u A} = 6.02\cdot 10^{23}\varrho_0\frac{Z}{A} \tag{A.4}$$

is the original number of ionization electrons, n_N is the number density of nuclei, ϱ_0 is the rest mass density, M_u is the atomic mass unit, Z is the mean number of free electrons per nucleus, A is the mean nuclear mass plus that of associated electrons in atomic mass units, and

$$n_1 = \frac{1}{\pi^2 z}\left(\frac{m_e c}{\hbar}\right)^3 K_2(z) \,. \tag{A.5}$$

In (A.5), $z = m_e c^2/kT$ and $K_2(z)$ is the modified Bessel function of second order. Numerically one has

$$n_1 \approx 1.521\cdot 10^{29}\, T_9^{\frac{3}{2}} \exp[-5.93/T_9]\ \mathrm{cm}^{-3}\,, \qquad T_9 < 3\,, \tag{A.6}$$

$$\approx 1.688\cdot 10^{28}\, T_9^3\ \mathrm{cm}^{-3}\,, \qquad T_9 > 3\,. \tag{A.7}$$

Because of the low density in massive stars for a given temperature, the number of positrons and paired electrons becomes comparable to the number of ionization electrons at relatively low temperatures, *e.g.* at $5\cdot 10^8$ °K in a star with $M = 10^8\, M_\odot$. This is above the temperature for hydrogen to helium conversion, however.

The factor x in eq. (A.1) is equal to $\frac{3}{2}$ for nonrelativistic, nondegenerate electrons and nuclei and has been tabulated for relativistic, nondegenerate electrons by CHANDRASEKHAR (1939) as U/PV in Table 24, p. 397. The entries in this table also apply to the pair positrons under relativistic nondegenerate conditions. Although the entries in the table range from $x = \frac{3}{2}$ up to maximum value, $x = 3$, there are circumstances (FOWLER and HOYLE 1964) under which x can be as high as 3.15, in which case $q = 1.05$. At low temperatures pairs can be neglected, the electrons and nuclei may recombine into atoms and molecules and in any case x can be found in terms of the specific heat at constant volume c_V or the radio of specific heats γ from

$$\frac{\mathrm{d}(xT)}{\mathrm{d}T} = c_V = \frac{1}{\gamma - 1}\,. \tag{A.8}$$

When x is constant, one has

$$x \approx c_V = \frac{1}{\gamma - 1}\,. \tag{A.9}$$

Under the circumstances of major interest in this paper, the nuclei are ionized the electrons are nonrelativistic and nondegenerate and pairs can be neglected Then $\gamma = \frac{5}{3}$ and $x = c_V = \frac{3}{2}$.

If $\beta = qnkT/p$ is introduced as the ratio of gas pressure to total pressure and $1 - \beta = aT^4/3p$ as the ratio of radiation pressure to total pressure, then from eqs. (A.1) and (A.2) the dimensionless ratio of internal energy density to pressure is given by

$$\frac{u}{p} = 3 - (\beta/q)[3q - x - z(2n_+/n)]\,. \tag{A.10}$$

As is required relativistically this ratio approaches 3 at very high temperatures independent of β since then $kT \gg m_e c^2$, $z \to 0$, $x/q \to 3$ and $2n_+ \to n$. When pairs are first copiously produced this ratio can exceed 3 under certain circumstances. The relativistic behavior for β is discussed in detail by FOWLER and HOYLE (1964); it passes through a minimum near zero in massive stars but increases to a limiting value, $\beta = 7/11$, at high temperatures when pairs become copious.

The customary nonrelativistic expression for u/p is found by setting $q = 1$, $x = (\gamma - 1)^{-1}$ and $n_+ = 0$ so that

$$\text{(A.11)} \qquad \frac{u}{p} \approx \frac{\beta}{\gamma - 1} + 3(1-\beta) = \frac{3(\gamma-1) - \beta(3\gamma - 4)}{\gamma - 1}, \qquad \text{NR}.$$

It is convenient at this point to introduce a quantity which is very similar to the adiabatic coefficients Γ_1, Γ_2 and Γ_3 defined by CHANDRASEKHAR (1939) p. 57 and 58. We denote this quantity by Γ_4 and define it by

$$\Gamma_4 - 1 \equiv p/u,$$

$$\text{(A.12)} \qquad = \frac{1}{3 - (\beta/q)[3q - x - z(2n_+/n)]},$$

$$\text{(A.13)} \qquad \approx \frac{\gamma - 1}{3(\gamma - 1) - \beta(3\gamma - 4)} = \frac{\gamma - 1}{1 + (1-\beta)(3\gamma - 4)}, \qquad \text{NR}.$$

Thus

$$\text{(A.14)} \qquad \Gamma_4 = \frac{4 - (\beta/q)[3q - x - z(2n_+/n)]}{3 - (\beta/q)[3q - x - z(2n_+/n)]}$$

$$\text{(A.15)} \qquad = \frac{4}{3} + \frac{(\beta/q)[3q - x - z(2n_+/n)]}{9 - 3(\beta/q)[3q - x - z(2n_+/n)]},$$

$$\text{(A.16)} \qquad \approx \frac{4(\gamma - 1) - \beta(3\gamma - 4)}{3(\gamma - 1) - \beta(3\gamma - 4)}, \qquad \text{NR},$$

$$\text{(A.17)} \qquad \approx \frac{4}{3} + \frac{\beta(3\gamma - 4)}{9(\gamma - 1) - 3\beta(3\gamma - 4)}, \qquad \text{NR}.$$

It will be clear from the definition of Γ_4 that averaging over the entire volume of the star yields

$$\text{(A.18)} \qquad \int p\,\mathrm{d}V = \int (\Gamma_4 - 1)\,u\,\mathrm{d}V = (\bar{\Gamma}_4 - 1)\int u\,\mathrm{d}V.$$

The appropriate mean value for Γ_4 is that obtained by averaging over each element of internal energy, $u\,\mathrm{d}V$.

Extreme relativistic conditions arise when $x = 3q$ and $z = 0$ in (A.14) or (A.15) in which case $\Gamma_4 = \frac{4}{3}$ as expected. Under intermediate circumstances Γ_4 can be found by using (A.14). However, under the circumstances of major interest in this paper, (A.16) with $\gamma = \frac{5}{3}$ is applicable and

$$\Gamma_4 \approx \frac{8-3\beta}{6-3\beta}, \qquad \gamma = \tfrac{5}{3}, \qquad \text{NR}, \tag{A.19}$$

$$\approx \frac{4}{3} + \frac{\beta}{6}, \qquad \beta \ll 1, \qquad \text{NR}, \tag{A.20}$$

where the second approximation holds for small β. This is the same approximation that holds for the first of Chandrasekhar's adiabatic coefficients, $\Gamma_1 \equiv -\,\mathrm{d}\ln p/d\ln V$ when β is small. As a matter of fact in massive stars during hydrogen burning β is quite small being given by (FOWLER and HOYLE 1964, Table BI)

$$\beta \approx \frac{4.28}{\mu}\left(\frac{M_\odot}{M}\right)^{\frac{1}{2}}, \qquad M > 10^3\, M_\odot, \qquad \text{NR}, \tag{A.21}$$

where $\mu = A/(Z+1)$ is the mean « molecular » weight. Note that $\beta \sim 10^{-3}$ for $M = 10^8\, M_\odot$ and $\mu = \frac{1}{2}$ (hydrogen). As discussed in the main text it is the smallness of β and the closeness of Γ_1 and Γ_4 to $\frac{4}{3}$ which makes the Newtonian terms in the binding energy and pulsation frequency correspondingly small and thus brings the rotational and general-relativistic terms into prominence in these quantities. It will be noted that Γ_1 and Γ_4 are effective ratios of specific heats under appropriate circumstances.

In the above analysis the ratio p/u at a given time and position in a star has been equated to $\Gamma_4 - 1$. In addition it is necessary to establish relationships between δp and δu and between $\delta\int p\,\mathrm{d}V$ and $\delta\int u\,\mathrm{d}V$ when the star is subject to an *adiabatic* perturbation at all points. The general-relativistic adiabatic relation is

$$\delta Q = \delta(\varrho c^2 V) + p\,\delta V = 0, \tag{A.22}$$

where it is required that the volume V apply to a fixed number of baryons throughout the adiabatic change. This requirement follows from the generally accepted physical law of the *conservation of baryons*. Under the conditions of interest in this paper the only baryons involved are protons and neutrons, free or incorporated in nuclei as nucleons.

In order to proceed it is necessary to recall once again the relation

$$\frac{\delta p}{p} \equiv -\,\Gamma_1 \frac{\delta V}{V} \tag{A.23}$$

by which Chandrasekhar's first adiabatic coefficient is defined. If eqs. (A.22) and (A.23) are appropriately manipulated it is found that

$$\frac{\delta p}{p} = \Gamma_1 \frac{\delta\varrho}{\varrho + p/c^2} \tag{A.24}$$

and

$$\frac{\delta(pV)}{\delta(\varrho c^2 V)} = \Gamma_1 - 1 . \tag{A.25}$$

Under some circumstances it is of interest to consider adiabatic changes during which no nuclear or atomic processes occur so that the rest mass associated with a given number of baryons (or nucleons) does not change. Under these circumstances $\varrho_0 V$ is an invariant and $\delta(\varrho c^2 V) = \delta(\varrho_0 c^2 V) + \delta(uV)$ becomes just equal to $\delta(uV)$. Then

$$\frac{\delta p}{p} = \Gamma_1 \frac{\delta \varrho_0}{\varrho_0} \qquad (\varrho_0 V = \text{const}) , \tag{A.26}$$

$$\frac{\delta(pV)}{\delta(uV)} = \frac{\delta(p/\varrho_0)}{\delta(u/\varrho_0)} = \Gamma_1 - 1 \qquad (\varrho_0 V = \text{const}) \tag{A.27}$$

and

$$\frac{\delta p}{\delta u} = \frac{\Gamma_1}{\Gamma_4}\frac{p}{u} = \frac{\Gamma_1}{\Gamma_4}(\Gamma_4 - 1) \qquad (\varrho_0 V = \text{const}) . \tag{A.28}$$

Now consider the variations $\delta\int p\,\mathrm{d}V$ and $\delta\int u\,\mathrm{d}V$ corresponding to adiabatic changes made throughout the entire star. These can be written respectively as

$$\delta\int p\,\mathrm{d}V = \delta\int (pV)\frac{\mathrm{d}V}{V} = \int \delta(pV)\frac{\mathrm{d}V}{V} = \int (\Gamma_1 - 1)\,\delta(uV)\frac{\mathrm{d}V}{V} \tag{A.29}$$

and

$$\delta\int u\,\mathrm{d}V = \delta\int (uV)\frac{\mathrm{d}V}{V} = \int \delta(uV)\frac{\mathrm{d}V}{V} . \tag{A.30}$$

The second equality in each of these equations derives from the fact that $\mathrm{d}V$ and V must each apply to a fixed number of baryons during any perturbation. Thus $\mathrm{d}V/V$ is replaceable by $\mathrm{d}N_\mathrm{B}/N_\mathrm{B}$ where N_B is the total number of baryons is the star and is therefore clearly invariant to any perturbation under consideration. In the last equality in (A.29), eq. (A.27) has been used. Then, since Γ_1 and its average $\bar{\Gamma}_1$ over $u\,\mathrm{d}V$ are constant to first order during any perturbation, it ultimately follows that

$$\begin{cases} \delta\int p\,\mathrm{d}V = \delta\int(\Gamma_4 - 1)\,u\,\mathrm{d}V , \\ \quad = (\bar{\Gamma}_1 - 1)\,\delta\int u\,\mathrm{d}V \qquad (\varrho_0 V = \text{const}) . \end{cases} \tag{A.31}$$

It will be clear that Γ_4 is not constant during an adiabatic perturbation and, in fact, it can be shown that

$$\frac{\delta\Gamma_4}{\Gamma_4 - 1} = (\Gamma_4 - \Gamma_1)\frac{\delta V}{V} . \tag{A.32}$$

Comparison of (A.31) with (A.18) indicates that $\bar{\Gamma}_1$ replaces $\bar{\Gamma}_4$ in relations involving adiabatic perturbations. To first order in small β, Γ_1 and Γ_4 and hence $\bar{\Gamma}_1$ and $\bar{\Gamma}_4$ are equal. This can be seen from Chandrasekhar's nonrelativistic expression for Γ_1 which corresponds to (A.16). This expression is

(A.33) $$\Gamma_1 \approx \beta + \frac{(4-3\beta)^2(\gamma-1)}{\beta+12(\gamma-1)(1-\beta)} \qquad \text{(NR)},$$

(A.34) $$\approx \frac{4}{3} + \frac{(4\beta-3\beta^2)(3\gamma-4)}{36(\gamma-1)-3\beta(12\gamma-13)} \qquad \text{(NR)},$$

(A.35) $$\approx \frac{32-24\beta-3\beta^2}{24-21\beta}, \qquad \gamma=\tfrac{5}{3}, \qquad \text{(NR)},$$

(A.36) $$\approx \frac{4}{3} + \frac{\beta}{6} \approx \Gamma_4, \qquad \beta \ll 1, \qquad \text{(NR)}.$$

FOWLER and HOYLE (1964), p. 289, give the relativistic expression for Γ_1 when pairs are included. Actually Γ_1 does not differ greatly from Γ_4 over the range $0 \leqslant \beta \leqslant 1$ as illustrated in Table I. The two are equal at the two extremes of this range with $\Gamma_1 = \Gamma_4 = 4/3$ at $\beta = 0$ and $\Gamma_1 = \Gamma_4 = 5/3$ at $\beta = 1$ for $\gamma = 5/3$. In addition for small β, Γ_1 and Γ_4 are equal for any γ since

TABLE I. – *Values of Γ_1 and Γ_4 for $\gamma = \frac{5}{3}$.*

β	0	0.01	0.1	0.2	0.3	0.4
Γ_1	1.333	1.335002	1.350	1.368	1.386	1.405
Γ_4	1.333	1.335008	1.351	1.370	1.392	1.417
β	0.5	0.6	0.7	0.8	0.9	1.0
Γ_1	1.426	1.449	1.476	1.511	1.563	1.667
Γ_4	1.444	1.476	1.512	1.556	1.606	1.667

(A.37) $$\Gamma_1 \approx \Gamma_4 \approx \frac{4}{3} + \frac{\beta}{3}\,\frac{\gamma-\frac{4}{3}}{\gamma-1}, \qquad \beta < 1, \qquad \text{(NR)}.$$

For convective stability it is necessary that

(A.38) $$\frac{\mathrm{d}\ln p}{\mathrm{d}r} > \Gamma_1 \frac{\mathrm{d}\ln \varrho}{\mathrm{d}r} \qquad \text{(conv. stab.)}.$$

CHANDRASEKHAR (1965*b*) has shown that this is a necessary and sufficient condition in general relativity except in very special physical situations involving only small regions in a star where the effect of general-relativistic modifications is not of crucial importance. Since p and ϱ usually decrease with r it is often convenient to use (A.38) rewritten as

$$\left|\frac{\mathrm{d}\ln p}{\mathrm{d}r}\right| < \Gamma_1 \left|\frac{\mathrm{d}\ln \varrho}{\mathrm{d}r}\right| \qquad \text{(conv. stab.)}\,. \tag{A.39}$$

For a polytrope at index n with $p \propto \varrho^{1+1/n}$ this yields

$$\left(1+\frac{1}{n}\right) < \Gamma_1$$

or

$$n > \frac{1}{\Gamma_1 - 1} \qquad \text{(conv. stab.)}\,, \tag{A.40}$$

$$> 3(1-\beta/2)\,, \qquad T_9 < 1\,.$$

Thus the polytrope $n=3$ which has been used extensively throughout this lecture is convectively stable except when electron-positron pair formation reduces Γ_1 below 4/3 in the range $1 < T_9 < 3$. Formation of other particles will reduce Γ_1 below 4/3 in additional ranges at still higher temperatures.

An important quantity in the considerations discussed in this lecture is $\bar{\beta}$, the ratio of gas pressure to total pressure averaged over the internal energy distribution in the star. See, for example, eqs. (55) and (56). It can be shown from the analysis of FOWLER (1964) and FOWLER and HOYLE (1964) that, for massive stars,

$$\frac{\overline{\mu\beta}}{(\mu\beta)_c} = \frac{\int \theta^{(5n+1)/4}\xi^2\,\mathrm{d}\xi}{\int \theta^{n+1}\xi^2\,\mathrm{d}\xi}\,, \tag{A.41}$$

where θ and ξ are the customary dimensionless variables in the Lane-Emden equation for the polytrope of index n and at the center (c) of the star

$$(\mu\beta)_c = \left(\frac{3}{4\pi}(n+1)^3\frac{\Re^4 M_n^2}{aG^3 M_\odot^2}\right)^{\frac{1}{4}}\left(\frac{M_\odot}{M}\right)^{\frac{1}{2}}. \tag{A.42}$$

Numerical values for $(\mu\beta)_c(M/M_\odot)^{\frac{1}{2}}$ and $\overline{\mu\beta}(M/M_\odot)^{\frac{1}{2}}$ are tabulated in Table II. Note that the latter quantity is approximately independent of n. In Table II R_n and M_n are the constants of integration corresponding to radius and mass respectively for the Lane-Emden equation. For μ=constant, (A.41) yields $\bar{\beta}/\beta_c$.

TABLE II.

n	R_n	M_n	$\varrho_c/\bar{\varrho}$	$\overline{\mu\beta}/(\mu\beta)_c$	$(\mu\beta)_c\left(\frac{M}{M_\odot}\right)^{\frac{1}{2}}$	$\overline{\mu\beta}(M/M_\odot)^{\frac{1}{2}}$
0	2.4494	4.8988	1.0000	1.8729	2.3569	4.4142
0.5	2.7528	3.7871	1.8361	1.5525	2.8088	4.3607
1.0	3.1416	3.1416	3.2899	1.3634	3.1743	4.3278
1.5	3.6538	2.7141	5.9907	1.2343	3.4879	4.3051
2.0	4.3529	2.4111	11.4025	1.1383	3.7691	4.2900
2.5	4.3553	2.1872	23.4065	1.0625	4.0299	4.2817
3.0	6.8969	2.0182	54.1825	1.0000	4.2788	4.2788
3.5	9.5358	1.8906	152.884	0.9465	4.5237	4.2817
4.0	14.9716	1.7972	622.408	0.8992	4.7734	4.2922
4.5	31.8365	1.7378	6189.47	0.8558	5.0416	4.3146
5.0	∞	1.7321	∞	0.8136	5.3727	4.3712

BIBLIOGRAPHY

BARDEEN, J. M., 1965, *Conference on Observational Aspects of Cosmology*, Miami Beach, Florida.

BARDEEN, J. M. and S. P. S. ANAND, 1966, *Ap. J.*, **144**, 953.

BURBIDGE, G. R., 1961, *Nature*, **190**, 1053.

CAUGHLAN, G. R. and W. A. FOWLER, 1962, *Ap. J.*, **136**, 453.

CHANDRASEKHAR, S., 1939, *An Introduction to the Study of Stellar Structure* (Chicago).

CHANDRASEKHAR, S., 1964*a*, *Phys. Rev. Letters*, **12**, 114, 437 E.

CHANDRASEKHAR, S., 1964*b*, *Ap. J.*, **140**, 417.

CHANDRASEKHAR, S., 1965*a*, *Phys. Rev. Letters*, **14**, 241.

CHANDRASEKHAR, S., 1965*b*, *Ap. J.*, **142**, 1488, 1513, 1519.

CHANDRASEKHAR, S. and N. R. LEBOVITZ, 1962, *Ap. J.*, **136**, 1082.

COLGATE, S. A. and R. H. WHITE, 1966, *Ap. J.*, **143**, 626.

DENT, W. A., 1965, *Science*, **148**, 1458.

FIELD, G. B., 1964, *Ap. J.*, **140**, 1434.

FOWLER, W. A., 1964, *Rev. Mod. Phys.*, **36**, 545, 1104 E.

FOWLER, W. A., 1965*a*, *Proc. Amer. Phil. Soc.*, **109**, 181.

FOWLER, W. A., 1965*b*, *Proc. Third Annual Science Conf. Belfer Grad. School of Science* (New York).

FOWLER, W. A., 1966, *Ap. J.*, **144**, 180.

FOWLER, W. A. and F. HOYLE, 1963, *Herstmonceux Bulletin*, **67**, E 302.

FOWLER, W. A. and F. HOYLE, 1964, *Ap. J. Suppl.*, **9**, 201; *Nucleosynthesis in Massive Stars and Supernovae* (Chicago, 1965).

GEYER, E. H., 1964, *Z. Astrophys.*, **60**, 112.

GOLD, T., W. I. AXFORD, and E. C. RAY, 1965, in *Quasi-Stellar Sources and Gravitational collapse*, ed., I. ROBINSON, A. SCHILD and E. L. SCHUCKING (Chicago), p. 93.

Gratton, L., 1964, Internal Report of the Astrophysical Laboratory of the University of Rome and the 4th Section of the Center of Astrophysics of the Italian National Research Council, Frascati, July 1964. Presented at the *Conference on Cosmology*, Padua, Italy, September 1964.

Greenstein, J. L. and T. A. Matthews, 1963, *Nature*, **197**, 1041.

Greenstein, J. L. and M. Schmidt, 1964, *Ap. J.*, **140**, 1.

Hebbard, D. F. and G. M. Bailey, 1963, *Nuclear Phys.*, **49**, 666.

Hoyle, F., 1960, *Quart. J. R.A.S.*, **1**, 28.

Hoyle, F. and G. R. Burbidge, 1965, *Conference on Observational Aspects of Cosmology*, Miami Beach, Florida.

Hoyle, F. and G. R. Burbidge, 1966, *Ap. J.*, **144**, 534.

Hoyle, F. and W. A. Fowler, 1963*a*, *M.N.R.A.S.*, **125**, 169.

Hoyle, F. and W. A. Fowler, 1963*b*, *Nature*, **197**, 533.

Hoyle, F. and W. A. Fowler, 1965, in *Quasi-Stellar Sources and Gravitational Collapse*, ed., I. Robinson, A. Schild and E. L. Schucking (Chicago), p. 17.

Hoyle, F., W. A. Fowler, G. R. Burbidge and E. M. Burbidge, 1964, *Ap. J.*, **139**, 909.

Iben, I., jr., 1963, *Ap. J.*, **138**, 1090.

Ledoux, P., 1941, *Ap. J.*, **94**, 537.

Lynds, C. R. and A. R. Sandage, 1963, *Ap. J.*, **137**, 1005.

Maltby, P. and A. T. Moffet, 1965, *Science*, **150**, 64.

Matthews, T. A., W. W. Morgan and M. Schmidt, 1964, *Ap. J.*, **140**, 35.

Matthews, T. A. and A. R. Sandage, 1963, *Ap. J.*, **138**, 30.

Misner, C. W. and D. H. Sharp, 1964, *Phys. Rev.*, **136**, B 571.

McVittie, G. C., 1964, *Ap. J.*, **140**, 401.

Ohyama, N., 1963, *Prog. Theoret. Phys.*, **30**, 170.

Oke, J. B., 1963, *Nature*, **197**, 1040.

Oke, J. B., 1965, *Ap. J.*, **141**, 6.

Ôno, Y., S. Sakashita and N. Ohyama, 1961, *Prog. Theoret. Phys. Suppl.*, n. 20.

Roxburgh, J. W., 1965, *Nature*, **207**, 363.

Sandage, A. R., 1964, *Ap. J.*, **139**, 416.

Schmidt, M., 1963, *Nature*, **197**, 1040.

Schwarzschild, M. and R. Härm, 1959, *Ap. J.*, **129**, 637.

Sharov, A. S. and Yu. N. Efremov, 1963, *Information Bulletin on Variable Stars*, Number 23, Commission 27 of I.A.U.

Smith, J. H. and D. Hoffleit, 1963, *Nature*, **198**, 650.

Stoeckly, R., 1965, *Ap. J.*, **142**, 208.

Teller, E., 1965, *Address Before the National Academy of Sciences*, Seattle, Washington.

Terrell, J., 1964, *Science*, **145**, 918.

Terrell, J., 1965, *Conference on Observational Aspects of Cosmology*, Miami Beach, Florida.

Tooper, R. F., 1964, *Ap. J.*, **140**, 434.

Ulam, S. M. and W. E. Walden, 1964, *Nature*, **201**, 1202.

Woltjer, L., 1964, *Nature*, **201**, 803.

Zel'dović, Ya. B., 1964, *Soviet Physics-Doklady*, **9**, 195.

Neutrino Astrophysics.

W. A. Fowler

California Institute of Technology - Pasadena, Cal.

1. – Introduction.

This lecture (Sects. **1** to **5**) and the following lecture (Sect. **6**) deal with the new scientific discipline, neutrino astrophysics. The designation, *neutrino astrophysics*, is used rather than *neutrino astronomy* since the practitioners in the field so far are mainly physicists and not astronomers. Although neutrino astrophysics is a relatively new field, large funds have alredy been spent on *experiments* and *preparations for observations* and much thought has been given to *theory* but *few positive effects* have been observed *to date*. In a sense it might be said that the whole business is « much ado about nothing ».

The two lectures will cover solar, stellar, galactic and extragalactic neutrino astrophysics. The general theme will be the estimation of the quantity

$$\mathscr{E}_\nu = \frac{\text{energy emitted as } \nu \text{ or } \bar{\nu}}{\text{rest mass-energy of emitting system}} . \tag{1}$$

This quantity has obvious cosmological implications and on *conservative* estimates is usually $\sim 10^{-4}$. In certain *speculative* cases the value is considerably greater. In terms of detection at the earth, one quantity calculated will be $(\varphi_\nu \sigma_\nu)$, where φ_ν is the expected neutrino flux at the earth and σ_ν is the neutrino absorption cross-section for a given process. This can be converted into counts per day expected in a detection system involving a stated mass of detector.

The literature on the subject of neutrino astrophysics is already quite extensive and the reader is especially referred to the excellent series of articles by Bahcall (1964*a*, *b*, *c*, *d*; 1965), who has made many theoretical contributions to neutrino astrophysics.

2. – Significance of neutrino detection.

The primary significance of observations on neutrinos derives from the extremely small interaction cross-section of these particles with matter. This cross-section is of the order of 10^{-44} cm^2 per nucleon or electron. In an object of characteristic dimension R and density ϱ, the number of nucleons along the neutrino line of passage is $\sim 10^{24}\varrho R$ and the number of interactions per neutrino is $\sim 10^{-20}\varrho R$. For the earth $\varrho \sim 10$, $R \sim 10^9$ so that $\sim 10^{34}$ nucleons are passed in the passage of a neutrino through the earth but only 10^{-10} of the incident neutrinos interact. For the sun, the corresponding numbers are $\varrho \sim 1$, $R \sim 10^{11}$, 10^{35} nucleons along the path and 10^{-9} of the neutrinos interact. For the universe, one has $\varrho \sim 10^{-29}$, $R \sim 10^{28}$, 10^{23} nucleons along the path and 10^{-21} of the neutrinos interact. Thus neutrinos bear direct information unscathed from the center of the sun and other stars and from the depths of the universe.

It is paradoxical that, in spite of the low interaction cross-sections, neutrinos can still be detected terrestrially. Consider a flux at the surface of the earth such as that for the ^{8}B neutrinos to be discussed in the next Section. This flux is of the order of 10^7 neutrinos cm^{-2} s^{-1} or 10^{12} neutrinos cm^{-2} day^{-1}. Consider a detector with $\varrho \sim 1$ and mass measured in kilotons ($\sim 10^9$ grams). The counting rate will be $\sim 10^{12} \times 10^{-44} \times 10^{24} \times 10^9 \sim 10$ events per day per kiloton. Sophisticated anticoincidence techniques have reduced background counting rates to a small fraction of this value and thus enough of the elusive neutrinos which have emerged from the sun or traversed the universe can be detected with assurance and compelled to yield the secrets of their birth and the nature of their birthplace.

3. – Neutrino emission by the sun.

FOWLER (1958) showed that the main nuclear processes in the sun are those in the pp-chain listed in Table I. All of the neutrinos indicated in Table I are those associated with electron capture or positron emission and are frequently designated by ν_e. BAHCALL (1964*b*) has pointed out that electron capture processes, such as ^{8}B$(e^-, \nu_e)^8$Be* and ^{3}He$(e^-, \nu_e)^3$T, will also occur but not with high probability except in the case of ^{7}Be as included in the Table. It can also be shown that the reaction ^{3}He$(p, e^+\nu_e)^4$He, either directly or through ^{4}Li, must be relatively infrequent. Note that there are two branchings in the reaction chain but that in any case the over-all result is the conversion of four protons into an alpha-particle plus two positrons and two neutrinos or, alternatively, the conversion of four protons and one electron into an alpha particle plus one positron and two neutrinos.

TABLE I. – *The* pp-*chain.*

	$^1H + {}^1H \to {}^2D + e^+ + \nu$	$^7Be + e^- \to {}^7Li + \nu$
	$^2D + {}^1H \to {}^3He + \gamma$	$^7Li + {}^1H \to {}^4He + {}^4He$
	$^3He + {}^3He \to {}^4He + {}^1H + {}^1H$	or
or		$^7Be + {}^1H \to {}^8B + \gamma$
	$^3He\ \ {}^4He \to {}^7Be + \gamma$	$^8B \to {}^8Be^* + e^+ + \nu$
		$^8Be^* \to {}^4He + {}^4He$
over-all		
	$4p \to \alpha + 2e^+ + 2\nu$	nuclear
	or	
	$4p + e^- \to \alpha + e^+ + 2\nu$	
	$4\,{}^1H \to {}^4He + 2\nu$	atomic

There are three main groups of neutrinos emitted in the pp-chain, namely ν(pp), $\nu(^7Be)$ and $\nu(^8B)$. Their energies and relative probabilities of emission depend on the results of *experiments* carried out in nuclear laboratories throughout the world. As an example, measurements made at the California Institute of Technology by PARKER and KAVANAGH (1963) on the cross-

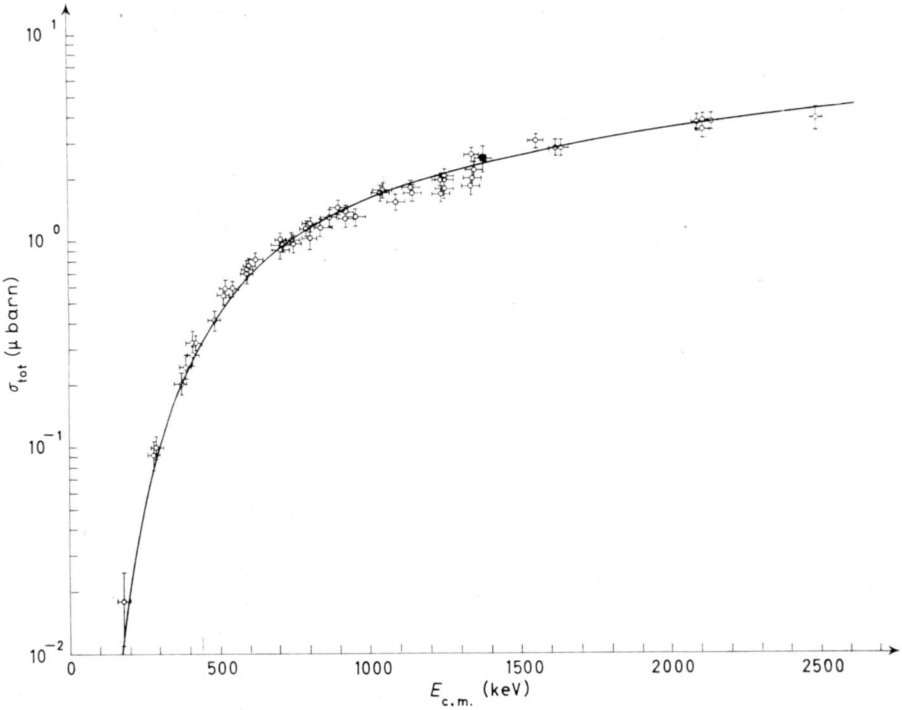

Fig. 1. – Cross-section *vs.* alpha-particle laboratory energy for the $^3He(\alpha, \gamma)^7Be$ reaction after PARKER and KAVANAGH (1963).

section for the production of ^{7}Be in the reaction ^{3}He$(\alpha, \gamma)^7$Be are shown in Fig. 1.

Measurements of the type illustrated in Fig. 1 are employed to determine the cross-section factors $S(E)$ in the equation

$$\sigma = \frac{S(E)}{E} \exp[-31.29\, Z_1 Z_0 A^{\frac{1}{2}} E^{-\frac{1}{2}}] \text{ barn}, \tag{2}$$

where E is the center-of-momentum reaction energy in keV, $A = A_0 A_1/(A_0 + A_1)$ is the reduced mass in atomic mass units (^{12}C $= 12$) and $S(E)$ is measured in keV·barn. Except in the case of low-lying resonances, $S(E)$ is found experimentally to be a slowly varying function of E which can be accurately extrapolated to the effective interaction energies in the sun and other stars. The effective interaction energy is given by

$$E_0 = 1.220(Z_0^2 Z_1^2 A T_6^2)^{\frac{1}{3}} \text{ keV}, \tag{3}$$

where $Z_0 Z_1$ are the charges of the interacting nuclei and $T_6 = T/10^6$ is the temperature in millions of degrees Kelvin. For the reactions of Table I, E_0 is the order of 10 keV, whereas it is possible to measure S only down to 100 keV in general. It is necessary to make a considerable extrapolation to obtain $S_0 = S(E_0)$ but this can usually be done with great accuracy. Experimental measurements on the pp-chain reactions are given in Table II. The

TABLE II. – *Reactions of the proton-proton or* pp *chain* (June, 1965).

The pp-chain	Energy release	S_0 (keV-barn) or $\bar{\tau}$	Solar $f_0 S_0$
^{1}H + ^{1}H → ^{2}D + β^+ + ν	1.19 × 2 = 2.38 MeV	$3.5 \cdot 10^{-22}$	$3.8 \cdot 10^{-22}$
^{2}D + ^{1}H → ^{3}He + γ	5.49 × 2 = 10.98	$3.0 \cdot 10^{-4}$	$3.2 \cdot 10^{-4}$
^{3}He + ^{3}He → ^{4}He + 2^{1}H	12.86	$1.1 \cdot 10^3$	$1.4 \cdot 10^3$
	26.22 (2% ν-loss)		
or			
^{3}He + ^{4}He → ^{7}Be + γ	1.59	0.47	0.59
^{7}Be + e$^-$ → ^{7}Li + ν + γ	0.05	$\bar{\tau}$ = 120 days (solar center)	
^{7}Li + ^{1}H → 2^{4}He	17.35	120 (nonres)	140
	25.67 (4% ν-loss)		
or			
^{7}Be + ^{1}H → ^{8}B + γ	0.13	$4.0 \cdot 10^{-2}$	$5.1 \cdot 10^{-2}$
^{8}B → ^{8}Be* + β^+ + ν	7.7	$\bar{\tau}$ = 1.1 s	
^{8}Be* → 2^{4}He	3.0	$\bar{\tau}$ = 10^{-16} s	
	19.1 (29% ν-loss)		
4^{1}H → ^{4}He	Total = = (26.7313 ± 0.0005) MeV		

quantity $f_0 \geqslant 1$ is the electron shielding factor which corrects for the fact that electron shileding at stellar densities increases the reaction rates over that measured in the laboratory.

When translated into reaction rates the experimental results in Table II indicate that in the sun the reaction $^3He(^3He, 2p)^4He$ occurs about $\frac{2}{3}$ of the

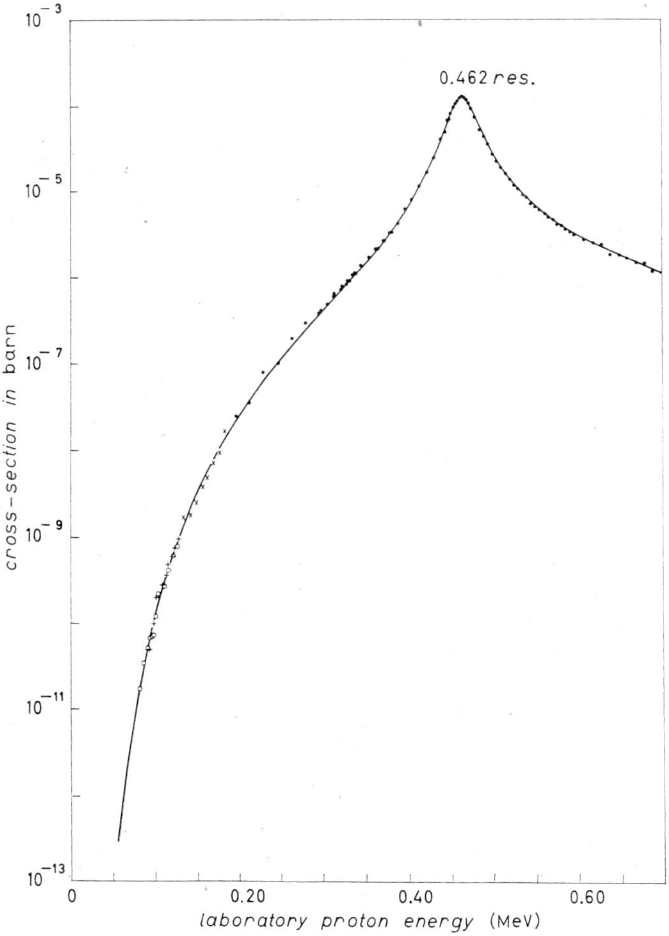

Fig. 2. – Cross-section *vs.* proton laboratory energy for the $^{12}C(p, \gamma)^{13}N$ reaction after VOGL (1963).

time, the reaction $^3He(\alpha, \gamma)^7Be$ about $\frac{1}{3}$ of the time and the reaction $^7Be(p, \gamma)^8B$ about 1/2500 of the time. The greatest experimental uncertainties lie in the rates of the first and the third of these reactions and new measurements are now in progress.

Measurements of the mass-energy balance in the neutrino reactions of

Table I can be summarized as follows:

$$(4)\quad \begin{cases} \text{Continuum} \quad 0 < E_\nu(\text{pp}) < 0.42\ \text{MeV}, & \langle E_\nu(\text{pp})\rangle = 0.25\ \text{MeV}, \\ \text{Lines} \quad E_\nu(^7\text{Be}) = 0.86\ \text{MeV and } 0.38\ \text{MeV}, & \\ \text{Continuum} \quad 0 < E_\nu(^8\text{B}) < 14.1\ \text{MeV}, & \langle E_\nu(^8\text{B})\rangle = 7.3\ \text{MeV}. \end{cases}$$

In connection with these results it is important to note that the cross-section for the detection of neutrinos varies roughly as the square of the energy above the threshold energy for the detecting reaction.

The effective energy released in the pp-chain is 26.0 MeV with 0.7 MeV or 3 per cent emitted in the form of neutrinos. The total energy emission is 0.7 per cent of the rest mass energies involved and we can assume that about $\frac{1}{3}$ of primordial hydrogen has been converted into helium during stellar evolution. Thus

$$(5)\qquad \mathscr{E}_\nu = \tfrac{1}{3}\times 0.03\times 0.07 = 7\times 10^{-5} \sim 10^{-4}\,.$$

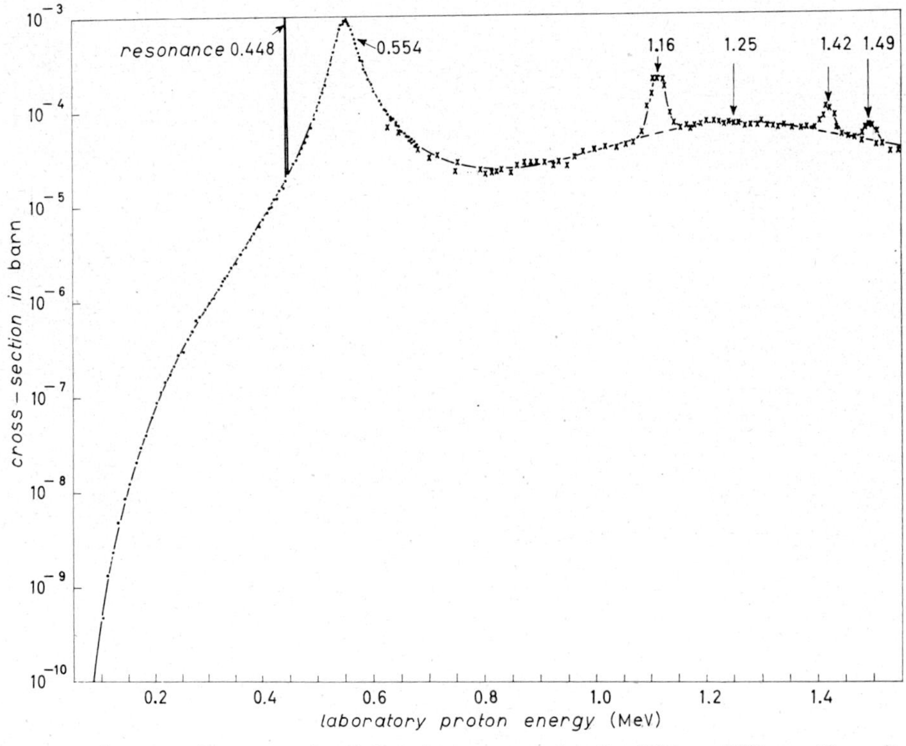

Fig. 3. – Cross-section *vs.* proton laboratory energy for the $^{13}C(p, \gamma_0)^{14}N$ reaction after Vogl (1963) and Seagrave (1951). Divide the ordinate by 0.82 to obtain the total $^{13}C(p, \gamma)^{14}N$ cross-section.

A similar result is obtained for helium production in the «big bang» of evolutionary cosmology or for helium production in massive stars early in the formation of the galaxy. For additional discussion see the end of Section 6·3.

The CNO bi-cycle reactions also take place in the sun. As examples, cross-section measurements for $^{12}C(p, \gamma)^{13}N$ and $^{13}C(p, \gamma)^{14}N$ made by VOGL (1963) and SEAGRAVE (1951) are shown in Fig. 2 and 3. Extrapolation of the cross-section factors are shown in Fig. 4. The experimental results for the complete CNO bi-cycle are shown in Table III. In the sun the energy generation is primarily due to the pp-chain as illustrated in Fig. 5. Nevertheless the rate of production of $\nu(^{13}N)$ and $\nu(^{15}O)$ can be calculated.

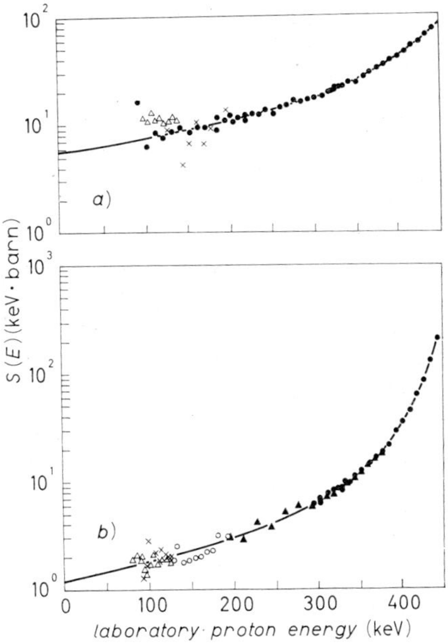

Fig. 4. – The cross-section factor, $S(E)$, *vs.* proton laboratory energy for the reactions: *a)* $^{13}C(p, \gamma)^{14}N$: × WOODBURY and FOWLER, △ HESTER and LAMB, • HEBBARD and VOGL; *b)* $^{12}C(p, \gamma)^{13}N$: ▲ • HEBBARD and VOGL, △ LAMB and HESTER, × HALL and FOWLER, ○ BAILEY and STRATTON.

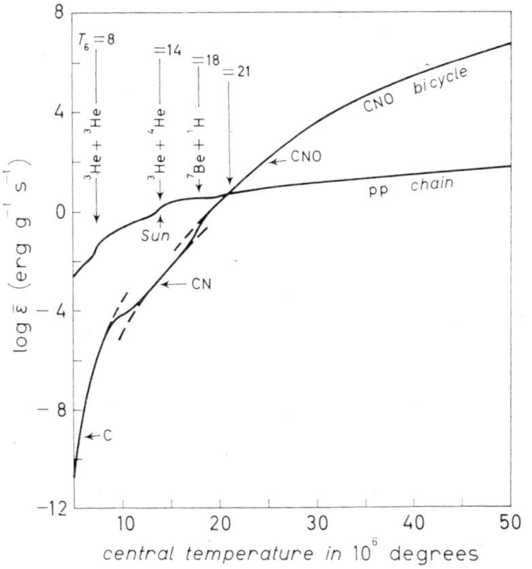

Fig. 5. – Average energy generation throughot a star in erg per gram-second as a function of central temperature for the p-p chain and the CNO cycle. The central density is taken as $\varrho = 100$ g/cm³, and the hydrogen concentration by weight as $X_H = 0.50$. Concentrations of C, N, and O by weight as given are those for a typical population I star ($X_C = 0.3\%$, $X_N = 0.1\%$, $X_O = 1.2\%$). The age of the star is taken to be $4.5 \cdot 10^9$ years. The points of inflection in the p-p chain arise from the onset of the indicated interactions. Similarly C, N and O are successively involved in the CNO cycle. Note that the sun and the cool stars operate on the p-p chain; hot stars operate on the CNO cycle. $\bar{\varepsilon}/\varepsilon_c = 0.1$, pp chain; $\bar{\varepsilon}/\varepsilon_c = 0.01$ CNO cycle.

Since two neutrinos are emitted in the conversion of $4\,{}^1H \rightarrow {}^4He$, the total neutrino flux at the earth can be easily computed from

$$(6) \qquad \varphi_\nu(\text{total}) = 2\times\frac{\text{solar constant}}{\langle\text{Energy from } 4\,{}^1H \rightarrow {}^4He\rangle} = $$

$$= \frac{2\times1.34\times10^6}{26\times1.6\times10^{-6}} = 6.5\times10^{10}\ \nu\ \text{cm}^2\ \text{s}^{-1}\ ,$$

where the solar constant (ABBOT and FOWLE, 1911) has been taken as 2 cal·$\cdot$cm^{-2} min^{-1} or $1.34\cdot10^6$ erg cm^{-2} s^{-1} and the energy release per pp-chain as 26.0 MeV or $4.17\cdot10^{-5}$ erg. The individual fluxes for the various types of neutrinos as calculated by BAHCALL (1964*d*) are shown in Fig. 6.

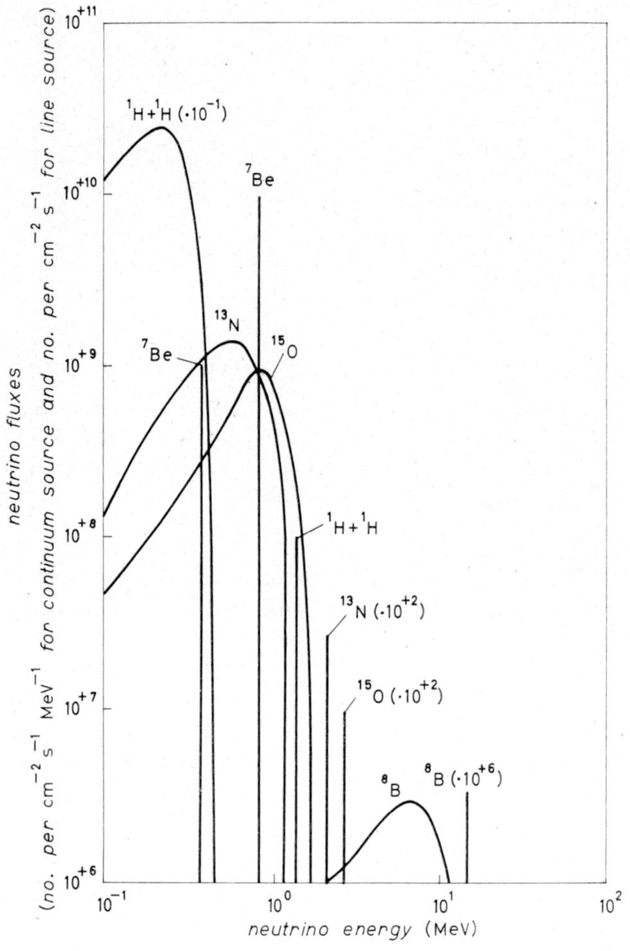

Fig. 6. – Predicted neutrino spectrum from the sun after BAHCALL (1965). Fluxes given are evaluated at the earth's surface. The neutrino lines are produced by the capture of free electrons; the small thermal widths ($\sim$1 keV) of these lines have been neglected in the figure.

TABLE III. – *Reactions of the* CNO-*cycle* (June, 1965).

The CNO-cycle	Energy release	S_0 (keV-barn) or $\bar{\tau}$	Solar $f_0 S_0$
$\rightarrow {}^{12}C + {}^{1}H \rightarrow {}^{13}N + \gamma$	1.94	1.53	2.2
${}^{13}N \rightarrow {}^{13}C + \beta^{+} + \nu$	1.50	$\bar{\tau} = 870$ s	
${}^{13}C + {}^{1}H \rightarrow {}^{14}N + \gamma$	7.55	5.9	8.4
$\rightarrow {}^{14}N + {}^{1}H \rightarrow {}^{15}O + \gamma$	7.29	3.0	4.5
${}^{15}O \rightarrow {}^{15}N + \beta^{+} + \nu$	1.73	$\bar{\tau} = 178$ s	
${}^{15}N + {}^{1}H \rightarrow {}^{12}C + {}^{4}He$	4.96	$7.5 \cdot 10^{4}$	$1.1 \cdot 10^{5}$
or (1/2200)	(6% ν-loss) 24.97 MeV		
${}^{15}N = {}^{1}H \rightarrow {}^{16}O + \gamma$	12.13	32	48
${}^{16}O + {}^{1}H \rightarrow {}^{17}F + \gamma$	0.60	9.9	16
${}^{17}F \rightarrow {}^{17}O + \beta^{+} + \nu$	1.76	$\bar{\tau} = 95$ s	
${}^{17}O + {}^{1}H \rightarrow {}^{14}N + {}^{4}He$	1.19	10	16
	(1/2200) 15.68 MeV		
$4{}^{1}H \rightarrow {}^{4}He$	Total = (26.7313 ± 0.0005) MeV		

4. – Detection of solar neutrinos.

DAVIS (1955, 1964) of the Brookhaven National Laboratory has developed a technique for the detection of neutrinos based on a reaction suggested by PONTECORVO and elaborated upon by ALVAREZ, namely

$$ {}^{37}Cl[J = \tfrac{3}{2}^{+},\ T = \tfrac{3}{2}] + \nu_e(\text{solar}) \rightarrow {}^{37}Ar[J = \tfrac{3}{2}^{+},\ T = \tfrac{5}{2}] + e^{-} - 0.814\ \text{MeV}\,, \tag{7} $$

which is the reverse of the electron capture reaction which can be observed terrestrially

$$ {}^{37}Ar + e^{-}(\text{orbital}) \rightarrow {}^{37}Cl + \nu_e\,, \tag{8} $$

for which the measured half-life is 35.1 days. The ${}^{37}Cl$ in the form of carbon tetrachloride, CCl_4, or of perchlorethylene, C_2Cl_4, is « exposed » to neutrinos with appropriate shielding in a deep mine and the rare gas ${}^{37}Ar$ is collected by bubbling helium through the CCl_4 or C_2Cl_4. The ${}^{37}Ar$ is then frozen out of the helium on to charcoal and is eventually deposited with carrier argon in a small, low-background counter. Counting is made possible by the Auger electrons and X-rays emitted by the excited ${}^{37}Cl$ atoms produced in the ${}^{37}Ar$ decay.

DAVIS has already performed experiments using 1000 to 3000 gallons of CCl_4 or C_2Cl_4 under the reactor at Savannah River, Georgia and in a deep mine at Barberton, Ohio. The reactor emits antineutrinos and Davis has already shown that the reaction

$$^{37}\mathrm{Cl} + \bar{\nu}_e(\mathrm{reactor}) \rightarrow {}^{37}\mathrm{Ar} + e^- \tag{9}$$

has a cross-section $\sigma(\bar{\nu}_e) < 0.02 \cdot 10^{-44}\ \mathrm{cm}^2$, whereas $\sigma(\nu_e) = 1.2 \cdot 10^{-44}\ \mathrm{cm}^2$ would be expected for neutrinos of the same energy spectrum. Thus he has shown that $\bar{\nu}_e$ and ν_e are not identical as postulated in some early theories of the weak interaction. (It is, of course, possible to argue that $\bar{\nu}_e$ and ν_e are the right- and left-handed varieties of the *same* particle and still be in keeping with experiment if the mass of the neutrino is taken to be very small and the deviation from completeness of the violation of parity in the weak interactions is assigned a suitably small value.)

The cross-section for the absorption of neutrinos in ^{37}Cl to form the ground state of ^{37}Ar is given by

$$\sigma(\nu_e) = \sigma_0 p_e \omega_e \left(\frac{F}{2\pi\alpha Z}\right), \tag{10}$$

where $F = F(\omega_e, Z)$ is the well known Fermi function and p_e and ω_e are the electron momentum in units $m_e c$ and the total electron energy in units $m_e c^2$ respectively. The cross-section $\sigma_0 = 1.9 \cdot 10^{-46}\ \mathrm{cm}^2$ can be calculated from the measured properties of the ^{37}Ar decay. From the energetics of the reaction the outgoing electron energy is given in terms of the incident neutrino energy by

$$E_e = W_e - 0.511\ \mathrm{MeV} = W_\nu - 0.814\ \mathrm{MeV}$$

or

$$\mathscr{E}_e = E_e / m_e c^2 = \omega_e - 1 = \omega_\nu - 1.59 \tag{11}$$

and

$$p_e = (\omega_e - 1)^{\frac{1}{2}}.$$

The threshold occurs for $E_e = 0$ or $W_\nu = 0.814$ MeV. Thus the reaction is only capable of detecting the most energetic of the ^{7}Be neutrino lines and that part of the ^{8}B continuum above 0.814 MeV. Because of the phase space factor, $p_e \omega_e$, for the emitted electron the reaction is ~ 250 times more sensitive to the $\nu(^8\mathrm{B})$ than to the $\nu(^7\mathrm{Be})$. This makes up in part for a factor of $\sim$ 500 in the relative fluxes favoring $\nu(^7\mathrm{Be})$.

Recently Bahcall (1964*b*) has suggested that the analogue state in ^{37}Ar corresponding to the $J = \frac{3}{2}$, $T = \frac{3}{2}$ ground state of ^{37}Cl should be produced with relatively high probability in the reaction

$$^{37}\mathrm{Cl}\left[J = \tfrac{3}{2}, T = \tfrac{3}{2}\right] + \nu_e \rightarrow {}^{37}\mathrm{Ar}^*\left[J = \tfrac{3}{2}^+, T = \tfrac{3}{2}\right] + e^- - 5.95\ \mathrm{MeV}, \tag{12}$$

since this is a super-allowed transition with a large matrix element for the transition. In this case $\sigma_0 \sim 10^{-44}$ cm^2 but only the ^{8}B neutrinos will produce the ^{37}Ar*. This changes the over-all cross-section factor for $\nu(^8\text{B})/\nu(^7\text{Be})$ to $\sim 10^4$. The threshold energy given above has been determined by experiments by McNally (1965) at the California Institute of Technology and elsewhere which isolated the $T = \frac{3}{2}$ state at 5.14 MeV excitation (*). The energy level diagram of ^{37}Ar before and after the experiments stimulated by Bahcall's suggestion is shown in Fig. 7.

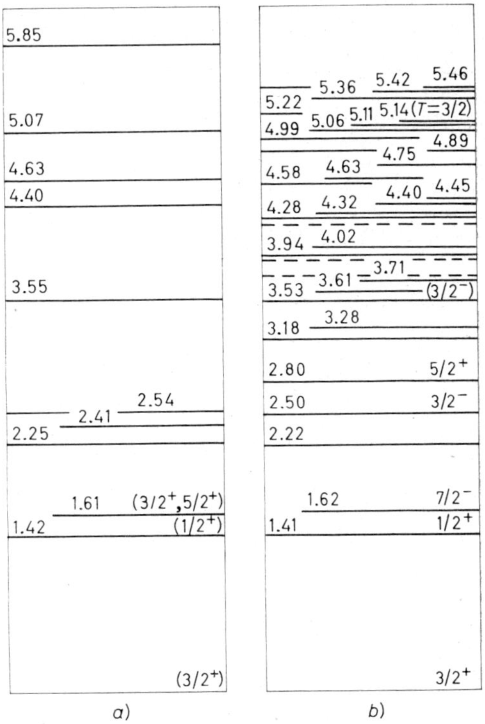

Fig. 7. – The energy level diagram of ^{37}Ar *a*) before and *b*) after experimental observations following the suggestion by Bahcall (1964*b*) that excited states of ^{37}Ar play a role in the interaction of neutrinos with ^{37}Cl.

On the basis of calculations involving the ground state, the analogue state and other known states in ^{37}Ar, Bahcall (1964*d*) has calculated the capture rates given in Table IV. The total flux cross-section product are

$$(\varphi\sigma)_\nu = (3.6 \pm 2)\cdot 10^{-35}\,\text{s}^{-1}\,\text{Cl}^{-1} \tag{13}$$

and the total expected counts per day in C_2Cl_4 are

$$(14)\quad \begin{cases} 100\,000 \text{ gal:} & (5.7 \pm 2.3) \text{ counts day}^{-1}, \\ 1\,000 \text{ gal:} & 0.06 \text{ counts day}^{-1}. \end{cases}$$

Davis has already found an upper limit of < 0.3 counts day^{-1} with the 1000 gallon apparatus set up in a mine at Barberton, Ohio. This is within a factor of $0.3/0.06 = 5$ of a significant result. The upper limit is set by background produced in the reaction ^{37}Cl(p, n)^{37}Ar by protons produced in turn by cosmic-ray muons which penetrate to the depth of the mine. Davis is now constructing a 100 000 gallon Neutrino Observatory in the Homestake Mine in South Dakota. Since this location is at a depth of 4700 meter water-

---

(*) The $T = \frac{3}{2}$ property may be shared by several of the $J^\pi = \frac{3}{2}^+$ states near this excitation energy.

equivalent he expects a background of < 0.2 counts day^{-1} which is less than the expected counting rate by a factor of ~ 30.

In his calculations BAHCALL used stellar-model calculations made by SEARS (1964). As pointed out by FOWLER (1958) the cross-section for the ^{7}Be(p, γ)^{8}B reaction is very sensitive to the central temperature, T_c, of the sun being given by

$$\sigma_{p,\gamma}(^7\text{Be}) \sim T_c^{14}\,. \tag{15}$$

Thus the Davis apparatus is a very sensitive « solar thermometer » and BAHCALL estimates that a measurement of the ^{8}B neutrino flux accurate to $\pm 50\%$ will determine the central temperature of the sun to $\pm 10\%$. The preliminary 1000 gal experiment of Davis puts an upper limit of $T_c < 20 \cdot 10^5$ °K. The models of SEARS (1964) indicate $T_c \sim 16 \cdot 10^5$ °K on the basis of currently accepted solar parameters and measured nuclear reaction rates. Thus neutrino astrophysics may soon provide us with direct information from the center of the sun which will serve as a check on current ideas of stellar structure and stellar energy generation.

5. – Additional observational techniques.

a) REINES and KROPP (1964) of the Case Institute of Technology have attempted to detect solar neutrinos using knock-on electrons produced in neutrino-electron scattering according to

$$\nu_e + e^- \to \nu_e + e^-\,. \tag{16}$$

This scattering process has not yet been observed in the laboratory but it is predicted on the basis of universality in current theories of the weak interactions. The cross-section should be of the order of 10^{-44} cm^2 for ^{8}B neutrinos.

The advantage of using this reaction for the observation of solar neutrinos is that it permits the measurement of the neutrino energy and direction in principle. The secondary electron is projected forward within a cone of $\pm 10°$ with respect to the primary neutrino; the angle and energy determine the neutrino energy by kinematics.

A modest experiment was performed by REINES and KROPP which enabled them to set certain limits and to assess the necessary full-scale effort. The experiment consisted of looking for unaccompanied counts in a 200-liter liquid scintillator detector ($5 \cdot 10^{28}$ target electrons) which was surrounded by a large Čerenkov anticoincidence detector and located 2000 feet underground in a salt mine. In a counting time of 4500 hours (~ 200 days) only three events were observed in the energy range 9 to 15 MeV, unaccompanied by pulses in the anticoincidence guard. This sets an upper limit on the flux of ^8B neutrinos

(17) $$\varphi_\nu(^8B) < 5 \cdot 10^8\ \nu_e\ cm^{-2}\ s^{-1}$$

which is 20 times that expected from the calculations given in Table IV.

REINES and KROPP estimated that a large detector with sensitive volume of 10^4 gallons would yield an expected rate ~ 100 counts y^{-1}. During the

TABLE IV. – $\nu + {}^{37}Cl \rightarrow {}^{37}Ar + e^-$.

Neutrino source	φ ($cm^{-2}\ s^{-1}$)	State in ^{37}Ar	σ (cm^{-2})	Capture rate per 10^5 gal. CCl_4
^7Be decay	$(1.2 \pm 0.5) \cdot 10^{10}$	Ground	$2.9 \cdot 10^{-4}$-	0.61 ± 0.25
^8B decay	$(2.5 \pm 1.0) \cdot 10^7$	Ground	$7.5 \cdot 10^{-44}$	0.32 ± 0.13
		1.4	$18.3 \cdot 10^{-44}$	0.83 ± 0.32
		2.7	$2.5 \cdot 10^{-44}$	0.13 ± 0.07
		5.1	$84.0 \cdot 10^{-44}$	3.80 ± 1.52
	Total neutrino capture rate in 10^5 gallons $= 5.7 \pm 2.3$			

CERN neutrino conference in January 1965, the possibility of a CERN-Case-Turin collaboration was discussed. The present laboratory in the Mont Blanc tunnel under 2000 meters of rock or 5000 meters water equivalent was suggested as a suitable location. On the basis of a predicted rate of 5 events per year per ton of detector it was argued that at least 5 tons of detector would be required. It was felt that the problem of light collection should be studied in a model. No approval for this project has yet been obtained as of July 1965.

b) REINES and WOODS (1965) have proposed the use of the inverse β-decay reactions

(18) $$\nu_e + {}^{11}B \rightarrow {}^{11}C + e^- - 1.98\ MeV$$

which is related to

(19) $$^{11}C \rightarrow {}^{11}B + e^+ + \nu_e + 0.96\ MeV$$

for which $\log ft = 3.6$ experimentally, and

(20) $$\nu_e + {}^7Li \rightarrow {}^7Be + e^- - 0.86\ MeV$$

which is the inverse of

(21) $$e^- + {}^7Be \rightarrow {}^7Li + \nu_e + 0.86\ MeV$$

for which $\log ft = 3.3$. All energies are computed from *nuclear*, not atomic, mass differences. The cross-sections for (18) and (20) can be calculated in terms of the ft-values of the related reactions.

In the suggested experimental arrangement thin, large-area slabs of target material containing Li or B are surrounded on both sides in layers by organic scintillator detectors. Several tons of Li and tens of tons of B are required to obtain counting rates of the order of 100 events per year. The angular correlation of the emitted electrons and incident neutrinos is not isotropic so the neutrino direction can be measured in principle. The advantage of this method over neutrino-electron scattering is that processes (18) and (20) are certain to occur while (16) is based on theoretical predictions. In the case (16), failure to observe events may mean that the weak interaction is not universal. The disadvantage is that reactions (18) and (20) have energy thresholds as indicated just as in the case of (7), whereas (16) does not.

c) REINES, CROUCH, JENKINS, KROPP, GURR, SMITH, SELLSCHOP, and MEYER (1965) are searching for high-energy neutrinos with apparatus installed 10 492 feet below the surface in a gold mine in South Africa. The venture is a collaborative effort of the Case Institute of Technology and the University of Witwatersrand. The idea of the experiment is to detect the energetic muons produced in neutrino interactions in the rock surrounding the mine tunnel by means of a large detector array located in the tunnel. Backgrounds are reduced by the large overburden and by utilizing the fact that the angular distribution of the unwanted residual muons from the earth's atmosphere is strongly peaked in the vertical direction at mine depth.

The detector array consists of two parallel vertical walls made up of 36 detector elements. The array is grouped into 6 « bays » with 3 elements, upper, middle, and lower, on each side. Each detector element is a lucite box containing 380 liters of liquid scintillator viewed at each end by two 5-inch photomultiplier tubes. Through coincidence counting the array constitutes a hodoscope which gives a rough measurements of the zenith angle of a charged particle passing through it. Only muons with zenith angle $> 45°$ are detected on both sides of the array. In addition, each event is located along the detector axis by the ratio of the photomultiplier responses at the two ends of the triggered element.

In 563 bay days of operation corresponding to 14 200 m^2 days sr of effective detection, a total of 7 events involving coincidences in one element on each side were recorded. We turn our attention to possible sources of these events.

The most likely source is the earth's atmosphere in which neutrettos $(\nu_\mu, \bar{\nu}_\mu)$ are produced by the decay of pions, kaons, and muons which in turn originate from collisions between primary cosmic particles with nuclei of the atmosphere. The angular distribution of the muons produced near the mine tunnel by neutretto interactions should show a slight peaking in the horizontal direction to which the coincidence arrangement of the detector array is most sensitive. This is in contrast as noted above to the angular distribution of muons coming directly from interactions in the atmosphere. REINES and his co-workers estimate 3 events from atmospheric neutrettos during the period of operation in which 7 events were recorded and state that there are reasons to believe that their estimate may be too low and that all the events can conceivably be from this source.

High-energy, cosmic neutrinos and neutrettos can trigger the detector array. BAHCALL and FRAUTSCHI (1964*a*, *b*) suggest that neutrinos and neutrettos may be emitted from supernovae, quasi-stellar objects and extended radio sources with energy comparable to that of the electrons which produce the radio noise from these objects.

The efficiency of detection for antineutrinos ($\bar{\nu}_e$) from these sources will be particularly high if a vector boson (W^-) serves as an intermediate stage in the reaction

$$\bar{\nu}_e(\text{cosmic}) + e^-(\text{terrestrial rock}) \to (W^-) \to \bar{\nu}_\mu + \mu^- . \tag{22}$$

Resonance in this reaction occurs at $4\cdot 10^{12}$ eV if the mass of the vector boson is $2\cdot 10^9$ eV/c^2. The μ^- would be the detected particle in the mine array.

If the earth is used as a target, BAHCALL and FRAUTSCHI estimate an antineutrino-induced counting rate at a depth of 1 km of 100 high-energy muons per m^2 per year from the direction of the Crab Nebula (supernova of July 4, 1054 A.D.). For a young radio source at the distance of *Cygnus* A, the counting rates would be 10^3 times those estimated for the Crab if all the $\bar{\nu}_e$ were emitted within the first 10^3 years of the lifetime of the source. Even so, highly directional sources of this nature would not contribute significantly to the counting rate expected in systems similar to those constructed by REINES and his co-workers. Furthermore, resonance effects cannot be detected at excessive depths.

d) The Tata Institute of Fundamental Research, Bombay, the Durham University, U.K., and the Osaka University, Japan, are jointly running a neutrino experiment in a gold mine at Kolar, India, about 2000 meters underground. Neutrinos react with nuclei in the rock and produce muons. The detector system has a collecting area of about 6 m^2 and consists of two outer banks of plastic scintillators and three banks of neon flash tubes with lead walls each of 2.5 cm between the flash tubes. The direction of individual particles can be estimated to an accuracy of about 1°. The detector has been in operation for about four months and 4 events have so far been observed,

3 of single particles and 1 of two particles. All 4 events made angles larger than 45° to the vertical, including the double-particle event which arrived along the horizontal direction.

e) KEUFFEL (1965) of the University of Utah is planning the installation of large detectors at 2000 feet depth near Park City, Utah. The detector consists of a block of concrete 10 m×10 m×6 m high with four vertical slots one meter wide filled with water used as Čerenkov counters. An additional nine vertical slots are filled with trays of cylindrical spark counters in which timing of the audible discharge with simple microphones permits localization of particle tracks to a few millimeters. Counting rates of 5 to 10 events per year are expected from atmospheric neutrettos.

f) COWAN, RYAN, ACOSTA, BUCKWALTER, CAREY, and CURTIN (1965) are engaged in the observation of muons appearing in massive detectors under the influence of a neutral component of the cosmic rays. The muons are of intermediate energies, 10 to 150 MeV, as they must be produced in and must stop in the detectors. They are identified by means of their decay electron through its energy and its delay time relative to the appearance of the muon. The detector consists of a block of plastic scintillator 2 ft.×4 ft.×1 ft. This presents a target of about 230 kg to the incident neutral particles. It is surrounded on all sides except the small east and west ends by sheets of plastic scintillator three-quarters of an inch thick which, with their photomultipliers provide the anticoincidence shielding. The top and bottom sheets overhang the detector somewhat. Twelve photomultipliers look into the target through the open east and west ends. A considerable number of events have been recorded but COWAN and his co-workers do not believe that incident neutrinos or neutrettos satisfy all the conditions implied by their experimental results to date.

6. – Theoretical problems concerning neutrino astrophysics (*).

6·1. *Introduction.* – The question of the number and energy of neutrinos and antineutrinos emitted by a star during its evolutionary lifetime was raised in the preceding Sections. The answer to this question depends in part on the universality of the weak interactions. Is the coupling constant the same for all possible four-particle interactions between pairs of protons and neutrons, pairs of electrons and electron-neutrinos and pairs of muons and muon-neu-

---

(*) This lecture is a revised and updated version of papers originally presented at the *Conference on Cosmology*, Padua, Italy, 1964 and at the *International Astronomical Union on Abundance Determination in Stellar Spectra*, Utrecht, The Netherlands, 1964.

trinos (neutrettos) or does the observed value only hold for those cases on which direct observations have been made: namely beta-decay, muon-decay, and muon-capture?

Complete universality is implied by the weak interaction theory of FEYNMAN and GELL-MANN (1958*a*, *b*). This theory has been shown to make correct predictions in a number of experimental tests by BARDIN, BARNES, FOWLER, and SEEGER (1960, 1962), FREEMAN *et al.* (1962, 1964), NORDBERG, MORINIGO and BARNES (1960, 1962), MAYER-KUCKUK and MICHEL (1961, 1962) and LEE, MO, and WU (1963), but the *completeness* of the universality was not directly in question in these experiments. Recent evidence for the existence of the parity-violating characteristic of the weak interaction in interactions involving only nucleons has been given by BOEHM and KANKELEIT (1964) and by ABOV, KRUPCHITSKY and ORATOVSKY (1964). These experiments are very suggestive but do not absolutely require that the extension to cases involving only leptons must be accepted as valid. From an analysis of the isotopic abundances in the iron-group elements on the basis of nucleosynthesis of these elements in an equilibrium process, FOWLER (1962, 1963) and FOWLER and HOYLE (1964) have suggested that there is strong circumstantial evidence for the emission of neutrinos and antineutrinos in electron-positron pair annihilation at just the rate predicted on the basis of the universality of the weak interaction. In the second part of this Section this suggestion is reviewed and in the third part a brief discussion of the extent of neutrino emission by astronomical objects is given on the basis that this suggestion is correct.

6·2. *Neutrino emission during the equilibrium process.* – In massive stars in the range $10\,M_\odot < M < 50\,M_\odot$, FOWLER and HOYLE (1964) show that nuclear evolution involving charged particle reactions proceeds from hydrogen-burning vie the CNO bi-cycle, through helium-burning with the production primarily of oxygen, to oxygen-burning with the production primarily of silicon. At the termination of oxygen-burning, photodisintegration into alpha-particles with subsequent capture of these particles, the so called α-process, leads to the synthesis of iron-group nuclei with mass number $A \sim 50$ to 60 which have the greatest binding energy and stability of all nuclear species.

These charged-particle reactions proceed primarily through nuclei which on the average have an equal number of neutrons and protons, $\bar{N} = \bar{Z}$. When the α-process comes to an end at $T_9 = T/10^9 = 3.5$, energy loss by neutrino emission leads to a mild contraction of the stellar core and a slight rise in temperature and density. At this point beta-processes, positron emission and electron capture, begin to play a role in the transformation to nuclei which have a greater number of neutrons than protons, *e.g.*, ^{56}Fe, and which are more stable than those with equal numbers, *e.g.*, ^{56}Ni.

The pertinent question is this. In the time scale permitted by the neutrino losses, how far will the beta-processes go in producing nuclei with a neutron excess? In other words, in the « equilibrium » or e-process in which the iron-group abundances are finally determined, does the material come to the complete equilibrium corresponding to the ambient temperature and density or does the limited reaction rate of the beta-processes impose an additional constraint? It has been emphasized by BURBIDGE, BURBIDGE, FOWLER and HOYLE (1957) and HOYLE and FOWLER (1960) that the abundances of the iron-group nuclei found in the solar system (particularly, terrestrial isotopic abundances) show definite effects of such a rate limitation. Figure 8 is adapted from B²FH (1957) and shows the excellent agreement between observed iron-group abundances and those calculated for equilibrium at $T_9 = 3.8$.

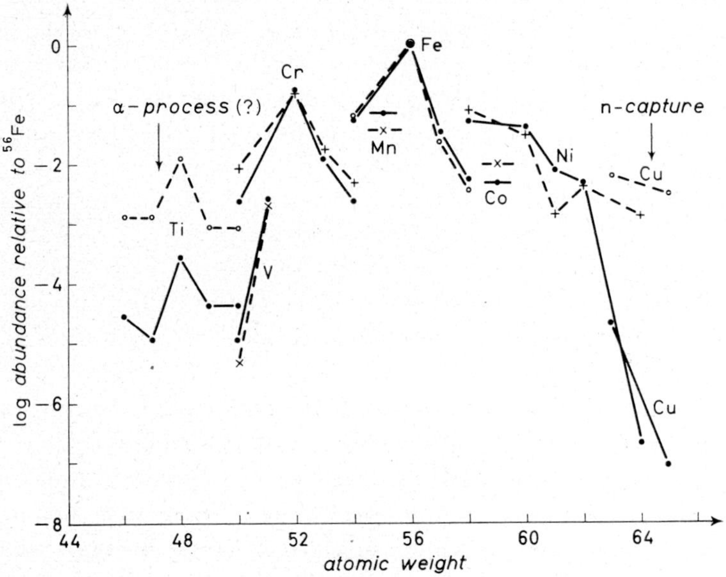

Fig. 8. – The abundance relative to ^{56}Fe of nuclei produced in the e-process: — — — solar, ——— calculated $T = 3.8 \cdot 10^9$ °K, $\varrho = 3.1 \cdot 10^6$ g·cm^{-3}, $\log(n_p/n_n) = 2.7$.

It is assumed that solar-system iron-group nuclei are typical of nuclei produced in the e-process just outside the imploding central regions of type II supernovae. These nuclei reside in the material which is swept out by the explosion of the mantle and envelope of the star. This explosion occurs in such a short time interval that the quasi-equilibrium abundances reached before the implosion-explosion are essentially unchanged. In what follows a most significant connection will be found between iron-group abundances and the time scale set by neutrino losses during the stellar stage just prior to core implosion and mantle-envelope explosion. The neutrino losses are taken to arise from the formation at high temperature of electron-positron pairs which can then annihilate with the production of neutrino-antineutrino pairs according to

$$e^{+} + e^{-} \rightarrow \nu + \bar{\nu} \,. \tag{23}$$

This process follows straightforwardly from the universal theory of the weak interactions proposed by FEYNMAN and GELL-MANN (1958*a*, 1958*b*).

The measure of beta-interaction rates appropriate for the present purposes is the rate of change of one-half the average neutron-proton difference per nucleus. This can be calculated from

$$\frac{1}{2}\frac{\mathrm{d}(\bar{N}-\bar{Z})}{\mathrm{d}t} = \frac{\mathrm{d}\bar{N}}{\mathrm{d}t} = -\frac{\mathrm{d}\bar{Z}}{\mathrm{d}t} = \frac{\sum \pm n(N, Z)/\tau(N, Z)}{\sum n(N, Z)} \,, \tag{24}$$

where $\bar{N} = \sum Nn(N, Z)/\sum n(N, Z)$, $\bar{Z} = \sum Zn(N, Z)/\sum n(N, Z)$, $n(N, Z)$ is the number of nuclei containing N neutrons and Z protons, and $\tau(N, Z)$ is the mean lifetime of these nuclei for beta-interactions. The positive sign is to be used for positron emission or electron capture and the negative sign for electron emission or positron capture. The problem at hand involves first of all the calculation of $n(N, Z)$ as a function of the ratio of protons to neutrons, $\bar{Z}/\bar{N}$. This is a task of considerable magnitude if temperature and density are also varied, and a computer program to accomplish the purpose has been undertaken by CLIFFORD and TAYLER (1964, 1965) at Cambridge University. Here we will fix on a temperature and density using some of their results and will discuss only in a general way what is essentially the « approach » to equilibrium in stellar nuclear processes.

Since B^2FH (1957) found that equilibrium calculations at $T_9 = 3.8$ gave excellent agreement with solar-system iron-group abundances, and since this temperature is just slightly above that at which the pure α-process ends, we will use this value in what follows. Then in a stellar core with effective mass $M_c = 20\,M_\odot$ FH (1964) show that $\varrho_6 = \varrho/10^6 = 3.1$, $N_e = 4.8\cdot10^{23}$ electrons and positrons per g, $n_e = 1.50\cdot10^{30}$ electrons and positrons per cm³, $N_- = 3.9\cdot10^{23}$ electrons per g, $n_- = 1.22\cdot10^{30}$ electrons per cm³, $N_+ = 0.9\cdot10^{23}$ positrons per g, and $n_+ = 0.28\cdot10^{30}$ positrons per cm³. The electron-positron numbers will change slightly as ^{56}Ni changes to ^{56}Fe as the dominant nucleus during the operation of the e-process.

The termination of the α-process at $T_9 = 3.5$ followed by a slight rise in temperature and density upon contraction brings the material to $T_9 = 3.8$ with $\bar{Z}/\bar{N} = 1$ and ^{56}Ni the most abundant nucleus. Beta-processes will now lower $\bar{Z}/\bar{N}$. For substitution in eq. (24) one thus needs relative values for $n(N, Z)$ for a series of values for $\bar{Z}/\bar{N}$ at $T_9 = 3.8$. A fixed value for $\bar{Z}/\bar{N}$

serves as a constraint on the equilibrium process in the manner described by B²FH (1957; see pp. 577, 578). CLIFFORD (1964) has carried out special abundance calculations for $\bar{Z}/\bar{N} = 1.00$, 0.975, 0.950, 0.925, 0.900, 0.875, 0.8725, 0.870, 0.865, and 0.860 at $\varrho_6 = 3.1$ and $T_9 = 3.8$. The interval between successive values corresponds to $\Delta\bar{N} = 0.4$ neutrons per nucleus when $\Delta(\bar{Z}/\bar{N}) = 0.025$. A total change of ~ 2 neutrons per nucleus is thus covered as expected for the typical case $^{56}_{28}Ni_{28} \to ^{56}_{26}Fe_{30}$. Table V lists the principal components of the material for various values of $\bar{Z}/\bar{N}$.

TABLE V. – *The approach to equilibrium at* $T = 3.8 \cdot 10^9$, $\varrho = 3.1 \cdot 10^6$, $M_c = 20 M_\odot$, $M \approx 30 M_\odot$.

	$\frac{1}{2}(\bar{N} - \bar{Z})$	$\bar{Z}/\bar{N}$	$\log n_p/n_n$	Time (10^4 s)		
1	0.0	1.000	8.62			0.0
2	0.4	0.975	7.36		0.1	0.1
3	0.8	0.950	6.61		0.1	0.2
4	1.2	0.925	5.18		0.2	0.4
2	1.6	0.900	4.04		0.8	1.2
6	2.0	0.875	2.94		1.6	2.8
7	2.04	0.8725	2.74		0.4	3.2
8	2.08	0.870	2.48		0.5	3.7
9	2.16	0.865	1.76	18.0	1.3	5.0
10	2.24	0.860	1.17		3.0	8.0
11	2.40	0.850	—		12.8	20.8

Methods for calculation of the $\tau(N, Z)$ under stellar conditions have been described by FH (1964). It will be clear that electron capture and positron emission are the important beta-processes since the trend in stability is toward nuclei with a neutron excess. Under terrestrial laboratory conditions positron emission is more rapid than electron capture if sufficient energy is available in the nuclear transformation to produce the positron rest mass and give the positron kinetic energy at least comparable to its rest-mass equivalent energy. However, in dense stellar interiors the electron density at the nucleus is considerably greater than in the undisturbed atom so that the rate of electron capture is greatly enhanced. The result is that the proton-to-neutron change in radioactive nuclei which normally capture electrons or emit positrons is increased in rate and even stable nuclei, *e.g.*, ^{58}Ni, have fairly short lifetimes for capture of electrons having high-energy in the tail of the thermal energy distribution.

Reference to Table V indicates that the nuclei which make important contributions in eq. (24) are: ^{56}Ni ($2 \cdot 10^3$ s), ^{57}Ni ($2 \cdot 10^3$ s), ^{58}Ni ($5 \cdot 10^4$ s), and ^{54}Fe ($4 \cdot 10^4$ s). The proton ($4 \cdot 10^3$ s), ^{55}Co ($2 \cdot 10^3$ s), and ^{55}Fe (10^4 s) also contribute. In general the transformation from $\bar{Z}/\bar{N}=1.00$ to smaller values can be followed in Fig. 9. At $\bar{Z}/\bar{N}=1$ the principal constituents are ^{56}Ni, ^{57}Ni, and ^{55}Co. These capture electrons or emit positrons to become ^{56}Co, ^{57}Co, and ^{55}Fe respectively. The ^{56}Co immediately becomes ^{54}Fe and ^{58}Ni through fast nuclear processes since $2\,^{56}\text{Co} \to {}^{54}\text{Fe} + {}^{58}\text{Ni} + 4.45$ MeV. ^{54}Fe and ^{58}Ni capture electrons to become ^{54}Mn and ^{58}Co which change by fast nuclear processes to ^{52}Cr, ^{56}Fe, and ^{60}Ni. ^{55}Fe and ^{57}Co produce ^{55}Mn and ^{57}Fe. Eventually nuclear processes produce the equilibrium abundances which mainly reside in the stable nuclei which form the shaded «steps» in Fig. 9, namely ^{52,53,54}Cr, ^{55}Mn, ^{56,57,58}Fe, ^{59}Co, and ^{60,61,62}Ni (the last two nuclei are not shown). Some material remains as stable ^{54}Fe and ^{58}Ni and also as stable ^{50}Cr (not shown) and the other rare iron-group nuclei.

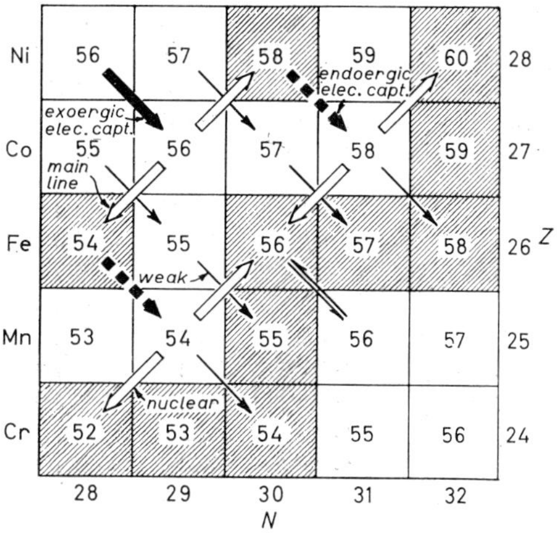

Fig. 9. – The flow of nuclear material in the N, Z plane during the equilibrium or e-process showing the effects of the slow beta interactions and the rapid nuclear interactions. The α-process results mainly in the production of ^{56}Ni with about 10 per cent ^{55}Co, ^{57}Ni, ^{54}Fe and ^{52}Fe (not shown). White squares: radioactive nuclei; shaded squares: stable nuclei.

Table V gives the time intervals calculated using eq. (24) for the changes through $\bar{Z}/\bar{N}=1.000$, $0.975, \ldots,$ to 0.860, and the total time to each value. Table V also gives the quantity $\theta = \log n_p/n_n$, the logarithm to the base 10 of the ratio of densities of free protons to free neutrons external to the complex nuclei. As pointed out by B²FH (1957) equilibrium calculations can be made quite simply using θ as a parameter. It will be clear, however, that $\bar{Z}/\bar{N}$ is the more significant parameter. The computer program of CLIFFORD and TAYLER (1964) essentially finds the values of θ which yield the chosen values of $\bar{Z}/\bar{N}$ and calculates the corresponding equilibrium abundances. The equilibrium abundances are given in Table VI. It will be noted immediately that, as expected, very large ratios of free protons to free neutrons are required external to the complex nuclei to maintain the larger values for $\bar{Z}/\bar{N}$, *e.g.*, $\theta=8.62$ for $\bar{Z}/\bar{N}=1.00$. In simple physical terms a dense atmosphere of protons is necessary to prevent the nuclei with $Z=N$ from decaying to the more stable nuclei with $Z<N$. The electrostatic repulsion between protons in the nucleus which leads to increased stability for $Z<N$ is seen to have a powerful effect.

B^2FH (1957) found the optimum correspondence between solar-system iron-group abundances and the calculated values for the case $T_9 = 3.8$ and $\theta = 2.5$. We have already seen that $T_9 = 3.8$ is reached naturally in the stellar and nuclear evolution under discussion. The new calculations of CLIFFORD

TABLE VI. – *Abundance in per cent by mass.* (Naturally radioactive nuclei in parentheses).

Nucleus	(^{55}Co)	(^{56}Ni)	(^{57}Ni)	^{58}Ni	^{54}Fe	(^{55}Fe)	^{56}Fe	^{57}Fe	^{58}Fe
Product	$(^{55}Fe)^{55}Mn$	$(^{56}Co)^{56}Fe$	$(^{57}Co)^{57}Fe$	(^{58}Co)	(^{54}Mn)	^{55}Mn	(^{56}Mn)	—	—
Energy diff. (MeV)	3.46	2.10	3.24	-0.38	-0.69	0.23	-3.71	—	—
τ_{star} (s)	$2\cdot10^{3}$	$2\cdot10^{3}$	$2\cdot10^{3}$	$5\cdot10^{4}$	$4\cdot10^{4}$	10^{4}	10^{8}	—	—
1	3.3	89.1	2.9	0.7	1.7	$3\cdot10^{-3}$	$6\cdot10^{-5}$	—	—
2	8.7	54.3	7.5	7.9	19.3	0.2	$1\cdot10^{-2}$	—	—
3	8.2	21.4	6.8	16.7	43.4	0.9	0.1	—	—
4	2.1	1.0	1.5	18.5	60.1	6.0	4.1	$2\cdot10^{-3}$	—
5	0.3	$3\cdot10^{-2}$	0.2	8.3	34.0	12.0	29.2	$6\cdot10^{-2}$	$4\cdot10^{-3}$
6	$2\cdot10^{-2}$	$5\cdot10^{-4}$	$9\cdot10^{-3}$	1.2	6.8	7.9	62.9	0.4	0.1
7	$8\cdot10^{-3}$	$2\cdot10^{-4}$	$5\cdot10^{-3}$	0.8	4.7	6.7	66.2	0.5	0.2
8	$4\cdot10^{-3}$	—	$2\cdot10^{-3}$	0.4	2.8	5.3	69.2	0.7	0.3
9	$4\cdot10^{-4}$	—	$2\cdot10^{-4}$	0.1	0.6	2.5	70.5	1.5	1.2
10	—	—	—	$2\cdot10^{-2}$	0.2	1.2	64.5	2.7	4.0

and TAYLER (1964, 1965) yield optimum results at $\theta = 2.7$ which differs insignificantly from the B^2FH values. Correspondingly $\bar{Z}/\bar{N} = 0.872$ and $\frac{1}{2}\Delta(\bar{N} - \bar{Z}) \approx 2.0$ showing that the beta-processes changed approximately two neutrons into protons in the transformation from material with ^{56}Ni the most abundant nucleus to material with ^{56}Fe the most abundant.

The correspondence between the observations and the calculations of CLIFFORD and TAYLER (1964, 1965) is illustrated for the stable iron isotopes $^{54,56,57,58}Fe$ in Table VII. The solar-terrestrial values are those found first by dividing the iron abundance by mass by the abundance of all the equilibrium process elements (V, Cr, Mn, Fe, Co, Ni) using the *solar* spectroscopic data given by ALLER (1961). The resulting value 73 per cent was then divided among the iron isotopes according to the *terrestrial* isotopic abundance ratios. The chondritic iron abundance given by SUESS and UREY (1956) is somewhat higher than the solar value. This higher value can be obtained from the equilibrium process calculations by employing a slightly lower value for the temperature without changing the isotope ratios significantly. The calculated values in Table VII have been obtained from the abundance of CLIFFORD and TAYLER (1964, 1965) given in part in Table VI by assigning all of the material at mass 56 to ^{56}Fe, for example, on the basis that if the equilibrium process terminated at a given value for $\bar{Z}/\bar{N}$ then ^{56}Ni and ^{56}Co would subsequently decay to ^{56}Fe and so forth.

The Table shows that almost exact correspondence is obtained at $\bar{Z}/\bar{N} = 0.872$ or $\theta = \log n_p/n_n = 2.7$ as noted previously. The time required for the electron captures up to this point is seen to be $3.2 \cdot 10^4$ s. This value holds for a star of mass $M = 30\, M_\odot$ with core mass $M_c = 20\, M_\odot$ where $T_6 = 3.8$

TABLE VII. – *Iron isotopes per cent of total* e*-process abundance by mass* $M_c = 20\, M_\odot$, $M \approx 30\, M_\odot$.

$\bar{Z}/\bar{N}$	$\log n_p/n_n$	^{54}Fe	^{56}Fe	^{57}Fe	^{58}Fe	Electron capture time (10^4 s)
1.000	8.6	1.7	89.1	2.9	0.0	0.0
0.950	6.6	43.4	21.9	7.2	0.0	0.2
0.900	4.0	34.0	29.6	4.7	0.04	1.2
0.872 (*)	2.7	4.3	66.6	2.5	0.23	3.2
0.860	1.2	0.2	64.5	3.0	4.0	8.0
0.850	—	—	—	—	—	20.8
Solar-terr. values		4.2	67.2	1.6	0.25	—

(*) Interpolated from calculated values of 0.8725 and 0.870.

and $\varrho_6 = 3.1$ are the assumed equilibrium conditions. The mass $M = 30\, M_\odot$ is taken as typical of the range $10\, M_\odot < M < 50\, M_\odot$ for type II supernovae. In the calculations positron emission, electron emission, and positron capture have been neglected relative to electron capture. At still lower $\bar{Z}/\bar{N}$, as complete equilibrium is attained, all processes, in particular positron capture, must be considered. The time required for the fast nuclear reactions to re-establish equilibrium as the electron captures take place has also been neglected. This is justified since, for example, the lifetime of ^{56}Co to ^{56}Co$(\gamma, n)^{55}$Co $- 10.07$ MeV is $\sim 10^{-4}$ s at $T_9 = 3.8$, $\varrho_6 = 3.1$.

It will be noted that the time required for a given change in $\bar{Z}/\bar{N}$ or in $\frac{1}{2}(\bar{N} - \bar{Z})$ rapidly increases after $\bar{Z}/\bar{N} = 0.872$. Table V shows that the change 0.875-0.850 requires more than ten times the interval required for the change 0.900-0.875. Table V shows that the total time from 1.000 to 0.850 is more than six times that required to reach 0.872. Thus we are in position to reach an answer to the question posed in the third paragraph of this Section. In the time scale permitted by the neutrino losses, how far will the beta-processes go in producing nuclei with a neutron excess?

To answer this question it is necessary to compute the neutrino time scale under the conditions of temperature and density which have been reached in a star with $M = 30\, M_\odot$ when the beta-processes operate to change ^{56}Ni and other $Z = N$ nuclei produced in the α-process to nuclei such as ^{56}Fe with $\frac{1}{2}(N - Z) = 2$. In the ^{56}Ni-^{56}Fe transformation the energy release is 6.6 MeV or $1.13 \cdot 10^{17}$ erg g^{-1} which is reduced to $\sim 10^{17}$ erg g^{-1} by direct neutrino losses. At $T_9 = 3.8$ and $\varrho_6 = 3.1$ FH (1964) show that $dU_\nu/dt \sim 10^{14}$ erg g^{-1} s^{-1} so the time scale is $t_\nu \sim 10^{17}/10^{14} \sim 1000$ s ~ 17 min. This calculation underestimates t_ν. Some ^{56}Ni begins to decay as soon as it is first produced at the beginning of the α-process. Thus an upper limit for t_ν is the sum of the interval for the α-process, which FH (1964) estimate to be 4000 s, plus that for the ^{56}Ni-^{56}Fe transformation. This sum is 4000 s + 1000 s = 5000 s. The intermediate value $t_\nu \sim 3000$ s, is tentatively adopted.

The value just adopted tentatively holds for the time scale at the center of the star. Since the neutrino loss decreases rapidly with decreasing temperature the time scale will be somewhat longer throughout the central region in which the ^{56}Ni-^{56}Fe transformation is taking place. Rough calculations lead to the final choice $t_\nu \sim 6000$ s. The ^{56}Ni-^{56}Fe transformation is relatively insensitive to temperature and no correction is necessary.

Thus we find $t_\nu \sim 6000$ s is considerably shorter than $t_e \sim 3 \cdot 10^4$ s. However, it must be recalled that these calculations have been made for a particular example, $M = 30\, M_\odot$, of the type of stars which HF (1960) suggested would evolve to become type II supernovae, namely, stars for which $10\, M_\odot < M < 50\, M_\odot$. The core mass was taken to be $M_c = \frac{2}{3} M = 20\, M_\odot$. Similar calculations for $M_c = \frac{1}{3} M$, which may be more realistic, show excellent correspondence between t_ν and t_e. In addition the lower range of stellar masses, $10\, M_\odot < M < 30\, M_\odot$, may well have contributed relatively more e-process material than the higher range, $30\, M_\odot < M < 50\, M_\odot$.

Thus, it would seem that quite close correspondence in the time scales exists for $e^- + e^+ \to \nu + \bar{\nu}$ and for $^{56}Ni + 2e^- \to {}^{56}Fe + 2\nu$ with a universal Fermi interaction for these two types of beta-interactions if the stars in which solar system e-process material was produced had masses 10-50$M_\odot$ as originally contemplated by HF (1960).

The point under discussion here can be sharpened by a consideration of the time scale if $e^- + e^+ \to \nu + \bar{\nu}$ was not operative. Photon losses in the interval $3 < T_9 < 4$ can be estimated to be $\sim 10^7$ erg g^{-1} s^{-1} rather than the value $\sim 10^{14}$ erg g^{-1} s^{-1} for dU_ν/dt. Thus the photon-loss time scale for ^{56}Ni-^{56}Fe is $\sim 6 \cdot 10^{10}$ s ~ 2000 years or ample time for the beta-interactions to reduce $\bar{Z}/\bar{N}$ well below the last values tabulated in Tables V and VI. The result, as shown in Table VI, would be, among other things, an enhancement in ^{58}Fe and a decrease in ^{54}Fe completely in variance with the terrestrial ratio. Clearly the time scale was not this long. Photon losses by the stellar material were not competent to decrease the time scale to the necessary value. On the other hand the neutrino time scale set by assigning the universal Fermi interaction strength to the process $e^+ + e^- \to \nu + \bar{\nu}$ in the pre-supernova stage of massive stars is closely that required to match the electron capture times involved in the formation of the Fe-isotopes and the other iron-group nuclei. The isotopic abundance ratios in any sample of terrestrial iron are circumstantial evidence for the universality of the beta-interactions.

This much can be asserted with some certainty: *The terrestrial iron-group isotopic abundance ratios strongly indicate the operation in massive stars of an energy loss mechanism having a loss rate of the same order of magnitude as that calculated for* $e^+ + e^- \to \nu + \bar{\nu}$ *on the basis of the universal Fermi interaction strength.*

A comment on the ultimate values for $\bar{Z}/\bar{N}$ or $\theta = \log n_p/n_n$ reached when the beta-interactions are in complete equilibrium is in order at this point. B²FH (1957) estimated $\theta = 1.4$ from a consideration of the equilibrium between free neutrons and free protons and electrons. This value is only an approximation at best. It does in principle cover the equilibrium between free protons and free neutrons and positrons. The difficulty involves the fact that neutrinos and antineutrinos escape and do not enter into reverse reactions once produced. This means, among other things, that energy must be supplied to maintain equilibrium at a given density and temperature. Granted this energy supply the equilibrium will depend more on the properties of the heavy nuclei than on those of the free neutrons and protons. The electron-positron ratio will be given as calculated by FH (1964) on the basis $\gamma \rightleftarrows e^+ + e^-$. Then when electron capture and positron emission are balanced exactly by positron capture and electron emission, equilibrium in the beta-interactions will have been reached. We found above that it was not necessary to carry the calculations this far. However, it is of considerable interest to know the value of θ and $\bar{Z}/\bar{N}$ for the ultimate equilibrium. Calculations to determine these values are being made by CLIFFORD (1964).

6·3. *Implications.* – Neutrinos and antineutrinos obey Fermi statistics and in an expanding universe they form a degenerate Fermi sea at very low energies. The effects of this universal Fermi degeneracy in various cosmologies has been discussed in detail by WEINBERG (1962) and the reader is referred to this paper for the basic treatment of neutrino cosmology. Neutrino and antineutrino effects in astronomy and astrophysics have been most extensively discussed by BAHCALL (1964*a*, *b*, *c*, *d*, 1965) and by BAHCALL and FRAUTSCHI (1964*a*, *b*). Here we will content ourselves with a discussion of the extent of neutrino and antineutrino emission by various astrophysical sources. Our discussion reviews and extends that given by WEINBERG (1962) in Part IV of his paper. Our results will be expressed as the ratio of energy emitted as neutrinos or antineutrinos to the rest mass energy equivalent of the emitting system and are given in Table VIII.

Nucleogenesis may occur through the creation of neutrons and antineutrons

TABLE VIII. – *Neutrino energy emission.*

		Neutrino energy / rest mass energy
Nucleogenesis	p, e^-	0
	$n \to p + e^- + \bar{\nu}$	$\sim 5 \cdot 10^{-4}$ ([a])
	$p, \bar{p}, n, \bar{n} \to e^{\pm}, \nu_e, \bar{\nu}_e, \nu_\mu, \bar{\nu}_\mu, \gamma$	< 0.25 ([b])
	$p, e^-, \nu_e, \bar{\nu}_e, \nu_\mu, \bar{\nu}_\mu$	arbitrary
Nucleosynthesis		
Hydrogen burning	$4p \to \alpha + 2e^+ + 2\nu_e$	$\sim 10^{-4}$
	$4p + e^- \to \alpha + e^+ + 2\nu_e$	
Helium burning	$3\,{}^4He \to {}^{12}C$, $4\,{}^4He \to {}^{16}O$	0
Carbon burning or oxygen burning		
$+\alpha$- and e-processes	${}^{12}C$ or ${}^{16}O \to {}^{56}Fe + 2\nu_e$	$\sim 10^{-4}$
+pair annihilation	$e^+ + e^- \to \nu + \bar{\nu}$	
Neutron *s*- and *r*-processes ($A > 60$)		$\sim 3 \cdot 10^{-10}$
Quasi-stellar objects (hydrogen burning)		$\sim 10^{-4}$
Radio galaxies ([c])	$p + p \to p, n, \pi^{\pm}, \pi^0$	$\sim 10^{-4}$ (?)
	$\pi \to e^{\pm}, \nu_e, \bar{\nu}_e, \nu_\mu, \bar{\nu}_\mu, \gamma$	
Gen. rel. collapse $\to$ invisible mass		
$e^+ + e^- \to \nu + \bar{\nu}$	$M \sim 10^3 M_\odot$	~ 0.03
	$M \sim 10^6 M_\odot$	$\sim 10^{-6}$
Average without rotation		$\sim 5 \cdot 10^{-3}$
Average with rotation		$\sim 2 \cdot 10^{-2}$

([a]) Continuos creation of neutrons excluded by cosmic X-ray observations at present time.

([b]) This value depends upon the fraction of nucleons and antinucleons which avoid annihilation. Continuous creation of nucleons and antinucleons with some annihilation is excluded by cosmic X-ray observations.

([c]) Note that muon neutrinos and antineutrinos are also emitted in this case and that high energy resonant scattering is possible for the electron neutrinos and antineutrinos (see references by BAHCALL and by BAHCALL and FRAUTSCHI).

or through the creation of protons and antiprotons. In the former case beta-decay probably occurs before other interactions but not, of course, in the latter case. In the former case the antineutrino or neutrino energy emitted is approximately 0.5 MeV or $\sim 5 \cdot 10^{-4}$ of the rest mass of the emitting particles.

Nucleosynthesis involving *matter* begins with the conversion of four protons into helium with the emission of two positrons and two neutrinos. The total energy emitted is $7 \cdot 10^{-3}$ of the original rest mass; of this, 2% is emitted as neutrino energy in the pp-chain and 6% in the CNO bi-cycle. In the main-sequence and red-giant evolution of a star a minimum of one-tenth and a maximum of two-thirds of the hydrogen is converted into helium. An average value can be estimated on the basis that observationally one-third of the hydrogen of the Galaxy has been converted into helium. Taking all of these factors into account it will be seen that to order of magnitude $\sim 10^{-4}$ of the rest mass energy is converted into neutrinos. A similar value holds for antineutrinos in nucleosynthesis involving *antimatter*.

Helium-burning either to carbon via $3\,{}^4\text{He} \rightarrow {}^{12}\text{C}$ or to oxygen via the additional reaction ${}^{12}\text{C} + {}^4\text{He} \rightarrow {}^{16}\text{O} + \gamma$ does not involve neutrino or antineutrino emission directly. Furthermore helium-burning takes place at such a low temperature that the pair-annihilation process, eq. (23), is not operative even if the universal strength of the weak interactions applies.

FOWLER and HOYLE (1964) show that helium-burning results in carbon production in stars with $M < \sim 10\,M_\odot$ and in oxygen production in stars with $M > \sim 10\,M_\odot$. There is considerable uncertainty in the critical mass because the rate of the ${}^{12}\text{C}(\alpha, \gamma){}^{16}\text{O}$ reaction has not yielded to experimental measurements to date and only approximate theoretical estimates can be made. Carbon-burning results in the production of nuclei near ${}^{24}\text{Mg}$ with little direct neutrino-antineutrino emission and takes place at too low a temperature for pair annihilation to be effective. Oxygen-burning results in the production of nuclei near ${}^{28}\text{Si}$ with little direct neutrino-antineutrino emission but does take place at high enough temperature ($> 2 \cdot 10^9$ degrees) for pair annihilation to be effective and to dissipate practically all of the nuclear energy if the universal strength of the weak interactions applied to reaction (23).

The nuclear energy release is $5 \cdot 10^{17}$ erg g^{-1} so the neutrino-antineutrino emission is $\sim 5 \cdot 10^{-4}$ of the rest mass. Subsequent to carbon- or oxygen-burning, the α- and e-processes occur in which heavier nuclei up to the iron group are produced. Pair annihilation is operative and again practically all of the available nuclear energy is radiated in the form of neutrinos and antineutrinos. The nuclear energy release is $3 \cdot 10^{17}$ erg g^{-1} so that the neutrino-antineutrino energy emission is $\sim 3 \cdot 10^{-4}$ of the rest mass. Thus in stars with $M < \sim 10\,M_\odot$ nucleosynthesis beyond hydrogen-burning releases $\sim 3 \cdot 10^{-4}$ of the rest-mass energy in neutrinos and antineutrinos while for $M > \sim 10\,M_\odot$ the total is $\sim 8 \cdot 10^{-4}$. However, in the smaller mass range a larger fraction, say one-third, of the mass is completely evolved to the nuclear end-point than in the larger mass range where a fraction more like one-eighth can be conveniently taken as a good average. Thus in both cases the over-all result is that $\sim 10^{-4}$ of the total rest mass is emitted as neutrino-antineutrino energy. If we include hydrogen-burning then in the full run of nuclear evolution in matter, $\sim 1.5 \cdot 10^{-4}$ of the rest mass energy appears as neutrinos, $0.5 \cdot 10^{-4}$ as antineutrinos and $2 \cdot 10^{-4}$ *in toto*. For nuclear evolution in antimatter the roles of neutrinos and antineutrinos are reversed. The arguments given in this paragraph are those used to justify the private communication referred to by WEINBERG (1962) in footnote 9, p. 1461.

We have so far neglected the neutron capture *s*- and *r*-processes by which the heavier elements beyond $A \sim 60$ are produced. On the basis of solar system element abundances only $\sim 10^{-6}$ of the original mass has been through the s-process. For the heavy nuclei averaged over abundances the mean atomic weight is $A \sim 75$. About twenty neutrons have been added to the typical seed nucleus but only about seven or eight of these have been converted into protons with the emission of an antineutrino so that one additional antineutrino per 10 nucleons is emitted in the s-process. The antineutrino energy is of the order of 2 MeV compared to the nucleon rest mass equivalent $\sim 10^3$ MeV so the over-all factor for antineutrino emission in the s-process is $\sim 2 \cdot 10^{-10}$. For the r-process, the abundance is $\sim 2 \cdot 10^{-7}$ according to recent estimates but the antineutrino energy is of the order of 6 MeV so that the over-all factor is $\sim 1 \cdot 10^{-10}$. It is thus clear that these processes can indeed be neglected in comparison to nucleosynthesis up to the iron-group elements.

The above discussion follows conventional ideas concerning nuclear evolution in stars and galaxies. We now turn to new and somewhat more speculative ideas which have been mainly put forward in attempts to understand the strong radio sources discovered in radio astronomy and the ultra-luminous quasi-stellar objects which exhibit large optical red shifts.

According to HOYLE and FOWLER (1963*a*, 1963*b*) and to FOWLER (1964, 1965, 1966) the energy generation in the quasi-stellar objects can be understood in terms of hydrogen-burning so that the neutrino emission factor is $\sim 10^{-4}$. We see no problem in meeting the energy requirements of the quasi-stellar objects, which we identify as massive stars with $M \sim 10^{8\pm1} M_\odot$, by means of the nuclear resources of the cores of these stars. There is a problem in the mechanism by which they are stabilized for periods as high as $\sim 10^5$ years. If spherically symmetric and nonrotating, the hydrostatic equilibrium of these stars requires large *inputs* of energy (FOWLER, 1964 and IBEN, 1963) and is unstable to general relativistic collapse (FOWLER, 1964; CHANDRASEKHAR, 1964*a*, *b*, *c* and GRATTON, 1964). However, rotation (FOWLER, 1966) and magnetoturbulence (BARDEEN and ANAND, 1966) are two of numerous mechanism which have been suggested as stabilizing agents.

The energy requirements for the strong radio emission from radio galaxies are so great according to some methods of calculation that HOYLE and FOWLER (1963*a*, 1963*b*) pointed out that nuclear reactions in a galactic nucleus limited to less than 1% of the total mass would not suffice as the energy source. The release of gravitational energy during gravitational collapse was suggested as an alternative but serious difficulties arise in the energy emission cut-off due to the large red shifts which develop during collapse to the Schwarzschild limit. The problem is under extensive study in many places and until such a time as a solution is reached we are compelled to proceed on the basis of direct analysis of the observations. If the high-energy electrons which yield the radio synchrotron emission are produced in proton-proton collisions (BURBIDGE, 1962) then electron neutrinos and antineutrinos plus muon neutrinos and antineutrinos are produced with roughly equal energies to that of the high-energy electrons. Take 10^{44} erg s^{-1} as a representative rate of emission over a maximum time scale of $5\cdot10^{8}$ years (MINKOWSKI, 1964) to obtain $\sim10^{60}$ erg for the energy emitted by the high-energy electrons and assign a similar value to the high-energy neutrinos of all types. On the grounds that the radio galaxies do not show internal evidence for spectacular violent events let us assume that at most 1% of the total mass, most probably in the galactic nucleus, was at one time involved in the energy production. SANDAGE (1964) has suggested that radio galaxies are probably quite massive of the order of $10^{12}\,M_\odot$. Thus we take $\sim0.01\cdot10^{12}\cdot10^{54}\sim10^{64}$ erg as the energy equivalent of the mass involved. Again the value $\sim10^{-4}$ is obtained for the neutrino energy relative to this energy but here there is considerably greater uncertainty to be attached to this value than even in our previous estimates. The value could be as high as 10^{-2}.

A still more speculative source of neutrino energy lies in the process of general-relativistic collapse, in which a nonrotating, supermassive star implodes at approximately the rate of free fall, releasing gravitational energy until the Schwarzschild limiting radius is reached. At this radius the star becomes invisible since all forms of radiation, including particles, are red-shifted to zero energy in the co-ordinates of a distant, external observer. The star becomes « hidden mass » except in so far as it exerts a static gravitational field. HOYLE, FOWLER, BURBIDGE, and BURBIDGE (1964) showed that during the collapse of a supermassive star the loss of energy in the form of neutrino-antineutrino pairs from eq. (2.3) was substantial even though not enough to reduce the externally observable mass to zero at the Schwarzschild limit.

BARDEEN (1965) has employed the analysis of ZEL'DOVICH and PODURETS (1964) to express the total energy radiated in the form of neutrinos from a collapsing supermassive star as

$$E_\nu=\int_0^{\varrho_{\max}}\frac{\mathrm{d}u_\nu/\mathrm{d}t}{(24\pi G\varrho)^{\frac{1}{2}}}\,\frac{(1-x)}{(1-x/3)^3}\,\frac{\mathrm{d}\varrho}{\varrho^2}\,. \tag{25}$$

In this expression, $\mathrm{d}u_\nu/\mathrm{d}t$ is the rate of neutrino energy loss and is given approximately by

$$\frac{\mathrm{d}u_\nu}{\mathrm{d}t}\approx4.58\cdot10^{15}\,T_9^{\,9}\ \text{erg cm}^{-3}\,\text{s}^{-1}\ (T_9>3)\,. \tag{26}$$

The free-fall characteristic time is $(24\pi G\varrho)^{-\frac{1}{2}}$ and the function involving $x=(\varrho/\varrho_{\max})^{\frac{1}{6}}$ is a general-relativistic correction which approaches unity for small x. This factor was ignored by HFB² (1964). The integration limit $\varrho_{\max}$ is the density at the stage of contraction when neutrinos emitted from the central region just reach the surface at the later time when the outer radius equals the Schwarzschild limit. It can be shown that

$$\varrho_{max} = \frac{4}{9}\,\varrho_{Sch} = 0.82\cdot 10^{16}\left(\frac{M}{M_\odot}\right)^2 \text{ g cm}^{-3} \tag{27}$$

where ϱ_{Sch} is the limiting Schwarzschild density.

The integral, eq. (25), may be evaluated once the appropriate ϱ, T relation has been established by the method used by HFB[2] (1964). An approximate solution for supermassive stars is

$$\mathscr{E}_\nu = \frac{E_\nu}{Mc^2} \sim 10^3\left(\frac{M_\odot}{M}\right)^{\frac{3}{2}} \qquad (M > 10^3 M_\odot). \tag{28}$$

Thus for $M = 10^6\,M_\odot$, $\mathscr{E}_\nu \sim 10^{-6}$ while for $M = 10^3\,M_\odot$, $\mathscr{E}_\nu \sim 0.03$. For smaller stars degeneracy leads to lower values of $\mathscr{E}_\nu$. If an average is taken over a reasonable stellar population the following figure is obtained

$$\langle \mathscr{E}_\nu \rangle \sim 5\cdot 10^{-3} \text{ (without rotation)}. \tag{29}$$

The above calculations assume that the collapsing mass is not rotating. Rotation leads to a longer time scale for collapse and to the value

$$\langle \mathscr{E}_\nu \rangle \sim 2\cdot 10^{-2} \text{ (with rotation)}. \tag{30}$$

The estimates given in eqs. (29) and (30) are admittedly quite speculative but it will be noted that these values are of the order of 100 times the neutrino losses which occur during the evolution of stars with $M < 100\,M_\odot$ or in the production of energy in radio sources. Furthermore it must be emphasized that these results depend on the assumption that the weak interaction is universal and that the coupling constant measured in beta-decay, muon decay and muon capture applies to the annihilation of electron-positron pairs with neutrino emission.

These speculations lead to a maximum value for $\mathscr{E}_\nu$ of the order of a few percent. We conclude that processes during stellar evolution never develop neutrino energies comparable to the rest mass-energies of the emitting systems. For this reason if the neutrino energy density in space is to be of cosmological significance, its origin must lie in cosmological processes.

Weinberg's calculations show that on the basis of current ideas the degenerate neutrino sea will be observable, it at all, only in the oscillating cosmologies. However, his results serve to illustrate the main thesis of this lecture. The mass density equivalent of the neutrino energy density is related to the

Fermi energy, E_F, by the well-known expression

$$\varrho_\nu = \frac{1}{8\pi^2}\left(\frac{E_F}{\hbar c}\right)^3 \frac{E_F}{c^2} \sim 3\cdot 10^{-21} E_F^4 \text{ g cm}^{-3} \tag{31}$$

for E_F in eV. E_F can be measured by observations on the behavior near the end point of the energy spectrum in beta-decay and present results set an upper limit, $E_F < 200$ eV. This corresponds to an upper limit, $\varrho_\nu < 5\cdot 10^{-12}$ g cm^{-3}, which is $\sim 10^{18}$ times the nucleon rest-mass density of 10^{-29} g cm^{-6} required in steady-state cosmology which in turn may be one or two orders of magnitude greater than that observed in luminous stars. Alternatively it will be noted that $E_F \sim 0.01$ eV if the « missing mass » energy is indeed in the form of neutrinos. Clearly this low value is impossible to detect experimentally in terrestrial laboratories with present techniques.

However, it is possible to set observational limits on the possible neutrino degeneracy in the universe from a consideration of the shape of the energy spectrum of the cosmic rays between 10^{10} and 10^{20} eV. COWSIK, PAL and TANDON (1964) have pointed out that the low-energy neutrinos in a Fermi sea appear to have quite large energies to a high-energy cosmic-ray proton in its rest mass system. Proton-neutrino interactions, elastic and inelastic, increase in probability quite rapidly with energy but eventually flatten off. This will have the result that the cosmic-ray energy spectrum should steepen at high energies and then eventually regain the original slope. Such an effect has been observed at 10^{15} to 10^{16} eV. If this is attributed entirely to proton-neutrino interactions then COWSIK, PAL and TANDON show that the height of the Fermi sea is at most a few eV.

Experiment, observation and theory in neutrino astrophysics will continue to be fruitful and productive in the quest for an understanding of astronomical systems and the Universe.

* * *

In the preparation of these lectures at Varenna, I wish to acknowledge the stimulating aid and cooperation of J. K. BIENLEIN, CERN, R. GALLINO, Torino, G. SILVESTRO, Torino, and D. FALLA, London. In the course of the studies on which these lectures are based I have been aided by S. P. S. ANAND, J. M. BARDEEN, J. N. BAHCALL, G. R. BURBIDGE, E. M. BURBIDGE, R. F. CHRISTY, J. FAULKNER, F. HOYLE, J. L. GREENSTEIN, I. IBEN, jr., C. C. LAURITSEN, F. C. MICHEL, I. W. ROXBURGH, M. SCHMIDT, R. STOECKLY, J. B. OKE, and B. ZIMMERMAN. I am especially indebted to J. M. BARDEEN and J. N. BAHCALL for many discussions and suggestions concerning supermassive stars and neutrino astrophysics respectively. The studies have been supported in part by the Office of Naval Research [Nonr-220(47)], National Science Foundation [GP-5391] and the National Aeronautics and Space Administration [NGR-05-002-028].

BIBLIOGRAPHY

ABBOT, C. G. and F. E. FOWLE, jr., 1911, *Ap. J.*, **33**, 191.

ABOV, YU. G., P. A. KRUPCHITSKY and YU. A. ORATOVSKY, 1964, *Congres International de Physique Nucléaire*, Paris.

ALLER, L. H., 1961, *The Abundance of the Elements* (New York).

BAHCALL, J. N., 1964*a*, *Phys. Rev. Letters*, **12**, 300.

BAHCALL, J. N., 1964*b*, *Phys. Rev.*, **135**, B 137.

BAHCALL, J. N., 1964*c*, *Phys. Rev.*, **136**, B1164.

BAHCALL, J. N., 1964*d*, *Proceedings of the Second Texas Symposium on Relativistic Astrophysics, Austin, Texas* (Chicago).

BAHCALL, J. N., 1965, *Science*, **147**, no. 3654, 115.

BAHCALL, J. N. and S. C. FRAUTSCHI, 1964*a*, *Phys. Rev.*, **135**, B 788.

BAHCALL, J. N. and S. C. FRAUTSCHI, 1964*b*, *Phys. Rev.*, **136**, B 1547.

BARDEEN, J. M., 1965, private communication.

BARDEEN, J. M. and S. P. S. ANAND, 1966, *Ap. J.*, **144**, 953.

BARDIN, R. K., C. A. BARNES, W. A. FOWLER and P. A. SEEGER, 1960, *Phys. Rev. Lett.*, **5**, 323.

BARDIN, R. K., C. A. BARNES, W. A. FOWLER and P. A. SEEGER, 1962, *Phys. Rev.*, **127**, 583.

BOEHM, F. and E. KANKELEIT, 1964, *Congrès International de Physique Nucléaire*, Paris.

BURBIDGE, G. R., 1962, *Prog. Theoret. Phys. Japan*, **27**, 999.

BURBIDGE, E. M., G. R. BURBIDGE, W. A. FOWLER and F. HOYLE, 1957, *Rev. Mod. Phys.*, **29**, 547; referred hereafter as B^2FH (1957).

CHANDRASEKHAR, S., 1964*a*, *Phys. Rev. Letters*, **12**, 114.

CHANDRASEKHAR, S., 1964*b*, *Phys. Rev. Letters*, **12** (E), 437.

CHANDRASEKHAR, S., 1964*c*, *Ap. J.*, **140**, 417.

CLIFFORD, F. E., 1964, private communication.

CLIFFORD, F. E. and R. TAYLER, 1964, *M.N.R.A.S.*, **127**, 185.

CLIFFORD, F. E. and R. TAYLER, 1965, *Memoirs R.A.S.*, **69**, 21.

COWAN, C. L., D. RYAN, V. ACOSTA, G. BUCKWALTER, W. CAREY and D. CURTIN, 1965, *Ninth International Conference on Cosmic Rays*, London September 15.

COWSIK, R., Y. PAL and S. V. TANDON, 1964, *Phys. Letters*, **13**, 265.

DAVIS, R., jr., 1955, *Phys. Rev.*, **97**, 766.

DAVIS, R., jr., 1964, *Phys. Rev. Letters*, **12**, 303.

FEYNMAN, R. P. and M. GELL-MANN, 1958*a*, *Phys. Rev.*, **109**, 193.

FEYNMAN, R. P. and M. GELL-MANN, 1958*b*, *Proceedings of the Second United Nations International Conference on the Peacedul Uses of Atomic Energy*, vol. **30**, 1958 (Geneva: United Nations).

FOWLER, W. A., 1958, *Astrophys. J.*, **127**, 551.

FOWLER, W. A., 1962, *Oral Presentation at Herstmonceux Conference*, April 17.

FOWLER, W. A., 1963, *Henry Norris Russell lecture to American Astronomical Society* at College, Alaska, July 13.

FOWLER, W. A., 1964, *Rev. Mod. Phys.*, **36**, 545.

FOWLER, W. A., 1965, *Proceedings of the Third Annual Science Conference of the Belfer Graduate School of Science* (Yeshiva University, New York).

FOWLER, W. A., 1966, *Ap. J.*, **144**, 180.

FOWLER, W. A. and F. HOYLE, 1964, *Ap. J. Suppl.*, **9**, 201; referred to hereafter as FH (1964).
FREEMAN, J. M., J. H. MONTAGUE, D. WEST and R. E. WHITE, 1962, *Physics Letters*, **3**, 136.
FREEMAN, J. M., J. H. MONTAGUE, G. MURRAY, R. E. WHITE and W. E. BURCHAM, 1964, *Physics Letters*, **8**, 115.
GRATTON, L., 1964, *Proceedings of Padua Symposium on Cosmology.*
HOYLE, F. and W. A. FOWLER, 1960, *Ap. J.*, **132**, 565; referred to hereafter as HF (1960).
HOYLE, F. and W. A. FOWLER, 1963*a*, *M.N.R.A.S.*, **125**, 169.
HOYLE, F. and W. A. FOWLER 1963*b*, *Nature*, **197**, 533.
HOYLE, F., W. A. FOWLER, G. R. BURBIDGE and E. M. BURBIDGE, 1964, *Ap. J.*, **139**, 909; referred to hereafter as HFB^2 (1964).
IBEN, I., 1963, *Ap. J.*, **138**, 1090.
KEUFFEL, J., 1965, private communication.
LEE, Y. K., L. W. MO, and C.-S. WU, 1963, *Phys. Rev. Letters*, **10**, 253.
MAYER-KUCKUK, T. and F. C. MICHEL, 1961, *Phys. Rev. Letters*, **7**, 167.
MAYER-KUCKUK, T. and F. C. MICHEL, 1962, *Phys. Rev.*, **127**, 545.
MCNALLY, J. H., 1965, *Ph. D. Thesis*, California Institute of Technology.
MINKOWSKI, R., 1964, *Proceedings of Padua Symposium on Cosmology.*
NORDBERG, M. E., jr., F. B. MORINIGO and C. A. BARNES, 1960, *Phys. Rev. Letters*, **5**, 321.
NORDBERG, M. E., jr., F. B. MORINGO and C. A. BARNES, 1962, *Phys. Rev. Letters*, **125**, 321.
PARKER, P. D. and R. W. KAVANAGH, 1963, *Phys. Rev.*, **131**, 2578.
REINES, F., M. F. CROUCH, T. L. JENKINS, W. R. KROPP, H. S. GURR, G. R. SMITH, J. P. F. SELLSCHOP and B. MEYER, 1965, *Phys. Rev. Letters*, **15**, 429.
REINES, F. and W. R. KROPP, 1964, *Phys. Rev. Letters*, **12**, 457.
REINES, F. and R. M. WOODS, jr., 1965, *Phys. Rev. Letters*, **14**, 20.
SANDAGE, A., 1964, *Proceedings of Padua Symposium on Cosmology.*
SEAGRAVE, J. D., 1951, *Phys. Rev.*, **84**, 1219.
SEARS, R. L., 1964, *Astroph. J.*, **140**, 477.
SUESS, H. E. and H. C. UREY, 1956, *Rev. Mod. Phys.*, **28**, 53.
VOGL, J. L., 1963, *Ph. D. Thesis*, California Institute of Technology.
WEINBERG, S., 1962, *Phys. Rev.*, **128**, 1457.
ZEL'DOVICH, YA. B. and M. A. PODURETS, 1964, *Soviet Physics-Doklady*, **9**, 373.

Symmetries of Strong Interactions.

N. DALLAPORTA
Istituto di Fisica dell'Università - Padova

I have been asked by Prof. GRATTON to try to summarize in this Lecture some of the relevant aspects of the so-called elementary-particle physics, because, although the connection of this field with astrophysics may not be very apparent up to now, it may be expected that sooner or later the two domains will happen to become more intimately interrelated with each other; and a first example of this possibility is offered by neutrino astrophysics which is developing quite rapidly, at least for what concerns its theoretical implications, as we have already learned from Prof. Fowler's lectures.

Owing to the enormous extension of elementary-particle physics and the short time available, I think the best I can do is to confine myself to one of the aspects of the problem in which the greatest advances have recently occurred; and which may presumably become one of the most interesting for astrophysical connections: this is the problem of the symmetries of the strong interactions.

I think the first step I have to take as a starting point is to make clear what concepts I have to discuss for those who may not be quite familiar with the subject. And these may be most easily understood and exemplified by the results obtained in the decade 1950-60 on the about 30 lowest-mass particles which were discovered up to that date, relevant data of which are contained in the following table (Table I). The main ideas contained in it concern mostly:

a) the different kinds of quantum numbers necessary to describe and differentiate the different particles;

b) the conservation laws which they imply;

c) the different kinds of interactions which they have allowed to distinguish.

I will try to summarize these results as follows.

TABLE I. – *Elementary particles.* The antiparticles are supposed to have the same spin, mass and mean life as the particles; strangeness and parity of the antibaryons are of opposite sign to those of the baryons.

Class	Name	Particle	antiparticle	Mass (MeV)	spin parity	Mean life (s)	Common decays and decay ratios (%)	Baryonic number	Isospin	Strangeness
photon	photon	γ			1	stable				
leptons	neutrino	ν_e	$\bar{\nu}_e$	< 0.00025	$\frac{1}{2}$	stable		0		
	neutretto	ν_μ	$\bar{\nu}_\mu$	< 2.5	$\frac{1}{2}$	stable		0		
	electron	e^-	e^+	0.510976 ± 0.000007	$\frac{1}{2}$	stable		0		
	muon	μ^-	μ^+	105.655 ± 0.010	$\frac{1}{2}$	$(2.210 \pm 0.002) \cdot 10^{-6}$	$e^-\bar{\nu}_e\nu_\mu(100)$	0		
mesons	pion	π^+	π^-	139.58 ± 0.05	0^-	$(2.547 \pm 0.027) \cdot 10^{-8}$	$\mu^+\nu_\mu(100)$	0	1	0
		π^0		134.97 ± 0.05	0^-	$(1.05 \pm 0.18) \cdot 10^{-16}$	$2\gamma(98.8)$, $\gamma e^+e^-(1.2)$	0	1	0
	K-meson	K^+	K^-	493.98 ± 0.14	0^-	$(1.227 \pm 0.008) \cdot 10^{-8}$	$\mu^+\nu_\mu(64.2 \pm 1.3)$	0	$\frac{1}{2}$	± 1
							$\pi^+\pi^0(18.6 \pm 0.9)$			
							$\mu^+\pi^0\nu_\mu(4.8 \pm 0.6)$			
							$e^+\pi^0\nu_e(5.0 \pm 0.5)$			
							$\pi^+\pi^+\pi^-(5.7 \pm 0.3)$			
							$\pi^+\pi^0\pi^0(1.7 \pm 0.2)$			
		K^0	$\bar{K}^0$	497.9 ± 0.6	0^-	$K_1^0(0.90 \pm 0.02) \cdot 10^{-10}$	$\pi^+\pi^-(69.4 \pm 1.0)$	0	$\frac{1}{2}$	± 1
							$\pi^0\pi^0(30.6 \pm 1.0)$			
						$K_2^0(6.3^{+1.6}_{-1.0}) \cdot 10^{-8}$	$\pi^+\pi^-\pi^0(8.7 \pm 2.3)$	0	$\frac{1}{2}$	
							$3\pi^0(38 \pm 7)$			
							$\pi^\pm e^\pm\nu_e(28.3 \pm 5.9)$			
							$\pi^\pm\mu^\pm\nu_\mu(25.0 \pm 5.9)$			
baryons	nucleon	p	$\bar{p}$	938.213 ± 0.010	$\frac{1}{2}^+$	stable		1	$\frac{1}{2}$	0
	nucleon	n	$\bar{n}$	939.507 ± 0.010	$\frac{1}{2}^+$	$(1.013 \pm 0.026) \cdot 10^{3}$	$pe^-\bar{\nu}_e(100)$	1	$\frac{1}{2}$	0
	Λ-hyperon	Λ^0	$\bar{\Lambda}^0$	1115.38 ± 0.10	$\frac{1}{2}^+$	$(2.57 \pm 0.30) \cdot 10^{-10}$	$p\pi^-(66^{+4}_{-3})$, $n\pi^0(34)$	1	0	-1
	Σ-hyperon	Σ^+	$\bar{\Sigma}^+$	1189.40 ± 0.20	$\frac{1}{2}^+$	$(0.78 \pm 0.03) \cdot 10^{-10}$	$p\pi^0$ (51), $n\pi^+(49)$	1	1	-1
		Σ^0	$\bar{\Sigma}^0$	1191.5 ± 0.5	$\frac{1}{2}^+$	$10^{-22} < \tau < 10^{-11}$	$\Lambda\gamma(100)$	1	1	-1
		Σ^-	$\bar{\Sigma}^-$	1195.96 ± 0.30	$\frac{1}{2}^+$	$(1.59 \pm 0.05) \cdot 10^{-10}$	$n\pi^-(100)$	1	1	-1
	Ξ-hyperon	Ξ^0	$\bar{\Xi}^0$	1314.3 ± 1.0	?	$(3.06 \pm 0.40) \cdot 10^{-10}$	$\Lambda\pi^0(100)$	1	$\frac{1}{2}$	-2
		Ξ^-	$\bar{\Xi}^-$	1320.8 ± 0.4	$\frac{1}{2}$	$(1.74 \pm 0.05) \cdot 10^{-10}$	$\Lambda\pi^-(100)$	1	$\frac{1}{2}$	-2

A) Conservation of energy and momentum applied to the decays of particles (column 8) has allowed to determine their mass.

B) Conservation of angular momentum applied to the decay or production reactions allows to determine their spin. This brings us to classify all the particles into two main groups: fermions (half-integer spin) and bosons or mesons (integer spin).

C) Lifetimes all of the same order, between 10^{-8} to 10^{-10} s with few exceptions, prove that decays occur through weak interactions (W.I.). This fact has suggested the concept of a universal Fermi interaction, which means universality of form and strength of all weak interactions.

D) If, leaving aside the photon and the neutrinos (ν_e and ν_μ) (they have zero mass so they cannot decay), we consider that the electron is stable because it is the lightest charged particle and its decay is therefore forbidden by the conservation of charge, we see that the stability of the proton p necessitates the introduction of another quantum number with a similar role as the electric charge, whose conservation should prevent the decay of the lightest particle (which happens to be the proton) bearing such a new type of « charge »: we call it the baryonic number. All fermions heavier than the proton have baryonic number $N \neq 0$ ($N = 1$ for baryons, $N = -1$ for antibaryons). Fermions lighter than the proton bear baryonic number N equal to zero and are called leptons. So fermions can be divided into two main groups according to the value of N: leptons and baryons. As the total number of mesons of any kind is not conserved, they are all assumed to have $N = 0$.

E) All baryons and mesons are found experimentally to interact strongly and therefore are called altogether hadrons. The mechanism usually adopted helping to visualize the interplay of S.I. (strong interactions) is the following: baryon number may be considered as a kind of charge which is the source of S.I. and mesons act as a kind of agents transmitting strong interactions between the sources, as photons do for the electromagnetic interaction (E.M.I.).

F) The existence of multiplets of particles having approximately the same mass and different charge state and therefore different E.M.I. suggests the introduction of a new quantum number I_3 (third isospin component) to differentiate each charge state within each multiplet.

G) The paradox of strong production and weak decays for K-mesons and hyperons (all baryon states except nucleons) necessitates the introduction of a new quantum number conserved by S.I. and violated by W.I. It is called the strangeness S. Conservation of strangeness by S.I. implies associated production for strangeness-bearing particles (ex. $\pi + p \to K + n$) and weak decays of them (with few exceptions) in *nonstrange* particles as only possible allowed channels (ex. $\Lambda \rightarrow p+\pi$). Electric charge Q, I_3, S, and the baryonic number N are related to each other by the so-called Gell-Mann–Nishijima relation

$$Q = I_3 + \frac{S+N}{2} \, . \tag{1}$$

H) Antiparticles have all quantum numbers (N, S, Q, I_3) equal and reversed in sign in respect to those of their respective particles.

I) Finally a further conservation law for S.I. is given by conservation of parity P. It has turned out that if we conventionally assume positive parity for all baryons (spin and parity state ($\frac{1}{2}^+$)), then mesons have opposite parity and therefore act as pseudoscalar fields (0^-).

Summarizing, we have 3 kinds of interactions: S.I., E.M.I. and W.I. and the conservation properties for each of them are illustrated by the following Table from which the obvious conservations of energy, momentum and angular momentum are omitted.

Possibly conserved quantities	S.I.	E.M.I.	W.I.
Q	yes	yes	yes
N	yes	yes	yes
S	yes	yes	no
I_3	yes	no	(not defined)
P	yes	yes	no

From it, we may presume the following general rule: the stronger the interaction is, the more symmetries and conservations it obeys.

Already before 1960 it was apparent that the connection of the hadrons with strong interactions was responsible for their appearance in different multiplets of mass, strangeness and charge. One of the main problems of particle physics turned then out to try to find a reason why the hadrons were so many (and this question of course has become more acute after 1960 when so many other new states have been discovered).

Since then, with alternate phases of success and fashion, two main currents of thought have competed with each other in order to explain the fact. The first is the idea that hadrons are compound structures built up from a few of them taken as fundamental; the second that the multiplicity of states is a consequence of some new kind of symmetry operating in a new kind of fictitious space, the charge or isospin space, introduced as a further internal degree of freedom of hadrons (as spin is an internal degree of freedom for fermions).

In a first period, compound models were considered and several types of them were proposed, the most famous one being the Fermi-Yang-Sakata model. Taking p, n, Λ (and their antiparticles $\bar{p}$, $\bar{n}$, $\bar{\Lambda}$) as fundamental states, their composition in order to obtain other particles is made in such a way that addition of quantum numbers is satisfied. Let us give some examples.

Mesons are considered to be composite states of two fundamental particles, a baryon and an antibaryon giving total $N=0$:

$$\pi^+ = p\bar{n}\,, \qquad \pi^- = \bar{p}n\,, \qquad \pi^0 = \text{linear combination}$$
$$K^+ = p\bar{\Lambda}\,, \qquad \bar{K}^- = \bar{p}\Lambda\,, \qquad \text{of } \bar{n}n \text{ and } p\bar{p}.$$
$$K^0 = n\bar{\Lambda}\,, \qquad \bar{K}^0 = \bar{n}\Lambda\,,$$

Other baryons are states formed by 3 fundamental particles (two baryons and an antibaryon), for instance:

$$\Sigma^+ = \bar{n}\Lambda p\,, \qquad \Sigma^- = \bar{p}n\Lambda\,, \qquad \Sigma^0 = \text{linear combina-}$$
$$\Xi^- = \bar{p}\Lambda\Lambda\,, \qquad \Xi^0 = \bar{n}\Lambda\Lambda\,, \qquad \text{tion of } \bar{n}\Lambda n \text{ and } \bar{p}\Lambda p.$$

For several reasons this and other attempts were met with some difficulties; so that after a while the fashion turned rather to look for the internal symmetries in isospace. This was mostly suggested by the regularities of the following diagrams (Fig. 1 and 2) in which the hypercharge Y, defined as $Y = S + N$, is plotted against I_3:

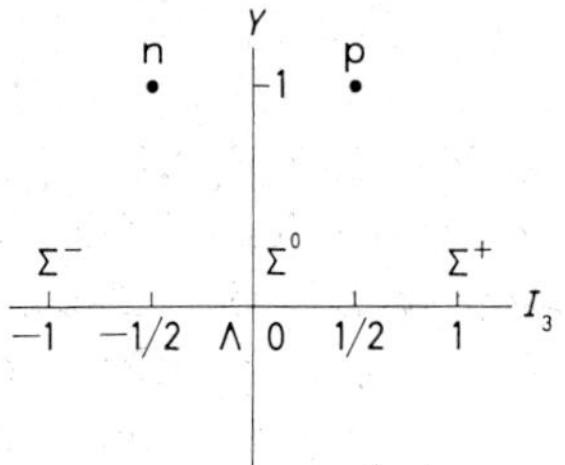

Fig. 1. – Baryons.

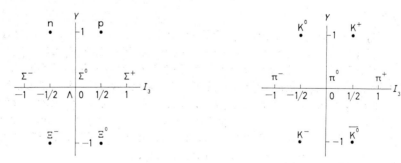

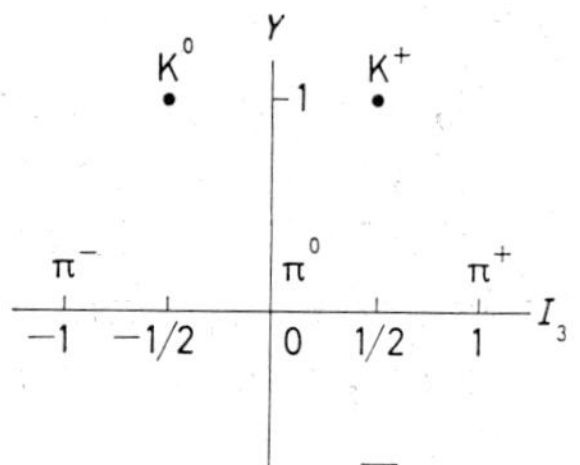

Fig. 2. – Mesons.

The great similarity of these two cases was the first strong support to the idea of underlying symmetries in charge and hypercharge space.

This idea may be considered as a generalization of isospace used in nuclear physics for interpreting the interactions of nucleons and pions. Why nucleons and pions exist in several charge states? Because, apart from Lorentz invariance and other possible symmetries concerned with ordinary space, S.I. are invariant for special operations called rotations in the isospin space.

In classical mechanics infinitesimal rotations are operations whose operators are at the same time conserved quantities (*i.e.* angular momentum). The transformations which correspond, in quantum mechanics, to the canonical transformations in classical mechanics are the unitary transformations of type $e^{i\alpha}$ (if α is the classical operator). If we consider an infinitesimal unitary transformation we can expand it as

$$e^{i\alpha} \sim 1 + i\alpha \,. \tag{2}$$

The easiest example is the intrinsic angular momentum of a spin-$\frac{1}{2}$ fermion. Such a particle can be represented by a two-component entity (more exactly a two-component spinor) in a 2-dimensional complex space.

In analogy with (2) an infinitesimal rotation in a 2-dimensional complex space is represented by the operation

$$1 + \varepsilon_i \sigma_i \qquad (i = 1, 2, 3)\,,$$

where the $\sigma_i = 2 \times 2$ are the Pauli matrices. This group of rotations in such a space is the unitary unimodular group called SU_2.

Of course the σ_i obey the well-known commutation relations

$$[\sigma_i, \sigma_k] = i\sigma_j\,, \qquad (i, k, j, \text{ cyclic})$$

so only one of them may be diagonalized; say σ_3: The eigenstates of this operator represent states with a well defined value of the 3-rd component of spin and its eigenvalues are the values of this quantity. Together with σ_3 also $\sigma^2 = \sum \sigma_i^2$ can be diagonalized and we have

$$\sigma^2 = S(S+1)I \qquad \text{with} \begin{cases} S = \frac{1}{2}\,, \\ I = \text{unit matrix}\,. \end{cases}$$

The group of all rotations acting on a 3-dimensional space is isomorphic to SU_2 and can be built from it.

Let us now consider the nucleons or the pions as being each a unique kind of particle which possesses a supplementary degree of freedom, related to the different charge states it can take (as ordinary spin is a supplementary co-ordinate related to the intrinsic angular momentum of fermions). This new degree of freedom needs the introduction of a supplementary fictitious space, the isospin space, and the co-ordinates in it have to label the different charge states the particle can take. Operations in this space (*i.e.* rotations) will transform the charge states one into the other. Requirement of invariance of the interaction against these rotations will give rise to the isobaric symmetries we are looking for.

A charge state multiplet like the nucleon may be represented by a two-component state in a two-dimensional fictitious charge space $\begin{vmatrix} p \\ n \end{vmatrix}$. The generators of the rotations in this two-dimensional space are the three τ_i matrices which are an equivalent representation of the Pauli matrices σ_i mentioned above. The group of rotations in this 2-dimensional charge space is again SU_2.

The same we can do for pions. Since they appear in 3 different charge states $\begin{vmatrix} \pi^+ \\ \pi^0 \\ \pi^- \end{vmatrix}$ we need a 3-dimensional representation for the rotation operators in SU_2 isomorphic to the τ_i; let us call them the θ_i; an infinitesimal transformation of charge in the pion charge space will be performed by the operator

$$1 + \varepsilon_i \theta_i$$

acting on the pion charge state vector.

The fundamental requirement is now that S.I. should be invariant under the group of transformations in isospace SU_2. This means that the Lagrangian of the interaction has to be a scalar under this group of transformations, and therefore does not change if we make an arbitrary transformation in the charge space of the particles taking part in the interaction; for instance if we go from one process to a different one obtained from the first by changing the charges of the particles in a suitable manner.

The simplest way to describe the interaction between pion and nucleons is then to construct the simplest scalar in charge space. Since the pion, in this space, is a 3-component object, that is to say a vector $\boldsymbol{\Pi}$, we must construct with the 2-component spinor ψ another isovector in order to obtain an isoscalar product between the two isovectors. We write therefore

$$\mathscr{L} = \sum_{i=1}^{3} \bar{\psi} \boldsymbol{\tau}_i \Gamma \psi \boldsymbol{\Pi}_i \,, \tag{4}$$

where Γ is a suitable space-time Dirac operator (in this precise case γ_5) $\psi = \begin{vmatrix} p \\ n \end{vmatrix}$, $\boldsymbol{\tau}$ is the vector whose three components are the three 2×2 Pauli matrices τ_i and $\boldsymbol{\Pi}$ an isovector whose three components π_i are related in a simple way to π^+, π^-, π^0.

In such an interaction, charge Q is of course conserved, $T_3 = \tau_3 + \theta_3$ and $\boldsymbol{T} = \boldsymbol{\tau} + \boldsymbol{\theta}$ are also conserved. This is what is called charge independence of nuclear forces.

We can easily extend this idea to all the interactions of pions with every other baryon multiplet; and we get terms of the type

$$\bar{\Sigma}\Sigma\pi\,, \qquad \bar{\Lambda}\Sigma\pi\,, \qquad \bar{\Xi}\Xi\pi\,;$$

we wish however to include also into a wider symmetry than SU_2 all the K-meson interactions, such as

$$\bar{\mathcal{N}}\Lambda K\,, \qquad \bar{\mathcal{N}}\Sigma K\,, \qquad \bar{\Lambda}\Xi K\,, \qquad \bar{\Sigma}\Xi K\,.$$

But then a new difficulty arises: if there were such a symmetry all masses of baryons should be equal; different masses violate higher symmetry.

One may try to overcome this point by supposing that the main part of strong interactions, let us call them V.S.I. (very strong interactions) have a wider symmetry which would be fully valid if all baryons had the same mass; and that there exists a subsidiary strong interaction, let us call it M.S.I. (medium strong interaction) about 25% as strong as V.S.I. which violates it and therefore destroys the equality of masses. Attention must be paid to the fact that these M.S.I. must be of such a type as not to destroy the isotopic multiplets already mentioned. The higher symmetries looked for are then related only to V.S.I.

Several approaches to interpret them have been tried until a successful one has been reached: SU_3.

SU_3 is the unitary unimodular group of rotations in a 3-dimensional complex space and therefore is mainly the 3×3 extension of the 2×2 unitary unimodular group SU_2.

The extension from SU_2 to SU_3 may be synthetized by the following Table:

	SU_2	SU_3
Dimensions	2	3
Number of fundamental operators	3	8
Fundamental operators	τ_i	λ_i
Commutation relations between fundamental operators	$(\tau_i, \tau_j) = i\tau_k$	$(\lambda_i, \lambda\ ) = 2if_{ijk}\,\lambda_k$
(the quantities f_{ijk} are the so-called structure coefficients of the group)		
Conserved quantities	τ_3	λ_3, λ_8
Dimensionality of fundamental representation	2	3
Dimensionality of regular representation (number of dimensions = number of operators)	3	8
Symbol of operators in regular representation	θ_i	F_i, D_i

The fact that in SU_2 we have only one conserved quantity τ_3 and in SU_3 we have two, λ_3 and λ_8, is the obvious consequence of the fact that according to the commutation relations

$$(\lambda_i, \lambda_j) = 2if_{ijk}\lambda_k$$

we have two operators which commute with each other and in fact two we need in order to conserve both isospin and hypercharge; the eigenvalues of λ_3 and λ_8, or F_3 and F_8, are respectively in fact the value of I_3 and Y for the different particle states.

In the SU_3 scheme, the 8 known baryons form an octet, that is a baryon is represented by a kind of spinor in an 8-dimensional space which is also the regular representation of SU_3:

$$\psi = \begin{vmatrix} p \\ n \\ \Xi^0 \\ \Xi^- \\ \Sigma^+ \\ \Sigma^0 \\ \Sigma^- \\ \Lambda^0 \end{vmatrix},$$

In analogy to (4) the SU_3 invariant interaction Lagrangian shall now be written

(5)
$$\mathscr{L} = \sum_{i=1}^{8} \psi F_i \Gamma \psi \varphi_i$$

with the F_i satisfying the commutation relations

$$[F_i F_j] = 2if_{ijk}F_k$$

taking the place of the τ_i and φ_i being a kind of SU_3 8-vector having as components simple combinations of the 8 meson states (K^+, K^0, $\overline{K}^0$, $\overline{K}^-$, π^+, π^0, $\overline{\pi}$, η).

In order to complete the octet it was necessary to introduce an 8-th meson η, which has in fact been afterwards discovered. In such an interaction the conserved quantities are $\sum F_3 =$ total isospin, $\sum F_8 =$ total hypercharge.

We must notice, at this point, that for antiparticles we must use in SU_3 the conjugate complex representations such as $\overline{3}$ which have opposite quantum numbers and in general are different in respect to the normal ones such as 3.

An exception is given by the 8-dimensional regular representation which coincides with its conjugate representation $\bar{8}$.

Now, according to the SU_3 model, baryons and mesons may easily be considered as compound states of each other; in effect generalizing the Fermi-Yang-Sakata model we may consider mesons as obtained by combining a baryon and an antibaryon

$$\mathrm{M} = \bar{\mathrm{B}} \times \mathrm{B} .$$

To choose the most suitable multiplet in which mesons can be arranged, we must form the direct product of the two octets of baryons and antibaryons and see in which irreducible representations it decomposes. From group theory we get the following decomposition:

$$8 \times 8 = 1 + 8 + 8 + 10 + \overline{10} + 27 .$$

We thus see that a suitable representation for mesons is again the 8-dimensional one. The direct product of an 8-meson with an 8-baryon is then again 8×8 and so on. We say that 8×8 generates always 8 and that is why this scheme is called the 8-fold way.

The violation of mass is performed, as we said above, by M.S.I. which must depend on the operator F_8 in order to split the masses of particles consequently to different values of hypercherge as is observed. With such a perturbation, a first order evaluation may be made. One of the main successes of the theory has in fact been the Gell-Mann–Okubo mass formula, obtained according to this program which gives the mass of the various hadrons according to their quantum numbers. The formula is

$$m = m_0\{1 + aY + b[I(I + 1) - \tfrac{1}{4} Y^2]\} ;$$

it is sufficient to determine the 3 constants m_0, a, b from the experimental values of three hadron states of a given supermultiplet, to predict then the mass of the remaining hadrons of this same supermultiplet. The agreement between this theoretical expectation and experimental data is extremely good; which is somewhat difficult to understand as the formula is obtained by a first-order perturbation calculation, while we know that, for strong interactions, perturbation methods generally fail.

SU_3 gave a settlement to all particles known up to 1960. However, since then, a lot of new hadronic states have been experimentally discovered. Apparently there is some difference between these new states and the old ones, from a phenomenological point of view; as in fact they generally appear as

TABLE II. – *Resonances*. Mesons.

Symbol	Mass (MeV)	Spin, parity J^{PG}	Width (MeV)	Principal decays: Partial modes	Principal decays: Fraction (%)	Isotopic spin	Strangeness
η	548.8 ± 5	(0^{-+})	< 10	$\gamma\gamma$ $3\pi^0$ or $\pi^0 2\gamma$ $\pi^+\pi^-\pi^0$ $\pi^+\pi^-\gamma$ $\pi^0 e^+e^-$	38.6 ± 2.7 30.8 ± 2.3 25.0 ± 1.6 5.5 ± 1.2 1.1 ± 1.1	0	0
ω	782.8 ± 0.5	(1^{--})	12.0 ± 1.7	$\pi^+\pi^-\pi^0$ $\pi^+\pi^-$ neutrals $(\pi^0\gamma)$ η+neutrals $\pi^+\pi^-\gamma$ e^+e^- $\mu^+\mu^-$	88 seen 10.6 ± 1 < 1.7 < 5 ≈ 0.01 < 0.10	0	0
X^0 or η'	958.6 ± 1.6	(0^{-+})	< 4	$\eta 2\pi$ $\pi^+\pi^-\gamma$	76 ± 4 24 ± 4	0	0
K_1K_1	≈ 1000						
φ	1019.5 ± 0.3	(1^{--})	3.3 ± 0.6	K_1K_2 K^+K^- $\pi\rho + 3\pi$ $\pi^0\gamma$ η+neutrals $\mu^+\mu^-$ e^+e^-	38 ± 3 30 ± 3 32 ± 8 < 12 < 0.5 < 0.4	0	0
f	1253 ± 20	(2^{++})	118 ± 16	$\pi\pi$ 4π $\bar{K}K$	large < 4 < 4	0	0

E	1420 ± 10		60 ± 10	K^*K $K\bar{K}\pi$	large	0	0
f′	1500	(2^{++})	80	K_1K_1 $K\bar{K}^*$ (890)		0	0
ρ	765 ± 3	(1^{-+})	124 ± 4	2π 4π $\pi\gamma$ e^+e^-	100 < 1 < 2 ≈ 0.0065	1	0
A_1	1072 ± 8	(1^{+-})	125	$\rho\pi$ $\bar{K}K$	~ 100 < 5	1	0
B	1220	$(\geqslant 1^{?+})$	125 ± 17	$\omega\pi$? $\pi\pi$ $\bar{K}K$ 4π	≈ 100 < 30 < 10 < 50	1	0
A_2	1300 ± 6	(2^{+-})	90 ± 10	$\rho\pi$ $\bar{K}K$ $\eta\pi$	≈ 91 5.5 ± 1.5 2^{+2}_{-1}	1	0
$\varkappa$	725 ± 2	(0^+)	< 12	$K\pi$	~ 100	$\frac{1}{2}$	±1
K^*	891.4 ± 0.2	(1^-)	49 ± 2	$K\pi$ $K\pi\pi$ $\varkappa\pi$	~ 100 < 0.2 < 0.2	$\frac{1}{2}$	±1
C	1215 ± 15		60 ± 10	$K\rho$ $K^*\pi$	? ?	$\leqslant \frac{3}{2}$	±1
K^*	1405 ± 8	(2^+)	95 ± 11	$K\pi$	?	$\frac{1}{2}$	±1

TABLE III. – *Resonances*. Baryons.

Symbol	Mass (MeV)	Spin, parity J^{PG}	Width (MeV)	Principal decays: Partial modes	Principal decays: Fraction (%)	Isotopic spin	Strangeness
$\mathcal{N}^*_{\frac{1}{2}}$ (1480)	1400—1500	($1/2^+$)	200 $\pm$ 20			$\frac{1}{2}$	0
$\mathcal{N}^*_{\frac{1}{2}}$ (1518)	1518 $\pm$ 10	($3/2^-$)	120	$\pi\mathcal{N}$ $\mathcal{N}\pi\pi$	75	$\frac{1}{2}$	0
$\mathcal{N}^*_{\frac{1}{2}}$ (1688) $\mathcal{N}^*_{\frac{1}{2}}$ (1674) $\mathcal{N}^*_{\frac{1}{2}}$ (1700)	1688 1674 $\sim$ 1700	($5/2^+$) ($5/2^-$) ($1/2^-$)	$\leqslant$ 100 $\sim$ 100	$\left\{ \begin{array}{l} \pi\mathcal{N} \\ \mathcal{N}\pi\pi \\ \eta\mathcal{N} \\ \Lambda K \end{array} \right.$	$\approx$ 85 < 2	$\frac{1}{2}$ $\frac{1}{2}$ $\frac{1}{2}$	0 0 0
$\mathcal{N}^*_{\frac{1}{2}}$ (2190)	2190	($7/2^-$)	$\approx$ 200	$\pi\mathcal{N}$ ΛK	$\approx$ 40 seen	$\frac{1}{2}$	0
$\mathcal{N}^*_{\frac{1}{2}}$ (2650)	2645 $\pm$ 10	($9/2^+$)	$\approx$ 200	$\pi\mathcal{N}$ $\eta\mathcal{N}$		$\frac{1}{2}$	0
$\mathcal{N}^*_{\frac{3}{2}}$ (1236)	1236.0 $\pm$ 0.4	($3/2^+$)	120.0 $\pm$ 1.5	$\pi\mathcal{N}$	100	$\frac{3}{2}$	0
$\mathcal{N}^*_{\frac{3}{2}}$ (1924)	1924	($7/2^+$)	$\approx$ 200	$\pi\mathcal{N}$ ΣK	60	$\frac{3}{2}$	0
$\mathcal{N}^*_{\frac{3}{2}}$ (2360)	2360	($9/2^-$)	$\sim$ 200	$\pi\mathcal{N}$	$\approx$ 15	$\frac{3}{2}$	0
$\mathcal{N}^*_{\frac{3}{2}}$ (2825)	2825	($11/2^+$)	260	$\pi\mathcal{N}$		$\frac{3}{2}$	0
Y^*_0 (1405)	1405	($1/2^-$)	35 $\pm$ 5	$\Sigma\pi$ $\Lambda\pi\pi$	100 < 1	0	—1
Y^*_0 (1520)	1518.9 $\pm$ 1.5	($3/2^-$)	16 $\pm$ 2	$\Sigma\pi$ $\bar{K}\mathcal{N}$ $\Lambda\pi\pi$	55 $\pm$ 7 29 $\pm$ 4 16 $\pm$ 2	0	—1

Y_0^* (1815)	1815 ± 5	(5/2⁺)	50	$\overline{K}\mathcal{N}$ $\Sigma\pi$ (mainly $Y_1^*(1385+\pi)\to\Lambda\pi\pi$ $\Lambda\eta$	≈75 ≈ 9 ≈15 ≈ 1	0	—1
Y_1^* (1385)	1382.7 ± 5	(3/2⁺)	44 ± 2	$\Lambda\pi$ $\Sigma\pi$	90 ± 2 10 ± 2	1	—1
Y_1^* (1660)	1660 ± 10	(⩾3/2)	44 ± 5	$\overline{K}\mathcal{N}$ $\Sigma\pi$ $\Lambda\pi$ (mainly $Y_0^*(1405+\pi)\to\Sigma\pi\pi$ $\Lambda\pi\pi$	≈15 ≈30 ≈ 5 ≈30 ≈20	1	—1
Y_1^* (1765)	1762 ± 17	(5/2⁻)	75 ± 7	$\overline{K}\mathcal{N}$ $\Lambda\pi$ $\Sigma\pi$ $Y_1^*(1385)+\pi$ $Y_0^*(1520)+\pi$	≈60 ≈16 ⩽ 3 ≈10 ≈10	1	—1
Y_1^* (2065)	2065	(7/2⁺)	≈160	$\overline{K}\mathcal{N}$ $\Lambda\pi$	∼35	1	—1
Ξ^* (1530)	1529.7 ± 0.9	(3/2⁺)	7.5 ± 1.7	$\Xi\pi$	≈100	½	—2
Ξ^* (1816)	1816 ± 3	(3/2⁻)	16 ± 4	$\Xi^*\pi$ $\Lambda\overline{K}$ $\Xi\pi$ $\Xi\pi\pi$	≈25 ≈65 ≈ 5 ≈ 5	½	—2
Ξ^* (1933)	1933 ± 16	(5/2⁺)	140 ± 35	$\Xi\pi$		½	—2
Ω^-	1675 ± 3	(3/2⁺)		$\Xi\pi$ $\Lambda\overline{K}$		0	—3

resonances in the scattering of different particles, or are indirectly observed in analysing 3-body final-state interaction processes (their masses being then deduced by considering the three- or more-body reaction as a two-body one, followed by a 2- or more-body decay of one of the products), and are therefore interpretable as unstable states rapidly decaying into lighter particles. The widths of the resonances in the scattering give the lifetimes which turn thus out to be of the order $10^{-18} \div 10^{-22}$, showing that these states decay through E.M.I. or S.I. A list of these so-called resonances is given in Table II and III. Their spin, parity and isospin values are gradually obtained from the conservation laws already quoted applied to different reactions.

What may be then the meaning of all these resonances from the point of view of SU_3? Up to now, only two octets (0^-) and a baryon octet ($\frac{1}{2}^+$) (of course all the particles of a same representation must have the same spin and parity) were experimentally identified; if the group has a real general meaning we ought to be able to form with the new states new representations. In fact this has been done and checked: the most important representations of SU_3 thus found are an octet (ρ, ω, K^* (892)) and a singlet (φ) of vector mesons (1^-), an octet (A_2, f, K^*(1405)) and a singlet (f′) of spin-two mesons (2^+), and a decuplet representation of baryons ($\mathcal{N}^*\Sigma^*\Lambda^*\Xi^*\Omega^-$)($\frac{3}{2}^+$). Other groups of baryons and mesons are still incomplete; new states are continuously discovered and masses run higher and higher.

What may now be the meaning of all these groups and why are there so many representations? Particularly why do we find the same SU_3 representations for different groups of particles with different values of spin and parity? The answer to these questions was looked for by searching for more extended groups including together symmetries in isospace and normal space; the final aim being to find a general group including both transformations in SU_3 and Lorentz transformations. Many attempts in this direction are recent and have been made only this last year; the most promising approach up to now is SU_6, which however solves the problem only partially, as it does not include Lorentz transformations but only three-dimensional space rotations; which means that the group is not relativistically invariant. However at low energies there is some evidence that it may be considered as a good approximation. The main feature is then that SU_6 can be factorized into the product of $SU_2 \times SU_3$, and every irreducible representation of SU_6 considered as the product of an irreducible representation of SU_2 times an irreducible representation of SU_3; we thus find definite combinations of the SU_3 F-spin and of normal spin and parity. The fundamental representation of SU_6 is, of course, 6-dimensional and is obtained by the product of SU_2 and SU_3 fundamental representations, that is

$$6 = 2 \times 3 \,,$$

where the first and second figure give respectively the dimensions of the representations of real spin and SU_3 spin.

Particles assigned to this fundamental representation would thus have two spin values and three charge states.

Higher most interesting representations are the following

$$35 = 1\times 8 + 3\times 8 + 3\times 1 \,,$$

$$56 = 2\times 8 + 4\times 10 \,.$$

As far as the 35-dimensional representation is concerned we have that it splits into an SU_3 octet of pseudoscalar particles, an SU_3 octet of vector particles and an SU_3 singlet of vector particles, if we choose parity — for all of them (according to data). In the same way we see that the 56-dimensional representation of SU_6 consists of an SU_3 octet of spin-$\frac{1}{2}$ particles and a decuplet of spin-$\frac{3}{2}$ particles. So we may summarize these results in the following Table:

Representations of SU_6	
$6 = 2\times 3$	$(\frac{1}{2})(3)$
$35 = 1\times 8 + 3\times 8 + 3\times 1$	$(0^-)(8) + (1^-)(8) + (1^-)(1)$
$56 = 2\times 8 + 4\times 10$	$(\frac{1}{2}^+)(8) + (\frac{3}{2}^+)(10)$

where now the two figures account for the spin and parity value and the SU_3 representation.

If we assign the right parities, we see that all the known lowest-lying meson and baryon states are gathered together in a single representation. This success, substantiated by several more other points which I cannot mention here represents the widest successful approach to include all known results as a consequence of a higher group operation.

One of the difficulties to proceed further than SU_6 is given by the following consideration. Up to now all groups we have considered were compact; which in group theory means that there are always unitary representations of a finite number of dimensions. If we want now to include the Lorentz group which is noncompact, one is forced to look for noncompact groups of which the unitary representations are always of an infinite number of dimensions. That is the number of excited states may become infinite continuous. One does not know if this should correspond to reality.

Finally, a further question which I would like to mention is connected with the following fact.

Why in SU_3 or SU_6, the representations realized in nature are not the lowest order ones, which are lacking, (3 for SU_3 and 6 for SU_6), but only the next higher ones? The idea which has been put forward to possibly explain this fact, is connected with an evolution in the concept of elementary particles and is a partial return to the idea of the compound model, or better, a compromise between symmetries and compound model. More exactly all known particles are now considered to be compound states on the same footing, all being states with a different excitation content of hadronic matter.

If then hadronic matter properties are invariant under SU_3 or SU_6 (of course we neglect here, as before, M.S.I. effects) and moreover all states we know are compound and are higher representations of the group, the easiest idea is to suppose that hadronic matter is composed of some underlying subnucleonic particles called *quarks*, which should constitute the elementary hadronic field, and of which the normal hadrons are composed. So the quarks should fill the lowest representations of the symmetry groups (SU_3 or SU_6). Let us refer to SU_3. The lowest representation being 3-dimensional, we have a triplet of quarks.

In order to obtain the normal hadrons we must compose together 2 or more quarks or antiquarks; if quarks belong to representation 3, then antiquarks belong to representation $\bar{3}$ which is the conjugate representation to 3. This corresponds to form the products of two or more 3-dimensional representations of SU_3.

The first idea is then of course to return to the Sakata model in which mesons are the compound states of a fundamental particle plus an antiparticle, and baryons the compound states of two fundamental particles plus an antiparticle. Applying now this scheme to quarks we get

$$\bar{3}\times 3 = 1 + 8\,,$$

$$\bar{3}\times 3\times 3 = 3 + 3 + \bar{6} + 15\,.$$

The first rule for mesons is all right since it yields the known 8-representation, but the second for baryons is not, since it leads to experimentally unknown representations. On the other hand we find that

$$3\times 3\times 3 = 1 + 8 + 8 + 10$$

which works very well because we obtain our beloved octets and decuplets. So we are led to think that baryons are compound states of 3 quarks and no antiquarks. This allows us to determine all the quantum numbers for the quarks keeping in mind the law of addition of quantum numbers in forming composite states.

The most important change to current ideas brought in by such a model is that now quarks must have baryonic number $\frac{1}{3}$. If all the other quantum numbers as strangeness, I_3 ... are obtained from the eigenvalues of λ_3 and λ_8 in the 3-representation of SU_3, we are then led for the electric charge Q, by applying the Gell-Mann–Nishijima formula

$$Q = I_3 + \frac{N+S}{2}$$

to fractional values for quarks. Using the symbols d_1, d_2, S_0 for the quarks we obtain the following Table of quantum numbers

	I	I_3	S	N	Y	Q
d_1	$\frac{1}{2}$	$\frac{1}{2}$	0	$\frac{1}{3}$	$\frac{1}{3}$	$\frac{2}{3}$
d_2	$\frac{1}{2}$	$-\frac{1}{2}$	0	$\frac{1}{3}$	$\frac{1}{3}$	$-\frac{1}{3}$
S_0	0	0	-1	$\frac{1}{3}$	$-\frac{2}{3}$	$-\frac{1}{3}$

and the following table of compound structure for mesons

$$\pi^+ = \bar{d}_2 d_1, \quad \pi^- = \bar{d}_1 d_2, \quad \pi^0 = \frac{1}{\sqrt{2}}(\bar{d}_1 d_1 - \bar{S}_0 S_0), \quad \eta_0 = \frac{1}{\sqrt{6}}(\bar{d}_1 d_1 + \bar{d}_2 d_2 - 2\bar{S}_0 S_0),$$

$$K^+ = \bar{S}_0 d_1, \quad K^- = \bar{d}_1 S_0, \quad K^0 = \bar{S}_0 d_2, \quad \bar{K}^0 = \bar{d}_2 S_0 .$$

The exact formulae for the compound structure of baryons are somewhat more complicated: it is enough here to indicate for each baryon the combination of quarks contributing to its formation.

$$\begin{aligned} &p \sim d_1 d_1 d_2, &&\Xi^0 \sim d_1 S_0 S_0, \\ &n \sim d_1 d_2 d_2, &&\Xi^- \sim d_2 S_0 S_0, \\ &\Lambda \sim d_1 d_2 S_0, &&\Sigma^+ \sim d_1 d_1 S_0, \\ &\Sigma^0 \sim d_1 d_2 S_0, &&\Sigma^- \sim d_2 d_2 S_0 . \end{aligned}$$

This model may fairly well account also for the breaking of the mass due to the M.S.I. perturbation if we suppose the S_0 quark to be heavier than the other two.

Up to now there is no evidence of quarks. They have been looked for owing to their peculiar characteristic of bearing fractional charge, so one could reveal them with magnetic deviations, but no trace was seen.

Cosmological Aspects of High-Energy Astrophysics.

D. W. Sciama
Department of Applied Mathematics and Theoretical Physics
University of Cambridge - Cambridge

1. – Mach's principle and the physical foundations of general relativity.

Mach's principle plays a dual role in this course; *a*) it provides the physical basis for general relativity, which is the theory used to discuss the behaviour of massive objects whose collapse may precede the formation of radio galaxies and quasi-stellar sources; *b*) it leads to the possibility that there exists an intergalactic gas comprising over 90 per cent of all the matter in the universe. This intergalactic gas may be the medium out of which galaxies and radio sources are formed. Its likely physical state is discussed in the next Section.

It is important to have a good understanding of the physical basis of general relativity because that theory lacks comprehensive experimental confirmation. If we wish to place confidence in its predictions about the behaviour of massive objects we must at least be able to judge the strength of its physical foundations. In my opinion most of the standard textbooks overstress the formal structure of the theory and pay insufficient attention to its physical aspects. In this lecture I shall try to redress the balance, while referring to these standard treatments for proofs of the mathematical results I need.

Mach's principle has been widely discussed in recent years, and indeed must still be regarded as controversial. I do not propose to repeat these arguments here, but refer the reader to three discussions (Sciama 1953, 1959*c*, 1964*a*; Dicke 1961*a*; Wheeler 1964*a* and *b*) to give him a sample of some of the different viewpoints that have been taken. The principle is concerned with the existence of the privileged class of *inertial* frames of reference which is basic to Newtonian dynamics and special-relativity alike. It seeks to relate this class of frames to the large-scale distribution of matter in the universe. Put more dynamically, it seeks a physical origin for the *inertial forces* which act in noninertial frames of reference. I shall take Mach's principle in the form:

Inertial forces are exerted by matter, not by absolute space.

In this form the principle contains two ideas:

i) inertial forces have a dynamical rather than a kinematical origin, and so must be derived from a field theory, in analogy with electromagnetic forces;

ii) the *whole* of the inertial field must be due to sources, so that in solving the inertial field equations the boundary conditions must be chosen appropriately.

The phrase « due to » in ii) gives rise to unsolved difficulties, owing to the nonlinearity which is characteristic of the field theory of i). We shall therefore restrict ourselves entirely to deriving this field theory.

The first question to decide is the stage in the argument at which *gravitation* is brought into the discussion. I differ from the textbooks by deferring the introduction of gravitation to the last possible moment. My reason is that Mach's principle is so desirable that I would be ready if necessary to introduce a new field into physics to carry the inertial forces, just as nuclear physicists introduced nuclear forces. It is a historical accident that this new field was in fact already well-known in a different connection, and this accident tends to conceal the logical structure of Einstein's theory.

1·1. *A field theory of inertial forces.*

1·1.1. The structure of inertial forces. The structure of inertial forces is well known in Newtonian theory and for our purpose it is convenient to start right away with their structure in special relativity. It is sometimes said that special relativity is not competent to deal with accelerated frames of reference for which general relativity must be used. This is not correct. What characterizes special relativity is its use of a *flat* (Minkowski) space-time. In this space-time any co-ordinate system can be used, although the fact that accelerated systems do not cover the whole of space-time in a nonsingular way can be a nuisance in practice.

We begin by writing down the equations of motion of a free particle in Minkoswki space-time in an inertial co-ordinate system. They are

$$m_0 \frac{\mathrm{d}^2 x^i}{\mathrm{d}s^2} = 0\,,$$

where m_0 is the rest-mass of the particle, the interval $\mathrm{d}s^2$ is given by

$$\mathrm{d}s^2 = g_{ij}\,\mathrm{d}x^i\,\mathrm{d}x^j$$

(summation convention used) and the metric tensor g_{ij} satisfies

$$g_{ij} = \begin{pmatrix} 1 & 0 & 0 & 0 \\ 0 & -1 & 0 & 0 \\ 0 & 0 & -1 & 0 \\ 0 & 0 & 0 & -1 \end{pmatrix} . \tag{1}$$

The velocity of the particle $\mathrm{d}x^i/\mathrm{d}s$ is a timelike vector, that is,

$$g_{ij} \frac{\mathrm{d}x^i}{\mathrm{d}s} \frac{\mathrm{d}x^j}{\mathrm{d}s} > 0 .$$

We now go over to a noninertial co-ordinate system x'^i by means of the transformation

$$x'^i = x'^i(x^0, x^1, x^2, x^3) .$$

The metric tensor g_{ij} transforms by the usual tensor transformation law (Einstein (1916)), and the equations of motion become

$$m_0 \frac{\mathrm{d}^2 x'^i}{\mathrm{d}s^2} + \begin{Bmatrix} i \\ j\,k \end{Bmatrix}' m_0 \frac{\mathrm{d}x'^j}{\mathrm{d}s} \frac{\mathrm{d}x'^k}{\mathrm{d}s} = 0 , \tag{2}$$

where the Christoffel brackets or three-index symbols $\begin{Bmatrix} i \\ j\,k \end{Bmatrix}'$ are given in terms of the g'_{ij} by

$$\begin{Bmatrix} i \\ j\,k \end{Bmatrix}' = \frac{1}{2} g'^{il} \left(\frac{\partial g'_{lj}}{\partial x'^k} + \frac{\partial g'_{lk}}{\partial x'^j} - \frac{\partial g'_{jk}}{\partial x'^l} \right) ,$$

and the interval $\mathrm{d}s^2$ is given by

$$\mathrm{d}s^2 = g'_{ij}\, \mathrm{d}x'^i\, \mathrm{d}x'^j \qquad (= g_{ij}\, \mathrm{d}x^i\, \mathrm{d}x^j) .$$

The equations of motion (2) express in an arbitrary co-ordinate system the co-ordinate-independent statement that the world-line of a free particle is a timelike geodesic of Minkowski space-time.

If we were given a metric tensor g_{ij} in an arbitrary co-ordinate system, we would need a means of telling whether it described a Minkowski space-time, that is, whether we could introduce an inertial frame in which the g_{ij} were reduced to the form (1) and the $\begin{Bmatrix} i \\ j\,k \end{Bmatrix}$ vanished everywhere. The necessary and sufficient condition for this to be possible is that (*)

$$(3)\qquad R^i{}_{jkl} \equiv \frac{\partial \begin{Bmatrix} i \\ j\ k \end{Bmatrix}}{\partial x^l} - \frac{\partial \begin{Bmatrix} i \\ j\ l \end{Bmatrix}}{\partial x^k} + \begin{Bmatrix} m \\ j\ k \end{Bmatrix}\begin{Bmatrix} i \\ m\ l \end{Bmatrix} - \begin{Bmatrix} m \\ j\ l \end{Bmatrix}\begin{Bmatrix} i \\ m\ k \end{Bmatrix} \delta = 0\,.$$

Here $R^i{}_{jkl}$ is the Riemann-Christoffel curvature tensor and its vanishing characterizes Minkowski space-time (except possibly for the topology in the large, which does not affect the present argument).

We see from this discussion that special relativity determines the structure of the inertial force field. Equation (2) shows that this force field is described by three-index symbols derived from a potential which is a symmetrical second-rank tensor. It is clear then that if we are to construct a field theory of inertial forces relating them to sources, *the potential of this field must also be a symmetrical second-rank tensor*, the simpler possibilities of a scalar or a vector potential are immediately ruled out. Equivalently we can say that the metric tensor g_{ij} which controls the inertial properties of matter must itself become a dynamical variable satisfying field equations which relate it to physical sources. In this way the geometry of space-time becomes « physicalized » (rather than as is sometimes said the physics becoming geometrized).

1·1.2. Field equations for the metric tensor. In setting up field equations for g_{ij} we must first decide how to describe its source. It is clear from (2) that the inertial force field $\begin{Bmatrix} i \\ j\ k \end{Bmatrix}$ acts on the energy-momentum tensor $m_0(\mathrm{d}x^j/\mathrm{d}s)(\mathrm{d}x^k/\mathrm{d}s)$ of the particle. Such a coupling would lead us to expect that the energy-momentum tensor acts back on the inertial-force field. It is precisely this back action which is missing in Newtonian theory where absolute space is unaffected by the matter on which it acts. Thus we assume that the source of the g_{ij} field is the energy-momentum tensor of matter or by an obvious extension of the argument of any field (such as the electromagnetic field) which has its own energy-momentum tensor. The correctness of this step is further guaranteed in Lagrangian field theory by the fact (BELINFANTE 1940; ROSENFELD, 1940) that the variational derivative of the Lagrangian density $\mathscr{L}$ with respect to g_{ij} is identically equal to the (symmetrized) energy-momentum tensor density $\sqrt{-g}T^{ij}$ or $\mathfrak{T}^{ij}$ of the matter or field:

$$\frac{\delta \mathscr{L}}{\delta g_{ij}} \equiv \mathfrak{T}^{ij},$$

where g is the determinant of g_{ij}.

(*) See any textbook on tensor analysis or general relativity.

We now ask how g_{ij} depends on the distance of the source. We can say immediately that it must be a long-range dependence, since the inertial behaviour of matter is not appreciably affected by its local environment. This question seems to have been studied first by NEWTON, who showed experimentally that the inertial mass of a body is not significantly changed if other bodies are brought nearby. This result is not decisive, however, since the externally applied force used in determining the mass may also be affected by the nearby bodies in a compensating manner. A somewhat similar remark applies to the recent attempts to detect an *anisotropy* in inertial mass, supposedly related to the anisotropy of the Milky Way (COCCONI and SALPETER, 1958; HUGHES *et al.*, 1960; SHERWIN *et al.*, 1960). Moreover, in this case, we would expect inertial effects to be isotropic *locally*, since in the local inertial frame g_{ij} will have the usual Galilean isotropic structure (as has been especially stressed by DICKE (1961*b*)). On the other hand, the anisotropy would be expected to show up *globally*, in that the local inertial frame would bear some special relationship to the Milky Way, and so the rest of the matter in the universe would have some anisotropic motions as seen from that frame.

A more decisive observational consideration comes precisely from the relation between the locally determined inertial frame and the pattern of motions of distant matter. NEWTON showed in his rotating bucket experiment that the rotation of the bucket had a negligible influence on the shape of the water surface, and so on the choice of the nonrotating reference frame. NEWTON himself illegitimately concluded from this that *no* matter in the universe was relevant for determining this frame. This error was pointed out by BERKELEY in 1721 (BERKELEY, 1721). He stressed that in such a frame the system of stars as a whole does not rotate. BERKELEY in fact believed that the centrifugal and Coriolis forces which arise in a rotating frame are *produced by the stars*, in the course of their rotation relative to that frame. MACH (1872, 1893) took the same view in 1872 and it was EINSTEIN (1918) who christened this view Mach's principle.

In 1896 a more precise experiment was carried out by B. and T. FRIEDLÄNDER (1896). They tried to detect centrifugal and Coriolis-type forces inside a heavy fast rotating flywheel, again without success. However, a more sensitive test is provided by the annual motion of the sun around the earth. If the sun were the dominant source of inertia one would expect, for example, that a Foucault pendulum which started off swinging towards the sun would remain swinging towards it, so that relative to the earth it would be dragged around once a year as well as once a day. In fact a Foucault pendulum does not behave in this way, and the local nonrotating frame follows the stars to an accuracy of a few seconds of arc per century (though to achieve this accuracy one must study the motion of the moon rather than of a Foucault pendulum) (SCHIFF, 1964).

This result rules out an inverse square law for the dependence of g_{ij} on distant masses, as we can see by considering the analogous problem of the brightness of the sun and the stars (Olbers' paradox (BONDI, 1960; SCIAMA, 1959)). The sun produces more light than all the other stars combined by a factor of the order of 10^7. Such a factor would be expected to apply to any inverse square effect (apart from a correction factor which could allow for the possibility that the amount of dark matter in the universe far exceeds the amount of bright matter. We shall see in the next Section that this correction factor is not less than 10^{-3}). We therefore conclude that if the distance dependence is a simple one, it must be at least as slow as the inverse first power. On the other hand if we make the dependence too slow we may face an Olbers-type divergence problem, even allowing for a Doppler cut-off associated with the expansion of the universe. We therefore provisionally adopt an inverse first power law. The relative importance of the sun in this case will be estimated later.

With the potential determined by an inverse first power law we have the familiar field-theoretical situation in which the potential satisfies a Poisson-type differential equation in the static case and a d'Alembertian-type in the general nonstatic case. However, we now face an unusual complication, because the g_{ij} here play a double role, namely, they are the variables on which the differential operator acts and they also enter into the structure of the differential operator itself, in place of the Galilean tensor that is used when the metric is not a dynamical variable. Moreover, the differentiated quantity must itself be a tensor. The problem of finding suitable field equations in this situation was beautifully solved by EINSTEIN, who pointed out that the Ricci tensor R_{jk} defined in terms of the Riemann tensor of (3) by

$$R_{jk} = R^i{}_{jki} \,,$$

has the general structure of a d'Alembertian operating on g_{ij}. If, in addition, we require that the source $\mathfrak{T}^{ij}$ should be conserved in the presence of inertial forces:

$$\frac{\partial \mathfrak{T}^{ij}}{\partial x^j} + \begin{Bmatrix} i \\ j\ k \end{Bmatrix} \mathfrak{T}^{jk} = 0 \,, \tag{4}$$

then we must adopt the field equations

$$E_{ij} \equiv R_{ij} - \tfrac{1}{2} R g_{ij} = f T_{ij} \,, \tag{5}$$

where the curvature scalar R is $g^{ij}R_{ij}$, and f is a coupling constant. The reason for the introduction of the extra term $\frac{1}{2}Rg_{ij}$ is, of course, that the contracted

Bianchi identities

$$\frac{\partial \mathscr{E}^{ij}}{\partial x_t} + \begin{Bmatrix} i \\ j\,k \end{Bmatrix} \mathscr{E}^{jk} = 0 ,$$

where

$$\mathscr{E}^{ij} = \sqrt{-g} E^{ij} ,$$

then ensure that the conservation equations are satisfied without further restriction. As is well known eqs. (5) are uniquely determined up to addition of the cosmical term λg_{ij} by the requirements that they contain no higher than second derivatives, that they are linear and homogeneous in these second derivatives, and that the divergence of the left-hand side vanishes identically (CARTAN, 1923).

One way of bringing out this uniqueness of Einstein's field equations is to attempt to construct field equations in flat space-time for a tensor potential coupled to the energy-momentum tensor. Let us try the equations (*)

$$\Box^2 \mathfrak{g}^{ji} = f \mathfrak{T}^{ij} ,$$

$$\frac{\partial \mathfrak{g}^{ij}}{\partial x^j} = 0 ,$$

$$\Box^2 A^i = J^i ,$$

where $\mathfrak{g}^{ij} = \sqrt{-g} g^{ij}$, in obvious analogy with Maxwell's equations

$$\partial A^i / \partial x^i = 0 ,$$

where the d'Alembertian $\Box^2 A_i = J^i$ is the flat space-time operator. However these equations for the inertial field lead to the conservation equation

$$\partial \mathfrak{T}^{ij} / \partial x^j = 0 ,$$

in analogy with $\partial J^i / \partial x^i = 0$, instead of with (4). To allow for the fact that inertial forces act on matter, we must introduce the energy-momentum tensor θ^{ij} of the inertial force-field itself (just as we introduce the Maxwell stress tensor to allow for the action of the electromagnetic field on matter). This new energy-momentum tensor is to be defined by the condition that

$$\begin{Bmatrix} i \\ j\,k \end{Bmatrix} \mathfrak{T}^{jk} = \frac{\partial \theta^{ij}}{\partial x^j} ,$$

so that the conservation eq. (4) becomes $(\partial/\partial x^j)(\mathfrak{T}^{ij} + \theta^{ij}) = 0$. We would

(*) The introduction of the scalar density $\sqrt{-g}$ facilitates our later comparison with Einstein's equations.

then be led to the equations

$$\Box^2 \mathfrak{g}^{ij} = f(\mathfrak{T}^{ij} + \theta^{ij}) ,$$

$$\frac{\partial \mathfrak{g}^{ij}}{\partial x^j} = 0 ,$$

which PAPAPETROU (1948) has shown to be equivalent to Einstein's equations. For some purposes this approach is more useful than the overtly geometrical one as it brings out the physical reason why the inertial field equations have to be nonlinear, namely, that the inertial force field acts as its own source. In addition, it makes the inertial field theory look as much as possible like other field theories. The first hint of this approach can be found in Einstein's original paper (1916), and since Papapetrou's work there have been further developments (GUPTA, 1957; FEYNMAN, 1957; THIRRING, 1961; HALPERN, 1963; WEINBERG, 1965). Nevertheless we shall not discuss this in detail here since, in an approach which stresses the role played by Mach's principle, there is really no room for a flat background metric.

1'2. *Estimation of the coupling constant and relation to gravitation.* – Our next step is to determine the value of the coupling constant f by imposing the requirement that the total potential g_{ij} due to all the matter in the universe should have the Minkowskian values in a local inertial frame. This will guarantee that in an accelerating frame the inertial force field $\left\{ {i \atop j\,k} \right\}$ due to the relative acceleration of this matter corresponds to the observed inertial force field.

A rigorous calculation of the total potential due to a given energy momentum tensor would involve the solution of the problem of *boundary conditions*—the second aspect ii) of Mach's principle. This problem has not yet been solved. However, we can make an estimate of f which is likely to be correct to within a factor of order unity by ignoring the nonlinear terms in Einstein's field equations. As we shall see, this rough estimate suffices for the drawing of a very important conclusion.

We can obtain this estimate by ignoring the stress terms in T_{ij} and considering just g_{00} and $T_{00} \sim \varrho$. We thus have

$$g_{00} \sim 1 \sim f \int \left[\frac{\varrho}{4\pi r} \right]_{\text{ret}} \mathrm{d}r .$$

Owing to the long-range of the $1/r$ potential, we can smooth out the distribution of distant matter and so take ϱ essentially uniform. We also disregard its possible change with time as we integrate along the past light-cone (*), but cut the integration off at $r = c\tau$ (τ the Hubble constant) to allow for the effects of the expansion of the universe. All these simplifications should still give us a result of the right general order.

Carrying out the integration we find

$$f \sim \frac{1}{\varrho\tau^2} . \tag{6}$$

The Hubble constant τ is known to about 30 percent, and is $\sim 10^{10}$ years. Unfortunately the mean density ϱ is not known with comparable accuracy. A detailed discussion is given in the next Section, where we find

$$10^{-30} < \varrho < 10^{-27} \text{ g cm}^{-3} .$$

By comparison with this uncertainty, the uncertainty in our calculation of g_{00} is likely to be unimportant. These values of τ and ϱ then give us the following range of possible values for the coupling constant f:

$$10^{-5} > f > 10^{-8} \cdot (\text{g} \cdot \text{s}^2)^{-1} .$$

This determination of f is important not only for its own sake but also because it enables us to calculate the perturbing effect of the annual motion of the sun on a Foucault pendulum at the earth. The resulting additional rotation rate ω is given approximately by

$$\omega \sim \frac{f M_\odot}{4\pi c^2 a} \Omega ,$$

where a is the distance of the sun and Ω is its period (1 year). Thus ω is given by

$$10 > \omega > 10^{-2} \text{ ''/century} .$$

This shows very clearly how with a $1/r$ law the importance of the sun is diminished as compared with a $1/r^2$ law. Even so, an ω of 10″ per century would be detectable. The observations show that the effect of the sun must be less than about 4″ per century (DE SITTER, 1916), so we can sharpen our previous estimate of f and obtain

$$4 \cdot 10^{-6} > f > 10^{-8} (\text{g s}^2)^{-1} . \tag{7}$$

In view of the roughness of our calculation of f in terms of ϱ, we cannot, of course, sharpen our estimate of ϱ from this consideration.

(*) No commitment to a particular cosmology is intended here. The assumption is made solely to obtain a quick estimate of f.

This perturbing effect of the sun arises from its acceleration relative to the local inertial frame, and depends inversely on the sun's distance. Our Poisson-type field equations also imply that there will be an inverse-square-type field produced by a static body. The contribution of distant matter to this field will vanish by symmetry, and the main source of this field at the earth will be the earth itself. This field will induce an acceleration α in a body at the surface of the earth where α is given by

$$\alpha = \frac{f M_E}{4\pi r^2} .$$

For the range of f given by (7) we have

$$3000 > \alpha > 15 \text{ cm} \cdot \text{s}^{-2} .$$

Now the observed acceleration of a body at the surface of the earth is 981 cm s^{-2} which lies within the predicted range of values. Moreover, this acceleration is observed to be the same for all bodies (ROLL *et al.*, 1964; SCHIFF, 1960; GOOD, 1961). We thus have striking confirmation of the correctness of Einstein's theory of inertial force fields. By a historical accident this acceleration was detected before it was predicted, and so it came to be described by a different name—gravitation. We thus arrive at Einstein's principle of equivalence of gravitational and inertial force fields. We also see that gravitation must be described, not in Newtonian fashion by a linear differential equation for a scalar potential, but by a nonlinear equation for a tensor potential. This equation leads to three small non-Newtonian effects which are in fair agreement with observation (the Einstein red shift, the bending of light and the perihelion motion of the planets) while further tests are under consideration (DICKE, 1964; BERTOTTI *et al.*, 1962; SCHIFF, 1961). However, what makes the theory convincing is not so much these small effects as the fact that our predicted α is close to the observed acceleration due to gravity g. An equivalent statement is that the calculated value of the coupling constant f is of the same order as the observed value of the Newtonian gravitational constant G.

If we accept the principle of equivalence we can use the observed value of G to determine f more precisely, and hence derive a value for the mean density ϱ which should be reliable to within a factor of order unity. We have

$$f/4\pi \sim G \sim 6.67 \cdot 10^{-8} \, (\text{g} \cdot \text{s}^2)^{-1} ,$$

so

$$f \sim 8 \cdot 10^{-7} \, (\text{g} \cdot \text{s}^2)^{-1} .$$

The corresponding value for ϱ, implied by (6) is

$$\varrho \sim 10^{-29} \, \text{g} \cdot \text{cm}^{-3} .$$

This value is some thirty times greater than recent estimates of the mean smoothed-out density of galaxies (OORT, 1958; ABELL, 1961). These estimates are rather uncertain, but it seems likely that Mach's principle and the principle of equivalence together require that the galaxies constitute only a small fraction of all the matter in the universe. Since these galaxies presumably condensed out of pre-existing gas, this result suggests that only a fraction of the gas has been used up in this way, the rest remaining in intergalactic space. If the gas actually exists, it would have great cosmological and astrophysical significance. Its likely physical state is examined in the next Section.

2. – Physical conditions in intergalactic space.

In the last Section we saw that Mach's principle leads to a relation of the form

$$4\pi G\varrho\tau^2 \sim 1 ,$$

between the Newtonian constant of gravitation G, the mean density of matter in the universe ϱ, and the Hubble constant τ. A precise relation was not derived because we could not integrate exactly the nonlinear inertial-gravitational field equations of Einstein. However, we can construct a heuristic argument which leads to a precise relation. According to this argument the parameter k in the Robertson-Walker cosmologies (BONDI, 1960) represents the excess of material energy over gravitational energy. If now we interpret Mach's principle as stating that the two forms of energy must be in exact balance since one arises from the other, then it follows that k has the value zero. In this case we have the exact relation (BONDI, 1960, p. 103)

$$\frac{8\pi}{3} G\varrho\tau^2 = 1 , \tag{8}$$

and the corresponding model universe is that of Einstein-de Sitter. Many cosmologists believe that the value of k and also of the cosmical constant λ should not be fixed by a priori arguments but should be determined directly from observation. In this case no prediction can be made for the value of ϱ. However, for the purposes of this lecture we shall adopt (8), which we believe to be implied by Mach's principle.

The same relation (8) also holds for the steady-state theory, as MCCREA (1951) has shown. Unfortunately the physical meaning of the quantity ϱ is not as clear-cut in this case as it is in the conventional theory, and different interpretations yield different values of the mean density of « ordinary » matter. All the interpretations so far suggested lead to a density of ordinary matter varying between the Einstein-de Sitter value (8) and 4 times this value. In this lecture we shall adopt the Einstein-de Sitter value, with an occasional reference to the implications of adopting a somewhat higher value.

For a Hubble constant of 10^{10} years we then have

$$\varrho = 2\cdot 10^{-29}\ \mathrm{g\ cm^{-3}}\,.$$

This theoretical density far exceeds the observational estimate (OORT, 1958; ABELL, 1961) of the smoothed-out density of galaxies, namely, $3\cdot 10^{-31}$ g cm^{-3} This latter estimate is very uncertain, and should probably be raised to allow for the existence of many faint galaxies, but it seems unlikely that the discrepancy can be completely resolved in this way. A more difficult question concerns the amount of matter contained in clusters of galaxies. There are strong indications (NEYMAN *et al.*, 1961) from the velocity dispersion in such clusters that the galaxies in them contribute only a fraction, perhaps ~ 10 per cent, of their total mass. If this is correct, the remaining 90 per cent of the matter in a cluster is probably in the form of ionized gas with a density $\sim 10^{-27}$ g cm^{-3}. The fraction of space occupied by clusters is rather uncertain, and it is possible that these clusters contribute most of the required theoretical over-all density of $2\cdot 10^{-29}$ g cm^{-3}. However, if the fraction 10 per cent of cluster material in the form of galaxies is at all representative, then in fact the clusters cannot contribute more than $\sim 3\cdot 10^{-30}$ g cm^{-3} to the total over-all density. We therefore assume for the purpose of this lecture that most of our theoretical density is in some other form. It has been suggested that this « missing matter » consists of a cosmic neutrino flux (FOWLER, this volume) of large masses collapsed into their Schwarzschild radius (HOYLE *et al.*, 1964), and of gravitational waves (WHEELER, 1962). However, we regard the most likely form as being an intergalactic gas. Since the galaxies have presumably condensed out of this gas, the relative concentration of gas and galaxies is determined by the efficiency of the condensation process. It does not seem a priori unreasonable that this efficiency is low, so that most of the matter is uncondensed. This point of view has the advantage of keeping the discussion in close contact with the astrophysical problem of the formation and evolution of galaxies and galaxy clusters. Moreover, as we shall see, such a hypothetical intergalactic gas is on the verge of being observable, and may indeed have already been observed.

We know from studies of our own galaxy that cosmic masses of gas have many different roles to play in astrophysics. They are likely to support significant magnetic fields and cosmic-ray fluxes. They exhibit intricate modes of energy interchange with compact luminous objects (stars) and intricate modes of instability. All these phenomena, and no doubt some new ones, are likely to have their counterparts in the intergalactic gas and in its relation to galaxies. In this lecture we have time to study in detail only one topic, the temperature and state of ionization of the gas. A more general discussion of the gas is given by SCIAMA (1964*c*).

The first point to note about the temperature of the intergalactic gas is that in the Einstein-de Sitter universe it must be very low unless the gas has been heated by the galaxies. The same is true for all evolutionary model universes that have developed from a highly condensed state. The reason is that at the early high-density stages matter and radiation would have been so strongly coupled as to have reached thermodynamic equilibrium in the time available. The matter and the radiation would then have cooled at the same rate until the density dropped to the point at which they became effectively decoupled. From this point on the matter must have cooled faster than the radiation. The reason is that in an adiabatic expansion the temperature T and volume V are related by

$$TV^{\gamma-1} = \text{const}\,,$$

where γ is the ratio of the specific heats. Now for dilute matter γ is approximately $\frac{5}{3}$ whereas for radiation $\gamma = \frac{4}{3}$. Thus

$$T_{\text{matter}} \propto \frac{1}{R^2}$$

$$T_{\text{rad}} \propto \frac{1}{R}\,,$$

where R is a typical length scale. During the expansion the radiation will remain in thermodynamic equilibrium despite the absence of work done against a piston—the red shift simply replaces the piston, as can be seen from the fact the black-body spectrum has the form $f(\nu/kT)$, while $\nu \propto 1/R$. Now the present black-body radiation temperature of space is certainly no greater than $\sim 3.5\ ^\circ$K (PENZIAS and WILSON, 1965), and so the temperature of the intergalactic gas must be less than this, in the absence of galactic heating. In the steady-state theory, on the other hand, there is the alternative possibility of *creation heating*, that is, matter coming into existence at an elevated temperature. We shall now examine what limits observation has placed on the possible kinetic temperature T of the intergalactic gas.

2·1. *The lower limit on the temperature of the intergalactic gas.*

2·1.1. Free-free absorption of low radio frequencies. The absorption coefficient of the intergalactic gas for radio waves of frequency ν is proportional to $n_e^2/\nu^2 T^{\frac{3}{2}}$, where n_e is the free electron density. Now distant radio sources are known which show no absorption down to 26 MHz (ERICSON and CRONYN, 1965) (it is difficult to observe from the ground at lower frequencies because of ionospheric absorption). This corresponds to less than 1 db absorption along a path $1.3 \cdot 10^9$ parsec in length through intergalactic space. If we were dealing with a fully ionized plasma, n_e would be $\sim 10^{-5}\ \text{cm}^{-3}$ and

$$T > 75\ °\text{K}.$$

If the gas were mainly neutral a weaker condition would hold.

2·1.2. HI absorption and emission at 21 cm. FIELD (1959, 1962), GOLDSTEIN (1963), DAVIES and JENNISON (1964), DAVIES (1964) have attempted to detect intergalactic neutral hydrogen (HI) by looking for both absorption and emission effects associated with the 21 cm line. The absence of detectable emission gives directly an upper limit on the neutral hydrogen concentration n_H:

(9) $$n_H < 2 \cdot 10^{-5}\ \text{cm}^{-3}.$$

The absence of detectable absorption gives the following relation between n_H and the spin temperature T_s °K which determines the relative populations of the two hyperfine states involved in the 21 cm transition

(10) $$n_H < 4 \cdot 10^{-8}\, T\ \text{cm}^{-3}.$$

FIELD has shown that if the gas is more than 42 per cent neutral T_s is mainly determined by Lyman-alpha radiation emitted by galaxies, and in that case he concludes that $T_s \sim 30$ °K. This would give a severe upper limit on n_H and so on n, inconsistent with our predicted value of n. However, FIELD further showed that if the gas is less than 42 per cent neutral the recombination Lyman-α radiation has the effect of pushing up T_s to the kinetic temperature T of the gas. In this case if $n_H = xn$, then

$$T > 250\, x\ °\text{K}.$$

This is as far as we can go by direct deduction from the observations. However, in view of the fact that the upper limit for n_H in (9) comes right in the range of densities we are considering, and that with this range (10) requires the gas to be at least 42 per cent ionized, we tentatively assume that the gas is in fact largely ionized. Assuming provisionally that it is pure hydrogen, its cooling time (owing to free-free and free-bound electronic transitions) is

(11) $$t_{\frac{1}{2}} \sim \frac{10^4 T^{\frac{1}{2}}}{n(1 + 3.8 \cdot 10^5/T)}\ \text{years}.$$

For $n \sim (1 \div 5) \cdot 10^{-5}$ cm^{-3} the cooling-time would be less than the Hubble time for $T < (10^4 \div 10^5)$ °K. Thus in this temperature-range a heat input would be required to maintain the ionization, and this input itself is likely to heat the gas to at least 10^4 °K (SPITZER, 1948). We thus arrive at the tentative conclusion that

$$T \geqslant 10^4 \text{ °K} .$$

Now such a hot gas would be thermally unstable (SCIAMA, 1964*c*; GOLD and HOYLE, 1959; FIELD, 1965; HUNTER, 1966), that is to say, regions of higher density than average would cool more rapidly than their surroundings to such an extent that the pressure within them would drop below the outside pressure. Such regions would accordingly become compressed and their density would increase further. This is an unstable situation and the regions would collapse and presumably eventually form galaxies. Since we require ~ 99 per cent of the matter in the universe not to be in the form of galaxies, the time-scale for the thermal instability must be at least of the same order as the Hubble time. Taking this time-scale to be of order $t_{\frac{1}{2}}$ as given in (11) we find

$$T \geqslant (10^4 \div 10^5) \text{ °K} , \tag{12}$$

with the larger lower limit corresponding to the larger values of n ($\sim 5 \cdot 10^{-5}$ cm^{-3}) given by some versions of the steady-state theory.

2·2. *The upper limit on the temperature of the intergalactic gas.*

2·2.1. The hot and lukewarm universes. It was suggested by GOLD and HOYLE (1959) that matter might be continuously created in the form of neutrons. When these neutrons decay the emitted electrons would have enough energy to heat the intergalactic gas to a temperature of about 10^9 °K. This would be an extreme case of what we have called creation heating. This suggestion is of particular interest not only for its identification of the form of the created matter, but also because at 10^9 °K the intergalactic gas would be in approximate hydrostatic equilibrium with the gas in clusters of galaxies ($T \sim 10^7$, $n \sim 10^{-3}$) and possibly even in galaxies themselves ($T \sim 10^4$, $n \sim 1$). Such a pressure balance throughout the universe would be of great astrophysical significance.

This hypothesis of a hot universe suffers from the difficulty that the cooling time $t_{\frac{1}{2}}$ of the gas at 10^9 °K would be about 10^{13} years, very much greater than the Hubble time of 10^{10} years. Thus no galactic condensations would be able to form. GOLD and HOYLE suggested that if a previous generation of galaxies were already present they might form a cold sink for the operation of a heat engine which would have extremely high efficiency owing to the large temperature difference involved. This heat engine could then cool the gas. However, they were unable to suggest a detailed mechanism for the operation of this heat engine, and it would appear to be difficult to resolve the problem in this way. Indeed we would prefer to reverse the argument and to suggest that an upper limit on the temperature of the intergalactic gas can be deduced from the requirement that the gas must be able to cool in a time comparable with the Hubble time, in order to form bound condensations. This condition gives us

$$T < (1 \div 4) \cdot 10^5 \ {}^\circ\mathrm{K} \, ,$$

according to the value chosen for n. Taken in conjunction with our previous lower limit (12) we arrive at a *lukewarm* universe (SCIAMA, 1964*c*).

2'2.2. The cosmic X-ray background. The free-free emission from an ionized intergalactic gas has a spectrum which is more or less flat up to a cut-off frequency related to the temperature T by $h\nu \sim kT$. Higher-frequency photons would be produced only by electrons in the Maxwell tail of the distribution. To avoid interference from the galaxy it is best to search for such free-free radiation at the highest possible frequencies, that is, in the X- or γ-ray region of the spectrum. As reported by GIACCONI (1965) an approximately isotropic flux of X-rays has been detected arriving at the earth in the $(3 \div 8)$ Å region, that is, in kilovolt X-rays. The corresponding temperature $(h\nu/k)$ is about 10^7 °K. Thus if the intergalactic gas were hotter than $\sim 10^7$ °K it would be emitting photons out to this X-ray region. However, the emission rate would be such that for $n \sim 10^{-5}$ cm^{-3} the expected flux of X-rays would be about 20 times greater than the observed flux (GOULD and BURBIDGE, 1963; FIELD and HENRY, 1964). A detailed calculation shows that to avoid this discrepancy we must have

$$T < 4 \cdot 10^6 \ {}^\circ\mathrm{K} \, .$$

It should be possible in the future to extend the X-ray observations out to longer wavelengths, and so either to detect the gas or to place a more stringent upper limit on T. The softest X-rays that can be used depends on the opacity of the galaxy. At high galactic latitudes observations out to 20 Å should be possible, and the limit might be extended even further, out to say 50 Å, in certain directions, where 21 cm maps indicate a minimum path length of the neutral absorbing hydrogen (GOULD and SCIAMA, 1964). A negative result at such a wavelength would imply

$$T \leqslant 4 \cdot 10^5 \ {}^\circ\mathrm{K} \, ,$$

an inequality which we expect to be satisfied according to the discussion in 2.2.1.

If the X-ray background has an extragalactic origin, as its isotropy and intensity suggest, its spectrum would give us information on the density of intergalactic neutral hydrogen. The reason is that such hydrogen is a strong absorber of X-rays. The absorption coefficient for wavelength λ is proportional to $(\lambda/\lambda_0)^3$, where λ_0 is the wavelength of the nearest absorption edge, in this case 912 Å (the threshold wavelength of the Lyman continuum). If no absorption is observed out to 50 Å, then the neutral hydrogen density must be less than about 10^{-31} g cm^{-3} (GOULD and SCIAMA, 1964). This would be a more stringent limit than that imposed by the absence of 21 cm absorption, although in the latter case effectively $\lambda \sim \lambda_0$. The reason for this weakness of the 21 cm absorption is that many atoms will be in the upper hyperfine level, so that stimulated emission will be important. The existence of so many excited atoms is a consequence of two facts: *a*) that the transition energy involved in the 21 cm line is so small ($5 \cdot 10^{-6}$ eV) that a background radiation temperature as low as 0.05 °K will excite many atoms, *b*) that the 21 cm transition is forbidden so that the atoms may be collisionally or radiatively excited in a time short compared with the lifetime of the upper state.

2.3. *The absorption of Lyman-alpha radiation by intergalactic neutral hydrogen.* – It is clear from the present discussion that the most powerful way of detecting intergalactic neutral hydrogen would be to use a transition for which $\lambda \sim \lambda_0$ and in which virtually all the neutral hydrogen atoms are in the ground state, that is, we need a permitted transition whose energy exceeds the energy of most of the background photons. Clearly we should use the Lyman transitions. The difficulty is that in these transitions λ lies in the range (912 ÷ 1216) Å, where the opacity not only of the earth's atmosphere but also of the galaxy is very large. Recently this problem has been ingeniously solved (SCHEUER, 1965*a*; GUNN and PETERSON, 1965) by making use of the large red-shift (~ 2) of 3C9 (SCHMIDT, 1965) (assumed here to be cosmological in origin). Radiation emitted by 3C9 with a wavelength somewhat less than 1216 Å will not be appreciably absorbed until it is red-shifted to 1216 Å (the Lyman-alpha wavelength). At this point the intergalactic neutral hydrogen would absorb it strongly. Thus the observed continuum of 3C9 should show absorption between the red-shifted and the unred-shifted wavelengths of the Lyman-alpha line, that is, in this case between 3666 Å and 1216 Å. In particular an absorption edge should be evident at 3666 Å. It so happens that one of the two observed spectral lines in 3C9 is at 3666 Å, that is, is the Lyman-alpha line itself. GUNN and PETERSON (1965) have measured Schmidt's spectrum, and have found that the continuum and the wing in the short-wavelength side of the line are depressed by about 40 per cent (*). We can get a quick estimate of the implications of this result by comparing it with our X-ray estimates of the previous Section. The absence of appreciable absorption at 50 Å corresponded to an upper limit of 10^{-31} g cm^{-3} for the density of intergalactic neutral hydrogen. The factor ~ 20 increase in wavelength to 1216 Å gives a factor $\sim (20)^3$ or $\sim 10^4$ in absorption cross-section. Thus the fairly small absorption found at 1216 Å corresponds to a density of about 10^{-35} g cm^{-3}. Detailed calculations (GUNN and PETERSON, 1965) show that in the Einstein-de Sitter universe $\varrho_H \sim 5 \cdot 10^{-35}$ g cm^{-3}, while in the steady-state universe $\varrho_H \sim 1.6 \cdot 10^{-35}$ g cm^{-3}.

We thus derive the remarkable result that if $\varrho \sim 2 \cdot 10^{-29}$ g cm^{-3} then only about one atom in 10^6 is neutral. Is this consistent with our previous estimate that T is in the range $(10^4 \div 4 \cdot 10^5)$ °K? The ionization level that would be maintained by collisions can be calculated as a function of the kinetic temperature of the gas if the collisional ionization and recombination cross-sections are known as functions of the energy of the incident electron. It is found that $n_p/n_H \sim 10^6$ for a temperature $\sim 3 \cdot 10^5$ °K in the steady state mode (REES and SCIAMA, 1966). Ultra-violet photons will be emitted during free-free and free-bound transitions, and so photoionization might be expected to alter the equilibrium value of n_H at a given temperature. However it turns out that photoionization is unimportant, for two reasons:

i) When n_H has the value 10^{-11} cm^{-3} the universe is almost transparent, so most ultra-violet photons will be red-shifted below the ionization threshold without having been observed.

ii) The photons that do eventually ionize an atom will not be absorbed immediately, but after a time $\sim \tau$. During this time the universe has expanded, so the photoionizations are spread over a larger volume and their effectiveness is consequently reduced.

We conclude that if $n \sim 10^{-5}$ cm^{-3}, T is likely to be $\sim 3 \cdot 10^5$ °K (**), which is close to the upper limit of our previous estimate. However if $n \sim 5 \cdot 10^{-5}$ cm^{-3}, a temperature $\sim 10^6$ °K would be necessary to produce the required level of ionization.

2'4. *Further effects of an ionized intergalactic gas.*

In **2**'1.1 we considered briefly the absorption effects of a ionized intergalactic gas at radio frequencies. If the temperature of the gas is about $3 \cdot 10^5$ °K, the « optical » depth of the gas only exceeds unity for frequencies

---

(*) This result was discussed at the *Miami Conference on Observational Cosmology* (Dec. 15th-17th 1965), and it appears possible that no depression is observable. In this case a temperature of at least $4 \cdot 10^5$ °K is required for a particle density of 10^{-5} cm^{-3}.

(**) See previous footnote.

below about 300 kHz, a region of the spectrum which has not yet been investigated. Since also the emission from the gas at this temperature would be hard to observe, the question arises: is it possible to detect this ionized gas directly, that is, not just through its neutral component?

Three possibilities have so far been suggested:

2·4.1. Thomson scattering. One of the well-known numerical coincidences of cosmology (BONDI, 1960, p. 60) is that the radius of the universe $c\tau$ divided by the classical radius of an electron e^2/mc^2 is roughly equal to the square root of the « number » of particles in the universe (that is, in a sphere of radius $c\tau$):

$$\frac{c\tau}{e^2/mc^2} \sim N^{\frac{1}{2}} (\sim 10^{40}) .$$

Writing $N \sim (4\pi/3) n (c\tau)^3$, we have

$$\frac{(c\tau)^2}{(e^2/mc^2)^2} \sim N \sim \frac{4\pi}{3} n (c\tau)^3 ,$$

or

$$c\tau \sim \frac{1}{n \cdot (4\pi/3)(e^2/mc^2)^2} .$$

Since the cross-section σ for Thomson scattering is $(8\pi/3)(e^2/mc^2)^2$, this coincidence implies that the ionized intergalactic gas in a Hubble radius has $\sim$ unit optical depth for Thomson scattering. Sources with large red shift z would thus be seriously affected (as has recently been stressed in (GUNN and PETERSON, 1965)). A straighforward integration shows that the optical depth p for a source with red shift z is given by

$$p = \tfrac{2}{3} n\sigma c\tau \{(1+z)^{\frac{3}{2}} - 1\} \qquad \text{Einstein-de Sitter model} ,$$

$$p = n\sigma c\tau \ln (1+z) \qquad \text{steady-state model} .$$

For 3C9 with $z \sim 2$, p has the values ~ 0.2, 0.1 for the Einstein-de Sitter and steady state models (with $n \sim 10^{-5}\ \text{cm}^{-3}$), respectively. The effect is thus beginning to be important for this value of z. As GUNN and PETERSON point out, the fact that the effect increases more rapidly with z for evolutionary universes than for the steady-state universe has the consequence that the red-shift apparent-magnitude relation for galaxies becomes a less sensitive tool for distinguishing between different cosmologies.

We might also note that the Thomson scattering cross-section is independent of frequency, and so the effect is as important for radio sources as it is for optical ones. The scattering might have an important influence on the radio source counts for sources with low flux densities, and must be taken account of in cosmological interpretations of these counts (see Sect. **4**).

2·4.2. Faraday rotation. Many extragalactic radio sources are plane polarized (BOLOGNA *et al.*, 1965) and the ionized intergalactic gas will contribute to the observed Faraday rotation of their plane of polarization (GARDNER and WHITEOAK, 1963). The size of this effect depends on the magnitude and scale of the intergalactic magnetic field, questions which are beyond the scope of this lecture. However, it is worth noting that with $n \sim 10^{-5}$ cm^{-3}, $H \sim 10^{-7}$ gauss (the value advocated by GINZBURG and SYROVATSKY (1964)) and a scale-length $\sim 10^{24}$ cm, the gas would produce a rotation measure ~ 200 rad/m^2 for a source with $z \sim 1$ (SCIAMA, 1964*c*). Typical observed rotation measures are much less than this, and the absence of any marked dependence of rotation measure on red shift suggests that the intergalactic field is unlikely to exceed about 10^{-8} gauss. A similar upper limit for the magnetic field holds if we follow FELTEN and MORRISON (1963) and attribute the observed X-ray background to inverse Compton photons produced by the scattering of starlight on intergalactic relativistic electrons. The electron flux required is about one per cent of the flux in our galaxy, and would produce synchrotron radiation in the intergalactic magnetic field. In order that this radiation should not exceed the estimated extragalactic radio background, we would again require $H < \sim 10^{-8}$ gauss (SCIAMA, 1964*c*; GOULD and BURBIDGE, 1965).

2·4.3. Dispersion. If any extragalactic radio sources have a variable intensity, it might be possible to detect a ionized intergalactic gas by the dispersion it would introduce (HADDOCK and SCIAMA, 1965). For $n \sim 10^{-5}$ cm^{-3} the plasma frequency ν_p of the intergalactic gas ~ 30 Hz. Radio waves of frequency $\nu > \nu_p$ would propagate through the gas with a time lag $\sim \frac{1}{2}\nu_p^2/\nu^2$ per unit time. For $\nu \sim 20$ MHz the fractional delay $\sim 10^{-12}$. The total propagation time for a source of large red shift is about 10^{10} years, so the delay at 20 MHz would be about 3 days. More local ionized regions would be expected to produce much less dispersion than this. Thus if a source varied on a time scale not too much longer than 3 days, it might be possible to detect the intergalactic gas.

At the time this idea was first worked out (July 1964) it was thought unlikely that sources would vary in the radio region on the required timescale, although the corresponding optical variations had been found for some quasi-stellar radio sources. However, radio variables are now known (see next Section). The chances of detecting dispersion are still unclear because

a) the sources appear to vary at high frequencies (>1000 MHz) only, where the dispersion is very small, *b*) the time-scale of the variations is rather long,

c) there may be frequency-dependent delays associated with the processes producing the variations.

If these difficulties can be avoided in the future it should be possible not only to detect the ionized intergalactic gas and to measure its density but also to distinguish between different cosmological models. The reason is that different models give a different relation between dispersion and red shift z. A straightforward calculation shows that the delay at an observed frequency ν is given by

$$\frac{1}{2}\frac{\nu_p^2}{\nu^2}\left(2\tau\{1-(1+z)^{-\frac{1}{2}}\}\right) \qquad \text{Einstein-de Sitter model},$$

$$\frac{1}{2}\frac{\nu_p^2}{\nu^2}\left(\tfrac{1}{2}\tau\{1-(1+z)^{-2}\}\right) \qquad \text{steady-state model},$$

where ν_p is the present value of the intergalactic plasma frequency. The expressions in round brackets differ by a factor ~ 2 at $z \sim 2$.

In the next Section we shall discuss the known radio variables and see whether there is any hope of avoiding the difficulties *a*), *b*) and *c*).

3. – Radio variables and their cosmological significance.

In February 1965 the Russian radio astronomer SHOLOMITSKY (1965) announced that the QSS CTA 102 (SANDAGE and WYNDHAM, 1965) varies by about 30 per cent at 940 MHz, the period being about 100 days. Now it was believed at that time that the angular diameter of the source is at least $(10^{-2})''$ (SLISH, 1963; WILLIAMS, 1963; Sect. 3·1). Since the source could hardly be larger than 100 light days (or the variations in the source would be smeared out (TERRELL, 1964)), SHOLOMITSKY concluded that it must be closer than 2 Mparsec, and might even be inside our galaxy. However, in April 1965 SCHMIDT (1965) reported that CTA 102 has a red shift of 1.037. This red shift is probably not gravitational in origin (GREENSTEIN and SCHMIDT, 1964), and if it is cosmological the distance of CTA 102 would be about 3 000 Mparsec (for a Hubble constant of 10^{10} years), 1500 times greater than Sholomitsky's upper limit. The behaviour of CTA 102 thus lends support to Terrell's (1964) suggestion that QSS's are inside or perhaps just outside our galaxy, their large red shifts signifying that they have velocities close to that of light relative to their immediate surroundings. This could be the case, if, for instance, they were expelled from the centre of our galaxy by a violent explosion which occurred a few million years ago. Recently, HOYLE and BURBIDGE (1966) have further explored this «local» hypothesis for the whereabouts of QSS's, and have pointed to the nearby galaxy NGC 5128 (*Centaurus A*) as a possible alternative seat of the explosion, on the basis of its clearly disturbed appearance.

In August doubt was cast on Sholomitsky's results by MOFFETT and MALTBY (1965*b*). They reported that CTA 102 did not vary appreciably at 970 MHz over a 3 year period ending about 2 years before Sholomitsky's observations began. It is, of course, possible that CTA 102 started to vary after MOFFETT and MALTBY completed their observations, and at the time of writing SHOLOMITSKY still believes that his results are essentially correct (private communication by SYROVATSKI). We must therefore wait for further observations to decide the question (*).

In the meantime there has been a second report of a varying QSS, this time the famous source 3C273. In May 1965 it was reported by DENT (1965) to have increased its flux density at 8000 MHz by about 40 per cent in the last 3 years. (DENT also found two other sources which may be varying, but the evidence in these cases was not so strong.) Dent's data appear to be reliable, and indeed they have recently been confirmed by MOFFETT and MALTBY (1965*a*) and by ADGIE *et al.* (1965). If the period of the radio variations is comparable with that of the optical variations, that is, $\sim$ 12 years (SMITH 1965) the size of the radio source cannot exceed 3 parsec. Now its angular diameter must exceed $\sim(3\cdot10^{-2})''$ (Sect. **3**.1) and so the source must be within 20 Mparsec. On the other hand if its red shift of 0.158 (SCHMIDT 1963) is cosmological its distance must be 470 Mparsec.

Our main aim in this lecture is to describe some possible models for 3 C 273 which would resolve this discrepancy while retaining the cosmological interpretation of the red shift. If this interpretation is correct, the existence of radio variables may also make possible the detection of ionized intergalactic gas, as we saw in Sect. **2**.4, *c*) of the last lecture. For this purpose, it will be necessary to understand the mechanism of the variations, so that frequency-dependent delays wich may occur in the source can be adequately allowed for. Thus models of varying radio sources have a double importance for us in this course.

3.1. *The angular diameters of* QSS'*s*. – One of the striking characteristics of QSS's is the smallness of their angular diameters. In many cases they are too small to be measured even by the Jodrell Bank-Malvern link (ADGIE *et al.* 1965) which can resolve sources down to 0.1″. In such cases the only information that can be obtained is from the presence or absence of *synchrotron self-absorption* in the source. This consideration sometimes gives an actual

(*) Meanwhile DENT has reported at the *Miami Conference on Observational Cosmology* (Dec. 15th-17th, 1965) that CTA 102 has not varied appreciably in the period since Sholomitsky's observations were completed.

value for the angular diameter, but usually gives a lower limit. The detailed theory of synchrotron self-absorption has been worked out by TWISS (1958) and LE ROUX (1961), and applied to actual sources by SLISH (1963) and WILLIAMS (1963). For our purposes it is sufficient to give a simplified discussion.

The brightness temperature $T_b(\nu)$ of a radio source is defined in terms of flux density $S(\nu)$ and (small) angular diameter θ by

$$kT_b = \frac{2}{\pi}\frac{c^2}{\nu^2}\frac{S(1+z)}{\theta^2},$$

where k is Boltzmann's constant and z is the red shift of the source. At high radio frequencies kT_b is usually much less than the energy E of the electrons mainly responsible for the high-frequency radiation and so the source is transparent. However, T_b usually increases with decreasing frequency, while E decreases. For a relativistic gas in thermal equilibrium at temperature T the mean energy per particle is $3\,kT$, so we can define an effective temperature $T(\nu)$ for the nonthermal radiating electrons as $E(\nu)/3k$ where $E(\nu)$ is given by the synchrotron formula

$$E = \gamma m_0 c^2 = m_0 c^2 \left(\frac{\nu(1+z)}{\nu_L}\right)^{\frac{1}{2}},$$

and ν_L is the Larmor frequency. Most radio sources have an electron energy-spectrum of the familiar cosmic-ray power-law type, for which most of the radiation at frequency ν is produced by electrons with energy close to E. It will therefore be a good approximation to say that when the frequency is low enough for T_b to become comparable with T self-absorption will be important.

For all lower frequencies we must have $T_b = T$. This requires that

$$\frac{2}{\pi}\frac{c^2}{\nu^2}\frac{S(1+z)}{\theta^2} = \frac{1}{3}m_0 c^2 \left(\frac{\nu(1+z)}{\nu_L}\right)^{\frac{1}{2}}. \tag{13}$$

Thus in the self-absorbing region we have

$$S \propto \nu^{2.5},$$

whereas in the transparent region we have

$$S \propto \nu^{-\alpha},$$

with α usually not less than zero.

In the transparent region we have $T_b > T$, and so at such frequencies, θ must exceed the value given by (13). Thus any observed absence of self-absorption, manifested by a departure from the $\nu^{2.5}$ spectrum, gives us a lower limit on the angular diameter. This limit is

$$\theta \geqslant 14\, S^{\frac{1}{2}} H^{\frac{1}{4}} \nu^{-\frac{5}{4}} (1+z)^{\frac{1}{4}}\,, \tag{14}$$

with θ in seconds of arc, S in flux units (1 flux unit is 10^{-26} w$\cdot$m^{-2}(Hz)$^{-1}$), H in gauss and ν in MHZ. The only quantity in (14) which is not directly measurable is the magnetic field H, and fortunately the dependence on H is rather weak. Thus estimates of H based on minimizing the energy requirements of the source, as described by BURBIDGE (this volume) should be adequate for determining a lower limit on θ.

SLISH and WILLIAMS used (14) to find lower limits on θ for several radio sources, including CTA 102. In this case they took $H \sim 10^{-3}$ G and used the fact that the spectrum of CTA 102 (CONWAY, KELLERMANN and LONG 1963) shows no self-absorption down to about 500 MHz. They thus obtained $\theta > 10^{-2}{}''$ the value quoted at the beginning of this Section. Similarly 3 C 273 shows no self-absorption down to 200 MHz, and for $H \sim 10^{-3}$ G we find $\theta > (3\cdot 10^{-2})''$, a value which was also quoted earlier. We have seen that these limits on the angular diameter are much larger than expected for the varying sources, and the most obvious explanation is that these sources are composite. On this hypothesis the varying region has an angular diameter less than the limit (14), its self-absorption not showing up in the spectrum because of the presence of a larger nonvarying component which dominates the spectrum at low frequencies. In the remainder of this Section we shall investigate some composite models, but it seems worth listing below some other possible explanations of the discrepancy. Preliminary studies suggest that none of them is likely to be correct (except perhaps 3)).

1) The variations may be produced outside the source by irregularities in the intervening medium.

2) If the electrons were radiating coherently, our discussion of self-absorption would break down and the angular diameter could be less than (14).

3) The source may not be radiating by the synchrotron mechanism.

4) The determination of the size of the source would be wrong if the variations were not in phase over the whole object, but had been triggered by an influence moving close to the speed of light, *e.g.* by a flux of relativistic particles. This would require a special geometry in the source.

3·2. *Composite models for radio variables.* – An attempt to construct a composite model for CTA 102 has been made by REES and SCIAMA (1965*a*) but in this case the discrepancy to be explained is so large than the attempt was not very successful. It was found necessary to adopt a special geometry for the smaller component, and then to assume that it had a special orientation with respect to the line of sight. The probability of the source having such a special orientation is very small. It seems advisable therefore to wait for the observational decision on whether this source does in fact vary before pursuing this question further theoretically.

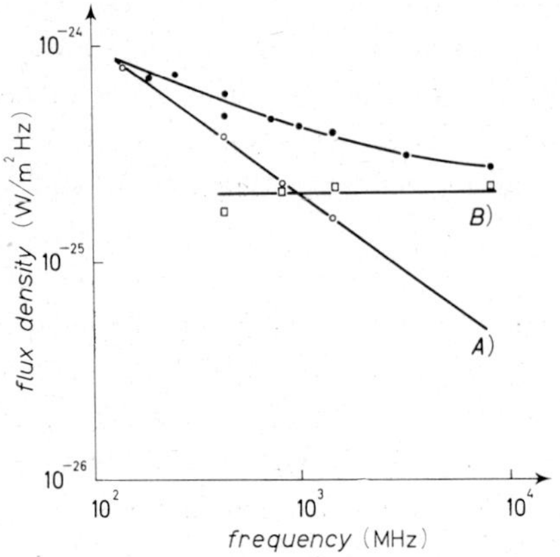

Fig. 1. – Components of 3 C 273.

The discrepancy for 3 C 273 is much smaller, however, and in this case REES and I were able (1965*b*) to construct several reasonable composite models, In fact this source is already known to be composite and to consist of a jet (3 C 273 A) and a quasi-stellar component (3 C 273 B). The spectra of these components are shown in Fig. 1 which is taken from an article by DENT and HADDOCK (1965). DENT's (1965) observations of the variations are shown in Fig. 2. They do not distinguish between components A and B but since at 8000 MHz A is much weaker than B, the amplitude of the variations suggests that it is B (the QSS) that is varying. Moreover B is known to vary optically (SMITH 1965, SANDAGE 1964)).

Now, as we have seen, the absence of self-absorption in the spectrum of 3 C 273 B down to 200 MHz implies that most of the radiation at these lower frequencies comes from a region with an angular diameter exceeding $(3\cdot10^{-2})''$. An attempt by HAZARD, MACKEY and SHIMMINS (1963) to measure the angular diameter at a lunar occultation led to a value of 0.5″ (see also SCHEUER (1965*b*)). However, the resolution set by the receiver characteristics is 0.3″, so that it is not certain that the source has in fact been resolved. Indeed a recent report from the Jodrell Bank-Malvern interferometer link-up (ADGIE *et al.* 1965) suggests that 3 C 273 B is actually double, with a component spacing of 0.4″, the individual components being less than 0.1″ across. These results would be consistent with the lower limit of $(3\cdot10^{-2})''$ derived above.

If the red shift of 3 C 273 is cosmological, the varying region cannot have an angular diameter exceeding $(10^{-3})''$. We shall thus assume that either one of the components of 3 C 273 B is at least $(3\cdot10^{-2})''$ across and the other less than $(10^{-3})''$ across, or that at least one of them is of the core-halo type with corresponding angular sizes. We now consider the simplest possible of such composite models.

Model I. This model consists of a source of angular diameter $<(3\cdot10^{-2})''$ and (roughly constant) flux density ~ 25 flux units down to at least 200 MHz, and a varying source of angular diameter $(1.3\cdot10^{-3})''$ (corresponding to a linear diameter of 3 parsec), and at minimum a flux density ~ 2.5 flux units down to the frequency ν_a at which self-absorption sets in.

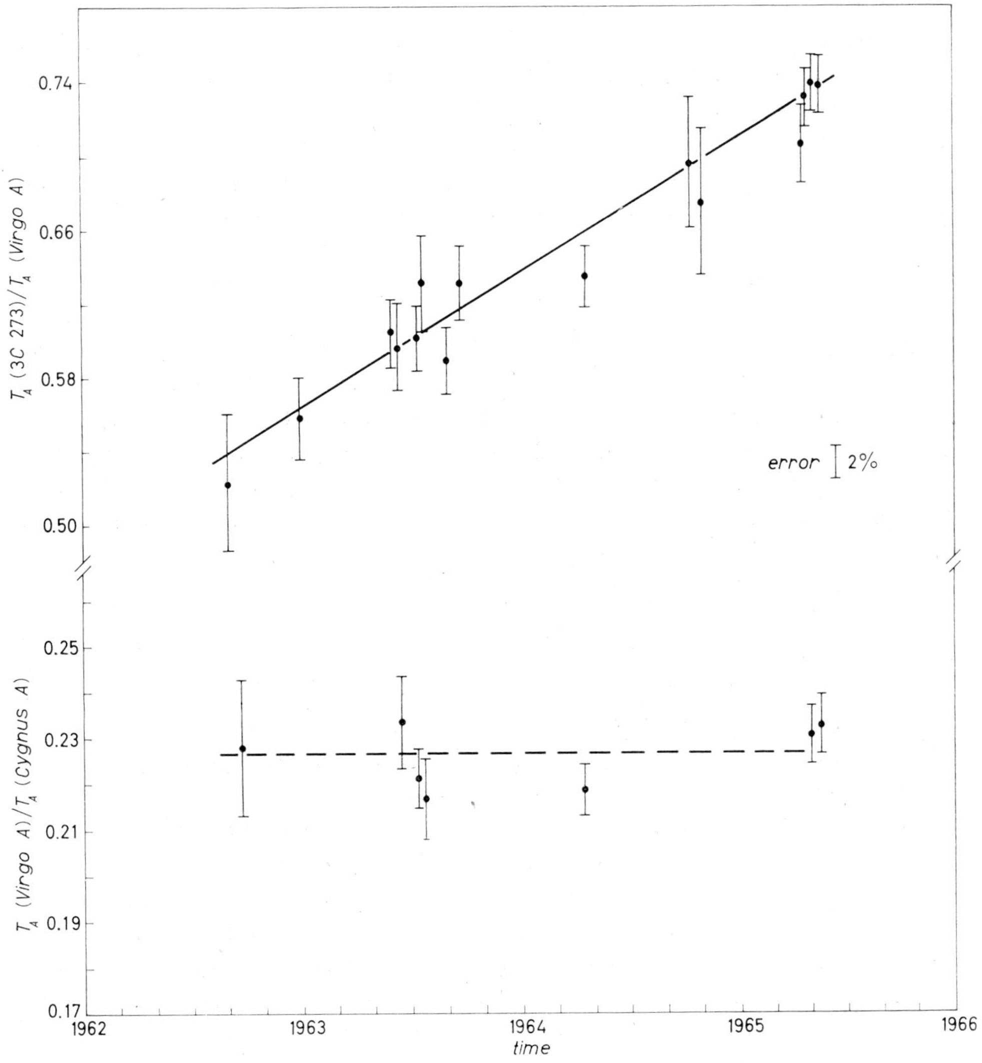

Fig. 2. – Observed radio variation of 3 C 273 (full line) (the broken line shows the observed ratio of *Virgo* A to *Cygnus* A).

Such self-absorption would not show up in the observed spectrum of this composite source. For a magnetic field H gauss in the central source, $\nu_a \sim 4000\, H^{\frac{1}{5}}$ MHz. For simplicity we assume that the central source varies because of an increase in its relativistic electron flux, while its angular diameter and magnetic field are unchanged. If the total flux density of the source is doubled at high frequencies at maximum, the flux from the central source must increase by a factor ~ 10. Thus the frequency ν_b at which self-absorption sets in at maximum is given by $(\nu_b/\nu_a)^{2.5} \sim 10$, so $\nu_b \sim 10\,000 H^{\frac{1}{5}}$ MHz.

We can now predict the time variations that would be observed at various frequencies. For simplicity we take the central source to vary sinusoidally at high frequencies. For $\nu < \nu_b$ no self-absorption occurs, so the observed variation would be sinusoidal. In the intermediate range $\nu_b < \nu < \nu_a$ the flux density would at first increase sinusoidally, but when it reaches the level at which it would be self-absorbed at that frequency the increase would be cut off, and the flux density would remain constant until it decreases again in the second half of the cycle. For $\nu > \nu_a$ the variations would be negligible.

A lower limit on H (whose value has not yet been specified) can be obtained if we require that the energy density of relativistic particles shall not exceed the magnetic density. If only $\sim 1\%$ of the total energy is in the electrons, we find that the field strength cannot be much less than 1 G. If $H = 1$ G ν_a and ν_b have the values ~ 4000 and $\sim 10\,0000$ MHz respectively, and the expected variations at 8000 MHz are large enough to account for the observations. Our estimates for ν_a and ν_b are only rough, but they indicate what might be expected, and the measurement of their values and of the variations at intermediate frequencies would be a useful test of the model and would provide considerable information about the structure of the source. For first steps in this direction see Maltby and Moffet 1965, Adgie *et al.* 1965.

It is not known how electrons attain relativistic energies in radio sources. The generation process may occur throughout the volume of the source, or the electrons may be ejected from a massive object at its centre. It is easily seen that the electrons must be produced by a mechanism of the former kind if the source in fact resembles Model I. The reason is that the lifetime of an electron which radiates at, say, 10^4 MHz in a field of 1 G is only $\sim 5 \cdot 10^5$ s, which is much less than the time taken to cross the source, even for an electron moving at the speed of light. If such an electron were ejected from the centre it would not reach the edge, unless it were emitting radiation at a frequency at which the source was opaque. Thus for frequencies exceeding ν_a our discussion of the variations will be incorrect. To allow for this we now introduce

Model II. In this model we assume that the electrons are all generated in a very small region (with diameter > 0.1 parsec), which presumably contains a massive object. As in Model I, nearly all the flux at frequencies $> \sim 4000$ MHz is assumed to come from a larger region, and we only concern ourselves with an intense spherically symmetric region with radius ~ 1 parsec, in which the variable higher-frequency radio flux is supposed to originate. We assume that $H \sim 1$ G throughout this region, and that its radio emission has a flux density $S(\nu)$ which may be variable. For each ν we can determine the minimum radius

$R(\nu)$ of a sphere from which $S(\nu)$ could come, if it in fact comes from a region which is opaque at all frequencies up to ν. We find that $R(\nu) \sim 0.3\big(S(\nu)\big)^{\frac{1}{2}}(\nu/10^4)^{-1.25}$ when S is measured in flux units and ν in MHz. This radius can be compared with the distance $r(\nu)$ which an electron radiating at frequencies $\sim \nu$ would travel in its lifetime, assuming that it moves with speed $\sim c$. This is $\sim 5\cdot 10^{-2}\cdot \cdot(\nu/10^4)^{-\frac{3}{2}}$ parsec. If $R(\nu) < r(\nu)$, electrons moving outward from the centre cannot radiate freely without producing a radiation field whose brightness temperature at frequency ν is higher than their kinetic temperature. Therefore they will conserve most of their energy until they reach a distance $\sim R(\nu)$ from the centre, where they can radiate freely.

The available data do not enable us to specificy the flux density of the core precisely, but it is consistent with the observations to take $S(\nu)$ to be $10 \div 30$ flux units in the frequency range from 5000 up to $\sim 10^5$ MHz. $R(\nu)$ is then several times greater than $r(\nu)$ throughout this range, and so we conclude that the radiation at frequency ν comes from the surface of a sphere of radius $R(\nu)$.

If electrons are ejected from the centre at a steady rate, $S(\nu)$ and $R(\nu)$ will adjust themselves to values which depend on the energy spectrum of the input electrons, and the flux of the source will be constant. If, however, the rate of input of electrons alters, $R(\nu)$ (and consequently $S(\nu)$)) will change after the lapse of an interval of the order of the time for light signals to travel a distance $R(\nu)$. Thus changes in the behaviour of the massive object will cause changes in the radio flux. The maximum rate of increase of flux will be attained if $R(\nu)$ expands with speed $\sim c$. An increase of $S(8.10^3)$ from 2.5 to 25 flux units, which corresponds to an increase in $R(8.10^3)$ from ~ 0.6 to ~ 1.9 parsec, could therefore certainly occur rapidly enough to explain Dent's observations. We can also predict, on the basis of this model, that more rapid variations could occur at higher frequencies. Furthermore, if a sudden change in the rate of injection of particles produces changes in $S(\nu)$ at different frequencies, we would expect to observe the variations at higher frequencies before those at lower (even in the absence of intergalactic dispersion).

We have seen that, if the core emits a significant amount of radiation at say, 10^5 MHz, this radiation must come mainly from a sphere which is opaque up to that frequency. The total energy density of all the radio frequency radiation up to 10^5 MHz within it will be $\sim 6\cdot 10^{-3}$ erg/cm^3 (compared with $\sim 10^{-6}$ erg/cm^3 within Model I), and this very high value suggests that inverse Compton scattering might be important. The Compton lifetime of an electron of energy $\gamma m_0 c^2$ in this radiation field is $8\cdot 10^9/\gamma$ s. If $S(10^5) \sim 25$ flux units, $R(10^5) \sim 0.1$ parsec, and the time which an electron takes to drift out of this sphere is $\sim 2\cdot 10^7$ s if its outward velocity $\sim c/2$. But the electrons radiating at 10^5 MHz have $\gamma \sim 300$, and so their Compton lifetime is of the same order. The most energetic photons would result from the scattering of 10^5 MHz photons by electrons with $\gamma \sim 300$, and their frequency would be (FEENBERG and PRIMAKOFF 1948) $\sim 10^{10}$ MHz, which is in the ultra-violet range. Photons of lower energy (including the whole visible range) would be produced, and the spectrum of the scattered radiation would have a low-energy cut-off at a frequency depending on the smallest value of γ represented in the electron energy spectrum. The energy radiated by this process in the visible range may well be greater than that of the synchrotron radio emission. The exact relative importance of the Compton and synchrotron losses is very sensitive to the high-frequency cut-off in the radio spectrum (which we have taken as 10^5 MHz), to the value of H, to the precise position where the electrons are accelerated, and to their mean rate of outward drift. It would therefore clearly not be worthwhile to base an exact calculation on this crude model.

The foregoing rough arguments do, however, suggest that at least a part of the visible light emitted by 3 C 273 B may have been produced by Compton scattering. Moreover, such a hypothesis woul provide a natural explanation for the observed optical fluctuations of the source, since, if electrons are accelerated in the massive object in irregular bursts, there will be variations in the scattered light. Nearly all of the scattering occurs in a region of radius ~ 0.1 parsec (since not only the radiation energy density, but also the particle density, is much higher near the centre). Therefore fluctuations with time-scales of the order of months, or even less, may occur, and these are in fact observed (SANDAGE 1964). The long-period variations (~ 12 years) in the optical luminosity may also arise from periodic variations in the rate of injection of electrons, which, as we have already seen, can produce the observed variation at radio frequencies. This model therefore suggests that the radio and the long-period optical variations may be connected.

The increase in the radio flux observed by DENT coincided with a decrease in the optical luminosity, which had the most recent of its 12-yearly maxima in 1962. But according to this model one would expect periodic radio variations to lag (perhaps by several years) behind the variations at the centre which cause them, so this fact also accords with our model, and suggests that the radio variations, when they are been observed for longer, will also turn out to have a period ~ 12 years.

The visible light from 3 C 273 B is unpolarized (MOROZ and YESIPOV 1963) whereas the radio flux (at ~ 3000 MHz) is $\sim 3\%$ polarized (MORRIS and BERGE 1964). It will not be possible to find out whether the central part of the source is polarized at radio frequencies until the extent to which the degree of polarization changes when the flux varies has been studied. However even if the radio flux from the core were polarized (implying large-scale uniformity in the direction of H), it would not follow that the scattered visible light must appear polarized, since it is mainly produced in an extremely opaque region where the radio frequency radiation will not be polarized even if the field is uniform.

It has been assumed in the foregoing that H does not change significantly when the density of the relativistic particles alters. This will be a good approximation if the magnetic energy is greater than the particle energy (a strength of 1 G is sufficient). The field is presumably « anchored » to the massive object.

It should be emphasized that the Compton losses are significant in this model mainly because of the occurrence of synchrotron self-absorption, which prevents the electrons from radiating away their energy as fast as they otherwise would. Any electrons which are accelerated to high energies ($\gamma < 300$, say), and which therefore emit synchrotron radiation at frequencies which can escape freely from the source, will lose their energy in a time much shorter than the Compton lifetime, so they will contribute to the radiation at high radio frequencies ($> 10^5$ MHz), rather than in the far ultra-violet ($> 10^{10}$ MHz).

Model III. The first two models have taken no account of the fact that lines are present in the optical spectrum of 3 C 273 B. According to GREENSTEIN and SCHMIDT (1964) these lines could be produced by gas of density $\sim 10^7$ particles/cm^3, temperature $\sim 2 \cdot 10^4$ °K and mass $\sim 10^5\, M_\odot$. Though this gas need not radiate all the optical continuum, it must be incorporated in a complete model of the source. The model which we shall now describe indicates one way in which this can be done.

If the gas were in the form of a uniform spherical cloud, its diameter would be $\sim \frac{1}{2}$ parsec, and it would be opaque to light of all frequencies because of scattering by free electrons. It would therefore be difficult to account for the observed flucutations in optical luminosity with a time-scale of a few months since if the variable flux were emitted by a small region within the cloud its variations would be smeared out and would not be observed. This difficulty would be eased if the density within the cloud were nonuniform, or if it had a filamentary structure, but there would remain the problem of feeding energy into the gas to balance its losses.

In an alternative configuration, suggested by SHKLOVSKY (1965), the gas is distributed in a thin spherical shell. We shall adopt this suggestion, and show that a model can be constructed on the basis of which the radio variations, and both the long and short period optical variations, can be explained.

If the radius of the shell is taken as $4 \cdot 10^{18}$ cm, and its density as $\sim 10^7$ particles/cm^3 its thickness will be $\sim 10^{17}$ cm if its total mass is $\sim 10^5\, M_\odot$. The observed broadening of the spectral lines places an upper limit of ~ 1500 km/s on the velocity of the shell if it is expanding. If there is a mass of $\sim 10^9\, M_\odot$ at its centre, a field of ~ 1 G would be strong enough to prevent the shell collapsing. Scattering by free electrons would be unimportant at all frequencies. The shell will be transparent to most photons of optical frequency, but will be opaque to radio waves at all frequencies below $\sim 10^5$ MHz because of free-free absorption. The observed radio flux must therefore originate outside the shell.

The gas in the shell would produce the observed line emission, and would radiate at a rate $\sim 10^{46}$ erg/s, mainly at visible wavelengths. Its thermal energy content is insufficient to maintain this rate of energy loss for more than a few weeks, and so it must be absorbing energy at an equal rate from the interior. Since the shell absorbs radio waves, intense but unobserved radio radiation may exist in the spherical region within it, and this suggests the possibility that the shell may be absorbing enough energy in the form of radio waves to compensate for its losses in the visible range. This would require the production of $\sim 10^{46}$ erg/s at frequencies below $\sim 10^5$ MHz, which is ~ 30 times as great as the observed power radiated in this frequency range. However such a high rate of energy production is not unreasonable since a sphere within which synchrotron self-absorption were taking place at all frequencies up to 10^5 MHz would need to have a radius of only ~ 0.8 parsec (little more than half the radius of the shell) to emit $\sim 10^{46}$ erg/s. Alternatively the required amount could be produced if the whole interior were opaque up to $\sim 7 \cdot 10^4$ MHz. The exact situation within the shell will depend on the energy spectrum of the electrons injected into it, but a sufficiently high rate of energy generation will be achieved if relativistic electrons with $\gamma < 300$ are produced at a rate $\sim 10^{46}$ erg/s. We must assume that there is a cut off in the electron energy spectrum for $\gamma > 300$, since otherwise there would be intense radiation at frequencies above 10^5 MHz which would excape through the shell and produce observable radiation with a higher flux-density than is observed.

The observed radiation at frequencies below 10^5 MHz (apart from the component which comes from the halo) is, according to this model, emitted outside the shell by electrons which have excaped from the interior. An electron ejected from the massive object at the centre will be absorbing and emitting radiation at the same rate until it approaches the shell. Since the synchrotron lifetime of the electrons (in the absence of self-absorption) is of the order of the time which they take to pass through the shell, most electrons will lose their energy before reaching the exterior. Thus their radiation will not be observed directly, but will simply heat the gas. However since the power of the observed radio radiation is much less than the power required to heat the gas, the observed radio flux would be produced even if only a few per cent of the electrons succeeded in escaping. Despite the high density of the gas in the shell, an electron passing through it has a 90 % chance of reaching the exterior without losing a significant amount of energy in ionization and collisional losses. If the field ~ 1 G extends outside the shell, these electrons will radiate away their energy before they have travelled a further distance ~ 0.1 parsec unless self-absorption occurs outside the shell as well. Such self-absorption will occur at sufficiently low frequencies, though the situation is somewhat complicated by the fact that the electrons can radiate energy inwards into the shell.

The production of the visible light is more complicated. Much of it, both in spectral lines and in the continuum, comes from the gas in the shell. However Compton scattering may also, as in Model II, produce radiation at optical frequencies. The radio radiation energy density in the volume enclosed by the shell is $\sim 2\cdot 10^{-3}$ erg/cm³ if synchrotron self-absorption occurs at frequencies up to $\sim 7\cdot 10^{4}$ MHz, and the corresponding Compton lifetime of an electron is $2\cdot 10^{10}/\gamma$ s. The highest-energy electrons whose synchrotron losses are balanced by self-absorption have $\gamma \sim 250$, and their Compton lifetimes are of the same order as the time they would take to travel outwards from the centre to the shell. The Compton losses therefore are significant, though their exact magnitude is highly sensitive to the precise model adopted. The frequencies of the scattered photons will, as in Model II, be mainly in the visible and near-ultra-violet, and most photons will escape through the shell, though those whose frequencies correspond to intense spectral lines may be absorbed. Compton scattering of radio frequency radiation outside the shell will be insignificant.

We now consider how the observed variations in flux can occur in this model. We discuss first the long-period variations. If there were fluctuations with a time scale ~ 12 years in the rate of production of relativistic particles at the centre, there would be changes in the radiation density in the sphere enclosed by the shell, and a consequent change in the temperature of the gas. The rate of radiation of visible light by the shell would therefore alter. There would also be changes in the rate at which electrons escape through the shell, and consequently in the observed radio flux. Variations with period less than, say, 5 years would be partly smeared out and so could not have a large amplitude.

The observed short-period fluctuations in the optical luminosity have a time scale of a few months, and obviously cannot be produced in the shell, which has a radius of ~ 4 light years. In Model II they were attributed to the inverse Compton effect. Since we have shown that light will be produced by Compton scattering in this model also, a similar explanation might be possible here. This would require the scattering to occur in a region smaller than a few light months in radius. However, the scattering will not be concentrated in such a small region as in Model II, where the radiation energy density was high enough for scattering to be significant only within a space of radius ~ 0.1 parsec. Nevertheless if all the electrons are ejected from a massive object, their number density will be higher near the centre, and the amount of scattering will be greater there even if the radiation density is no higher. Consequently the variations in the component of the optical continuum produced by the Compton effect may be sufficiently rapid to account for the observed variations with time scales of a few months.

We note that whereas the line strengths will alter with the slow period ~ 12 years, it would be inconsistent with this model for them to be involved in the rapid fluctuations in optical luminosity. We understand that attempts are currently being made to see whether the lines do in fact vary in intensity. This feature of our model will thus soon be tested.

If we could construct a complete model of this kind, we would be able to calculate the expected phase lag between the variations in luminosity at optical frequencies and the related radio variations. However, we lack sufficient information to enable us to do this. To illustrate the complexity of the problem we enumerate some of the factors which would determine the magnitude of the lag.

1) The variations in particle density and radiation energy density propagate outwards with different velocities.

2) The phase delay of the radio variations will depend on whether self-absorption is taking place outside the shell at the frequency of observation. If it is taking place the observed flux would come from the surface of a sphere with radius greater than 1.5 parsec, rather than from just outside the shell, thus increasing the lag of the radio variations. At 8000 MHz, the frequency of Dent's observations, self-absorption would occur if more than ~ 14 flux units of the observed flux density were coming from the compact source (rather than from the halo). Since the observed variations amount to 10 flux units (and this flux cannot come from the halo) it is likely, though not certain, that self-absorption is in fact occurring.

3) The sense in which the emission rate of the gas in the shell varies as additional radio energy falls on it must be known.

4) The relative intensity of the light produced by the inverse Compton effect and the light emitted by the shell must be known. These two components will have the same period, but may be out of phase with one another. The times at which maxima in the resultant optical luminosity occur will thus depend on the phase lag between the two components, and on the ratio of the amplitude of their variations.

3·3. *Conclusions.* – This discussion shows that existing observations do not suffice to determine a well-defined working model of 3 C 273 B nor to assess with certainty whether intergalactic dispersion will be measurable. However we can draw the important conclusion that neither the optical nor the radio variations require the source to be closer to us than the 470 Mparsec implied by a cosmological red-shift of 0.158. This conclusion considerably weakens the case for the local model of quasi-stellar radio sources which places them a few megaparsec away and in which the observed red-shift implies a large velocity relative to their surroundings. More detailed observations of optical variations, and of radio variations as a function of frequency, should enable us to decide whether models of the type described here are appropriate for 3 C 273 B, and other quasi-stellar sources as well.

4. – The interpretation of the radio source counts,

In this Section we discuss the current status of the attempts that have been made to determine the structure of the universe from analysis of the radio source counts. As we shall see, more observations are needed before a definite decision is possible.

Before describing the source surveys that are relevant it is convenient to set up a zeroth-order model for the distribution of radio sources. This model refers to sources at high galactic latitudes, where well-known types of source associated with the disc of our galaxy (supernova remnants, nebulosities, H II regions etc.) are rare compared with extragalactic sources. We therefore make the following assumptions in the zeroth-order model;

a) The sources are extragalactic.

b) They are distributed throughout the whole of Euclidean space.

c) They are at rest.

d) They are distributed uniformly, with a concentration ϱ and an intrinsic radio brightness P at the frequency of observation.

Under these circumstances the number of sources whose measured flux-density exceeds S consists of all the sources within a sphere of radius $(P/S)^{\frac{1}{2}}$ and so is $(4\pi/3)\varrho P^{\frac{3}{2}} S^{-\frac{3}{2}}$. The number N per unit solid angle is then $\frac{1}{3}\varrho P^{\frac{3}{2}} S^{-\frac{3}{2}}$. We can immediately generalize *d*) and introduce a spread of intrinsic brightness, and obtain

$$N = \tfrac{1}{3}\left(\sum \varrho P^{\frac{3}{2}}\right) S^{-\frac{3}{2}}\,, \tag{1}$$

where the sum is over the various brightness classes (and can be replaced by an integral if desired).

This is the famous three-halves power law, which dominates the discussion of the radio source counts.

The first attempt to test this law was made in Cambridge by RYLE and SCHEUER (1955). Their survey of sources led to a log N-log S relation with a slope of -3 instead of -1.5. Later observations by the Sydney group, MILLS, SLEE and HILL (1958) led to a slope of -1.8. Three further surveys from Cambridge (EDGE *et al* 1959, SCOTT and RYLE 1961, GOWER 1966) have given slopes of -2, -1.8 and -1.8 respectively while a recent Australian survey by BOLTON *et al.* (1964) also gave -1.8. The first results from Bologna (BRACCESI *et al.*, 1965) suggest a slope of -2, but the Italian workers stress that their results are only preliminary. We shall therefore provisionally adopt a slope of -1.8. As we shall see, the significant feature of the counts is that the log N-log S curve is *steeper* than the zeroth-order model would predict. In Fig. 3 we show the latest Cambridge results (Gower 1966) which combine the counts made by Ryle and Neville (1962) in the North Polar Survey at very low flux densities with the recently completed 4 C survey. It will be seen that the slope is beginning to flatten off at the lowest flux-densities. The new Cambridge radio-telescope, amongst others, should provide us with reliable counts down to lower flux-levels still, how low depending on the counts themselves since one of the limiting factors is the number of sources per beam-width. In Fig. 4 we show (as far as the present identifications permit) a breakdown due to Veron (1966) of the counts into radio galaxies and QSS's separately. It will be seen that the radio galaxies follow the three-halves power law rather well, and that it is the QSS's that have a steep slope, in this case about -2. A similar result has been obtained by Longair (1966). As we shall see, this result is of great significance for the interpretations.

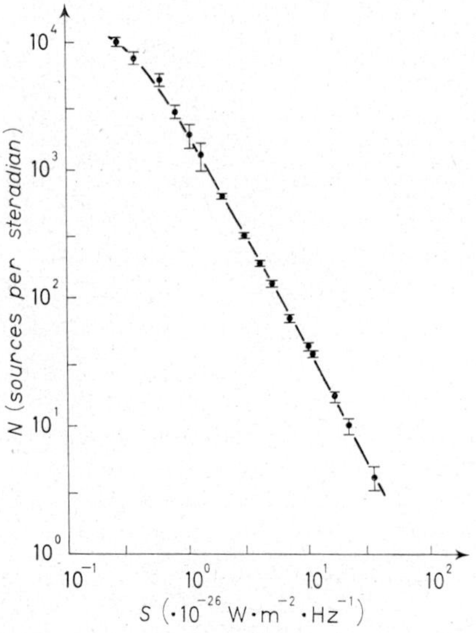

Fig. 3.

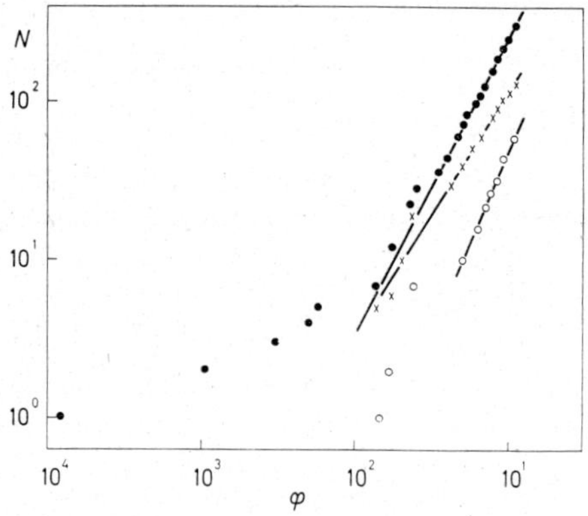

Fig. 4. – Radio-source counts: • all radio sources, slope = 1.85; × radiogalaxies, slope = 1.55; ∘ QSS, slope = 2.20.

4·1. *The red-shift corrections.* – Since many of the optically identified radio sources have substantial red shifts it is clear that assumption *c*) of our zeroth-order model is incorrect. Any realistic interpretation of the counts must therefore begin by considering the red-shift corrections to the three-halves power law. There are three such corrections, each of which increases as S decreases.

i) The effective value of P will depend on the red shift since we are observing in one small frequency-band radiation emitted in a different small frequency-band. Allowance must therefore be made for the change in band-width and for the spectrum of the source.

ii) The red shift weakens the measured brightness of the source over and above the effect of the inverse square law, so that the sphere corresponding to S is reduced in size. This has the effect of reducing N.

iii) If the red shift is taken to imply an evolutionary universe then the sources were more congested in the past than they are now, that is, ϱ was greater. Now the greater the red shift the further the source, and so the longer we are looking into the past. Thus the effective ϱ should increase with increasing red shift and so with decreasing S. This has the effect of increasing N.

In practice effect i) is small. Most sources have a spectrum of the form $S \propto \nu^{-0.7}$ in the vicinity of the Cambridge observing frequency of 178 MHz and if we allow for the effect of red shift on the bandwidth we find that the effective luminosity P increases with red shift z like $(1+z)^{-0.3}$, a fairly weak dependence. By contrast, effects ii) and iii) are important, and calculation shows that in all plausible cosmological models ii) is more important than iii) (which of course is completely absent in the steady-state model). Thus in all plausible cosmological models the red-shift corrections serve *to flatten the slope of the* log N-log S *relation*. Now in the range of flux density S where this slope can be distinguished for radio galaxies and QSS's, we saw that radio galaxies showed no appreciable deviation from the three-halves power law. This is understandable because in this range of S the red shifts of most radio galaxies are small, and so the red-shift correction is also small. By contrast, the QSS's in this flux range have large red shifts, and we would expect their log N-log S relation to be affected. This is indeed the case, but the observed deviation from the three-halves power law *is in the opposite direction*, the slope (-2) is steeper and not flatter than -1.5.

Various explanations for this discrepancy have been proposed in the past, and have been surveyed by SCIAMA (1965). However, the recent discovery that only the QSS's show a steep slope has rendered several of these explanations untenable, unless one is willing to contemplate the existince of irregularities in the distribution of QSS's which have a scale of the order of the Hubble radius of the universe ($\sim 10^{10}$ light years), or to assume that the red shift is not cosmological. In my opinion it is premature to introduce a hypothesis of extremely large-scale irregularities into theoretical cosmology, since it essentially robs the theory of any predictive power, and would permit almost any observations to be consistent with theory. Only as a last resort should such a hypothesis be considered seriously. It is possible that the red shifts of the QSS are not cosmological, but this question should be settled by observation fairly soon, and in this lecture we shall neglect the possibility.

There are then two surviving explanations, the orthodox one due to RYLE (1958, RYLE and CLARKE 1961) which requires the universe to be evolutionary, and an unorthodox one due to SCIAMA (1963, 1964*b*, 1964*a*, SCIAMA and SASLAW

1966) which would permit the universe to be in a steady state. We consider these explanations in turn.

4·2. *Ryle's interpretation.* – Ryle's interpretation is based on the consideration that in an evolving universe objects with large red shift are being observed at an earlier stage in the development of the universe than are nearby objects of small red shift. The possibility then arises that there has been a significant evolution in the intrinsic properties and distribution of radio sources over the time interval involved in the observations. Since we lack a detailed understanding of the origin and development of these sources, we are free at this stage to suppose that the sources have evolved in whatever manner is required to account for the observed $\log N$-$\log S$ relation. In particular we would obtain a slope steeper than -1.5 if we assumed that in the past sources had on the average a sufficiently higher intrinsic luminosity P, or a sufficiently higher concentration ϱ (over and above the kinematical effects of the expansion). Such an explanation is clearly not available to the steady-state theory, which requires P and ϱ to have the same average values at all times and in all places in the universe.

The first detailed attempt to account for the observed slope of -1.8 in this way was made by DAVIDSON (1962, DAVIDSON and DAVIES 1964*a* and *b*) His analysis has been recently criticized by LONGAIR (1966) in a comprehensive re-discussion in which the latest radio data have been used to determine the mode of evolution which would best account for the observations. In the remainder of this Section I give a brief account of Longair's work, which was kindly communicated to me before publication.

In its most general form the unknowns in the problem are

a) the local $\varrho(P)$ distribution at the present epoch,

b) the geometrical properties of the cosmological model,

c) the evolution of the properties of radio sources with epoch.

In a satisfactory cosmological model these parameters must be specified in such a way that the following observational data are accounted for:

d) the source counts for all radio sources and for quasi-stellar sources,

e) the luminosity distributions at several flux levels,

f) the integrated emission from extragalactic sources.

The disadvantage of this approach lies in the large number of unknown parameters, associated, in particular, with possible modes of evolution and the geometries of the cosmologies. On this account, no attempt was made to treat the problem generally. Instead, advantage was taken of the susceptibility of the method to numerical analysis and a computer was used to test a number of specific models which illustrate the requirements of any satisfactory model

Longair's actual procedure was as follows:

a) The local $\varrho(P)$ distribution was determined from identifications of sources with small red shifts, following the discussion of LONGAIR and SCOTT (1965).

b) The Einstein-de Sitter model was adopted.

c) Various evolutionary schemes were considered as follows:

i) Luminosity evolution: $P \propto t^{-x}$ for all sources.
ii) Luminosity evolution: $P \propto t^{-x}$ for the brightest sources only ($P > P_0$)
iii) Density evolution (in addition to the expansion of the universe): $\varrho \propto t^{-y}$ for all sources.
iv) Density evolution (in addition to the expansion of the universe): $\varrho \propto t^{-y}$ for the brightest sources ($P > P_1$).

d) The resulting source counts were then computed and compared with observation.

e) Luminosity distributions were computed at 40, 20 and 0.25 flux units and compared with the observations as discussed by LONGAIR and SCOTT (1965).

f) The integrated emission at 178 MHz (the frequency of the Cambridge surveys) was computed and compared with the observational estimates of this quantity. The integrated emission corresponding to the source counts themselves down to 0.25 flux units is 10 °K, whereas the background emission in the direction of minimum sky brightness is observed (TURTLE and BALDWIN 1962) to be about 80 °K at 178 MHz. Part of this background emission appears to be isotropic, and if this part is attributed to extragalactic sources of mean spectral index 0.8 between 13 and 178 MHz, it amounts to (23 ± 5) °K. By comparison, normal galaxies contribute about 4 °K assuming Einstein-de Sitter cosmology with no evolution. As mentioned in the last Section there may also be significant synchrotron emission from intergalactic relativistic electrons, even if the intergalactic magnetic field strength is no greater than 10^{-8} G. In the absence of any well-established information on these parameters, LONGAIR provisionally neglects this possibility, and takes the value 23 °K for the integrated emission from extragalactic radio sources, other than normal galaxies.

In this way Longair found the following models to be compatible with observation:

$$\text{luminosity evolution: } P \propto t^{-2.2} \qquad (P \geqslant 2.5 \cdot 10^{25}\ \text{W} \cdot \text{Hz}^{1-} \cdot \text{sr}^{-1}),$$

$$\text{density evolution: } \varrho \propto t^{-3.8} \qquad (P \geqslant 6 \cdot 10^{26}\ \text{W} \cdot \text{Hz}^{-1} \cdot \text{sr}^{-1}),$$

if an addition a cut-off is introduced at $z = 3.3$ (luminosity evolution) or $z = 4$ (density evolution), that is, no sources with larger red shifts must contribute to the counts or to the integrated emission. This cut-off is required to account for the flattening of the log N-log S curve at the lowest Ryle-Neville point

(0.27 flux units on the new flux-density scale (GOWER 1966)). The critical value of z is rather less than that arising from Thomson scattering (see 2.4, a)), and might perhaps be associated with the epoch of formation of the radio sources (it corresponds to a time $5 \cdot 10^8$ years after the singularity at $t = 0$). LONGAIR explains the result that only the brightest sources evolve by assuming that these are essentially the QSS's.

We can summarize this Section by saying that it is possible to find evolutionary models which fit the data, and that these models have some rather specific properties such as that only the brightest sources evolve appreciably, and that there must be a sharp cut-off at $z \sim 3.5$.

4·3 *Sciama's interpretation.* – The fact that the observed slope of the log N-log S relation is steeper than expected can be regarded in either of two ways, namely, that there is an excess of faint sources or a deficit of bright ones. Ryle's interpretation is based on the first of these, that is, on an excess of faint sources. Such an excess would be likely to involve distant sources and so to have a cosmological origin. Alternatively, as stressed by HANBURY BROWN (1962), there may be a deficit of bright sources. Such a deficit would be likely to involve nearby sources, and so to have a purely local origin.

HANBURY BROWN attempted to relate the possible existence of a local deficit to the known irregularity in the distribution of galaxies out to about 35 Mparsec. However, we now know that if there is a local deficit it must occur in the distribution of QSS's, whose red-shifts show that even the nearest (3 C 273) is five-hundred Mparsec away (on the cosmological interpretation of the red shifts, which we are here adopting). The same difficulty holds for the Hoyle-Narlikar (1961, 1962) hypothesis that in a steady-state universe irregularities as large as a few hundred Mparsec could arise. Moreover even this hypothesis depended critically on the Gold-Hoyle (1959) theory of a hot universe, which has now been disproved by observation (see 2·2.2).

We can, however, avoid this difficulty if we notice that most of the QSS's whose red shifts have been determined lie in the flux density range where the deficit is greatest. *The red shifts, distances and luminosities of the missing* QSS's *are thus not determined*, for they are simply not there to be measured. Accordingly we may introduce the hypothesis that the required local deficit occurs in the distribution of a class of sources which are intrinsically weaker and more concentrated than the QSS's of known red shift. The scale of the local irregularity could then be smaller than our previous estimate. This hypothesis was first proposed early in 1963 (SCIAMA 1963) before much was known about QSS's. At that time it was not possible to make any statement about the optical properties or angular diameters of this second, hypothetical, population. Now, however, it is clear that our hypothesis requires QSS's themselves to consist of two populations, and also requires many of the QSS's of low flux density to have very much smaller red shifts than the QSS's of high flux density ($S \geqslant \sim 16$ flux units). This requirement will probably be tested observationally in the next few months.

We can estimate a lower limit on the intrinsic radio luminosity of a typical member of our hypothetical class of QSS's by imposing the requirement that their integrated emission should not exceed the extragalactic background. This limit arises because $\varrho P^{\frac{3}{2}}$ for this class can be estimated from the counts. If it is, say, X, then ϱP is $X/P^{\frac{1}{2}}$, so the smaller we make P the larger we make ϱP, that is, the larger we make the volume emissivity. In this way it is possible to show that $P \geqslant \sim 4 \cdot 10^{23}\ \mathrm{W \cdot Hz^{-1} \cdot sr^{-1}}$ a limit about 1000 times less than the luminosity of a typical QSS of known red shift. The required scale of the local deficit in this fainter class is now more nearly comparable with the scale of the known irregularities in the distribution of nearby galaxies.

Unfortunately for this explanation, there is another condition that must be satisfied, namely, that the counts be correctly reproduced right down to 0.27 flux units, the lower limit of the Ryle-Neville survey. Now it will be recalled that the counts at this flux level are so low that in order to explain them. Longair was forced to introduce a sharp cut-off in the sources at $z \sim 3.5$. By contrast, from the present point of view the observed counts at 0.27 flux units turn out to be too high for comfort. The difference arises because in Longair's analysis the steepness of the $\log N$-$\log S$ relation is explained by introducing intrinsic evolutionary effects; owing to the spread in the observed luminosity dispersion it is then difficult to explain why the slope flattens off so soon. On the other hand, here the steepness is explained by a local deficit, and it is difficult to explain how the counts remain so high at 0.27 flux units in face of the severe red-shift corrections. This difficulty is not perhaps decisive, but it makes the present model rather implausible. We would expect to find about 7000 sources per unit solid angle brighter than 0.27 flux units, whereas RYLE and NEVILLE observed $10\,500 \pm 1300$. In view of all the uncertainties this discrepancy might be resolvable. The decisive test will come when the counts are extended down to, say, 0.1 flux units or below, a range which is accessible to radio telescopes now in existence. The present model predicts that there are about 23 000 sources per steradian brighter than 0.1 flux units.

The fact that the Ryle-Neville counts are so high can be explained if we assume that the second population of QSS's lies *inside our own galaxy*, since they will then not be subject to any red-shift corrections at all. Indeed, this was Sciama's original proposal early in 1963, although at that time it was expressed solely in terms of a second population of radio sources of unknown optical characteristics. The recently-discovered fact that they must actually be starlike in appearance is thus gratifyingly consistent with the requirements of the model.

The most important parameter of this model is the ratio N_g/N_e of galactic to extragalactic sources in a given flux range (before corrections have been applied for the local deficit in N_g and the red shift effect on N_e). If the local irregularity in N_g is to be kept within reasonable bounds this ratio cannot differ greatly from unity. For if the ratio were very small the local deficit in N_g would not show up so clearly in the $\log N$-$\log S$ relation. On the other hand if the ratio were very large we could not account for the optical identifications, which imply that for $S > 20$ flux units nearly all the sources are extragalactic.

A detailed analysis (SCIAMA 1963, 1964*a* and *b*, SCIAMA and SASLAW 1966) of the source counts shows that the optimum value of N_g/N_e is about 0.8, and that beyond 10 flux units there are no more missing sources (which total about 24 per steradian). With this choice for N_g/N_e and no further adjustable parameter involved, the model reproduces correctly all the counts from 10 flux units right down to 0.27 flux units. In particular, the last Ryle-Neville point, which is so troublesome for other models, is here obtained to within the observational errors, viz. 10 800 as compared with $10\,500 \pm 1300$. The number count corresponding to 0.1 flux units is 40 000, compared with 23 000 for the previous model.

It remains to check that the integrated emission from the galactic sources does not exceed the galactic background discussed earlier, and that these sources would not exhibit anisotropies, which the source counts themselves are not observed to posses. As we shall see, these two requirements constrain us in opposite directions: the first leads to a lower limit on the intrinsic brightness of a typical source, and the second leads to an upper limit. Indeed, at one time RYLE (1958, RYLE and CLARKE 1961) claimed that the lower limit exceeded the upper limit, so that no solution was possible, implying that only a small fraction of the sources involved in the counts could be galactic and that the steep slope had to be explained in some other way. Using more recent data however, it turns out that the two limits more or less coincide, which implies that a solution is possible, but only if most of the background at high galactic latitudes arises from the sources, and if anisotropy shows up at flux densities not far below the present limit.

To see this we note first that $\varrho_g P_g$ for the galactic sources is known from the source counts and is X, say. We also have an upper limit, Y, say, on $\varrho_g P_g r$, where r is the effective thickness of the distribution in the direction where the sky temperature is least. We thus have a lower limit X^2/Y^2 on P_g/r^2, which is the flux density produced by a source at the nearest edge of the distribution. This is the flux density at which anisotropy would begin to set in. At this point we must allow for a spread in intrinsic luminosities, which for the galactic sources is quite unknown. It is perhaps reasonable to introduce a factor of 10 to allow for this, although this is clearly an arbitrary choice. We thus find for the critical flux S_0 at which anisotropy sets in the relation

$$S_0 \geqslant \frac{10X^2}{Y^2}\,.$$

If we choose for X the value obtained from the counts, and for Y the value derived from the estimated galactic background of 60 °K, we find

$$S_0 \geqslant \sim 0.1 \text{ flux units} .$$

Now the Cambridge workers have shown that there is no anisotropy down to 0.2 flux units, so we see that there is not much leeway, and that most of the 60 °K background temperature must be due in this model to the integrated effect of the galactic sources.

We thus return to the original theory (RYLE 1949, WESTERHOUT and OORT 1951, PRIESTER 1954, UNSÖLD 1955) of the origin of the galactic background, that it is due to a large number of faint point sources. This theory was displaced in the early 1950's by the hypothesis that the emission is due to synchrotron radiation from cosmic-ray electrons moving in interstellar magnetic fields. This latter hypothesis is reasonable in its requirements on the electron flux and the magnetic field strength, but has by no means been established beyond doubt. Perhaps the main objection to the radio-star hypothesis came with the discovery in the mid-1950's of the galactic radio halo, which had a distribution quite different from that of any known population of stars. Whatever this argument was worth it has now been much weakened by the discovery (BALDWIN 1963, TURNER and BURKE 1965) that the galaxy may after all have little or no radio halo. A second objection, which has been stressed by SCOTT (1963), is that the sources and the background have different spectra. This argument is also inconclusive, however. In the first place the spectrum of the galaxy is not yet well established. At the time SCOTT wrote (1963) the Cambridge workers believed that the spectral index was zero at 38 MHz and 0.9 at 178 MHz. More recent measurements by themselves (ANDREW 1966) and by other workers (YATES and WIELEBINSKI 1965) suggest that the spectral index is fairly constant in this frequency range at about 0.5. The median spectral index of the sources is also constant in this range at about 0.7. The difference can hardly be said to be significant. Moreover, the intrinsically weaker sources contribute more to the integrated emission (through $\sum \varrho P$) than they do to the sample of sources to which the spectral measurements apply (this sample being mainly determined by S and so by $\sum \varrho P^{\frac{3}{2}}$). Thus if there is a correlation between intrinsic radio luminosity and spectrum we would not expect exact agreement between the spectra of the background and of the sources (selected by flux density).

It thus appears that the model is a possible one, although future work may show it to be wrong. Meanwhile we can derive values for ϱ_g and P_g separately by using Baldwin's (1963) estimate that the thickness of the galactic background is about 400 parsec on each side of the galactic plane. Putting $r \sim 400$ parsec we find

$$P_g \sim 3 \cdot 10^{10} \text{ W} \cdot \text{Hz}^{-1} \cdot \text{sr}^{-1} ,$$

$$\varrho_g \sim 10^{-2} \text{ parsec}^{-3} .$$

Thus a typical source-strength is about 10^{-6} that of the Crab, and the concentration of sources about 10^{-1} that of the known stars. These values are similar to those used in earlier versions of the radio source hypothesis (PRIESTER 1954, UNSÖLD 1955). It has been suggested (SCIAMA 1964*b*) that the sources may be faint low-mass stars still undergoing gravitational contraction from a dispersed state and passing through a rotationally unstable phase which produces a radio source. We must add now that they are required to have QSS-like colours (SANDAGE, this volume). The requirement is not unreasonable since the discussion (KINMAN 1965) aroused by Sandage's (1965) hypothesis about QSS's has shown that certain types of star and extragalactic QSS's cannot be distinguished on grounds of colour alone.

One last point. With a concentration $\sim 10^{-2}$ parsec^{-3}, the nearest galactic QSS's must be a matter of only a few parsecs away. At such a distance their proper motions are likely to be very large, a few tenths of a second of arc per year. We thus predict that once one is looking beyond the local deficit, that is, below about 16 flux units, a growing proportion of QSS's as the flux level drops should be found to have almost zero red shifts and large proper motions. This prediction should be tested soon, perhaps even before this lecture sees the light of day. Meanwhile the steady-state model remains in the field, bloody but unbowed.

Note added in proof.

Recent red shift determinations for QSS's show that the steady-state model can probably be ruled out, if the red shifts are cosmological in origin. (D. W. SCIAMA and M. J. REES: *Nature*, **211**, 1283 (1966)).

BIBLIOGRAPHY

ABELL, G. O., 1961, *A. J.*, **66**, 607.

ADGIE, R. L., H. GENT, O. B. SLEE, A. D. FROST and H. P. PALMER, Rowson, 1965, **208**, 275.

ALLEN, C. W., 1963, *Astrophysical Quantities* (London), p. 34.

ANDREW, B. H., 1966, *M.N.R.A.S.* **132**, 79.

BALDWIN, J. E., 1963, *Observatory*, **83**, 153.

BELINFANTE, F. J., 1940, *Physica*, **7**, 449.

BERKELEY, G., 1721, *De Motu*.

BERTOTTI, B., D. BRILL and R. KROTKOV, 1962, *Gravitation*, ed. WITTEN (New York), p. 1.

BOLOGNA, J. M., E. F. MCCLAIN, W. K. ROSE and R. M. SLOANAKER, 1965, *Ap. J.*, **142**, 106.

Bolton, J. G., F. F. Gardner and M. B. Mackey, 1964, *Aust. J. Phys.*, **17**, 340.
Bondi, H., 1960, *Cosmology* (Cambridge).
Braccesi, A., M. Ceccarelli, R. Fanti, G. Gelato, C. Giovannini, D. Harris, C. Rosatelli, G. Sinigaglia and L. L. Volders, 1965, *Nuovo Cimento*, **40**, 267.
Cartan, E., 1923, *Ann. Ecole Normale*, **40**, 23.
Cocconi, G. and E. E. Salpeter, 1958, *Nuovo Cimento*, **10**, 646.
Conway, R. G., K. I. Kellermann and R. J. Long, 1963, *M.N.R.A.S.*, **125**, 261.
Davidson, W., 1962, *M.N.R.A.S.*, **124**, 79.
Davidson, W. and M. Davies, 1964*a*, *M.N.R.A.S.*, **127**, 241.
Davidson, W. and M. Davies, 1964*b*, *M.N.R.A.S.*, **128**, 363.
Davies, R. D., 1964, *M.N.R.A.S.*, **128**, 133.
Davies, R. D. and R. C. Jennison, 1964, *M.N.R.A.S.*, **128**, 123.
Dent, W. A., 1965, *Science*, **148**, 1458.
Dent W. A. and F. T. Haddock, 1965, *Quasi-Stellar Sources and Gravitational Collapse* (Chicago), p. 381.
Dicke, R. H., 1961*a*, *Proc. S.I.F.* Course, XX, p. 1.
Dicke, R. H., 1961*b*, *Phys. Rev. Letters*, **7**, 359.
Dicke, R. H., 1964, *Relativity Groups and Topology* (New York), p. 165.
Drever, R. W. P., 1961, *Phil. Mag.*, **6**, 683.
Edge, D. O., J. R. Shakeshaft, W. B. McAdam, J. E. Baldwin and S. Archer, 1959, *Mem. Roy. Ast. Soc.*, **67**, 37.
Einstein, A., 1916, *Ann. Phys.*, **49**, 769 see the *Principle of Relativity* (New York), 1923, 148.
Einstein A., 1918, *Ann. Phys.*, **55**, 241.
Ericson, W. C. and W. M. Cronyn, 1965, *Ap. J.*, **142**, 1156.
Feenberg, E. and H. Primakoff, 1948, *Phys. Rev.*, **73**, 449.
Felten, J. E. and P. Morrison, 1963, *Phys. Rev. Letters*, **10**, 453.
Feynman, R. P., 1957, *Chapel Hill Conference*, and unpublished lectures at the *California Institute of Technology*.
Field, G. B., 1959, *Ap. J.*, **129**, 525, 536.
Field, G. B., 1962, *Ap. J.*, **135**, 684.
Field, G. B., 1965, *Ap. J.*, **142**, 531.
Field, G. B. and R. C. Henry, 1964, *Ap. J.*, **140**, 1002.
Fowler, W. A., this volume p. 313.
Friedländer, B. and T. Friedländer, 1896, *Absolute und Relative Bewegung* (Berlin).
Gardner, F. F. and J. B. Whiteoak, 1963, *Nature*, **197**, 1162.
Giacconi, R., this volume p. 73.
Ginzburg, V. L. and S. I. Syrovatsky, 1964, *The Origin of Cosmic Rays* (London), p. 241.
Gold, T. and F. Hoyle, 1959, *Paris Symposium on Radio Astronomy* (Stanford), p. 583.
Goldstein, S. J., 1963, *Ap. J.*, **138**, 978.
Good, M. L., 1961, **121**, 311.
Gould, R. J. and G. R. Burbidge, 1963, *Ap. J.*, **138**, 969.
Gould, R. J. and G. R. Burbidge, 1965, *Ann. d'Astr.*, **28**, 171.
Gould, R. J. and D. W. Sciama, 1964, *Ap. J.*, **140**, 1634.
Gower, J. F. R., 1966, *M.N.R.A.S.*, **133**, 151.
Greeenstein, J. L. and M. Schmidt, 1964, *Ap. J.*, **140**, 1.
Gunn, J. E. and B. A. Peterson, 1965, *Ap. J.*, **142**, 1633.
Gupta, S., 1957, *Rev. Mod. Phys.*, **29**, 334.
Haddock, F. T. and D. W. Sciama, 1965, *Phys. Rev. Letters*, **14**, 1007.
Halpern, L., 1963, *Annals of Physics*, **25**, 387.

Hanbury Brown, R., 1962, *M.N.R.A.S.*, **124**, 35.
Hazard, C., M. B. Mackey and A. J. Shimmins, 1963, *Nature*, **197**, 1037.
Hoyle, F. and G. R. Burbidge, 1966, *Ap. J.*, **144**, 534.
Hoyle, F., W. A. Fowler, G. R. Burbidge and E. M. Burbidge, 1964, *Ap. J.*, **139**, 909.
Hoyle, F. and J. V. Narlikar, 1961, *M.N.R.A.S.*, **123**, 133.
Hoyle, F. and J. V. Narlikar, 1962, *M.N.R.A.S.*, **125**, 13.
Hughes, V. W., H. G. Robinson and V. Beltran-Lopez, 1960, *Phys. Rev. Letters*, **4**, 342.
Hunter, J. H., 1966, *M.N.R.A.S.*, **133**, 181.
Kinman, T. D., 1965, *Ap. J.*, **142**, 1241.
Le Roux, E., 1961, *Ann. d'Astro.*, **24**, 71.
Longair, M. S., 1966, *M.N.R.A.S.*, **133**, 421.
Longair, M. S. and P. F. Scott, 1965, *M.N.R.A.S.*, **130**, 379.
Mach, E., 1872, *History and Root of the Principle of the Conservation of Energy.*
Mach, E., 1893, *The Science of Mechanics.*
Maltby, P. and A. T. Moffett, 1965*a*, *Science*, **150**, 63.
Maltby, P. and A. T. Moffett, 1965*b*, *Ap. J.*, **142**, 409.
McCrea, W. H., 1951, *Proc. Roy. Soc. A.*, **206**, 562.
Mills, B. Y., O. B. Slee and E. R. Hill, 1958, *Aust. J. Phys.*, **11**, 360.
Moroz, V. I. and V. R. Yesipov, 1963, *I.A.U. Inf. Bull. on variable stars*, No. 31.
Morris, D. and G. L. Berge, 1964, *Astron. J.*, **69**, 641.
Neyman, J., T. Page and E. Scott, 1961, *Conference on the Instability of Systems of Galaxies* (ed.), *A. J.*, **66**, 533.
Oort, J. H., 1958, *Solvay Conference on Structure and Evolution of the Universe* (Brussels).
Papapetrou, A., 1948, *Proc. Roy. Irish. Acad. A.*, **52**, 11.
Penzias, A. A. and R. W. Wilson, 1965, *Ap. J.*, **142**, 419.
Priester, W., 1954, *Zeit. f. Astrophys.*, **34**, 295.
Rees, M. and D. W. Sciama, 1965*a*, *Nature*, **207**, 738.
Rees, M. and D. W. Sciama, 1965*b*, *Nature*, **208**, 371.
Rees, M. and D. W. Sciama, 1966, *Ap. J.*, **145**, 6.
Roll, P. G., R. Krotkov and R. H. Dicke, 1964, *Annals of Physics*, **26**, 442.
Rosenfeld, L., 1940, *Acad. Roy. Belg.*, **19**, 6.
Ryle, M., 1949, *Proc. Phys. Soc. A.*, **62**, 491.
Ryle, M., 1958, *Proc. Roy. Soc. A.*, **248**, 289.
Ryle, M. and R. W. Clarke, 1961, *M.N.R.A.S.*, **122**, 349.
Ryle, M. and A. C. Neville, 1962, *M.N.R.A.S.*, **125**, 39.
Ryle, M. and P. A. G. Scheuer, 1955, *Proc. Roy. Soc. A.*, **230**, 448.
Sandage, A., 1964, *Ap. J.*, **139**, 416.
Sandage, A., 1965, *Ap. J.*, **141**, 1560.
Sandage, A. and J. B. Wyndham, 1965, *Ap. J.*, **141**, 328.
Scheuer, P. A. G., 1965*a*, *Nature*, **207**, 963.
Scheuer, P. A. G., 1965*b*, *Quasi-stellar sources and Gravitational Collapse* (Chicago), p. 373.
Schiff, L. I., 1960, *Proc. Nat. Acad. Sci.*, **46**, 871.
Schiff, L. I., 1961, *Physics Today*, p. 42.
Schiff, L. I., 1964, *Rev. Mod. Phys.*, **36**, 507.
Schmidt, M., 1963, *Nature*, **197**, 1040.
Schmidt, M., 1965, *Ap. J.*, **141**, 1295.
Sciama, D. W., 1953, *M.N.R.A.S.*, **113**, 34.

SCIAMA, D. W., 1959, *The Unity of the Universe* (London).
SCIAMA, D. W., 1963, *M.N.R.A.S.*, **126**, 195.
SCIAMA, D. W., 1964*a*, *Rev. Mod. Phys.*, **36**, 463.
SCIAMA, D. W., 1964*b*, *M.N.R.A.S.*, **128**, 49.
SCIAMA, D. W., 1964*c*, *Quart. J. Roy. Astr. Soc.*, **5**, 196.
SCIAMA, D. W., 1964*d*, *Observatory*, **84**, 161.
SCIAMA, D. W., 1965, *Science Progress*, **53**, 1.
SCIAMA, D. W. and W. C. SASLAW, 1966, *Nature*, **210**, 348.
SCOTT, P. F., 1963, *M.N.R.A.S.*, **127**, 37.
SCOTT, P. F. and M. RYLE, 1961, *M.N.R.A.S.*, **122**, 389.
SHAPIRO, I. I., 1964, *Phys. Rev. Letters*, **13**, 789.
SHERWIN, C. W., H. FRAUENFELDER, E. L. GARWIN, E. LUSCHER, S. MARGULIES and R. N. PEACOCK, 1960, *Phys. Rev. Letters*, **4**, 399.
SHKLOVSKY, I. S., 1965, *Sov. Astron.*, **8**, 638.
SHOLOMITSKY, G. B., 1965, Feb. 27, I.A.U. Information Bulletin on variable stars, No. 83.
DE SITTER, W., 1916, *M.N.R.A.S.*, **76**, 699.
SLISH, V. I., 1963, *Nature*, **199**, 682.
SMITH, H. J., 1965, *Quasi-stellar sources and gravitational collapse* (Chicago), p. 221.
SPITZER, L., 1948, *Ap. J.*, **107**, 6.
TERRELL, J., 1964, *Science*, **145**, 918.
THIRRING, W., 1961, *Annals of Physics*, **16**, 96.
TURNER, K. C. and B. F. BURKE, 1965, *Astron. J.*, **70**, 332.
TURTLE, A. J. and J. E. BALDWIN, 1962, *M.N.R.A.S.*, **124**, 459.
TWISS, R. G., 1958, *Phil. Mag.*, **45**, 249.
UNSÖLD, A., 1955, *Physik der Sternatmosphären*, 2nd ed. (Berlin), p. 768.
VERON, P., 1966, *Nature*, **211**, 724.
WEINBERG, S., 1965, *Phys. Rev.*, **138**, 988.
WESTERHOUT, G. and J. H. OORT, 1951, *Bull. Astr. Neth.*, **11**, 323.
WHEELER, J. A., 1962, *Royaumont Conference on General Relativity* (CNRS, Paris), p. 269.
WHEELER, J. A., 1964*a*, *Relativity, Groups and Topology* (New York), p. 317.
WHEELER, J. A., 1964*b*, *Relativistic Theories of Gravitation, Warsaw Conference* (London), p. 223.
WILLIAMS, P. J. S., 1963, *Nature*, **200**, 56.
YATES, K. W. and R. WIELEBINSKI, 1965, *Nature*, **208**, 64.

Tipografia Compositori - Bologna - Italy

PROCEEDINGS OF THE INTERNATIONAL SCHOOL OF PHYSICS
« ENRICO FERMI »

Course XIV
Ergodic Theories
edited by P. CALDIROLA

Course XV
Nuclear Spectroscopy
edited by G. RACAH

Course XVI
Physicomathematical Aspects of Biology
edited by N. RASHEVSKY

Course XVII
Topics of Radiofrequency Spectroscopy
edited by A. GOZZINI

Course XVIII
Physics of Solids (Radiation Damage in Solids)
edited by D. S. BILLINGTON

Course XIX
Cosmic Rays, Solar Particles and Space Research
edited by B. PETERS

Course XX
Evidence for Gravitational Theories
edited by C. MØLLER

Course XXI
Liquid Helium
edited by G. CARERI

Course XXII
Semiconductors
edited by R. A. SMITH

Course XXIII
Nuclear Physics
edited by V. F. WEISSKOPF

Course XXIV
Space Exploration and the Solar System
edited by B. ROSSI

Course XXV
Advanced Plasma Theory
edited by M. N. ROSENBLUTH

Course XXVI
Selected Topics on Elementary Particle Physics
edited by M. CONVERSI

Course XXVII
Dispersion and Absorption of Sound by Molecular Processes
edited by D. SETTE

Course XXVIII
Star Evolution
edited by L. GRATTON

Course XXIX
Dispersion Relations and Their Connection with Causality
edited by E. P. WIGNER

Course XXX
Radiation Dosimetry
edited by F. W. SPIERS and G. W. REED

Course XXXI
Quantum Electronics and Coherent Light
edited by C. H. TOWNES and P. A. MILES

Course XXXII
Weak Interactions and High-Energy Neutrino Physics
edited by T. D. LEE

Course XXXIII
Strong Interactions
edited by L. W. ALVAREZ

Course XXXIV
The Optical Properties of Solids
Edited by J. TAUC

Information about Courses 1-13 may be obtained from the Italian Physical Society.